Vector Spaces
and
Matrices

Robert M. Thrall
Professor of Mathematics
University of Michigan

and

Leonard Tornheim
Research Mathematician
California Research Corporation

John Wiley & Sons, Inc.

New York · London · Sydney

Preface

The past several decades have witnessed a growing interest in the theory of vector spaces and matrices. One evidence of this interest is the replacement of the traditional course on theory of equations as the basic required course in algebra in many colleges by one on matrix theory. Aside from many uses in various parts of mathematics, matrices and vectors find use in circuit analysis (in electrical engineering), quantum mechanics, statistics, numerical analysis, econometrics, and operations research.

The wide range of applications of vectors spaces and matrices both inside and outside of pure mathematics has led to development of the subject at many different levels. Each higher level sheds new light and gives deeper insight into the basic facts. After having looked down from the heights the mathematician is sometimes tempted to feel impatient with lower level approaches. However, he must realize that the beginning student who is not yet equipped to climb to the heights needs to approach the subject at a level within his grasp.

At the lowest level everything is kept concrete. A matrix is regarded as an array of real (or complex) numbers, and the pages of a textbook written at this level are generously filled with summation signs applied to sequences of numbers. At a slightly higher level the matrices and vectors become the basic elements although one still must occasionally deal with the components. At this level vectors are defined as n-tuples, and more general types of vector spaces are not considered. At a still higher level vector spaces are defined axiomatically, and the theory is developed over an arbitrary (commutative) field, but without recourse to the theory of groups with operators. At the higher strata of this level matrices are replaced by linear transformations and bilinear functions; the theory proceeds without mention of n-tuples. At still higher levels the numerical scalars are replaced by elements of a ring and the theory of vector spaces becomes a corollary to general theorems about groups, rings, and algebras.

Each level carries with it many advantages and disadvantages. The lower levels do not give enough insight into the basic facts and the higher levels are too abstract for the beginner. In the present textbook we have chosen to proceed simultaneously at two levels, one concrete and one axiomatic. Thus in the first chapter we introduce n-tuples and abstract from them a set of axioms for a vector space. Each new property of a vector space is first discussed at one level and then at the other. Sometimes the concrete approach precedes and sometimes it follows the axiomatic one. We feel that this dual approach has many advantages. It introduces the student to the elegance and power of mathematical reasoning based on a set of axioms and helps bridge the gap that lies between the pre-eminence of problem solving found in most elementary undergraduate courses and the axiomatic approach that characterizes much modern research in mathematics. On the other hand, the frequent return to concrete formulations helps keep the student's feet on solid ground. We have tried to develop understanding and conceptual grasp, rather than mere manipulation.

In the early chapters we have supplied a far more detailed exposition than is found in many textbooks. It has been our experience that this fullness in detail is extremely important for the student who is having his first experience with mathematical rigor. Only after he has won his spurs can he afford to replace the sometimes tedious details which clinch a proof by a phrase such as "continuing in this fashion $\cdots$." Moreover, such statements frequently gloss over an induction argument, and we believe that an objective of this course should be to give the student a thorough grounding in proof by induction.

The book is designed for a one-year course meeting three times per week. We have found that in a one-semester course one can cover the first five chapters and some topics from the sixth and seventh chapters.

The first two chapters introduce the concepts of vector space, linear transformation, and matrix. The third chapter applies these concepts to the problem of solving systems of linear equations. Although these three chapters are closely knit, the instructor who wishes to will find it possible to rearrange the order of presentation so as to come to the solution of equations somewhat earlier. In particular Sections 1.9, 1.10, 2.7, and 2.8 can be omitted or postponed.

Chapter 4 gives a self-contained development of the theory of determinants. The first four sections can be skipped if the students have already had an introduction to determinants.

Chapter 5 is intended to introduce the student to the general concept of invariant and serves as a summary of what has preceded. It also includes a brief introduction to the theory of similarity.

Chapters 6 and 7 present the usual material on bilinear and quadratic forms and on orthogonal equivalence.

The last four chapters are more advanced in nature, and the level of exposition is somewhat higher. The first part of Chapter 8 gives the standard theory of polynomials in one indeterminate. The last six sections develop the general theory of simple algebraic extensions of a field. By removing the usual restriction to extensions which are again fields we get a development which can be used not only as a foundation for Galois theory but also for the general similarity theory. To the best of our knowledge this is the first elementary presentation of this material available in textbook form (in English). In Chapter 9 we present the standard canonical forms for matrices with integral or with polynomial elements. These results are applied to differential equations with constant coefficients, and also to finitely generated abelian groups to obtain the fundamental theorem. Chapter 10 presents the similarity theory with the usual canonical forms. It includes applications to geometry and to differential equations. Many further applications are considered in the exercises in this chapter.

The final chapter on linear inequalities presents a brief introduction to this important topic, which has until now been neglected in elementary texts on matrix theory. We hope that what we have given will provide the student with sufficient background so that he can read books and papers on game theory and linear programming.

We have chosen in this book to break off our treatment of group theory just short of a formal, development of the concept of factor group. This decision was based on the conviction that, if we went as far as factor groups, it would be difficult to avoid raising the level of the entire book to such a point that it would have become a textbook on "groups with operators with applications to matrix theory." However, in cases where more group theory is available or suitable we recommend that the instructor point out how some of our proofs can be simplified. This holds especially in the last four chapters.

We wish to acknowledge the help and suggestions of many friends who read and tested the manuscript in an early version. Included among these are E. A. Cameron, G. K. Kalisch, J. E. McLaughlin, C. J. Nesbitt, J. A. Nyswander, H. Raiffa, G. L. Thompson, and A. W. Tucker.

ROBERT M. THRALL
LEONARD TORNHEIM

March 1957

Contents

CHAPTER 1 **Vector Spaces**

1.1 Introduction   1
1.2 Scalars   4
1.3 Cartesian space   8
1.4 Vector spaces   10
1.5 Independence of vectors   13
1.6 Dimension and basis   19
1.7 Isomorphism   21
1.8 Subspaces   24
1.9 Sums and intersections of subspaces   26
1.10 Subspaces of $\mathcal{V}_n(\mathcal{F})$ 29

CHAPTER 2 **Linear Transformations and Matrices**

2.1 Linear transformations   32
2.2 Matrix of a linear transformation   36
2.3 Examples of linear transformations   41
2.4 Multiplication of linear transformations   45
2.5 Multiplication of matrices   50
2.6 Sums and products by scalars   55
2.7 Sets of linear transformations of a vector space   59
2.8 Submatrices, partitioned matrices   63
2.9 Row and column matrices   68

CHAPTER 3 **Systems of Linear Equations**

3.1 Rank; row and column spaces of a matrix   73
3.2 Systems of linear homogeneous equations   78
3.3 Elementary transformations   82
3.4 Row-echelon matrices   86

ix

3.5 Triangular and Hermite matrices   89
3.6 Properties of Hermite matrices   93
3.7 Elementary matrices   94
3.8 Equivalence of matrices   101
3.9 Nonhomogeneous linear equations   106

CHAPTER **4** **Determinants**

4.1 Definition of determinant   110
4.2 Basic properties of determinants   115
4.3 Proofs of the properties of determinants   118
4.4 Classical definition of determinant; Laplace expansion by
     minors   120
4.5 Determinants of products of square matrices;
     determinantal criterion for rank   125
4.6 Determinants of products of rectangular matrices   127
4.7 Adjoints and inverses of square matrices; Cramer's Rule   129

CHAPTER **5** **Equivalence Relations and Canonical Forms**

5.1 Equivalence relations   132
5.2 Canonical forms and invariants   134
5.3 Alias and alibi   136
5.4 Change of basis   139
5.5 Similarity of matrices; eigenvalues   142
5.6 Equivalence and similarity of linear transformations   147

CHAPTER **6** **Functions of Vectors**

6.1 Bilinear forms   149
6.2 Canonical forms for skew-symmetric and symmetric
     matrices   152
6.3 Quadratic forms   158
6.4 Bilinear functions; dual spaces   160
6.5 Bilinear scalar functions and matrices; dualities   163
6.6 Quadratic functions   167
6.7 Hermitian functions   171
6.8 Determinants as multilinear functions   174

CHAPTER **7** **Orthogonal and Unitary Equivalence**

7.1 Euclidean space and inner products   179
7.2 Schwartz's inequality, distance, and angle   181
7.3 Orthogonality   183
7.4 Orthogonal subspaces   185
7.5 Orthogonal transformations   185

7.6   Diagonalization of symmetric matrices   187
7.7   Unitary transformations   191
7.8   Adjoint of a linear transformation   193

CHAPTER **8** **Structure of Polynomial Rings**

8.1   Rings and subrings   196
8.2   Existence and uniqueness of transcendental extensions   199
8.3   Division algorithm; greatest common divisor   203
8.4   Factorization of polynomials   207
8.5   Algebraic extensions of a field   210
8.6   Congruence of polynomials   213
8.7   Direct sums of vector spaces   214
8.8   Idempotents and direct sums   218
8.9   Decomposition of algebras   221
8.10 Decomposition of simple algebraic extensions   224

CHAPTER **9** **Equivalence of Matrices over a Ring**

9.1   Matrices over a ring   229
9.2   Equivalence of matrices with polynomial elements   230
9.3   Matrices with integer elements   236
9.4   Vector spaces over the integers   238
9.5   Finitely generated vector spaces over the integers   240
9.6   Systems of linear differential equations with constant
         coefficients   244

CHAPTER **10** **Similarity of Matrices**

10.1 Minimum function   247
10.2 Invariant subspaces   250
10.3 Cayley-Hamilton Theorem   256
10.4 Primary linear transformations   258
10.5 Similarity, general case   263
10.6 Segre characteristics   269
10.7 Pairs of bilinear forms; systems of linear differential
         equations   271
10.8 Pairs of quadratic forms   273
10.9 Applications to projective geometry   275
10.10 Roots of matrices   279

CHAPTER **11** **Linear Inequalities**

11.1 Definitions and notation   284
11.2 Inequalities and convex sets   285

11.3 Convex cones   288
11.4 Polar cones and double description   290
11.5 Linear programming   293
11.6 The Minimax Theorem   295
11.7 Matrix games   298

      Appendix I   Mathematical Induction   302

      Appendix II   Relations and Mappings   306

      Appendix III Bibliography   309

      Glossary of Special Symbols   311

      Index   313

Chapter 1 | Vector Spaces

1.1. Introduction. In arithmetic and elementary algebra we study operations on numbers and on symbols which represent numbers. In plane geometry we describe each point by a pair of numbers and so can bring the tools of algebra to bear on geometry. In solid geometry a triple of numbers is employed, and for higher dimensions we merely use more numbers to describe each point and proceed algebraically much as in the two- and three-dimensional cases. Even though for dimensions greater than three we have no direct physical representation for the geometry, it is still useful to employ geometric language in describing the algebraic results.

The next stage in the development usually is the introduction of vectors* into geometry. Frequently vectors are initially defined as directed line segments. Two line segments with equal length, the same direction numbers, and the same sense define equal vectors. Vectors find applications in many parts of mathematics. Since they arise in geometry vectors are apt to appear in any mathematical problem that has a geometric setting. Topics in which vectors are used extensively include mechanics, dynamics, linear differential equations, statistics, differential geometry, mathematical economics, function spaces, algebraic number theory, systems of linear equations, and theory of games.

It is our purpose in the present book to give a development of the theory of vector spaces in such a way as to facilitate applications in all of these theories, and we shall include introductory treatments of several of these applications. With such a broad list of applications in mind it seems appropriate (indeed almost essential) to employ an axiomatic approach. The axiomatic approach has the additional advantage of providing an introduction to modern abstract algebra.

---

* The brief discussion of vectors that follows is to be regarded only as descriptive. Formal introduction of vectors is made in Section 1.4.

There is also an economy of thought and simplicity of proof made possible by the use of the abstract approach. However, since the beginner may need or wish for something concrete with which to work, most of the presentation is arranged so that whenever a concept is introduced in one section it is accompanied by a concrete interpretation in that section or the preceding or following section. For example, we first define linear transformation and then matrix, and following each development of some portion of the theory of linear transformations we give the corresponding theory for matrices.

We now summarize the earlier part of the book. First the idea of a field is introduced; the set of all real numbers or of all complex numbers is an example of a field. Next vector spaces are defined; the most important example is the set of all ordered n-tuples $(a_1, \cdots, a_n)$, where the a_i lie in a field. This leads to the consideration of a special function, called a linear transformation, which maps a vector of one vector space into a vector of another or possibly the same vector space. The usefulness of linear transformations in the theory of matrices arises not only from the fact that in a certain way is there a one-to-one correspondence between such transformations and matrices which preserves addition and multiplication, but also many of the operations with matrices have a simple interpretation in terms of linear transformations. Thus the use of these transformations not only provides simpler proofs but our comprehension of matrices, e.g., of which statements about them may be true or false and the discovery of proofs, is deepened when put in a context of linear transformations. Thus Section 2.1, where linear transformations are defined, is central for an understanding of much of the book. And this conviction of the helpfulness of linear transformations will grow the further the reader advances in the book.

The reader may recall the use of vectors in physics and in geometry. In these cases various properties of vectors and operations with them are studied; in particular, the ideas of *length* and *direction* of vectors are important. In many parts of mathematics, where vectors are used, however, neither length nor direction are important (or even defined); the concepts which always appear are *addition of vectors* and *multiplication of vectors by scalars*. In most of the early chapters we focus attention on these operations and later (Chapter 7) examine special cases in which length and direction are meaningful.

In the plane a vector is determined by two points, an initial point (a_1, a_2) and a terminal point (b_1, b_2), or more simply by a single point (c_1, c_2) which is the terminal point when the origin $(0, 0)$ is chosen as the initial point. Then $c_1 = b_1 - a_1$ and $c_2 = b_2 - a_2$. Similarly, in three dimensions a vector γ may be represented by a point C with coordinates c_1, c_2, c_3, these coordinates being real numbers and depending upon the coordinate system. For simplicity we write $\gamma = (c_1, c_2, c_3)$ and call c_1, c_2, c_3 the *components* of γ with respect to the coordinate system.

Consider the vector $\alpha = (a_1, a_2, a_3)$ and its representative point A. The

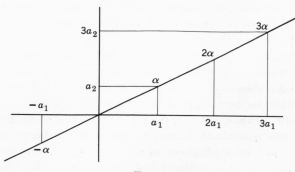

FIG. 1

product $c\alpha$ of α by a real number c is the vector (ca_1, ca_2, ca_3). The point corresponding to $c\alpha$ lies at a distance from the origin O which is $|c|$ times the distance of A from O, and in the same direction if $c > 0$, but in the opposite direction if $c < 0$ (see Fig. 1).

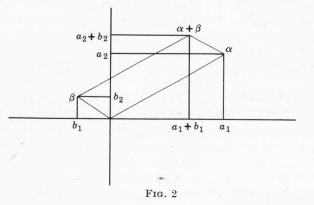

FIG. 2

If $\alpha = (a_1, a_2, a_3)$ and $\beta = (b_1, b_2, b_3)$ are two vectors with representative points A and B, respectively, their sum $\alpha + \beta$ is the vector $\gamma = (a_1 + b_1, a_2 + b_2, a_3 + b_3)$. Geometrically the representative point C for γ is obtained as the fourth vertex of a parallelogram having A, B, O as vertices and with A and B opposite each other (see Fig. 2).

1.2. Scalars. In the preceding discussion the only properties of real numbers that we have used are that they can be added and multiplied to yield real numbers; i.e., the closure under addition and multiplication. Soon we shall require other simple properties of addition and multiplication. Not only does the set $\Re$ of real numbers have the needed properties, but also the set $\mathfrak{C}$ of all complex numbers and the set $\mathfrak{Q}$ of all rational numbers, and in certain applications, even in geometry, it is desirable that the set of numbers be not always $\Re$, but sometimes $\mathfrak{C}$ or $\mathfrak{Q}$. For a considerable portion of this book we shall be using properties that all these sets have. These properties are listed below and define a field. The abstraction of field includes more than that of the special cases $\mathfrak{Q}$, $\Re$, and $\mathfrak{C}$; other common examples are given later.

Before embarking on our discussion of fields we say a few words about the axiomatic method. It frequently happens in mathematics that several systems arise which have a number of common properties. It may also be that the applications of these systems depend primarily on these common properties. When this is so, it is usually advantageous to set up an abstract system with these common properties as axioms (or postulates). One important advantage of using an axiomatically defined system is that any theorem that follows from the axioms holds for every system that satisfies these axioms, whereas without the axiomatic approach the theorem would have to be proved separately for each system.

A *field* $\mathscr{F}$ is composed of a set of elements called *scalars* or *numbers*, here denoted by $a, b, c, \cdots$, and two operations, addition and multiplication, satisfying the following axioms.

	Addition	Multiplication
Closure	$a + b$ is in $\mathscr{F}$	ab is in $\mathscr{F}$
Associativity	$(a + b) + c = a + (b + c)$	$(ab)c = a(bc)$
Commutativity	$a + b = b + a$	$ab = ba$
Existence of a zero scalar 0	$a + 0 = 0 + a = a$	
Existence of a unit scalar $1\ (1 \neq 0)$		$a \cdot 1 = 1 \cdot a = a$
Existence of a negative $-a$ for every a	$a + (-a) = (-a) + a = 0$	
Existence of a reciprocal a^{-1} for every $a \neq 0$		$aa^{-1} = a^{-1}a = 1$
Left distributivity		$a(b + c) = ab + ac$
Right distributivity		$(a + b)c = ac + bc$

Some of the axioms are superfluous. For example, right distributivity is a consequence of left distributivity and the commutativity of multiplication. These excess axioms have been included because we are interested here not in the briefest description of a field but in the simple properties that are to be used and also because we shall compare fields with other axiomatic algebraic systems which will be introduced later.

The fields $\mathfrak{Q}$, $\mathfrak{R}$, and $\mathfrak{C}$ each have special properties, not resulting from the axioms for a field, which will be disregarded in all that follows except in a few applications. The proofs of some of these properties are not short, and we do not give them in this book.

A real number may be defined as an infinite decimal. The set $\mathfrak{R}$ has the property, not possessed by all fields, that every number in it is either the square or the negative of the square of an appropriate number in $\mathfrak{R}$.

The set $\mathfrak{C}$ of complex numbers consists of all quantities of the form $a + bi$ with a, b in $\mathfrak{R}$ and $i^2 = -1$. It has the special property of being *algebraically closed*: i.e., every nonconstant polynomial with coefficients in $\mathfrak{C}$ has a root in $\mathfrak{C}$ and can be factored into linear factors.

A rational number is a real number that can be expressed as p/q, where p, q are integers and $q \neq 0$. The set $\mathfrak{Q}$ has the property that, no matter how many times 1 is added to itself, the sum is never 0. This property is also true of $\mathfrak{R}$ and $\mathfrak{C}$, but not of $\mathscr{F}_5$ given below. If in a field $\mathscr{F}$, zero is the sum of p 1's and if p is the smallest such positive integer, then $\mathscr{F}$ is said to have *characteristic* p.

In all that follows $\mathscr{F}$ will stand for an arbitrary field unless there is some contrary stipulation. Of course any theorem involving number systems which can be proved assuming only the field axioms is automatically valid for $\mathfrak{Q}$, $\mathfrak{R}$, and $\mathfrak{C}$. Without the abstract concept of field such a theorem would have to be proved separately for each of the three cases, and would then be established only for these three cases. *However, the reader who is unfamiliar with fields will be able to comprehend all the essential parts of the theory of vector spaces and matrices if he ignores the field axioms and thinks of $\mathscr{F}$ merely as being an unspecified one of the three systems $\mathfrak{Q}$, $\mathfrak{R}$, or $\mathfrak{C}$.*

We next consider some consequences of the field axioms. A complicated appearing product such as $\{[a(bc)][(de)f]\}[(gh)k]$ can be reduced to the simple left-to-right multiplication $(((((((ab)c)d)e)f)g)h)k$ by repeated applications of the associative law. This equality justifies the use of the simpler notation $abcdefghk$ for both products. The following theorem generalizes and formalizes this result.

THEOREM 1.2A. GENERALIZED ASSOCIATIVE LAW. *Let $a_1, \cdots, a_n$ be elements of a field $\mathscr{F}$, let $a_1 a_2 \cdots a_n$ denote the left-to-right product $(\cdots (a_1 a_2) a_3 \cdots) a_n$, and let $g(a_1, \cdots, a_n)$ denote any other product defined by inserting parentheses in the ordered sequence $a_1, \cdots, a_n$. Then $g(a_1, \cdots, a_n) = a_1 a_2 \cdots a_n$.*

We prove this theorem by induction on n (see appendix on mathematical induction). For $n = 1$ there is no product, and so $g(a_1) = a_1$ trivially. For $n = 2$ the only product is $a_1 a_2$, and so $g(a_1, a_2) = a_1 a_2$. For $n = 3$

there are only the two products $a_1a_2a_3 = (a_1a_2)a_3$ and $a_1(a_2a_3)$, and the equality of these is just what the associative law states. Now make the induction hypothesis that the theorem is true for all products with less than r factors. Among the parentheses that define the product $g(a_1, \cdots, a_r)$ consider only the outermost pair. They give

$$g(a_1a_2 \cdots a_r) = g_1(a_1 \cdots a_s)g_2(a_{s+1} \cdots a_r),$$

where $1 \leq s < r$ and g_1, g_2 are products with $s, r - s$ factors, respectively.

First suppose $s = r - 1$. Then by our induction hypothesis $g_1(a_1, \cdots, a_{r-1}) = a_1 \cdots a_{r-1}$ and $g(a_1, \cdots, a_r) = (a_1 \cdots a_{r-1})a_r = a_1 \cdots a_r$ by definition of the product $a_1 \cdots a_r$. Next, if $s < r - 1$, then by our induction hypothesis we have $g_1(a_1, \cdots, a_s) = a_1 \cdots a_s$, $g_2(a_{s+1}, \cdots, a_r)$ $= (a_{s+1} \cdots a_{r-1})a_r$, and hence $g(a_1, \cdots, a_r) = (a_1 \cdots a_s)[(a_{s+1} \cdots a_{r-1})a_r]$. Apply the associative law to this product, and we have $g(a_1, \cdots, a_r)$ $= [(a_1 \cdots a_s)(a_{s+1} \cdots a_{r-1})]a_r$. Now, once again, by our induction hypothesis $(a_1 \cdots a_s)(a_{s+1} \cdots a_{r-1}) = a_1 \cdots a_{r-1}$, and finally $g(a_1, \cdots, a_r)$ $= (a_1 \cdots a_{r-1})a_r = a_1 \ldots a_r$ as required by the theorem.

For later applications we point out that the proof of the generalized associative law required only closure and the associative law for products of three factors. Hence it will hold in any system closed under an associative product or other associative operation. In particular, it holds for addition in fields, so that we may write simply $a_1 + \cdots + a_n$ for any way of summing the ordered summands $a_1, \cdots, a_n$.

Let us now turn to the axioms concerning the existence of zero and negatives. We know for the real, the rational, and the complex number fields that zero and negatives not only exist but are unique. We now prove this for all fields. First suppose that $a = a + 0^*$ for a pair 0^* and a in $\mathscr{F}$. Then we have $0 = (-a) + a = (-a) + (a + 0^*)$ $= ((-a) + a) + 0^* = 0 + 0^* = 0^*$, and hence $0 = 0^*$. We have shown not only that 0 is unique but that, if $a + 0^* = a$ for a single quantity a in $\mathscr{F}$, then $0^* = 0$. Similarly, if b and b^* are both negatives for a, we get $b = b + 0 = b + (a + b^*) = (b + a) + b^* = 0 + b^* = b^*$; i.e., $b = b^*$.

We leave as an exercise to the reader the analogous proof that the unit element and reciprocals are unique. As a simplification we sometimes write $a - b$ for $a + (-b)$, and a/b for $a(b^{-1})$.

We next show that $0a = a0 = 0$. We have $a0 = a(0 + 0) = a0 + a0$ by the distributive law. Thus we have an equation $b + 0^* = b$, where $b = a \cdot 0$ and $0^* = a \cdot 0$, and hence as proved above $a \cdot 0 = 0$. The other equality $0a = 0$ follows at once from the commutative law of multiplication or can be proved from the equation $0a = (0 + 0)a = 0a + 0a$. The latter method has the advantage of not using the commutative law and hence will apply even in systems where multiplication is not commutative.

The remainder of the present section deals with some additional examples of fields and is not essential to the theory of vector spaces and matrices.

First consider the set $\mathscr{F}$ of all real numbers of the form $a + b\sqrt{2}$ where a and b are rational numbers. Since the elements of $\mathscr{F}$ are real numbers, they automatically satisfy the associativity, commutativity, and distributivity axioms. The zero element is the real number 0, and it has the appropriate form, viz. $0 = 0 + 0\sqrt{2}$. Similarly the unit element is 1 which equals $1 + 0\sqrt{2}$. The negative of $a + b\sqrt{2}$ is $(-a) + (-b)\sqrt{2}$. The reciprocal (or inverse) of $a + b\sqrt{2}$ is $\dfrac{a}{a^2 - 2b^2} + \dfrac{-b}{a^2 - 2b^2}\sqrt{2}$, a fact that can be verified by forming the product, provided that the denominator $a^2 - 2b^2 \neq 0$. Suppose $a^2 - 2b^2 = 0$. If $b = 0$, then $a = 0$ and $a + b\sqrt{2} = 0$ and no inverse is required. But, if $b \neq 0$, then $\sqrt{2} = a/b$, which is rational when a and b are; this is a contradiction to the fact that $\sqrt{2}$ is irrational. Finally the closure axioms can be easily checked. In particular for multiplication the product $(a + b\sqrt{2})(c + d\sqrt{2}) = (ac + 2bd) + (ad + bc)\sqrt{2}$.

As a second example consider the set $\mathscr{F}$ of all rational functions $f(x) = p(x)/q(x)$ where $p(x)$ and $q(x)$ are polynomials with real coefficients and $q(x) \neq 0$. That the axioms hold in $\mathscr{F}$ follows readily from this being so in $\mathfrak{R}$ together with the properties of fractions. The details of the proof that $\mathscr{F}$ is a field are left to the reader.

For our final example we use the remainders of integers on division by 5. These five numbers 0,1,2,3,4 form a field $\mathscr{F}_5$ with addition defined using the remainder of the ordinary sum, e.g., $2 + 4 = 1$ and multiplication by means of the remainder after forming the ordinary product, e.g., $2 \cdot 4 = 3$. The reader can check that the field axioms all hold in $\mathscr{F}_5$. An interesting property of this field is that it has characteristic 5.

Exercises 1.2

1. Show that the integers under ordinary addition and multiplication do not form a field.

2. Show that the rational functions $f(x) = p(x)/q(x)$, where $q(x) \neq 0$ and $p(x)$, $q(x)$ are polynomials with real coefficients, form a field.

3. Show that the six remainders of integers on division by 6 do not form a field, if addition is defined by adding as usual and taking remainders, and if multiplication is defined analogously.

4. Show that the commutativity of addition follows from the other axioms for a field.

5. In any field $\mathscr{F}$ prove the uniqueness of the unit scalar and of the reciprocal a^{-1} of any nonzero scalar a.

6. Prove the generalized distributive law in a field $\mathscr{F}$: If $c, a_1, a_2, \cdots, a_n$ are in $\mathscr{F}$ then

$$(a_1 + a_2 + \cdots + a_n)c = a_1c + a_2c + \cdots + a_nc.$$

7. Prove that in a field $-a = (-1)a$.

8. Is division associative?

9. Show that $\sqrt{2}$ is irrational. (Hint: show that no fraction a/b in lowest terms can have 2 as its square.)

10. Given that multiplication is associative, prove (without use of the generalized associative law) that $(ab)(cd) = a((bc)d)$.

11. Show, similarly, that $\{[a(bc)][(de)f]\}[(gh)k] = (((((((ab)c)d)e)f)g)h)k$.

1.3. Cartesian space. Let $\mathscr{F}$ be a field. Consider the set of all ordered n-tuples $(a_1, a_2, \cdots, a_n)$ of scalars $a_1, a_2, \cdots, a_n$ in $\mathscr{F}$. We say that $(a_1, a_2, \cdots, a_n) = (b_1, b_2, \cdots, b_n)$ if and only if $a_1 = b_1$, $a_2 = b_2, \cdots$, $a_n = b_n$.

If $\alpha = (a_1, a_2, \cdots, a_n)$ and $\beta = (b_1, b_2, \cdots, b_n)$ are two n-tuples, then their sum $\alpha + \beta$ is defined to be the n-tuple

$$\alpha + \beta = (a_1 + b_1, a_2 + b_2, \cdots, a_n + b_n).$$

The same symbol $+$ is being used for addition of n-tuples and addition of scalars; strictly, different symbols should be used. However, it is almost always clear from the context which type of addition is to be performed and no confusion should arise from the double role of the symbol $+$.

It is easy to see that $\alpha + \beta = \beta + \alpha$; i.e., that addition of n-tuples is commutative, as a consequence of the commutativity of addition in $\mathscr{F}$. Other simple properties will soon be given.

The product $c\alpha$ of an n-tuple $\alpha = (a_1, a_2, \cdots, a_n)$ by a scalar c is defined to be the n-tuple

$$(3.1) \qquad\qquad c\alpha = (ca_1, ca_2, \cdots, ca_n).$$

The set of all such n-tuples, together with equality, addition, and multiplication by scalars as defined above, is called the *Cartesian space of dimension n over* $\mathscr{F}$ and will be denoted by $\mathscr{V}_n(\mathscr{F})$. Here, of course, the term "space" has a generalized meaning. In particular $\mathscr{V}_2(\mathfrak{R})$ is the ordinary plane and $\mathscr{V}_3(\mathfrak{R})$ is ordinary space discussed in Section 1.1. The n-tuples which comprise $\mathscr{V}_n(\mathscr{F})$ will be called *vectors* in $\mathscr{V}_n(\mathscr{F})$.

If $\alpha = (a_1, a_2, \cdots, a_n)$ is a vector in $\mathscr{V}_n(\mathscr{F})$, then the scalars $a_1, a_2, \cdots$, a_n are called the *components* of α. From our definitions we see that (1) two vectors in $\mathscr{V}_n(\mathscr{F})$ are equal if and only if corresponding components are equal, (2) two vectors are added by adding corresponding components, and (3) a vector is multiplied by a scalar by multiplying each component by the scalar. Thus all operations in $\mathscr{V}_n(\mathscr{F})$ are reduced to operations in $\mathscr{F}$.

From the properties of $\mathscr{F}$ we can deduce properties for $\mathscr{V}_n(\mathscr{F})$.

First $\mathscr{V}_n(\mathscr{F})$ is closed under addition; i.e., $\alpha + \beta$ always exists. This follows from the fact that the components of $\alpha + \beta$ are simply $a_i + b_i$ ($i = 1, \cdots, n$), and each of these sums exists because of the closure of $\mathscr{F}$ under addition.

Next, $(\alpha + \beta) + \gamma = \alpha + (\beta + \gamma)$. The ith component of $\alpha + \beta$ is $a_i + b_i$. If $\gamma = (c_1, c_2, \cdots, c_n)$, the ith component of $(\alpha + \beta) + \gamma$ is $(a_i + b_i) + c_i$. Similarly the ith component of $\alpha + (\beta + \gamma)$ is $a_i + (b_i + c_i)$. Hence, by the associativity of addition in $\mathscr{F}$, we have associativity of addition in $\mathscr{V}_n(\mathscr{F})$.

The vector $0 = (0, 0, \cdots, 0)$ acts as a zero for addition of vectors. For $\alpha + 0 = (a_1, a_2, \cdots, a_n) + (0, 0, \cdots, 0) = (a_1 + 0, a_2 + 0, \cdots, a_n + 0) = (a_1, a_2, \cdots, a_n)$ because of the analogous property for 0 in $\mathscr{F}$.

If $\alpha = (a_1, a_2, \cdots, a_n)$ and $\delta = (-a_1, -a_2, \cdots, -a_n)$ then $\alpha + \delta = 0$ because the ith component of the left side is $a_i + (-a_i)$ which equals 0. Similarly $\delta + \alpha = 0$. Now δ is in $\mathscr{V}_n(\mathscr{F})$ because of the existence of negatives in $\mathscr{F}$. Hence for every vector α there exists a δ such that $\alpha + \delta = \delta + \alpha = 0$.

The ith component of $\alpha + \beta$ is $a_i + b_i$ which equals $b_i + a_i$, the ith component of $\beta + \alpha$. Hence $\alpha + \beta = \beta + \alpha$. Thus commutativity of addition of vectors in $\mathscr{V}_n(\mathscr{F})$ is a consequence of commutativity of addition in $\mathscr{F}$.

Next, $c\alpha$ defined by (3.1) is an element of $\mathscr{V}_n(\mathscr{F})$ because of the closure of multiplication in $\mathscr{F}$. Hence $\mathscr{V}_n(\mathscr{F})$ is closed under multiplication of a vector by a scalar.

If c is a scalar, then $c(\alpha + \beta)$ has as its ith component $c(a_i + b_i)$. This equals $ca_i + cb_i$, by the distributive law in $\mathscr{F}$, and this is the ith component of $c\alpha + c\beta$. Consequently $c(\alpha + \beta) = c\alpha + c\beta$.

Also if c, d are scalars, $(c + d)\alpha$ has $(c + d)a_i$ for its ith component. By the distributive law in $\mathscr{F}$, this equals $ca_i + da_i$, which is the ith component of $c\alpha + d\alpha$. Thus $(c + d)\alpha = c\alpha + d\alpha$.

Furthermore $(cd)\alpha = c(d\alpha)$. For, the ith component of $(cd)\alpha$ is $(cd)a_i$, and this equals $c(da_i)$, the ith component of $c(d\alpha)$.

Finally $1\alpha = (1 \cdot a_1, 1 \cdot a_2, \cdots, 1 \cdot a_n) = (a_1, a_2, \cdots, a_n) = \alpha$ from the property of the 1 element in $\mathscr{F}$.

The properties of $\mathscr{V}_n(\mathscr{F})$ proved above, ten in number, will be taken as axioms for the more general structure called a vector space defined in the next section. Although $\mathscr{V}_n(\mathscr{F})$ has all these properties, it is only a special example of a vector space. It is, however, an exceedingly important case, as will become clear in Section 1.7 below.

Exercises 1.3

1. In $\mathscr{V}_3(\mathscr{F})$ if $\alpha = (3, 0, 1)$ and $\beta = (1, 2, -2)$, find
    (a) $\alpha + \beta$,   (b) 2β,   (c) $3\alpha + (-2)\beta$.

Verify that

    (d) $2(\alpha + \beta) = 2\alpha + 2\beta$,

    (e) $(3 + 2)\beta = 3\beta + 2\beta$.

    2. In $\mathscr{V}_5(\mathscr{F})$ let $\alpha = (2, 1, 2, 0, -1)$, $\beta = (3, 1, 2, -1, 0)$, $\gamma = (-3, -2, 1, 8, 1)$. Find $2\alpha + 3\beta - 4\gamma$, $-3\alpha + \beta + 2\gamma$.

    3. In $\mathscr{V}_4(\mathscr{F})$ let $\varepsilon_1 = (1, 0, 0, 0)$, $\varepsilon_2 = (0, 1, 0, 0)$, $\varepsilon_3 = (0, 0, 1, 0)$, $\varepsilon_4 = (0, 0, 0, 1)$, $\alpha = (-3, 1, -2, 4)$, $\beta = (b_1, b_2, b_3, b_4)$. Show that $\alpha = -3\varepsilon_1 + \varepsilon_2 - 2\varepsilon_3 + 4\varepsilon_4$ and that $\beta = b_1\varepsilon_1 + b_2\varepsilon_2 + b_3\varepsilon_3 + b_4\varepsilon_4$.

    4. Let ε_1, ε_2, ε_3, ε_4 be as in Exercise 3. Show that $c_1\varepsilon_1 + c_2\varepsilon_2 + c_3\varepsilon_3 + c_4\varepsilon_4 = 0$ if and only if $c_1 = c_2 = c_3 = c_4 = 0$.

    5. If $\alpha = (3, -2, -1, 1)$, $\beta = (-3, 1, -2, 1)$, find a vector $\gamma = (c_1, c_2, c_3, c_4)$ for which $2\alpha + 3\gamma = \beta$.

    6. Let $\alpha = (2, 1, -2)$, $\beta = (-4, 2, 3)$, $\gamma = (-8, 8, 5)$, $\delta = (1, 3, 5)$. Show that there exists a scalar x for which $2\alpha + x\beta = \gamma$. Show that there are no scalars x and y for which $x\alpha + y\beta = \delta$.

1.4. Vector spaces.

The Cartesian space $\mathscr{V}_n(\mathscr{F})$ is an example of what we shall call a vector space. The concept of a vector space comes essentially from abstracting the properties of $\mathscr{V}_n(\mathscr{F})$.

A *vector space* $\mathscr{V}$ *over a field* $\mathscr{F}$ consists of a set of elements called *vectors* together with two operations, addition of vectors and multiplication of a vector by a scalar, satisfying the following axioms. Here α, β, γ stand for arbitrary vectors in $\mathscr{V}$ and c, d for arbitrary scalars.

Axioms for Addition of Vectors

(A1)   Closure: for every two vectors α, β there is a vector in $\mathscr{V}$ called the *sum* of α and β, written $\alpha + \beta$.

(A2)   Associativity: $(\alpha + \beta) + \gamma = \alpha + (\beta + \gamma)$.

(A3)   Zero vector: a vector 0 exists such that, for any vector α, always $\alpha + 0 = 0 + \alpha = \alpha$.

(A4)   Negative of a vector: for every α, there is a vector δ such that $\alpha + \delta = \delta + \alpha = 0$ (such a vector δ is usually written $-\alpha$).

(A5)   Commutativity: $\alpha + \beta = \beta + \alpha$.

Axioms for Multiplication of a Vector by a Scalar

(S1)   Closure: for every vector α and scalar c there is a vector in $\mathscr{V}$ called the *product of α by c* and written $c\alpha$.

(S2) $c(\alpha + \beta) = c\alpha + c\beta$.

(S3) $(c + d)\alpha = c\alpha + d\alpha$.

(S4) $(cd)\alpha = c(d\alpha)$.

(S5) $1\alpha = \alpha$.

Note that the symbol 0 is used both for the zero scalar and for the zero vector. Just which meaning is to be given to the symbol is always clear from the context. However, for additional emphasis and clarity we sometimes use the symbol $0_{\mathscr{V}}$ for the zero vector in the vector space $\mathscr{V}$.

Observe that S2 and S3 are in a sense distributive laws. Also S2, S3,

S4 account for all of the simplest combinations of operations on vectors with operations on scalars.

That $\mathscr{V}_n(\mathscr{F})$ is a vector space over $\mathscr{F}$ was verified in the preceding section. We recall that $0_{\mathscr{V}} = (0, 0, \cdots, 0)$ and, if $\alpha = (a_1, a_2, \cdots, a_n)$, then $-\alpha = (-a_1, -a_2, \cdots, -a_n)$. Consequently $-\alpha = (-1)\alpha$.

Another example of a vector space over $\mathscr{F}$ is the set $\mathscr{L} = \mathscr{L}_n(\mathscr{F})$ whose elements are all linear homogeneous polynomials in $x_1, x_2, \cdots, x_n$ with coefficients in $\mathscr{F}$. An element α in $\mathscr{L}_n(\mathscr{F})$ thus has the form

$$\alpha = a_1 x_1 + a_2 x_2 + \cdots + a_n x_n,$$

where $a_1, a_2, \cdots, a_n$ are in $\mathscr{F}$. If $\beta = b_1 x_1 + b_2 x_2 + \cdots + b_n x_n$ is another vector in $\mathscr{L}_n(\mathscr{F})$, then, using ordinary addition of polynomials and multiplication of a polynomial by a number, we have

$$\alpha + \beta = (a_1 + b_1)x_1 + (a_2 + b_2)x_2 + \cdots + (a_n + b_n)x_n,$$

and, if c is a scalar,

$$c\alpha = (ca_1)x_1 + (ca_2)x_2 + \cdots + (ca_n)x_n.$$

This shows the closure of $\mathscr{L}_n(\mathscr{F})$ under these two operations. The remaining axioms of a vector space are easily verified. In particular the zero vector $0_{\mathscr{L}}$ is $0_{\mathscr{L}} = 0 \cdot x_1 + 0 \cdot x_2 + \cdots + 0 \cdot x_n$.

The next example comes from solutions of equations. A set of equations

$$
\begin{aligned}
a_{11}x_1 + a_{12}x_2 + \cdots + a_{1n}x_n &= 0, \\
a_{21}x_1 + a_{22}x_2 + \cdots + a_{2n}x_n &= 0, \\
\cdot \quad \cdot \quad \cdot \quad \cdots \quad \cdot \\
a_{m1}x_1 + a_{m2}x_2 + \cdots + a_{mn}x_n &= 0,
\end{aligned}
$$

(4.1)

where the coefficients a_{ij} are scalars chosen from some field $\mathscr{F}$ is said to be a system of *m homogeneous linear equations in n unknowns*. (The adjective "homogeneous" refers to the fact that the right-hand sides are all zero; in a nonhomogeneous system the right-hand sides could be arbitrary scalars in $\mathscr{F}$.) By a solution of the system (4.1) we mean a vector $\gamma = (c_1, \cdots, c_n)$ in $\mathscr{V}_n(\mathscr{F})$ such that the m equations

$$a_{i1}c_1 + a_{i2}c_2 + \cdots + a_{in}c_n = 0 \qquad (i = 1, \cdots, m)$$

are identities in $\mathscr{F}$. The zero vector $(0, \cdots, 0)$ is clearly a solution no matter what coefficients a_{ij} are selected; this solution is said to be *trivial* and all other solutions are said to be *nontrivial*.

As an illustration let $\mathscr{F}$ be the rational field $\mathfrak{Q}$, and consider the system

(4.2)

$$
\begin{aligned}
2x_1 + x_3 - x_4 &= 0, \\
x_2 - 2x_3 - 3x_4 &= 0;
\end{aligned}
$$

the vectors $\alpha_1 = (0, 5, 1, 1)$, $\alpha_2 = (-1, 4, 2, 0)$, $\alpha_3 = (1, 6, 0, 2)$, α_4

$= (1, 11, 1, 3)$, and $\alpha_5 = (3, -12, -6, 0)$ in $\mathscr{V}_4(\mathscr{F})$ are readily seen to be solutions of the system (4.2). Note that $\alpha_4 = \alpha_1 + \alpha_3$ and that $\alpha_5 = -3\alpha_2$.

More generally if $\alpha = (a_1, \cdots, a_n)$ and $\beta = (b_1, \cdots, b_n)$ are any two solutions of (4.1) and if c is any scalar, then $\gamma = \alpha + \beta$ and $\delta = c\alpha$ are also solutions of (4.1). (This can be proved by direct substitution in (4.1) of the components of γ and δ.)

The set $\mathscr{W}$ of all solutions of the system (4.1) is a subset of $\mathscr{V}_n(\mathscr{F})$. We have just noted that axioms A1 and S1 hold in $\mathscr{W}$. The remaining axioms for a vector space are also satisfied in $\mathscr{W}$ (the reader should check this). Thus we see that *the set of all solutions of any system of homogeneous linear equations is a vector space.*

The set of solutions of a linear nonhomogeneous system of equations is not a vector space because the sum of two solutions is not necessarily a solution nor is the product of a solution by a scalar.

Another example of a vector space over a field $\mathscr{F}$ is the set of all infinite sequences $(a_1, a_2, \cdots)$, where $a_1, a_2, \cdots$ lie in $\mathscr{F}$, with addition defined by

$$(a_1, a_2, \cdots) + (b_1, b_2, \cdots) = (a_1 + b_1, a_2 + b_2, \cdots),$$

and multiplication by a scalar c defined by

$$c(a_1, a_2, \cdots) = (ca_1, ca_2, \cdots).$$

We now prove some simple properties of a general vector space $\mathscr{V}$ from the axioms.

If there is a vector β for which $\alpha + \beta = \alpha$, then necessarily $\beta = 0_{\mathscr{V}}$. For on adding $-\alpha$ to both sides we obtain on the left $-\alpha + (\alpha + \beta) = (-\alpha + \alpha) + \beta = 0_{\mathscr{V}} + \beta = \beta$, while getting on the right $-\alpha + \alpha = 0_{\mathscr{V}}$. We conclude that $\beta = 0_{\mathscr{V}}$.

Another fact is that $0\alpha = 0_{\mathscr{V}}$ for any α. For, $0\alpha = (0 + 0)\alpha = 0\alpha + 0\alpha$. But, by the preceding paragraph, using 0α in place of α and β, we conclude that $0\alpha = 0_{\mathscr{V}}$.

Next we show that $-\alpha$ is unique. For, suppose that $\alpha + \beta = \alpha + \gamma = 0_{\mathscr{V}}$. Then $\beta = \beta + 0_{\mathscr{V}} = \beta + (\alpha + \gamma) = (\beta + \alpha) + \gamma = 0_{\mathscr{V}} + \gamma = \gamma$; i.e., $\beta = \gamma$ or, in other words, a vector has only one negative.

Finally we show that $-\alpha = (-1)\alpha$. This follows from the relation $0_{\mathscr{V}} = 0\alpha = (1 + (-1))\alpha = 1\alpha + (-1)\alpha = \alpha + (-1)\alpha$, where we have used successively the preceding paragraphs, and axioms S4 and S5. This shows that $(-1)\alpha$ is a negative for α. But, since there can be only one negative, $(-1)\alpha = -\alpha$ as claimed.

We shall mean by $\alpha - \beta$ the vector $\alpha + (-\beta)$. In particular $\alpha - \alpha = 0_{\mathscr{V}}$.

Notice that some of the results presented here for vector spaces were given for fields in Section 1.2. Indeed several of the proofs differ only in the notation.

Exercises 1.4

1. Let c be a scalar and α, β vectors. Prove that $c(\alpha - \beta) = c\alpha - c\beta$.

2. Let $c, c_1, \cdots, c_n$ be scalars and $\alpha, \alpha_1, \cdots, \alpha_n$ vectors. Show that $c(\alpha_1 + \cdots + \alpha_n) = c\alpha_1 + \cdots + c\alpha_n$ and $(c_1 + \cdots + c_n)\alpha = c_1\alpha + \cdots + c_n\alpha$.

3. Verify that $\mathscr{L}_n(\mathscr{F})$ satisfies the postulates for a vector space.

4. Show that all polynomials in a single variable x with coefficients in the field $\mathfrak{Q}$, with addition and multiplication by scalars defined as ordinary addition and multiplication of a function by a constant, form a vector space.

5. Show that all real single-valued functions of x on the interval $a \leq x \leq b$, with addition and multiplication by scalars defined as ordinary addition and multiplication of a function by a real number, form a vector space.

6. Do likewise using the set composed only of 0 and those polynomials in x with coefficients in a field $\mathscr{F}$ whose degree does not exceed some fixed positive integer n.

7. Let $\mathscr{F}_5$ be as in Section 1.2. How many vectors are there in $\mathscr{V}_2(\mathscr{F}_5)$? In $\mathscr{V}_3(\mathscr{F}_5)$? In $\mathscr{V}_n(\mathscr{F}_5)$?

8. Prove that, for any pair of vectors α, β, there is a vector ξ such that $\alpha + \xi = \beta$.

9. Prove that $-0_{\mathscr{V}} = 0_{\mathscr{V}}$.

10. Prove that a field $\mathscr{F}$ is, in particular, a vector space over $\mathscr{F}$.

11. Prove that $\mathfrak{R}$ is a vector space over $\mathfrak{Q}$.

12. Let $\mathscr{L} = \mathscr{L}_4(\mathscr{F})$. If $\alpha = x_1 + 3x_4$, $\beta = -x_2 + x_3 - 2x_4$, $\gamma = 2x_1 + x_2$, show that $(\alpha + \beta) + \gamma = \alpha + (\beta + \gamma)$ and that $3(\alpha + \beta) = 3\alpha + 3\beta$. Find $-\beta, 2\alpha - \beta + 3\gamma, 2\gamma - \alpha$. Find a vector δ such that $\alpha + 2\beta - \gamma + \delta = 0_{\mathscr{L}}$.

1.5. Independence of vectors.

Let $\mathscr{V}$ be a vector space over $\mathscr{F}$, and let $\mathscr{S} = \{\alpha_1, \alpha_2, \cdots, \alpha_r\}$ be a finite nonvacuous ordered set of vectors in $\mathscr{V}$. The set $\mathscr{S}$ is said to be *dependent* (sometimes called *linearly dependent*) if there exist scalars $c_1, c_2, \cdots, c_r$ not all zero such that

$$(5.1) \qquad 0 = c_1\alpha_1 + c_2\alpha_2 + \cdots + c_r\alpha_r.$$

[Although we have defined addition of only two vectors at a time, it is a consequence of the associativity of addition that the sum in (5.1) is unambiguous; see Theorem 1.2A.]

The set $\mathscr{S}$ is said to be *independent* if the only solution of (5.1) is $c_1 = c_2 = \cdots = c_r = 0$. An arbitrary set of vectors is said to be independent if every finite ordered subset is independent, and is otherwise said to be dependent.

We also agree to call the vacuous set independent. This decision may seem arbitrary and, from some points of view, unreasonable, but it does make most theorems hold without change whenever the case of a vacuous set occurs, e.g., Lemma 1.5A. Usually in the proof of such theorems the case of a vacuous set requires special consideration, but the proof is almost always trivial. Ordinarily no reference to this case will be made, its verification being left to the reader.

In an independent set $\{\alpha_1, \cdots, \alpha_r\}$ no two vectors can be equal. For suppose $\alpha_i = \alpha_j$ $(i \neq j)$. If we set $c_i = 1$, $c_j = -1$, and $c_h = 0$ for $h \neq i$ or j, then (5.1) holds. Hence *the set $\mathscr{S} = \{\alpha_1, \cdots, \alpha_r\}$ is dependent if any two of its elements are equal.* We now consider some examples of dependent and independent sets.

In $\mathscr{V}_2(\mathscr{F})$ consider $\mathscr{S} = \{\alpha_1, \alpha_2, \alpha_3\}$ where $\alpha_1 = (1, 0)$, $\alpha_2 = (0, 1)$, $\alpha_3 = (2, 4)$; then the equation $0 = 2\alpha_1 + 4\alpha_2 - \alpha_3$ shows that $\mathscr{S}$ is dependent. On the other hand any pair of the α_i constitute an independent set.

In $\mathscr{L}_4(\mathscr{F})$ consider $\alpha_1 = x_1 + x_2$, $\alpha_2 = x_2 + x_3$, $\alpha_3 = x_3 + x_4$, $\alpha_4 = x_4 + x_1$. Then $\alpha_1 + \alpha_3 - \alpha_2 - \alpha_4 = 0$, so that $\mathscr{S} = \{\alpha_1, \alpha_2, \alpha_3, \alpha_4\}$ is dependent.

Next consider the equations:

$$
\begin{aligned}
x_1 - x_2 &= 0, \\
x_1 - 2x_3 &= 0, \\
x_1 + x_2 - x_4 &= 0.
\end{aligned}
$$

One solution is $\alpha_1 = (2, 2, 1, 4)$. All other solutions are dependent on this one.

Consider the equation

$$x_1 + x_2 + x_3 - x_4 = 0.$$

Its solutions include

$$\alpha_1 = (1, -1, 0, 0), \qquad \alpha_2 = (1, 0, -1, 0), \qquad \alpha_3 = (1, 0, 0, 1),$$
$$\alpha_4 = (0, 1, -1, 0), \qquad \alpha_5 = (1, 1, 1, 3).$$

The set $\mathscr{S} = \{\alpha_1, \alpha_2, \alpha_3\}$ is independent whereas any four of the α_i constitute a dependent set.

LEMMA 1.5A. *If $\mathscr{S} = \{\alpha_1, \alpha_2, \cdots, \alpha_r\}$ is independent, then any subset $\mathscr{T}$ of $\mathscr{S}$ is also independent.*

For suppose 0 can be expressed in the form (5.1), but using only some of the α_i, and with coefficients that are not all zero. Then by introducing the remaining α's with zeros as coefficients we obtain an expression of 0 in the form (5.1) where the scalars are not all zero, contrary to the hypothesis that the set $\mathscr{S}$ is independent. Thus no subset of $\mathscr{S}$ is dependent.

Let $\mathscr{S}$ be any nonvacuous set of vectors (finite or infinite). A vector α is said to be *dependent on $\mathscr{S}$* if there exist vectors $\alpha_1, \alpha_2, \cdots, \alpha_r$ in $\mathscr{S}$ and scalars $a_1, a_2, \cdots, a_r$ such that

$$\alpha = a_1\alpha_1 + a_2\alpha_2 + \cdots + a_r\alpha_r.$$

We say that α is a *linear combination* of $\alpha_1, \cdots, \alpha_r$.

By taking all $a_1, a_2, \cdots, a_r$ equal to 0 we see that the zero vector is dependent on any nonvacuous set $\mathscr{S}$.

The above definition applies only to nonvacuous sets. If $\mathscr{S}$ is the vacuous set we say that the zero vector is dependent on $\mathscr{S}$ and that no other vector is dependent on $\mathscr{S}$. Thus the zero vector is dependent on every set $\mathscr{S}$ vacuous or nonvacuous.

LEMMA 1.5B.   *Let* $\mathscr{S} = \{\alpha_1, \alpha_2, \cdots, \alpha_r\}$ *be an independent set. Suppose that* $\alpha = a_1\alpha_1 + \cdots + a_r\alpha_r$ *and also that* $\alpha = b_1\alpha_1 + \cdots + b_r\alpha_r$. *Then* $a_1 = b_1, \cdots, a_r = b_r$; *i.e., a vector can be expressed in at most one way as a linear combination of vectors belonging to an independent set.*

We have $0 = \alpha - \alpha = (a_1\alpha_1 + \cdots + a_r\alpha_r) - (b_1\alpha_1 + \cdots + b_r\alpha_r)$ $= (a_1 - b_1)\alpha_1 + \cdots + (a_r - b_r)\alpha_r$.   Now, since $\mathscr{S}$ is independent, $a_1 - b_1 = 0, \cdots, a_r - b_r = 0$, or $a_1 = b_1, \cdots, a_r = b_r$.

LEMMA 1.5C.   *Let* $\mathscr{S}$ *be an independent set of vectors and* α *a vector independent of* $\mathscr{S}$. *Then the set composed of* α *and the vectors of* $\mathscr{S}$ *is also independent.*

Suppose $\alpha_1, \cdots, \alpha_r$ are in $\mathscr{S}$ and there exist scalars $a, a_1, a_2, \cdots, a_r$ such that

(5.2) $0 = a\alpha + a_1\alpha_1 + \cdots + a_r\alpha_r$.

Then $a = 0$, for otherwise we could solve for α,

$$\alpha = (-a_1/a)\alpha_1 + \cdots + (-a_r/a)\alpha_r,$$

which contradicts the assumption that α is independent of $\alpha_1, \cdots, \alpha_r$. Thus $a = 0$ and using this in (5.2) we conclude that also $a_1, \cdots, a_r$ are all 0 since $\mathscr{S}$ is independent. Thus, $\alpha, \alpha_1, \cdots, \alpha_r$ are independent, and the proof is complete.

A set $\mathscr{S}$ is said to be *dependent* on a set $\mathscr{T}$ if every vector in $\mathscr{S}$ is dependent on $\mathscr{T}$.

THEOREM 1.5D.   *Let* $\mathscr{S} = \{\alpha_1, \cdots, \alpha_s\}$ *be an independent set, and let* $\mathscr{T} = \{\beta_1, \cdots, \beta_t\}$ *be any finite set such that* $\mathscr{S}$ *is dependent on* $\mathscr{T}$. *Then* $s \leq t$.

Since $\mathscr{S}$ is dependent on $\mathscr{T}$ we have scalars c_{ij} such that

(5.3) $\alpha_i = c_{i1}\beta_1 + \cdots + c_{it}\beta_t$ $(i = 1, \cdots, s)$.

The theorem is trivial for $s = 1$ since then $\alpha_1 \neq 0$ and so there must be at least one β_j in the expression for α_1; therefore $s \leq t$. We proceed by induction on the number of elements in $\mathscr{S}$ and take as our induction hypothesis that the theorem is true for all independent sets with less than s elements $(s > 1)$. Let $\mathscr{S}' = \{\alpha_1, \cdots, \alpha_{s-1}\}$ be the independent set obtained by deleting α_s from $\mathscr{S}$.

It may happen that $c_{1t} = \cdots = c_{st} = 0$: i.e. that β_t is not really used in (5.3). If this is true, then $\mathscr{S}$ is actually dependent on $\mathscr{T}' = \{\beta_1, \cdots, \beta_{t-1}\}$, and hence $\mathscr{S}'$ is dependent on $\mathscr{T}'$. Now $\mathscr{S}'$ has $s' = s - 1 < s$ elements, and so by our induction hypothesis $s' = s - 1 \leq t - 1$. Hence in this case $s \leq t$ as required by the theorem.

If not every one of $c_{1t}, \cdots, c_{st}$ is zero we may suppose the notation so chosen that $c_{st} \neq 0$. Thus we let

$$(5.4) \qquad \gamma_i = \alpha_i - (c_{it}/c_{st})\alpha_s \qquad (i = 1, \cdots, s-1),$$

and let $\mathscr{S}'' = \{\gamma_1, \cdots, \gamma_{s-1}\}$. The purpose of this step is to obtain an independent set $\mathscr{S}''$ with $s - 1$ elements which is dependent on a set $\mathscr{T}'$ with $t - 1$ elements. In effect we eliminate β_t by adding a suitable multiple of α_s to each α_i in turn.

We first show that $\mathscr{S}''$ is independent. For suppose we have scalars $d_1, \cdots, d_{s-1}$ such that

$$(5.5) \qquad d_1\gamma_1 + \cdots + d_{s-1}\gamma_{s-1} = 0.$$

Substituting (5.4) in (5.5), we get

$$d_1\alpha_1 + \cdots + d_{s-1}\alpha_{s-1} - (d_1 c_{1t}/c_{st} + \cdots + d_{s-1} c_{s-1,t}/c_{st})\alpha_s = 0.$$

Now, since $\mathscr{S}$ is independent, $d_1 = \cdots = d_{s-1} = 0$; this shows that $\mathscr{S}''$ is independent.

Next, we observe that the coefficient of β_t in the expression (5.4) for γ_i is

$$c_{it} - (c_{it}/c_{st}) \cdot c_{st} = 0 \qquad (i = 1, \cdots, s-1).$$

Hence β_t does not actually appear in the equations (5.4) which express the dependence of $\mathscr{S}''$ on $\mathscr{T}$; in other words $\mathscr{S}''$ is dependent on $\mathscr{T}'$. But since $\mathscr{S}''$ is an independent set with $s'' = s - 1 < s$ members it follows from our induction hypothesis that $s'' \leq t - 1$; i.e., $s - 1 \leq t - 1$. Hence $s \leq t$ in this case also. This completes our induction argument, and so the theorem holds for all s.

We give an application of this theorem to the theory of homogeneous linear equations.

THEOREM 1.5E. FUNDAMENTAL THEOREM ON LINEAR EQUATIONS. *A system of homogeneous linear equations always has a nontrivial solution if the number of unknowns exceeds the number of equations.*

Suppose we have n vectors $\alpha_1, \cdots, \alpha_n$ in $\mathscr{V}_m(\mathscr{F})$, say

$$\alpha_j = (a_{1j}, \cdots, a_{mj}) \qquad (j = 1, \cdots, n).$$

If the set $\mathscr{S} = \{\alpha_1, \cdots, \alpha_n\}$ is dependent then there exist scalars $c_1, \cdots, c_n$ not all 0 such that

$$(5.6) \qquad c_1\alpha_1 + \cdots + c_n\alpha_n = 0.$$

This vector equation is equivalent to the following system of m scalar equations obtained by setting each component equal to 0:

(5.7)
$$a_{11}c_1 + \cdots + a_{1n}c_n = 0,$$
$$\cdots$$
$$a_{m1}c_1 + \cdots + a_{mn}c_n = 0.$$

Thus the system of m linear equations in n unknowns

(5.8)
$$a_{11}x_1 + \cdots + a_{1n}x_n = 0,$$
$$\cdots$$
$$a_{m1}x_1 + \cdots + a_{mn}x_n = 0$$

has a nontrivial solution if $\mathscr{S} = \{\alpha_1, \cdots, \alpha_n\}$ is dependent. The converse statement, that $\mathscr{S}$ is dependent if (5.8) has a nontrivial solution $c_1, \cdots, c_n$, is also true since (5.6) is equivalent to (5.7).

Now every vector $\alpha = (a_1, \cdots, a_m)$ in $\mathscr{V}_m(\mathscr{F})$ is dependent on the set $\mathscr{T} = \{\varepsilon_1, \cdots, \varepsilon_m\}$, where

$$\varepsilon_1 = (1, 0, \cdots, 0),$$
$$\varepsilon_2 = (0, 1, \cdots, 0),$$
$$\cdots$$
$$\varepsilon_m = (0, 0, \cdots, 1)$$

(i.e., ε_j has jth component 1 and all other components 0). For

$$\alpha = a_1\varepsilon_1 + a_2\varepsilon_2 + \cdots + a_m\varepsilon_m.$$

Thus $\mathscr{S}$ is dependent on $\mathscr{T}$. Also $\mathscr{S}$ has n vectors and $\mathscr{T}$ has m vectors. According to Theorem 1.5D, $\mathscr{S}$ cannot be independent if $n > m$. Hence if the number of unknowns exceeds the number of equations, (5.7) has a solution with $c_1, c_2, \cdots, c_n$ not all 0, and this is also a nontrivial solution of (5.6).

Although this theorem guarantees the existence of a nontrivial solution when the number of unknowns exceeds the number of equations, its proof provides very little aid in actually finding such a solution. In a later chapter we will develop methods for obtaining all solutions. Meanwhile those systems that are encountered can be solved by the elimination method of elementary algebra.

The question of whether a given set of vectors in $\mathscr{V}_m(\mathscr{F})$ is dependent or independent can always be reduced to finding whether or not a related system of homogeneous linear equations does or does not have a nontrivial solution. Similarly, the question of whether a given vector in $\mathscr{V}_m(\mathscr{F})$ is dependent on some set of vectors can be reduced to finding a solution of a related system of nonhomogeneous linear equations. The proof of the preceding theorem illustrates the way the system is found. The condition of dependence or independence gives a single vector equation [e.g. (5.6)]. The components of this vector equation form a system of m scalar equations.

As an illustration of the foregoing discussion consider the following problem. Let $\mathscr{S} = \{\alpha_1, \alpha_2, \alpha_3\}$ where $\alpha_1 = (2, -1, 3, 0)$, $\alpha_2 = (1, -2, 1, 2)$, $\alpha_3 = (0, -1, 4, 1)$, let $\alpha = (3, -1, 9, -1)$, and determine whether or not α is dependent on $\mathscr{S}$. If α is dependent on $\mathscr{S}$, then there exist scalars c_1, c_2, c_3 which satisfy the vector equation

$$x_1\alpha_1 + x_2\alpha_2 + x_3\alpha_3 = \alpha.$$

The components of this vector equation give the scalar system

$$\begin{aligned}
2x_1 + x_2 &= 3, \\
-x_1 - 2x_2 - x_3 &= -1, \\
3x_1 + x_2 + 4x_3 &= 9, \\
2x_2 + x_3 &= -1.
\end{aligned}$$

We leave the solving of this system as an exercise. A solution is $(c_1, c_2, c_3) = (2, -1, 1)$. The existence of a solution shows that α is dependent on $\mathscr{S}$.

Exercises 1.5

1. Show that in $\mathscr{V}_2(\mathfrak{R})$ the vector $(6, 5)$ is dependent on $(1, 2)$ and $(2, -1)$.

2. Determine whether these three vectors in $\mathscr{V}_4(\mathfrak{Q})$ are independent:

$$(2, -1, 3, 2), \qquad (-1, 1, 1, -3), \qquad (1, 1, 9, -5).$$

3. Show that the vector $\beta = (3, -1, 0, -1)$ is not dependent on the set $\mathscr{S}$ considered in the illustrative example above.

4. Find a nontrivial dependence relation on the set $\mathscr{S} = \{\beta_1, \beta_2, \beta_3, \beta_4\}$, where $\beta_1 = (1, 0, 1)$, $\beta_2 = (0, 1, 1)$, $\beta_3 = (1, 1, 0)$, $\beta_4 = (2, -1, 3)$.

5. Prove that if $\mathscr{S} = \{\alpha_1, \cdots, \alpha_r\}$ is independent then no α_i is 0.

6. Prove that if $\mathscr{S} = \{\alpha_1, \cdots, \alpha_r\}$ is independent then α_1 is independent of $\mathscr{T} = \{\alpha_2, \cdots, \alpha_r\}$.

7. Give a counterexample to the false statement that if $\mathscr{S} = \{\alpha_1, \cdots, \alpha_r\}$ is dependent then α_1 is dependent on $\mathscr{T} = \{\alpha_2, \cdots, \alpha_r\}$.

8. Find a nontrivial dependence relation on the set $\mathscr{S} = \{\beta_1, \beta_2, \beta_3, \beta_4\}$, where $\beta_1 = (1, 0, i)$, $\beta_2 = (1 + i, 1, -i)$, $\beta_3 = (2 - i, i, 3)$, $\beta_4 = (0, i, 1)$.

9. Show that every solution of the system

$$\begin{aligned}
x_1 - x_3 + 2x_4 &= 0, \\
x_2 + 3x_3 + x_4 &= 0
\end{aligned}$$

is dependent on the set $\mathscr{S} = \{\alpha_1, \alpha_2\}$, where $\alpha_1 = (-2, -1, 0, 1)$ and $\alpha_2 = (1, -3, 1, 0)$.

10. If α and β are dependent on γ show that the set $\{\alpha, \beta\}$ is dependent. Is α necessarily dependent on β?

11. Show that if α is dependent on $\{\alpha_1, \cdots, \alpha_r\}$ then the set $\{\alpha, \alpha_1, \cdots, \alpha_r\}$ is dependent.

12. Prove that if $\mathscr{S}$ is independent and $\{\mathscr{S}, \alpha\}$ is dependent then α is dependent on $\mathscr{S}$.

13. Let $\mathscr{S} = \{\alpha_1, \cdots, \alpha_m\}$ and $\mathscr{T} = \{\beta_1, \cdots, \beta_t\}$ be independent sets, and let $\mathscr{S}$ be dependent on $\mathscr{T}$. Prove that there exists an independent set $\mathscr{T}' = \{\mathscr{S}, \beta_{i_1}, \cdots, \beta_{i_r}\}$ with $r = t - m$ such that $\mathscr{T}$ is dependent on $\mathscr{T}'$. (Hint: use the preceding exercise and induction.) Use this result to give another proof of Theorem 1.5D.

14. Let $\mathscr{S}$ be independent, and let β be a nonzero vector dependent on $\mathscr{S}$. Prove that $\mathscr{S}$ is dependent on an independent set $\{\mathscr{S}', \beta\}$ where $\mathscr{S}'$ is obtained from $\mathscr{S}$ by deleting a suitable vector.

15. Let $\mathscr{S} = \{\alpha_1, \cdots, \alpha_s\}$, $\mathscr{T} = \{\beta_1, \cdots, \beta_t\}$ be independent sets spanning (see page 25 below) the same space $\mathscr{V}$. Prove that there exists a sequence of sets $\mathscr{S}_0 = \mathscr{S}$, $\mathscr{S}_1, \cdots, \mathscr{S}_s = \mathscr{T}$ such that, for each i, $\mathscr{S}_i$ is an independent set which spans $\mathscr{V}$ and which is obtained from $\mathscr{S}_{i-1}$ by deleting an element originally of $\mathscr{S}$ and adjoining an element of $\mathscr{T}$. (Hint: use the preceding exercise.) Use this result to construct another proof of Theorem 1.5D.

16. Prove that, if $n > m$, any set of n vectors in $\mathscr{V}_m(\mathscr{F})$ is dependent.

1.6. Dimension and basis.

Let $\mathscr{V}$ be a vector space over a field $\mathscr{F}$. If $\mathscr{V}$ consists of the zero vector alone we say that $\mathscr{V}$ has dimension 0. Next, suppose that $\mathscr{V} \neq \{0\}$. If $\mathscr{V}$ contains at least one independent set of n vectors and if every set in $\mathscr{V}$ with more than n vectors is dependent then we say that $\mathscr{V}$ has *dimension n*. If there is no upper bound to the number of independent vectors in an independent subset of $\mathscr{V}$, then we say that $\mathscr{V}$ has infinite dimension. We sometimes use the notation dim $\mathscr{V}$ for the dimension of $\mathscr{V}$.

A set $\mathscr{S}$ is said to be a *basis* for $\mathscr{V}$ if (i) $\mathscr{S}$ is independent and (ii) $\mathscr{V}$ is dependent on $\mathscr{S}$. A basis is essentially a coordinate system (not necessarily rectangular). To obtain a coordinate system for the set of vectors in the plane it is sufficient to choose two independent vectors α_1, α_2; then the origin is given (by the vector 0) and the lines determined by α_1, α_2 are the coordinate axes, the units on the axes being α_1 and α_2.

For example the set $\mathscr{S} = \{(1, 0, 0), (0, 1, 0), (0, 0, 1)\}$ is a basis for $\mathscr{V}_3(\mathscr{F})$. First $\mathscr{S}$ is independent since

$$(6.1) \qquad a_1(1, 0, 0) + a_2(0, 1, 0) + a_3(0, 0, 1) = (a_1, a_2, a_3),$$

and this is 0 only if $a_1 = a_2 = a_3 = 0$. Second, if (a_1, a_2, a_3) is any vector in $\mathscr{V}_3(\mathscr{F})$ it can be expressed in terms of the basis as is demonstrated by (6.1).

Another basis of $\mathscr{V}_3(\mathscr{F})$ is $(0, 0, 1)$, $(1, 1, 0)$, $(-1, 0, 0)$. We shall show only that $\mathscr{V}_3(\mathscr{F})$ depends on them. For if (a_1, a_2, a_3) is any vector in $\mathscr{V}_3(\mathscr{F})$ then

$$(a_1, a_2, a_3) = a_3(0, 0, 1) + a_2(1, 1, 0) + (a_2 - a_1)(-1, 0, 0).$$

THEOREM 1.6A. *If a vector space $\mathscr{V}$ has finite dimension n then any independent set with n vectors is a basis for $\mathscr{V}$, and every basis for $\mathscr{V}$ has n vectors.*

Since dim $\mathscr{V} = n$ there exists an independent subset $\mathscr{S}$ with n members, and every subset $\mathscr{T}$ with more than n members is dependent. Let α be any vector in $\mathscr{V}$. If α is not dependent on $\mathscr{S}$ then by Lemma 1.5C the set $\mathscr{T} = \{\mathscr{S}, \alpha\}$ is independent; but since $\mathscr{T}$ has $n + 1$ members it is dependent. Thus we conclude that every vector α in $\mathscr{V}$ is dependent on $\mathscr{S}$, or in other words $\mathscr{V}$ is dependent on $\mathscr{S}$. Hence $\mathscr{S}$ is a basis for $\mathscr{V}$. We next show that every basis has the same number of vectors. Let $\mathscr{S}'$ be another basis for $\mathscr{V}$ having n' members. Since $\mathscr{S}'$ is a basis for $\mathscr{V}$ we have $\mathscr{S}$ dependent on $\mathscr{S}'$, and, by Theorem 1.5D, $n \leq n'$. Similarly $n' \leq n$. Hence, $n' = n = \dim \mathscr{V}$ as claimed. (This proof requires some modification for the case dim $\mathscr{V} = 0$; the details are left as an exercise.)

LEMMA 1.6B. *Let $\mathscr{V}$ have finite dimension n and let $\mathscr{S} = \{\alpha_1, \cdots, \alpha_r\}$ be any independent set in $\mathscr{V}$. Then if $r < n$ there exist vectors $\alpha_{r+1}, \cdots, \alpha_n$ such that $\mathscr{T} = \{\alpha_1, \cdots, \alpha_n\}$ is a basis for $\mathscr{V}$.*

Another statement of this lemma is that any independent set can be extended to become a basis.

Since $r < n$, according to Theorem 1.6A, $\mathscr{S}$ cannot be a basis for $\mathscr{V}$. Hence there is a vector α_{r+1} not dependent on $\mathscr{S}$, and by Lemma 1.5C the set $\{\alpha_1, \cdots, \alpha_r, \alpha_{r+1}\}$ is independent. If $r + 1 < n$, then this process is repeated. Finally by induction an independent set $\mathscr{T} = \{\alpha_1, \cdots, \alpha_n\}$ is obtained, and it forms a basis by Theorem 1.6A.

Exercises 1.6

1. Find the dimension of the vector space of all solutions of the system of equations $x_1 + 2x_2 - x_3 + x_4 = 0$, $x_2 + x_3 = 0$, $x_4 = 0$.

2. Show that the set of all vectors of $\mathscr{L}_4(\mathscr{F})$ dependent on $x_1 - x_2 + x_3 - x_4$, $x_1 + x_2 + x_3 + x_4$, and $3x_1 + 2x_2 + 3x_3 + 2x_4$ is a vector space, and find its dimension.

3. Show that $\mathscr{V}_n(\mathscr{F})$ has dimension n.

4. Show that $\mathscr{L}_n(\mathscr{F})$ has dimension n.

5. Show that the space of polynomials (Ex. 1.4–4) has infinite dimension.

6. Show that the space of functions (Ex. 1.4–5) has infinite dimension.

7. Show that the empty set is a basis for the space $\mathscr{V} = \{0\}$ which consists of only the zero vector.

8. Find a basis for $\mathscr{V}_3(\mathscr{F})$ which includes the vectors $\alpha = (1, 2, 3)$, $\beta = (3, 4, 6)$.

9. Show that no basis for $\mathscr{V}_3(\mathscr{F})$ can include both of the vectors $\alpha = (1, 2, 3)$, $\gamma = (2, 4, 6)$.

1.7. Isomorphism.* Let $\mathscr{S} = \{\alpha_1, \alpha_2, \cdots, \alpha_n\}$ be a basis of a vector space $\mathscr{V}$. Then any vector α in $\mathscr{V}$ can be expressed as

$$(7.1) \qquad \alpha = a_1\alpha_1 + a_2\alpha_2 + \cdots + a_n\alpha_n.$$

Since $\mathscr{S}$ is independent the scalars $a_1, a_2, \cdots, a_n$ are unique (Lemma 1.5B). Thus to every α there corresponds a unique n-tuple $(a_1, a_2, \cdots, a_n)$. Also, given an n-tuple $(a_1, a_2, \cdots, a_n)$ a unique vector α is determined by (7.1). Thus the mapping T:

$$\alpha \to (a_1, a_2, \cdots, a_n) = \alpha\mathsf{T}$$

is a one-to-one mapping of $\mathscr{V}$ onto $\mathscr{V}_n(\mathscr{F})$.

We next study the connections between the mapping T and the operations in the vector spaces. Let β be another vector in $\mathscr{V}$, say

$$\beta = b_1\alpha_1 + b_2\alpha_2 + \cdots + b_n\alpha_n.$$

Then we have

$$\beta \to (b_1, b_2, \cdots, b_n) = \beta\mathsf{T}.$$

The sum of α and β is

$$\alpha + \beta = (a_1 + b_1)\alpha_1 + (a_2 + b_2)\alpha_2 + \cdots + (a_n + b_n)\alpha_n,$$

and consequently

$$
\begin{aligned}
(7.2) \qquad (\alpha + \beta)\mathsf{T} &= (a_1 + b_1, a_2 + b_2, \cdots, a_n + b_n) \\
&= (a_1, a_2, \cdots, a_n) + (b_1, b_2, \cdots, b_n) \\
&= \alpha\mathsf{T} + \beta\mathsf{T}.
\end{aligned}
$$

Next, if c is a scalar, then

$$c\alpha = (ca_1)\alpha_1 + (ca_2)\alpha_2 + \cdots + (ca_n)\alpha_n,$$

so that

$$
\begin{aligned}
(7.3) \qquad (c\alpha)\mathsf{T} &= (ca_1, ca_2, \cdots, ca_n) \\
&= c(a_1, a_2, \cdots, a_n) \\
&= c(\alpha\mathsf{T}).
\end{aligned}
$$

From (7.2) and (7.3) we see that any sequence of operations on the vectors of $\mathscr{V}$ yields a vector whose image can be obtained by carrying out the same sequence of operations on the corresponding vectors of $\mathscr{V}_n(\mathscr{F})$. Thus, with respect to the two vector operations, $\mathscr{V}$ and $\mathscr{V}_n(\mathscr{F})$ will have the same properties. This discussion leads us to the following definition.

* The student should read Appendix II on relations and mappings before reading this section.

A vector space $\mathscr{V} = \{\alpha, \beta, \cdots\}$ is said to be *isomorphic* to a vector space $\mathscr{V}' = \{\alpha', \beta', \cdots\}$ if there is a one-to-one mapping T:

$$\alpha \to \alpha' = \alpha\mathsf{T}$$

of $\mathscr{V}$ onto $\mathscr{V}'$ which has the properties that it is one-to-one, and

(7.4) $$(\alpha + \beta)\mathsf{T} = \alpha\mathsf{T} + \beta\mathsf{T}$$

and

(7.5) $$(c\alpha)\mathsf{T} = c(\alpha\mathsf{T})$$

for all vectors α, β in $\mathscr{V}$ and for all scalars c in $\mathscr{F}$. Note that for two spaces to be isomorphic they must have the same field of scalars.

From (7.4) it follows by induction that, if $\alpha_1, \cdots, \alpha_m$ are in $\mathscr{V}$,

(7.6) $$(\alpha_1 + \cdots + \alpha_m)\mathsf{T} = \alpha_1\mathsf{T} + \cdots + \alpha_m\mathsf{T}.$$

More generally, if also $c_1, \cdots, c_m$ are in $\mathscr{F}$, then

(7.7) $$(c_1\alpha_1 + \cdots + c_m\alpha_m)\mathsf{T} = c_1(\alpha_1\mathsf{T}) + \cdots + c_m(\alpha_m\mathsf{T});$$

i.e., the image of a linear combination of any set of vectors is the same linear combination of the image vectors. For

$$(c_1\alpha_1 + \cdots + c_m\alpha_m)\mathsf{T} = (c_1\alpha_1)\mathsf{T} + \cdots + (c_m\alpha_m)\mathsf{T} \qquad \text{(by 7.6)}$$
$$= c_1(\alpha_1\mathsf{T}) + \cdots + c_m(\alpha_m\mathsf{T}) \qquad \text{(by 7.5)}.$$

We write $\mathscr{V} \cong \mathscr{V}'$ to signify that $\mathscr{V}$ is isomorphic to $\mathscr{V}'$. Since T is a one-to-one mapping of $\mathscr{V}$ onto $\mathscr{V}'$, it has an inverse S (see Appendix II). Here, if β is in $\mathscr{V}'$, $\beta\mathsf{S}$ is defined to be that vector α in $\mathscr{V}$ such that $\alpha\mathsf{T} = \beta$; i.e.

$$\beta\mathsf{S} = \alpha \quad \text{if and only if} \quad \alpha\mathsf{T} = \beta.$$

Such a vector α exists since T is a mapping onto; α is uniquely determined by β since T is one-to-one. Then S is a one-to-one mapping of $\mathscr{V}'$ onto $\mathscr{V}$. It is easy to check that S satisfies the conditions (7.4) and (7.5), and, hence, if $\mathscr{V} \cong \mathscr{V}'$ then $\mathscr{V}' \cong \mathscr{V}$. The mapping T is said to be an *isomorphism* of $\mathscr{V}$ onto $\mathscr{V}'$.

The discussion at the beginning of this section yields the following important result.

THEOREM 1.7A.   *If a vector space $\mathscr{V}$ over the field $\mathscr{F}$ has finite dimension n, then $\mathscr{V} \cong \mathscr{V}_n(\mathscr{F})$.*

Thus the properties of $\mathscr{V}$ as a vector space depend only upon its dimension n and field of scalars $\mathscr{F}$. One need study only the model $\mathscr{V}_n(\mathscr{F})$.

COROLLARY 1.7B.   *Two finite dimensional vector spaces over the same field $\mathscr{F}$ are isomorphic if they have the same dimension n.*

This result follows immediately from Theorem 1.7A and Exercise 2 below.

The reader might well ask why we defined vector spaces by a long list of postulates rather than by isomorphism with $\mathscr{V}_n(\mathscr{F})$. One answer is, of course, that the axiomatic approach includes infinite dimensional spaces also and so is more general. But a more important reason is that in many applications it is easier to check that a set $\mathscr{V}$ satisfies the vector space postulates than it is to set up a basis and give an isomorphism with $\mathscr{V}_n(\mathscr{F})$. This is true even for subsets of $\mathscr{V}_n(\mathscr{F})$ which are themselves vector spaces; e.g., solutions of a system of homogeneous linear equations. Hence, even if we defined a vector space as a system isomorphic to $\mathscr{V}_n(\mathscr{F})$ we would find avoiding the postulates so awkward that we would show, as a substitute for Theorem 1.7A, that any system having the properties described by the postulates is a vector space. A third reason is that the axiomatic approach to a mathematical subject is usually considered esthetically more desirable.

An *isomorphism* T of $\mathscr{V}$ into $\mathscr{V}'$ is a mapping $\alpha \to \alpha' = \alpha\mathsf{T}$ of $\mathscr{V}$ into $\mathscr{V}'$ which is one-to-one and satisfies (7.4) and (7.5). The set of images $\alpha' = \alpha\mathsf{T}$ need not exhaust all of $\mathscr{V}'$. If it does then $\mathscr{V} \cong \mathscr{V}'$. In any case $\mathscr{V} \cong \mathscr{W}'$ where $\mathscr{W}'$ is the set of all images. Of course, $\mathscr{W}' \subseteq \mathscr{V}'$. This set $\mathscr{W}'$ will sometimes be denoted by $\mathscr{V}\mathsf{T}$ to indicate that it is the set of all images of vectors in $\mathscr{V}$. In the special case when $\mathscr{V}\mathsf{T} = \mathscr{V}'$ then T is, of course, an isomorphism of $\mathscr{V}$ onto $\mathscr{V}'$.

LEMMA 1.7C. *Let* T *be an isomorphism of a vector space* $\mathscr{V}$ *into a vector space* $\mathscr{V}'$. *Let* $\mathscr{S} = \{\alpha_1, \cdots, \alpha_r\}$ *be any finite set of vectors in* $\mathscr{V}$ *and let* $\mathscr{S}' = \{\alpha'_1, \cdots, \alpha'_r\}$ *where* $\alpha'_i = \alpha_i\mathsf{T}$ $(i = 1, \cdots, r)$. *Then* $\mathscr{S}'$ *is independent if and only if* $\mathscr{S}$ *is independent.*

We first show that $0_{\mathscr{V}}\mathsf{T} = 0_{\mathscr{V}'}$. For $0_{\mathscr{V}}\mathsf{T} = (00_{\mathscr{V}})\mathsf{T} = 0(0_{\mathscr{V}}\mathsf{T}) = 0_{\mathscr{V}'}$, by (7.5) and the fact that the product of the scalar 0 with any vector always gives the zero vector.

Next, if $\mathscr{S}$ is dependent, then there exist scalars $c_1, \cdots, c_r$ not all 0 such that

$$c_1\alpha_1 + \cdots + c_r\alpha_r = 0_{\mathscr{V}}.$$

Thus

$$(c_1\alpha_1 + \cdots + c_r\alpha_r)\mathsf{T} = 0_{\mathscr{V}}\mathsf{T},$$

which gives

$$c_1(\alpha_1\mathsf{T}) + \cdots + c_r(\alpha_r\mathsf{T}) = 0_{\mathscr{V}'}$$

by the preceding paragraph and (7.7); now, substituting $\alpha_i\mathsf{T} = \alpha'_i$, we get

$$c_1\alpha'_1 + \cdots + c_r\alpha'_r = 0_{\mathscr{V}'}.$$

Consequently $\mathscr{S}'$ is dependent. If we reverse all the steps we see that $\mathscr{S}$

is dependent if $\mathscr{S}'$ is dependent, where to reverse the first step we use the fact that T is one-to-one. Now, since a set is either dependent or independent, it follows that $\mathscr{S}'$ is independent if and only if $\mathscr{S}$ is independent.

It follows from Lemma 1.7C that, when $\mathscr{V} \cong \mathscr{V}'$, the maximum number of independent vectors in $\mathscr{V}$ is the same as in $\mathscr{V}'$. Hence dim $\mathscr{V}$ = dim $\mathscr{V}'$. The converse, that dim $\mathscr{V}$ = dim $\mathscr{V}'$ implies $\mathscr{V} \cong \mathscr{V}'$, has been stated as Corollary 1.7B. These two results put together give the next theorem.

Theorem 1.7D. *Two finite dimensional vector spaces over the same field are isomorphic if and only if they have the same dimension.*

Exercises 1.7

1. Show that, if T is an isomorphism of $\mathscr{V}$ onto $\mathscr{V}'$, then its inverse T^{-1} is an isomorphism of $\mathscr{V}'$ onto $\mathscr{V}$.

2. Show that, if T is an isomorphism of $\mathscr{V}$ onto $\mathscr{V}'$ and if S is an isomorphism of $\mathscr{V}'$ onto $\mathscr{V}''$, then the mapping R of $\mathscr{V}$ onto $\mathscr{V}''$ obtained by applying first T and then S (written $\mathsf{R} = \mathsf{TS}$ and called the *product* of T and S) is an isomorphism of $\mathscr{V}$ onto $\mathscr{V}''$.

3. Show that a vector space is isomorphic to itself.

4. Prove formula (7.6) by induction.

5. Let $\mathscr{U}$ be the set of all vectors in $\mathscr{V}_3(\mathscr{F})$ having the first component zero (i.e. the vectors in the "yz plane "). Show that $\mathscr{U}$ is a vector space of dimension 2 and find an isomorphism of $\mathscr{U}$ onto $\mathscr{V}_2(\mathscr{F})$.

6 Let $\mathscr{U}$ be a set satisfying axioms A1 and S1, let $\mathscr{V}$ be a vector space, and let T be an isomorphism of $\mathscr{V}$ into $\mathscr{U}$. Show that $\mathscr{V}\mathsf{T}$ is a vector space.

1.8. Subspaces. Let $\mathscr{V}$ be a vector space over a field $\mathscr{F}$. A subset $\mathscr{W}$ which is itself a vector space is said to be a *subspace* of $\mathscr{V}$. Thus the set $\mathscr{W}$ of all vectors $(x_1, x_2, 0)$ is a subspace of $\mathscr{V}_3(\mathscr{F})$. Also the set of all solutions of a set of homogeneous linear equations in n unknowns is a subspace of $\mathscr{V}_n(\mathscr{F})$ (this was proved in Section 1.4). The set consisting of 0 alone is a subspace called the *zero space*; and $\mathscr{V}$ itself is a subspace of $\mathscr{V}$.

The following theorem reduces from ten to two the number of axioms that need to be checked in order to show that a subset of a vector space is a subspace.

Theorem 1.8A. *A nonempty subset of $\mathscr{W}$ of a vector space $\mathscr{V}$ is a subspace if for every scalar c and every pair α, β of vectors in $\mathscr{W}$ the vectors $\alpha + \beta$ and $c\alpha$ again lie in $\mathscr{W}$.*

We sometimes paraphrase this theorem by saying that *a subset is a subspace if it is closed under addition and under multiplication by scalars.*

Certain of the axioms hold automatically in any subset by virtue of holding in the space itself. These are A2, A5, S2, S3, S4, and S5. These axioms all refer to the way various elements combine under addition and under multiplication by scalars and in each case state that two formally distinct combinations yield equal results. We call such axioms *combinatorial*.

The remaining axioms are called *existential*. Each of these axioms states that certain vectors belong to the set under consideration.

The hypothesis of the theorem states that A1 and S1 are satisfied in $\mathscr{W}$; hence the proof will be complete as soon as we check A3 and A4. By hypothesis $\mathscr{W}$ is a nonempty subset of $\mathscr{V}$; let α be any element of $\mathscr{W}$. We proved in Section 1.4 that $0\alpha = 0$ and $(-1)\alpha = -\alpha$. Thus, in the case of subsets, A3 and A4 are consequences of S1.

Notice how much simpler this proof is compared with showing that the subset is isomorphic with some $\mathscr{V}_m(\mathscr{F})$, as would have had to be done if we had defined a vector space to be an isomorphic image of some $\mathscr{V}_m(\mathscr{F})$.

THEOREM 1.8B.   *Let $\mathscr{V}$ be any vector space over a field $\mathscr{F}$, and let $\mathscr{S}$ be any subset (finite or infinite) of $\mathscr{V}$. Then the set $\mathscr{W}$ of all vectors dependent on $\mathscr{S}$ is a subspace of $\mathscr{V}$.*

We need show only closure under addition and under multiplication by scalars. Suppose that c is any scalar and that α, β are two vectors dependent on $\mathscr{S}$. By the definition of dependence (cf. Section 1.5) there exist vectors $\alpha_1, \cdots, \alpha_r, \beta_1, \cdots, \beta_s$ in $\mathscr{S}$ and scalars $a_1, \cdots, a_r, b_1, \cdots, b_s$ such that $\alpha = a_1\alpha_1 + \cdots + a_r\alpha_r$ and $\beta = b_1\beta_1 + \cdots + b_s\beta_s$. Then we have

$$\begin{aligned}
c\alpha &= c(a_1\alpha_1 + \cdots + a_r\alpha_r) \\
&= c(a_1\alpha_1) + \cdots + c(a_r\alpha_r) \\
&= (ca_1)\alpha_1 + \cdots + (ca_r)\alpha_r,
\end{aligned}$$

which shows that $c\alpha$ is dependent on $\mathscr{S}$, and

$$\begin{aligned}
\alpha + \beta &= (a_1\alpha_1 + \cdots + a_r\alpha_r) + (b_1\beta_1 + \cdots + b_s\beta_s) \\
&= a_1\alpha_1 + \cdots + a_r\alpha_r + b_1\beta_1 + \cdots + b_s\beta_s,
\end{aligned}$$

which shows that $\alpha + \beta$ is dependent on $\mathscr{S}$. Consequently $\mathscr{W}$ is a subspace of $\mathscr{V}$ (cf. Theorem 1.8A).

We say that $\mathscr{W}$ is the space *spanned* or *generated* by $\mathscr{S}$ and sometimes write $\mathscr{W} = \langle \mathscr{S} \rangle$. Note, in particular, that a vector space is spanned by any basis for it, and that a basis for a vector space can be characterized as an independent set which spans the space. Also a subset $\mathscr{W}$ is a subspace if and only if $\mathscr{W} = \langle \mathscr{W} \rangle$.

LEMMA 1.8C.   *Let $\mathscr{W}$ be a subspace of a finite-dimensional vector space $\mathscr{V}$. Then $\mathscr{W} = \mathscr{V}$ if and only if $\dim \mathscr{W} = \dim \mathscr{V}$. Moreover, if* dim $\mathscr{W} = r$, *then for any given basis of $\mathscr{W}$ there exists a basis for $\mathscr{V}$ in which the first r vectors are the given basis for $\mathscr{W}$.*

Such a basis is said to be *adapted* to $\mathscr{W}$.

This lemma is an immediate consequence of Theorem 1.6A and Lemma 1.6B when $\mathscr{S}$ is chosen as the given basis for $\mathscr{W}$.

The first part of this lemma does not hold for infinite-dimensional spaces, as can be seen by taking $\mathscr{F} = \mathfrak{Q}$, $\mathscr{V} = \mathfrak{C}$, and $\mathscr{W} = \mathfrak{R}$.

THEOREM 1.8D. *Let T be an isomorphism of a vector space $\mathscr{V}$ into a vector space $\mathscr{V}'$, let $\mathscr{W}$ be a subspace of $\mathscr{V}$, and let $\mathscr{W}' = \mathscr{W}\mathsf{T}$ be the set of all images $\beta' = \beta\mathsf{T}$ for β in $\mathscr{W}$. Then $\mathscr{W}'$ is a subspace of $\mathscr{V}'$ and* dim $\mathscr{W} = $ dim $\mathscr{W}'$.

Let c be any scalar, and let $\beta' = \beta\mathsf{T}$ and $\gamma' = \gamma\mathsf{T}$ be two vectors in $\mathscr{W}'$. Then we have

$$c\beta' = c(\beta\mathsf{T}) = (c\beta)\mathsf{T}$$

and

$$\beta' + \gamma' = \beta\mathsf{T} + \gamma\mathsf{T} = (\beta + \gamma)\mathsf{T},$$

which shows that $\mathscr{W}$ is a subspace. The equality of dimension follows from Lemma 1.7C.

Exercises 1.8

1. Find a basis for the set of all solutions of the system
$$x_1 + x_2 - x_4 = 0, \qquad x_1 - x_3 + 2x_4 = 0.$$

2. Which of the following sets are subspaces of $\mathscr{L}_4(\mathscr{F})$: (a) the set of all forms $a_1x_1 + a_2x_2 + a_3x_3 + a_4x_4$ having $a_1 = 0$, (b) those forms having $a_1 = 2$, (c) those forms having $a_1 = 2a_2$, (d) those forms for which a_1, a_2, a_3, a_4 are all solutions of the system of equations $2y_1 - y_4 = 0$, $y_2 = 0$, (e) those forms for which $a_1 + a_2 + a_3 = 1$?

3. Show that a nonempty subset $\mathscr{W}$ of a vector space $\mathscr{V}$ is a subspace if and only if $a\alpha + b\beta$ lies in $\mathscr{W}$ for all scalars, a, b and all vectors α, β in $\mathscr{W}$.

4. Show that $\mathscr{W}$ is a subspace if and only if $\mathscr{W} = \langle \mathscr{W} \rangle$.

5. Find the dimension of the subspace

$$\mathscr{W} = \langle (1, 2, -3, 6), (2, 2, 1, -2), (6, -1, 7, 10), (1, -7, 6, 0) \rangle \text{ of } \mathscr{V}_4(\mathscr{F}),$$

and give a basis for this space.

6. Give a basis for the subspace

$$\mathscr{W} = \langle (2, -3, 4), (4, -6, 8), (6, -8, 12), (9, -11, 18) \rangle \text{ of } \mathscr{V}_3(\mathscr{F}).$$

1.9. Sums and intersections of subspaces. Let $\mathscr{V}$ be a vector space over a field $\mathscr{F}$, and let $\mathscr{U}$ and $\mathscr{W}$ be subsets of $\mathscr{V}$. We denote by $\mathscr{U} + \mathscr{W}$ the set of all sums $\alpha + \beta$ for α in $\mathscr{U}$ and β in $\mathscr{W}$, and call this new set the *sum* of $\mathscr{U}$ and $\mathscr{W}$. Notice that, if $\mathscr{U}$ is a subspace, $\mathscr{U} + \mathscr{U} = \mathscr{U}$. We denote by $\mathscr{U} \cap \mathscr{W}$ the set of all vectors that are in both $\mathscr{U}$ and $\mathscr{W}$, and call this new set the *intersection* of $\mathscr{U}$ and $\mathscr{W}$. (The intersection is sometimes called *common part* or *crosscut*.) In particular, for any subset $\mathscr{U}$, $\mathscr{U} \cap \mathscr{U} = \mathscr{U}$.

The reader is cautioned against confusing the sum of two subsets with the set-theoretic sum which consists of all vectors that lie in at least one of the two subsets. The sum defined above is algebraic in character. (Notice that $\mathscr{U} + \mathscr{U} \subseteq \mathscr{U}$ is equivalent to the closure of $\mathscr{U}$ under addition.) On the other hand, the intersection operation defined above is just the set-theoretic intersection. Although the operations sum and intersection are defined for arbitrary subsets of $\mathscr{V}$, they are of most interest in the case of subspaces.

THEOREM 1.9A. *Let $\mathscr{V}$ be a vector space over a field $\mathscr{F}$, let $\mathscr{U}_1$ and $\mathscr{U}_2$ be subspaces of $\mathscr{V}$. Then, $\mathscr{U}_1 \cap \mathscr{U}_2$ and $\mathscr{U}_1 + \mathscr{U}_2$ are subspaces of $\mathscr{V}$, and*

$$(9.1) \quad \dim\,(\mathscr{U}_1 \cap \mathscr{U}_2) + \dim\,(\mathscr{U}_1 + \mathscr{U}_2) = \dim\,\mathscr{U}_1 + \dim\,\mathscr{U}_2.$$

This last result is so fundamental that we restate it in words: *The sum of the dimensions of any two subspaces is equal to the dimension of their intersection plus the dimension of their sum.*

Let $\mathscr{W}_1 = \mathscr{U}_1 \cap \mathscr{U}_2$ and $\mathscr{W}_2 = \mathscr{U}_1 + \mathscr{U}_2$. Clearly 0 lies in both $\mathscr{W}_1$ and $\mathscr{W}_2$; hence neither is empty. We first prove that $\mathscr{W}_1$ is a subspace. Let c be any scalar, and let α and β be elements of $\mathscr{W}_1$. Then, by definition of intersection, α and β belong to $\mathscr{U}_1$. Now, since $\mathscr{U}_1$ is a subspace, $c\alpha$ and $\alpha + \beta$ again belong to $\mathscr{U}_1$. By the same argument $c\alpha$ and $\alpha + \beta$ also belong to $\mathscr{U}_2$, and therefore (again by definition) to the intersection $\mathscr{W}_1 = \mathscr{U}_1 \cap \mathscr{U}_2$. This shows that $\mathscr{W}_1$ is a subspace (cf. Theorem 1.8A).

Next, to see that $\mathscr{W}_2$ is a subspace, let α and β belong to $\mathscr{W}_2$, and let c be any scalar. Then by definition of sum there exist vectors α_1, β_1 in $\mathscr{U}_1$ and α_2, β_2 in $\mathscr{U}_2$ such that $\alpha = \alpha_1 + \alpha_2$ and $\beta = \beta_1 + \beta_2$. Then

$$\alpha + \beta = (\alpha_1 + \alpha_2) + (\beta_1 + \beta_2) = (\alpha_1 + \beta_1) + (\alpha_2 + \beta_2)$$

and

$$c\alpha = c(\alpha_1 + \alpha_2) = c\alpha_1 + c\alpha_2$$

again belong to $\mathscr{W}_2$ since both $\alpha_1 + \beta_1$, $c\alpha_1$ belong to $\mathscr{U}_1$ and $\alpha_2 + \beta_2$, $c\alpha_2$ belong to $\mathscr{U}_2$. This proves that $\mathscr{W}_2$ is a subspace.

We observe that, if either $\mathscr{U}_1$ or $\mathscr{U}_2$ has infinite dimension, then so has $\mathscr{W}_2$, and so (9.1) holds. This leaves us only the case where $\dim \mathscr{U}_1 = r$ and $\dim \mathscr{U}_2 = s$ are both finite. We shall establish (9.1) by construction of a basis for $\mathscr{W}_2$ which has, as subsets, bases for $\mathscr{U}_1$, $\mathscr{U}_2$, and $\mathscr{W}_1$.

Let $\mathscr{S}_1 = \{\alpha_1, \cdots, \alpha_m\}$ be a basis for $\mathscr{W}_1$. Since $\mathscr{W}_1$ is a subspace of

$\mathscr{U}_1$, we have $\dim \mathscr{W}_1 = m \leq r$. Then by Lemma 1.8C there exist vectors $\beta_1, \cdots, \beta_{r-m}$ such that $\mathscr{R}_1 = \{\alpha_1, \cdots, \alpha_m, \beta_1, \cdots, \beta_{r-m}\}$ is a basis for $\mathscr{U}_1$. Similarly we can find a basis $\mathscr{R}_2 = \{\alpha_1, \cdots, \alpha_m, \gamma_1, \cdots, \gamma_{s-m}\}$ for $\mathscr{U}_2$.

Let $\mathscr{S}_2 = \{\alpha_1, \cdots, \alpha_m, \beta_1, \cdots, \beta_{r-m}, \gamma_1, \cdots, \gamma_{s-m}\}$. We now show that $\mathscr{S}_2$ is a basis for $\mathscr{W}_2$; i.e., that $\mathscr{S}_2$ spans $\mathscr{W}_2$ and that $\mathscr{S}_2$ is independent. When this is done we will have

$$\dim \mathscr{W}_2 = m + (r - m) + (s - m) = r + s - m$$

as required by (9.1).

To see that $\mathscr{S}_2$ spans $\mathscr{W}_2$ consider any vector δ in $\mathscr{W}_2$. By definition of sum we can write $\delta = \beta + \gamma$ where β belongs to $\mathscr{U}_1$ and γ belongs to $\mathscr{U}_2$. Then, since $\mathscr{R}_1$ is a basis for $\mathscr{U}_1$, we can write

$$\beta = a_1\alpha_1 + \cdots + a_m\alpha_m + b_1\beta_1 + \cdots + b_{r-m}\beta_{r-m}.$$

Similarly,

$$\gamma = d_1\alpha_1 + \cdots + d_m\alpha_m + c_1\gamma_1 + \cdots + c_{s-m}\gamma_{s-m}.$$

Now we have

$$\delta = (a_1 + d_1)\alpha_1 + \cdots + (a_m + d_m)\alpha_m$$
$$+ b_1\beta_1 + \cdots + b_{r-m}\beta_{r-m} + c_1\gamma_1 + \cdots + c_{s-m}\gamma_{s-m},$$

which shows that $\mathscr{S}_2$ spans $\mathscr{W}_2$.

Finally, to see that $\mathscr{S}_2$ is independent consider a relation

$$(9.2) \quad a_1\alpha_1 + \cdots + a_m\alpha_m + b_1\beta_1 + \cdots + b_{r-m}\beta_{r-m} + c_1\gamma_1$$
$$+ \cdots + c_{s-m}\gamma_{s-m} = 0.$$

Then

$$(9.3) \quad c_1\gamma_1 + \cdots + c_{s-m}\gamma_{s-m} = -a_1\alpha_1 - \cdots - a_m\alpha_m - b_1\beta_1 - \cdots$$
$$- b_{r-m}\beta_{r-m}.$$

Call the common value of these two expressions γ. From the left side, we see that γ is in $\mathscr{U}_2$; from the right, γ is in $\mathscr{U}_1$; hence γ belongs to $\mathscr{U}_1 \cap \mathscr{U}_2 = \mathscr{W}_1$. As an element of $\mathscr{W}_1$, γ has an expansion

$$\gamma = d_1\alpha_1 + \cdots + d_m\alpha_m.$$

Equating this expression for γ with the left side of (9.3) gives a dependence relation on the independent set $\mathscr{R}_2$; hence all of the coefficients d_j and c_j are zero. But, if the c_j are all zero, (9.2) becomes a dependence relation on $\mathscr{R}_1$, and so the a_j and b_j are also all zero. This shows that $\mathscr{S}_2$ is an independent set, and completes the proof of the theorem.

Exercises 1.9

1. Let $\mathscr{U}_1$ be the space spanned by the set $\mathscr{R}_1 = \{(1, 0, 0), (0, 1, 0)\}$, and let $\mathscr{U}_2$ be the space spanned by the set $\mathscr{R}_2 = \{(0, 1, 2), (2, 1, 3)\}$. Find a basis for $\mathscr{U}_1 \cap \mathscr{U}_2$ and a basis for $\mathscr{U}_1 + \mathscr{U}_2$.

2. Let $\mathscr{U}_1$ be the set of all solutions of the system $x_1 + x_2 - x_4 = 0$, $x_1 - x_3 + 2x_4 = 0$, and let $\mathscr{U}_2$ be the set of all solutions of the "system" $x_1 - x_4 = 0$. Find bases for $\mathscr{U}_1$, $\mathscr{U}_2$, $\mathscr{U}_1 \cap \mathscr{U}_2$, and $\mathscr{U}_1 + \mathscr{U}_2$.

3. In $\mathscr{L}_5(\mathscr{F})$ let $\mathscr{U}_1$ be the space spanned by the set $\mathscr{R}_1 = \{x_1 - x_2, x_3 + x_5\}$, and let $\mathscr{U}_2$ be the space spanned by the set $\mathscr{R}_2 = \{x_1 - x_4, x_5, x_2, x_3 + x_4\}$. Find bases for $\mathscr{U}_1$, $\mathscr{U}_2$, $\mathscr{U}_1 \cap \mathscr{U}_2$, $\mathscr{U}_1 + \mathscr{U}_2$.

4. Show that $\langle \mathscr{S} \rangle$ is the intersection of all subspaces that contain $\mathscr{S}$.

5. Prove that $\mathscr{U} + \mathscr{W} = \langle \mathscr{U}, \mathscr{W} \rangle$.

1.10. Subspaces of $\mathscr{V}_n(\mathscr{F})$.

Although for theoretical developments it is convenient to deal with vector spaces in abstract form, for actual applications it is almost always $\mathscr{V}_n(\mathscr{F})$ and to a lesser extent $\mathscr{L}_n(\mathscr{F})$ [or some similar model such as $\mathscr{V}_n{}^r(\mathscr{F})$ (cf. Section 2.9)] which appears. In the present section we shall study subspaces of $\mathscr{V}_n(\mathscr{F})$.

As an example we first consider the space $\mathscr{V} = \mathscr{V}_3(\mathfrak{R})$ of solid analytic geometry. Its subspaces are of four kinds: (1) the zero vector alone, (2) lines through the origin, (3) planes through the origin, and (4) $\mathscr{V}$ itself. Their dimensions are 0, 1, 2, and 3, respectively. We recall that a plane through the origin can be described as the set of vectors $\alpha = (a_1, a_2, a_3)$ whose components satisfy a single homogeneous linear equation $c_1 x_1 + c_2 x_2 + c_3 x_3 = 0$. A line through the origin can be specified by giving the equations of two planes which intersect on the line; i.e., it is the set of vectors whose components satisfy both equations. Also the plane can be specified by giving a set of two vectors which form a basis for it; and the line by a single nonzero vector on it, usually called a set of direction numbers.

The situation in $\mathscr{V}_3(\mathfrak{R})$ illustrates that for $\mathscr{V}_n(\mathscr{F})$ in general. Let $\mathscr{W}$ be a subspace of $\mathscr{V}_n(\mathscr{F})$. Then $\mathscr{W}$ has finite dimension, and so according to Theorem 1.6A it has a basis. Since a basis is in particular a finite set which spans $\mathscr{W}$, we see that *any subspace of $\mathscr{V}_n(\mathscr{F})$ can be defined as the set of all vectors dependent on some finite set.*

A linear form $a_1 x_1 + \cdots + a_n x_n$ is said to *vanish on a subspace* $\mathscr{W}$ of $\mathscr{V}_n(\mathscr{F})$ if each vector in $\mathscr{W}$ is a solution of the equation $a_1 x_1 + \cdots + a_n x_n = 0$. It is easy to see that *the set of all forms that vanish on $\mathscr{W}$ is a subspace of $\mathscr{L}_n(\mathscr{F})$*; we denote this subspace by $\mathscr{L}(\mathscr{W})$. Now $\mathscr{L}(\mathscr{W})$ has a finite spanning set $\{a_{11} x_1 + \cdots + a_{1n} x_n, \cdots, a_{m1} x_1 + \cdots + a_{mn} x_n\}$. A major result which will be proved later (Section 3.2) is that $\mathscr{W}$ is the space of all solutions of the system of equations

$$(10.1) \qquad a_{i1} x_1 + \cdots + a_{in} x_n = 0 \qquad (i = 1, \cdots, m);$$

and hence in particular *any subspace of $\mathscr{V}_n(\mathscr{F})$ can be defined as the set of all solutions of some system of homogeneous linear equations.*

A familiar example of this occurs in $\mathscr{V}_3(\mathfrak{R})$ in the problem of finding the coefficients in the equation $a_1x_1 + a_2x_2 + a_3x_3 = 0$ of a plane through the origin, given two points on it.

The question of finding a spanning set for $\mathscr{W}$, when $\mathscr{W}$ is given as the space of all solutions of a system of equations (10.1), will be answered when the theory of systems of homogeneous linear equations has been developed (Theorem 3.6C).

Let $\phi = (f_1, \cdots, f_n)$ be a vector of $\mathscr{V}_n(\mathscr{F})$. To determine if ϕ is in $\mathscr{W}$, where $\mathscr{W}$ is given as the set of solutions of the system of equations (10.1), is trivial. Simply find if the components of ϕ satisfy every equation. But, if $\mathscr{W}$ is defined by means of a spanning set $\alpha_1, \cdots, \alpha_w$, where $\alpha_i = (a_{i1}, \cdots, a_{in})$, then ϕ is in $\mathscr{W}$ if and only if there exist scalars $c_1, \cdots, c_w$ such that

$$\phi = c_1\alpha_1 + \cdots + c_w\alpha_w.$$

On equating the ith components of these two expressions for ϕ we find that $(c_1, \cdots, c_w)$ is a solution of the nonhomogeneous system

$$f_j = x_1a_{1j} + \cdots + x_wa_{wj} \qquad (j = 1, \cdots, n).$$

The solution of such a system is given in Section 3.9.

If the α_i are actually a basis for $\mathscr{W}$, we may consider instead the homogeneous equations

$$y_0f_j + y_1a_{1j} + \cdots + y_wa_{wj} = 0 \qquad (j = 1, \cdots, n)$$

obtained by taking components from $y_0\phi + y_1\alpha_1 + \cdots + y_w\alpha_w = 0$. For, if this vector equation has any solution other than the trivial one $y_0 = \cdots = y_w = 0$, it has one with $y_0 = -1$, since otherwise the α_i would not be independent.

· To determine whether a subspace $\mathscr{U}$ is contained in $\mathscr{W}$, it is sufficient to ascertain whether all vectors of a spanning set of $\mathscr{U}$ lie in $\mathscr{W}$. If $\mathscr{U}$ is defined as the space of solutions of a system of equations it is usually simplest to solve the equations, find a spanning set for $\mathscr{U}$, and verify whether each member of the set is in $\mathscr{W}$. For this purpose it is most convenient to have $\mathscr{W}$ given as the space of solutions of a system of equations.

We next describe a process for obtaining a basis for $\mathscr{W}$ from a finite spanning set $\alpha_1, \cdots, \alpha_w$. We examine the α_j in order. If α_j is independent of $\alpha_1, \cdots, \alpha_{j-1}$ we keep it; otherwise we discard it. The vectors that remain will be a basis for $\mathscr{W}$.

We now consider sums and intersections of subspaces. If $\mathscr{U} = \langle \alpha_1, \cdots, \alpha_u \rangle$ and $\mathscr{W} = \langle \beta_1, \cdots, \beta_w \rangle$, then $\mathscr{U} + \mathscr{W} = \langle \alpha_1, \cdots, \alpha_u, \beta_1, \cdots, \beta_w \rangle$.

But, if $\mathscr{U}$ and $\mathscr{W}$ are defined by means of equations of the form (10.1), then it is difficult to find a set of equations defining $\mathscr{U} + \mathscr{W}$. On the other hand $\mathscr{U} \cap \mathscr{W}$ is simply the set of all solutions of both sets of equations simultaneously. But a generating set of vectors for $\mathscr{U} \cap \mathscr{W}$ cannot usually be readily found from the sets $\alpha_1, \cdots, \alpha_u$ and $\beta_1, \cdots, \beta_w$. Thus for addition of subspaces it is desirable to have spanning sets, while for intersection it is better to have defining equations.

We say that we have a *double description* for a subspace $\mathscr{W}$ if we have both a spanning set for it and a system of equations for which it is the set of all solutions. The foregoing discussion shows the advantage of double description for subspaces. One important property of Hermite matrices (which are introduced in Section 3.5) is that they supply a handy means of providing double description for subspaces. The fact that double description is always possible is proved in Section 3.2 (Theorem 3.2D).

Exercises 1.10

In Exercises 1 and 2 find defining equations for $\mathscr{U}$ and $\mathscr{W}$ and find bases of $\mathscr{Y}$ and $\mathscr{Z}$. Find bases for $\mathscr{U} \cap \mathscr{W}$, $\mathscr{Y} \cap \mathscr{Z}$, $\mathscr{Z} \cap \mathscr{U}$, $\mathscr{U} + \mathscr{W}$, $\mathscr{Y} + \mathscr{Z}$ and $\mathscr{Y} + \mathscr{U}$.

1. Let $\mathscr{U} = \langle (1, -1, 2), (2, 1, 1) \rangle$;
   let $\mathscr{W} = \langle (0, 1, -1), (1, 2, 1) \rangle$;

   let $\mathscr{Y}$ be the set of all solutions of
   $$\begin{cases} 4x_1 - x_3 = 0, \\ x_1 + x_2 = 0; \end{cases}$$

   and let $\mathscr{Z}$ be the set of all solutions of
   $$\begin{cases} 3x_1 - x_2 - x_3 = 0, \\ x_3 = 0. \end{cases}$$

2. Let $\mathscr{U} = \langle (1, 0, 1, 0, 0), (1, -1, 1, 0, 1), (2, -1, 1, 0, 1) \rangle$;
   let $\mathscr{W} = \langle (1, 0, 0, 1, -1), (2, 1, 0, 1, 2), (4, 1, 1, 2, 1) \rangle$;
   let $\mathscr{Y}$ be defined by the equations

   $$\begin{aligned} x_1 - 2x_2 + x_3 - x_4 + x_5 &= 0, \\ x_1 \quad\quad + x_3 + x_4 \quad\quad &= 0, \\ x_2 \quad\quad + x_4 + x_5 &= 0; \end{aligned}$$

   and let $\mathscr{Z}$ be defined by the equations

   $$\begin{aligned} x_1 \quad\quad\quad - x_4 - 2x_5 &= 0, \\ x_2 \quad + x_4 + x_5 &= 0. \end{aligned}$$

3. Prove that a basis can be obtained from a finite spanning set by discarding in turn each vector dependent on the preceding vectors.

Chapter 2

Linear Transformations and Matrices

In Chapter 1 we introduced the concept of vector space and developed some of the properties of vectors. In Chapter 2 we study mappings from one vector space into another. These mappings appear in the abstract as linear transformations and in concrete analytic form as matrices; the theory is developed both in abstract and in concrete form so as to utilize the advantages of each.

2.1. Linear transformations. The concept of isomorphism was introduced in Section 1.7. We now consider an important generalization of that concept obtained by discarding the requirement that the mapping be one-to-one. Let $\mathscr{V}$ and $\mathscr{W}$ be vector spaces over a field $\mathscr{F}$. A mapping $\mathsf{T}: \alpha \to \beta = \alpha\mathsf{T}$ of $\mathscr{V}$ into $\mathscr{W}$ is said to be a *linear transformation* (homomorphism) if it satisfies the following two conditions:

(L1)   *For every pair of vectors α_1 and α_2 in $\mathscr{V}$*

$$(\alpha_1 + \alpha_2)\mathsf{T} = \alpha_1\mathsf{T} + \alpha_2\mathsf{T},$$

and

(L2)   *For every scalar c and every vector α in $\mathscr{V}$*

$$(c\alpha)\mathsf{T} = c(\alpha\mathsf{T}).$$

The requirement that a mapping T be a linear transformation may be stated simply as that T preserves the two basic operations of a vector space. Examples of linear transformations are given in Section 2.3.

The conditions L1 and L2 are equivalent to the single condition

(L3)   *For every pair of scalars c_1, c_2 and every pair of vectors α_1, α_2 in $\mathscr{V}$,*

$$(c_1\alpha_1 + c_2\alpha_2)\mathsf{T} = c_1(\alpha_1\mathsf{T}) + c_2(\alpha_2\mathsf{T}),$$

as well as to the single condition

(L4)   *For every set of scalars $c_1, c_2, \cdots, c_r$, and for every set of vectors $\alpha_1, \alpha_2, \cdots, \alpha_r$,*

$$(c_1\alpha_1 + c_2\alpha_2 + \cdots + c_r\alpha_r)\mathsf{T} = c_1(\alpha_1\mathsf{T}) + c_2(\alpha_2\mathsf{T}) + \cdots + c_r(\alpha_r\mathsf{T}).$$

This condition can be paraphrased: *A mapping* T *is a linear transformation if the image of a linear combination of any set of vectors is the same linear combination of the image vectors.* We leave the proofs of the equivalence of L1 and L2 to L3 and to L4 as exercises.

We recall (cf. Appendix II) that to say that T is a mapping of $\mathscr{V}$ into $\mathscr{W}$ requires that for each vector α in $\mathscr{V}$ there corresponds a unique image vector $\beta = \alpha$T in $\mathscr{W}$; the term "into" means that we do not require that every vector β in $\mathscr{W}$ shall appear as an image; if the mapping has this additional property we may speak of a mapping of $\mathscr{V}$ *onto* $\mathscr{W}$. We call $\mathscr{V}$ the *domain* of T and denote by $\mathscr{V}$T the *range* (also called *image space*) of T; i.e., the set of all vectors β in $\mathscr{W}$ that are of the form $\beta = \alpha$T. We call the set of all vectors α in $\mathscr{V}$ for which αT $= 0_{\mathscr{W}}$ the *kernel* of T and denote it by $\mathscr{K}$(T). Another term frequently used is *null space* of T.

THEOREM 2.1A. *The kernel and the range of a linear transformation are vector spaces.*

Clearly, neither $\mathscr{V}$T nor $\mathscr{K}$(T) is empty since the equation $0_{\mathscr{V}}$T $= (00_{\mathscr{V}})$T $= 0(0_{\mathscr{V}}$T$) = 0_{\mathscr{W}}$ shows that $\mathscr{V}$T contains $0_{\mathscr{W}}$ and $\mathscr{K}$(T) contains $0_{\mathscr{V}}$. Let c be any scalar and suppose that α_1 and α_2 belong to $\mathscr{K}$(T). Then applying L1 we have $(\alpha_1 + \alpha_2)$T $= \alpha_1$T $+ \alpha_2$T $= 0_{\mathscr{W}} + 0_{\mathscr{W}} = 0_{\mathscr{W}}$, and applying L2 we have $(c\alpha_1)$T $= c(\alpha_1$T$) = c0_{\mathscr{W}} = 0_{\mathscr{W}}$. This shows that $\mathscr{K}$(T) is a subspace of $\mathscr{V}$. We leave to the reader the proof that $\mathscr{V}$T is a subspace of $\mathscr{W}$. Note that this theorem provides two new sources of subspaces.

LEMMA 2.1B. *A linear transformation is an isomorphism if and only if its kernel is* $\{0_{\mathscr{V}}\}$.

Let T be a linear transformation of $\mathscr{V}$ into $\mathscr{W}$. Then $0_{\mathscr{V}}$ is in $\mathscr{K}$(T). Furthermore, if T is an isomorphism and hence one-to-one, then $0_{\mathscr{V}}$ is the only vector with image $0_{\mathscr{W}}$; thus $\mathscr{K}$(T) $= \{0_{\mathscr{V}}\}$.

Conversely, if αT $= \beta$T, then $(\alpha - \beta)$T $= \alpha$T $- \beta$T $= 0_{\mathscr{W}}$; hence $\alpha - \beta$ is in $\mathscr{K}$(T). If $\mathscr{K}$(T) $= \{0_{\mathscr{V}}\}$, then we must have $\alpha = \beta$, and T is an isomorphism of $\mathscr{V}$ into $\mathscr{W}$.

It may happen that $\mathscr{V}$ and $\mathscr{W}$ are the same space. In this case we say that T is a linear transformation *on* $\mathscr{V}$. (Note that this does not require that T be a mapping of $\mathscr{V}$ *onto* $\mathscr{V}$.)

We recall that two linear transformations S and T are *equal* if they define the same mapping; that is, if they have the same domain $\mathscr{V}$ and if for each vector α in $\mathscr{V}$ we have αS $= \alpha$T.

Suppose that T is a linear transformation of $\mathscr{V}$ into $\mathscr{W}$ and that $\mathscr{U}$ is a subspace of $\mathscr{V}$. Then we can define a mapping S of $\mathscr{U}$ into $\mathscr{W}$ by the equation γS $= \gamma$T for all γ in $\mathscr{U}$. Clearly S is a linear transformation.

Except for the trivial case $\mathscr{V} = \mathscr{U}$, the transformations S and T are not equal since they do not have the same domain. We say that S is *induced in* $\mathscr{U}$ *by* T, and also say that S is the *restriction of* T *to* $\mathscr{U}$. If $\mathscr{U}$, $\mathscr{V}$, and $\mathscr{W}$ are as above and S is a linear transformation of $\mathscr{U}$ into $\mathscr{W}$, then a linear transformation T of $\mathscr{V}$ into $\mathscr{W}$ is said to be an *extension of* S *to* $\mathscr{V}$ if S is the restriction of T to $\mathscr{U}$.

Evidently an isomorphism is a transformation which besides being linear is one-to-one.

LEMMA 2.1C.   *A restriction of an isomorphism is also an isomorphism.*

As mentioned above, the restriction is a linear transformation. The one-to-one property is also clearly preserved under restriction.

LEMMA 2.1D.   *Let* T *be a linear transformation of* $\mathscr{V}$ *into* $\mathscr{W}$. *If* $\alpha_1, \cdots, \alpha_n$ *are dependent, then their images* $\alpha_1 T, \cdots, \alpha_n T$ *are also dependent.*

If $c_1\alpha_1 + \cdots + c_n\alpha_n = 0$, then

$$(c_1\alpha_1 + \cdots + c_n\alpha_n)T = 0T.$$

The left-hand side equals

$$c_1(\alpha_1 T) + \cdots + c_n(\alpha_n T),$$

and the right-hand side $0T = 0$. Hence $\alpha_1 T, \cdots, \alpha_n T$ are dependent when $\alpha_1, \cdots, \alpha_n$ are.

COROLLARY 2.1E.   *The dimension of the range of a linear transformation cannot exceed the dimension of the domain;* i.e.,

$$\dim \mathscr{V}T \leq \dim \mathscr{V}.$$

If $\mathscr{V}$ has infinite dimension the corollary is obviously true. Suppose, otherwise, $\dim \mathscr{V} = v$. Take any $v + 1$ vectors in $\mathscr{V}T$; call them $\beta_1 T, \cdots, \beta_{v+1}T$, where $\beta_1, \cdots, \beta_{v+1}$ are in $\mathscr{V}$. Since $\dim \mathscr{V} < v + 1$, the vectors $\beta_1, \cdots, \beta_{v+1}$ are dependent. Hence $\beta_1 T, \cdots, \beta_{v+1}T$ are dependent by Lemma 2.1D. Since any $v + 1$ vectors in $\mathscr{V}T$ are dependent, $\dim \mathscr{V}T \leq v = \dim \mathscr{V}$.

A more general result follows.

THEOREM 2.1F.   *Let* T *be a linear transformation whose domain is a finite dimensional vector space* $\mathscr{V}$. *Then*

$$\dim \mathscr{V}T + \dim \mathscr{K}(T) = \dim \mathscr{V};$$

i.e., *the dimension of the range plus the dimension of the kernel is equal to the dimension of the domain.*

The kernel of T is a subspace of $\mathscr{V}$ and therefore has finite dimension, say $\dim \mathscr{K}(T) = s$. Let $\mathscr{S} = \{\gamma_1, \cdots, \gamma_s\}$ be a basis for $\mathscr{K}(T)$, and let

$\beta_1, \cdots, \beta_r$ be additional vectors such that $\mathcal{T} = \{\gamma_1, \cdots, \gamma_s, \beta_1, \cdots, \beta_r\}$ is a basis for $\mathcal{V}$. Then $v = \dim \mathcal{V} = r + s$.

Let $\beta_i \mathsf{T} = \beta'_i \; (i = 1, \cdots, r)$. We establish the theorem by showing that the set $\mathcal{R} = \{\beta'_1, \cdots, \beta'_r\}$ is a basis for $\mathcal{V}\mathsf{T}$, and thus that $\dim \mathcal{V}\mathsf{T} = r = v - s = \dim \mathcal{V} - \dim \mathcal{K}(\mathsf{T})$.

We first show that $\mathcal{R}$ spans $\mathcal{V}\mathsf{T}$. Each vector α' in $\mathcal{V}\mathsf{T}$ has the form $\alpha' = \alpha\mathsf{T}$ where α is in $\mathcal{V}$. Since $\mathcal{T}$ is a basis for $\mathcal{V}$, there exist scalars $c_1, \cdots, c_s, b_1, \cdots, b_r$ such that

$$\alpha = c_1\gamma_1 + \cdots + c_s\gamma_s + b_1\beta_1 + \cdots + b_r\beta_r.$$

Then by L4 we have

$$\alpha' = \alpha\mathsf{T} = c_1(\gamma_1\mathsf{T}) + \cdots + c_s(\gamma_s\mathsf{T}) + b_1(\beta_1\mathsf{T}) + \cdots + b_r(\beta_r\mathsf{T})$$
$$= 0 + \cdots + 0 + b_1\beta'_1 + \cdots + b_r\beta'_r.$$

Therefore $\mathcal{V}\mathsf{T}$ is dependent on $\mathcal{R}$. We next show that $\mathcal{R}$ is independent. Suppose that

$$b_1\beta'_1 + \cdots + b_r\beta'_r = 0.$$

Then, if $\beta = b_1\beta_1 + \cdots + b_r\beta_r$, we have from L4 that

$$\beta\mathsf{T} = (b_1\beta_1 + \cdots + b_r\beta_r)\mathsf{T}$$
$$= b_1\beta'_1 + \cdots + b_r\beta'_r = 0,$$

and hence β lies in $\mathcal{K}(\mathsf{T})$. Now, since $\mathcal{S}$ is a basis for $\mathcal{K}(\mathsf{T})$ there exist scalars $c_1, \cdots, c_s$ such that

$$\beta = b_1\beta_1 + \cdots + b_r\beta_r = c_1\gamma_1 + \cdots + c_s\gamma_s.$$

From the last two members of this equation we get the dependence relation

$$(-c_1)\gamma_1 + \cdots + -(c_s)\gamma_s + b_1\beta_1 + \cdots + b_r\beta_r = 0$$

on $\mathcal{T}$, and now since $\mathcal{T}$ is an independent set we conclude that $b_1 = \cdots = b_r = 0$. This establishes the independence of $\mathcal{R}$ and completes the proof of the theorem.

Exercises 2.1

1. Show that L1 and L2 are equivalent to L3.
2. Show that L3 is equivalent to L4.
3. Show that L1 and L2 are equivalent to L4.
4. Prove that $\mathcal{V}\mathsf{T}$ is a subspace of $\mathcal{W}$.
5. Show that the perpendicular projection T in $\mathcal{V}_3$ defined by $(a_1, a_2, a_3)\mathsf{T} = (a_1, a_2, 0)$ is a linear transformation. Find its kernel and range.
6. Let $\mathcal{W} = \langle \mathcal{S} \rangle$ where $\mathcal{S} = \{\alpha_1, \cdots, \alpha_r\}$ is not necessarily a basis for $\mathcal{W}$. Prove that the image $\alpha\mathsf{T}$ of any vector α in $\mathcal{W}$ under a linear transformation T is determined when $\alpha_1\mathsf{T}, \cdots, \alpha_r\mathsf{T}$ are given.

7. Show that the mapping $(b_1, b_2, b_3)\mathsf{T} = (2b_1, 3b_2, -b_3)$ is a linear transformation.

8. Show that the mapping $(b_1, b_2, b_3)\mathsf{T} = (2b_1 + b_3, -b_2 + 2b_3)$ is a linear transformation.

9. Show that the mapping $(b_1, b_2, b_3)\mathsf{T} = (b_1 + 1, b_2, b_3)$ is not a linear transformation.

10. Under a linear transformation T on $\mathscr{V}_2(\mathfrak{Q})$ the images of $(2, -3)$ and $(1, 4)$, respectively, are $(1, 2)$ and $(2, -1)$. What is the image of (x, y)?

11. Is there any linear transformation T on $\mathscr{V}_2(\mathfrak{Q})$ for which $(2, 3)\mathsf{T} = (-1, 2)$, $(1, -1)\mathsf{T} = (3, 1)$, and $(-1, -9)\mathsf{T} = (11, 2)$?

12. Let T be a linear transformation. Show that if the set $\{\alpha_1\mathsf{T}, \cdots, \alpha_r\mathsf{T}\}$ is independent then $\{\alpha_1, \cdots, \alpha_r\}$ is independent.

2.2. Matrix of a linear transformation.

Let $\mathscr{V}$ and $\mathscr{W}$ be finite dimensional vector spaces over a field $\mathscr{F}$; let $\{\alpha_1, \cdots, \alpha_v\}$ be a basis for $\mathscr{V}$ and $\{\beta_1, \cdots, \beta_w\}$ a basis for $\mathscr{W}$. Consider a linear transformation T of $\mathscr{V}$ into $\mathscr{W}$. Then since for each basis vector α_i the image $\alpha_i\mathsf{T}$ is in $\mathscr{W}$ we have equations

(2.1) $$\alpha_i\mathsf{T} = a_{i1}\beta_1 + \cdots + a_{iw}\beta_w \qquad (i = 1, \cdots, v),$$

or

$$\alpha_1\mathsf{T} = a_{11}\beta_1 + \cdots + a_{1w}\beta_w,$$
$$\alpha_2\mathsf{T} = a_{21}\beta_1 + \cdots + a_{2w}\beta_w,$$
$$\cdots,$$
$$\alpha_v\mathsf{T} = a_{v1}\beta_1 + \cdots + a_{vw}\beta_w.$$

The form of these equations suggests writing down the vw scalars a_{ij} in the rectangular array

(2.2)
$$A = \left\| \begin{array}{cccccc}
a_{11} & a_{12} & \cdots & a_{1j} & \cdots & a_{1w} \\
a_{21} & a_{22} & \cdots & a_{2j} & \cdots & a_{2w} \\
\cdot & \cdot & \cdots & \cdot & \cdots & \cdot \\
a_{i1} & a_{i2} & \cdots & a_{ij} & \cdots & a_{iw} \\
\cdot & \cdot & \cdots & \cdot & \cdots & \cdot \\
a_{v1} & a_{v2} & \cdots & a_{vj} & \cdots & a_{vw}
\end{array} \right\|.$$

Any rectangular array A of the form (2.2), with v and w any natural numbers, is said to be a *matrix*, more precisely a *v-by-w $\mathscr{F}$ matrix*. We call v the *row degree* and w the *column degree of A* and write $v = \deg_r A$ and $w = \deg_c A$. The scalars a_{ij} are called the *elements* (or *entries*) of the matrix. The elements $a_{i1}, a_{i2}, \cdots, a_{ij}, \cdots, a_{iw}$ are said to constitute the *i*th *row* of the matrix A; similarly the elements $a_{1j}, a_{2j}, \cdots, a_{ij}, \cdots, a_{vj}$ are said to constitute the *j*th *column* of A. We sometimes use the abbreviated symbol $\| a_{ij} \|$ for the matrix A. When this is done the row and column degrees must also be specified in some way. (Some writers use parentheses or brackets instead of the double vertical bars to indicate a matrix.)

We say that two matrices $A = \| a_{ij} \|$ and $B = \| b_{ij} \|$ are *equal* if and only if they have the same degrees and all corresponding elements are equal; in more detail $A = B$ if and only if

(a) $\deg_r A = v = \deg_r B$.

(b) $\deg_c A = w = \deg_c B$.

(c) $a_{ij} = b_{ij}$ $(i = 1, \cdots, v; \ j = 1, \cdots, w)$.

The matrix A of (2.2) is uniquely determined by the transformation T when bases of $\mathscr{V}$ and $\mathscr{W}$ are prescribed. For the elements a_{ij} are given from (2.1) as the coordinates of $\alpha_i \mathsf{T}$ and are uniquely defined since $\beta_1, \cdots, \beta_w$ is a basis of $\mathscr{W}$.

For any vector α in $\mathscr{V}$, the image $\alpha \mathsf{T}$ is uniquely determined by the images $\alpha_1 \mathsf{T}, \cdots, \alpha_v \mathsf{T}$ of the basis vectors. For α is a linear combination of the basis vectors, say

$$(2.3) \qquad \alpha = x_1 \alpha_1 + \cdots + x_v \alpha_v.$$

Since T is a linear transformation, it follows from L4 that

$$(2.4) \qquad \alpha \mathsf{T} = (x_1 \alpha_1 + \cdots + x_v \alpha_v)\mathsf{T} = x_1(\alpha_1 \mathsf{T}) + \cdots + x_v(\alpha_v \mathsf{T});$$

and we conclude that $\alpha \mathsf{T}$ is the same linear combination of the vectors $\alpha_1 \mathsf{T}, \cdots, \alpha_v \mathsf{T}$ as α is of $\alpha_1, \cdots, \alpha_v$.

The image $\alpha \mathsf{T}$ is in $\mathscr{W}$ and hence is a linear combination of $\beta_1, \cdots, \beta_w$:

$$(2.5) \qquad \alpha \mathsf{T} = y_1 \beta_1 + \cdots + y_w \beta_w.$$

We shall find formulas expressing each component y_j in terms of the x_i and a_{ij}; i.e., in terms of the components of α [see (2.3)] and the elements of the matrix A determined by T.

But before doing this we first discuss a convenient notation useful in handling sums. For example, if $f(x)$ is any function defined for integer values of x and if r and s are integers with $r \leq s$, the sum

$$f(r) + f(r + 1) + \cdots + f(s)$$

will be written

$$(2.6) \qquad \sum_{\lambda = r}^{s} f(\lambda).$$

This symbol is read "the sum from $\lambda = r$ to $\lambda = s$ of $f(\lambda)$."

The integers r and s are called, respectively, the *lower limit* and *upper limit* of the sum; the variable λ is called the *summation index*; and $f(\lambda)$ is sometimes called the *general term* of the sum. In this book we shall follow the convention of always designating summation indices by lower-case Greek letters, typically λ, μ, ν.

Note the formal resemblance of (2.6) to the definite integral $\int_r^s f(x)\,dx$. We give a few examples:

$$\sum_{\lambda=1}^{4} a_\lambda = a_1 + a_2 + a_3 + a_4,$$

$$\sum_{\lambda=3}^{5} (1 + \lambda^2) = (1 + 3^2) + (1 + 4^2) + (1 + 5^2),$$

$$\sum_{\lambda=0}^{n} a_\lambda x^\lambda = a_0 + a_1 x + a_2 x^2 + \cdots + a_n x^n.$$

As an exercise in the use of the Σ notation we express the sum S of the elements in the matrix A. The sum R_i of the elements in the ith row is

$$R_i = \sum_{\lambda=1}^{w} a_{i\lambda},$$

and so

$$S = \sum_{\mu=1}^{v} R_\mu = \sum_{\mu=1}^{v} \left(\sum_{\lambda=1}^{w} a_{\mu\lambda} \right).$$

If we sum by columns first, and denote by C_j the sum of the elements in the jth column, we have

$$C_j = \sum_{\mu=1}^{v} a_{\mu j},$$

and then (by virtue of the associative and commutative laws in $\mathscr{F}$)

$$S = \sum_{\lambda=1}^{w} C_\lambda = \sum_{\lambda=1}^{w} \left(\sum_{\mu=1}^{v} a_{\mu\lambda} \right).$$

Equating these two expressions for S, we obtain finally

(2.7)
$$\sum_{\mu=1}^{v} \left(\sum_{\lambda=1}^{w} a_{\mu\lambda} \right) = \sum_{\lambda=1}^{w} \left(\sum_{\mu=1}^{v} a_{\mu\lambda} \right);$$

or, in words, *the order of summation can be interchanged without changing the over-all sum*, provided the inner limits are independent of the outer summation variable.

Using this Σ notation we rewrite various equations:

(2.1')
$$\alpha_i \mathsf{T} = \sum_{\lambda=1}^{w} a_{i\lambda} \beta_\lambda \qquad (i = 1, \cdots, v),$$

(2.3')
$$\alpha = \sum_{\lambda=1}^{v} x_\lambda \alpha_\lambda,$$

$$(2.4') \qquad \alpha\mathsf{T} = \sum_{\lambda=1}^{v} x_\lambda(\alpha_\lambda\mathsf{T}),$$

$$(2.5') \qquad \alpha\mathsf{T} = \sum_{\lambda=1}^{w} y_\lambda\beta_\lambda.$$

We are now ready to express the y_j in terms of the x_i and the a_{ij}. We see that

$$\alpha\mathsf{T} = \sum_{\lambda=1}^{v} x_\lambda(\alpha_\lambda\mathsf{T}) \qquad \text{(by 2.4′)}$$

$$= \sum_{\lambda=1}^{v} x_\lambda \left(\sum_{\mu=1}^{w} a_{\lambda\mu}\beta_\mu \right) \qquad \text{(by 2.1′)}$$

$$= \sum_{\lambda=1}^{v} \left(\sum_{\mu=1}^{w} x_\lambda a_{\lambda\mu}\beta_\mu \right) \qquad \text{(by axioms S2, S3)}$$

$$= \sum_{\mu=1}^{w} \left(\sum_{\lambda=1}^{v} x_\lambda a_{\lambda\mu}\beta_\mu \right) \qquad \begin{matrix}\text{(by (2.7) with } a_{\lambda\mu}\text{ re-}\\ \text{placed by } x_\lambda a_{\lambda\mu}\beta_\mu)\end{matrix}$$

$$= \sum_{\mu=1}^{w} \left(\sum_{\lambda=1}^{v} x_\lambda a_{\lambda\mu} \right) \beta_\mu \qquad \text{(by S2, S3).}$$

On comparing this last result with (2.5′) and realizing that the coefficients of β_μ are unique since $\{\beta_1, \cdots, \beta_w\}$ is a basis for $\mathscr{W}$, we finally obtain the formula

$$(2.8) \qquad y_j = \sum_{\lambda=1}^{v} x_\lambda a_{\lambda j} \qquad (j = 1, \cdots, w).$$

We restate this in words: The coefficient of β_j in $\alpha\mathsf{T}$ is found by multiplying the λth coordinate of α by the λth element in the jth column of the matrix A defined by T and then summing over the range $\lambda = 1$ to $\lambda = v$.

Formulas (2.8) and (2.5′) show that (in the finite dimensional case) each linear transformation can be completely described by a matrix.

We next show that the converse is true. Suppose that A is any v-by-w matrix given by (2.2) and then define a mapping T of $\mathscr{V}$ into $\mathscr{W}$ by formula (2.5); more precisely, if α is a vector given by (2.3) then we define $\beta = \alpha\mathsf{T}$ to be the vector with coordinates $y_1, \cdots, y_w$ (relative to the basis of $\mathscr{W}$) where y_j is given by (2.8). To check that T is well defined (i.e., defined and single-valued for each α in $\mathscr{V}$) we observe that each vector α has a unique expression (2.3) in terms of the given basis vectors for $\mathscr{V}$.

We now show that T is a linear transformation by checking the linearity properties L1 and L2.   Let α be as in (2.3), let $\alpha' = x'_1\alpha_1 + \cdots + x'_v\alpha_v$, and let c be a scalar.   Then we have

$$(\alpha + \alpha')\mathsf{T} = \left[\sum_{\lambda=1}^{v} (x_\lambda + x'_\lambda)\alpha_\lambda \right] \mathsf{T}$$

$$= \sum_{\mu=1}^{w} \left(\sum_{\lambda=1}^{v} (x_\lambda + x'_\lambda)a_{\lambda\mu} \right) \beta_\mu \qquad \text{[by (2.5) and (2.8)]}$$

$$= \sum_{\mu=1}^{w} \left(\sum_{\lambda=1}^{v} x_\lambda a_{\lambda\mu} \right) \beta_\mu + \sum_{\mu=1}^{w} \left(\sum_{\lambda=1}^{v} x'_\lambda a_{\lambda\mu} \right) \beta_\mu \qquad \text{(by S4, S3, A5)}$$

$$= \alpha\mathsf{T} + \alpha'\mathsf{T} \qquad \text{[by (2.5)],}$$

which checks L1, and

$$(c\alpha)\mathsf{T} = \left(\sum_{\lambda=1}^{v} (cx_\lambda)\alpha_\lambda \right) \mathsf{T} = \sum_{\mu=1}^{w} \left(\sum_{\lambda=1}^{v} (cx_\lambda)a_{\lambda\mu} \right) \beta_\mu$$

$$= c \left(\sum_{\mu=1}^{w} \left(\sum_{\lambda=1}^{v} x_\lambda a_{\lambda\mu} \right) \beta_\mu \right) = c(\alpha\mathsf{T}),$$

which checks L2.

If T determines a matrix A as described in the first part of this section and if A determines a linear transformation S by the process described just above, then $\mathsf{S} = \mathsf{T}$.   Indeed, for the basis vector α_i, all of whose components are 0 except $x_i = 1$, we see that (2.8) gives $y_j = a_{ij}$ so that

$$\alpha_i\mathsf{S} = \sum_{\lambda=1}^{w} a_{i\lambda}\beta_\lambda,$$ which is equal to $\alpha_i\mathsf{T}$ by (2.1').   Since the images of the basis vectors completely determine a linear transformation this shows that $\mathsf{S} = \mathsf{T}$.

Thus, *given two vector spaces $\mathscr{V}$ and $\mathscr{W}$, together with a fixed basis for each, there is a one-to-one correspondence between the set of all linear transformations T of $\mathscr{V}$ into $\mathscr{W}$ and the set of all v-by-w $\mathscr{F}$ matrices A.*   This correspondence is exhibited by the numbered formulas of this section. From A, we find T by employing (2.3), (2.5), and (2.8).   From T we obtain A by using (2.1) and (2.2).   We state this more explicitly.   The matrix A of T has v rows and w columns.   The ith row consists of the coordinates of the image under T of the ith basis vector; i.e.,

$$(2.9) \quad A = \left\| \begin{array}{l} \text{1st row: coordinates relative to the } \beta_j \text{ of } \alpha_1\mathsf{T} \\ \text{2nd row: coordinates relative to the } \beta_j \text{ of } \alpha_2\mathsf{T} \\ \qquad \cdots \\ i\text{th row: coordinates relative to the } \beta_j \text{ of } \alpha_i\mathsf{T} \\ \qquad \cdots \\ v\text{th row: coordinates relative to the } \beta_j \text{ of } \alpha_v\mathsf{T} \end{array} \right\| .$$

In other words the element a_{ij} of A which lies in the ith row and the jth column of A is the coefficient of β_j in the expression for $\alpha_i\mathsf{T}$ as a linear combination of $\beta_1, \cdots, \beta_w$.

This can be compactly described if we introduce the following notation. Let the ordered set $\mathscr{A} = \{\alpha_1, \cdots, \alpha_v\}$ be a basis for $\mathscr{V}$. Then for every vector α in $\mathscr{V}$ there is a unique set of coordinates $a_1, \cdots, a_v$ such that

$$\alpha = a_1\alpha_1 + \cdots + a_v\alpha_v.$$

Let $\| \alpha \|_{\mathscr{A}}$ denote the single-rowed matrix

$$\| \alpha \|_{\mathscr{A}} = \| a_1 \cdots a_v \|.$$

Let $\mathscr{B} = \{\beta_1, \cdots, \beta_w\}$. Then the ith row of A is $\| \alpha_i\mathsf{T} \|_{\mathscr{B}}$. If we denote the matrix A of the transformation T relative to the bases $\mathscr{A}$ of $\mathscr{V}$ and $\mathscr{B}$ of $\mathscr{W}$ by $A = \| \mathsf{T} \|_{\mathscr{A}\mathscr{B}}$, then

$$\| \mathsf{T} \|_{\mathscr{A}\mathscr{B}} = \left\| \begin{matrix} \| \alpha_1\mathsf{T} \|_{\mathscr{B}} \\ \cdot \\ \cdot \\ \cdot \\ \| \alpha_v\mathsf{T} \|_{\mathscr{B}} \end{matrix} \right\|.$$

Consider the case of a linear transformation T on a space $\mathscr{V}$ (i.e., $\mathscr{V} = \mathscr{W}$). Although, in applying the formula to determine the matrix A of T, it would be possible to use one basis $\alpha_1, \cdots, \alpha_v$ for $\mathscr{V}$ considered as domain of T, and another basis $\beta_1, \cdots, \beta_v$ for $\mathscr{V}$ considered as image space, we shall always assume that when $\mathscr{V} = \mathscr{W}$ we have also $\beta_1 = \alpha_1, \cdots, \beta_v = \alpha_v$ (unless we specify to the contrary for some particular argument).

2.3. Examples of linear transformations. The developments of the preceding section show how to get a large variety of linear transformations. All we need to do is to choose bases for each of two vector spaces and then write down any matrix with the proper numbers of rows and columns. In the following examples we do not proceed in this way, but instead begin by defining a mapping in some other way and then show that the mapping is a linear transformation.

EXAMPLE 1. The ordinary Euclidean plane studied in analytic geometry can be regarded as $\mathscr{V}_2(\Re)$ where we take as basis vectors $\varepsilon_1 = (1, 0)$ and $\varepsilon_2 = (0, 1)$. The vector (x, y) can be identified with the directed line segment $\overrightarrow{OP}$ where O is the origin and P the point with ordinary rectangular coordinates x, y. Consider a rotation T of the plane with the origin as center and through an angle θ. Then, if $\overrightarrow{OP'} = (x', y')$ is the position of the vector $\overrightarrow{OP}$ after the rotation, we recall that

$$x' = (\cos \theta)x + (-\sin \theta)y,$$
$$y' = (\sin \theta)x + (\cos \theta)y.$$

These equations are in the form of (2.8) if we take $\mathscr{V} = \mathscr{W} = \mathscr{V}_2(\mathfrak{R})$ and $\alpha_1 = \beta_1 = \varepsilon_1$, $\alpha_2 = \beta_2 = \varepsilon_2$. Hence T is a linear transformation, and its matrix is

$$\left\|\begin{array}{cc} \cos\theta & \sin\theta \\ -\sin\theta & \cos\theta \end{array}\right\|.$$

We can also check L1 and L2 by direct geometric arguments.

EXAMPLE 2.   Let $\mathscr{V}$ be any vector space, and let c be a scalar.   Consider the mapping T of $\mathscr{V}$ into itself given by

(3.1) $\mathsf{T}: \alpha \to \beta = \alpha\mathsf{T} = c\alpha.$

We check L1 and L2 as consequences of S2 and S4.   We say that T is a *scalar transformation on $\mathscr{V}$*.

To determine a matrix for T, first take a basis $\alpha_1, \cdots, \alpha_v$ for $\mathscr{V}$.   Then $\alpha_i\mathsf{T} = c\alpha_i$ by (3.1) so that T has the matrix $A = \|\, a_{ij} \,\|$ with $a_{ii} = c$ $(i = 1, \cdots, v)$ and $a_{ij} = 0$ if $i \neq j$ $(i, j = 1, \cdots, v)$.

If, in particular, $\mathscr{V} = \mathscr{V}_4(\mathscr{F})$, we have for the matrix A of T

$$A = \left\|\begin{array}{cccc} c & 0 & 0 & 0 \\ 0 & c & 0 & 0 \\ 0 & 0 & c & 0 \\ 0 & 0 & 0 & c \end{array}\right\|,$$

and, in general, if $\mathscr{V} = \mathscr{V}_v(\mathscr{F})$, we have the v-by-v matrix

(3.2) $$A = \left\|\begin{array}{cccc} c & 0 & \cdots & 0 \\ 0 & c & \cdots & 0 \\ \cdot & \cdot & \cdots & \cdot \\ 0 & 0 & \cdots & c \end{array}\right\|.$$

A v-by-w matrix is said to be *square* if $v = w$.   We use the expression "A is a matrix of *degree* v" to indicate that A is a square matrix with v rows.   In a square matrix $A = \|\, a_{ij} \,\|$ of degree v we say that the elements $a_{11}, a_{22}, \cdots, a_{vv}$ constitute the *diagonal* of A.   A square matrix is *diagonal* if its nondiagonal elements are all zero.   A diagonal matrix (such as the A in (3.2)) is said to be a *scalar matrix* if its diagonal elements are all equal.

An interesting and important property of a scalar transformation T on a finite dimensional vector space $\mathscr{V}$ is that, regardless of the basis chosen for $\mathscr{V}$, the matrix A corresponding to T is scalar with the same scalar c on its diagonal as is used to define T. This was essentially proved while finding A.

The special case of (3.1) in which $c = 1$ is called the *identity transformation on* $\mathscr{V}$ and is denoted by $\mathsf{I}_{\mathscr{V}}$. For it we have $\alpha\mathsf{I}_{\mathscr{V}} = \alpha$ for all α in $\mathscr{V}$. The corresponding scalar matrix

$$
I_v = \left\|
\begin{matrix}
1 & 0 & \cdots & 0 \\
0 & 1 & \cdots & 0 \\
\cdot & \cdot & \cdots & \cdot \\
0 & 0 & \cdots & 1
\end{matrix}
\right\|,
$$

is called the *identity matrix* of degree v. (Sometimes when it will cause no confusion we may delete the subscripts $\mathscr{V}$ and v.)

EXAMPLE 3. Consider the vector space $\mathscr{V}$ consisting of all polynomials $f(x)$ in one variable and with real coefficients. Vector addition is taken as ordinary addition of polynomials, and for any scalar c and vector $f(x)$ we define $g(x) = cf(x)$ to be the polynomial in which each coefficient is c times the corresponding coefficient in $f(x)$. We leave checking that $\mathscr{V}$ is a vector space as an exercise for the reader. This is an instance of a vector space whose dimension is not finite, since for every n the vectors $x^0 = 1$, $x, x^2, \cdots, x^{n-1}$ are independent.

We now introduce two linear transformations of $\mathscr{V}$ into itself. The first is

$$\mathsf{D}\colon f(x) \to f(x)\mathsf{D} = f'(x),$$

where the prime indicates ordinary differentiation. Formulas L1 and L2 for D follow from the formulas for derivative of a sum and of a constant times a function. The second is

$$\mathsf{T}\colon f(x) \to f(x)\mathsf{T} = \int_0^x f(t)\, dt.$$

The ordinary properties of definite integrals insure that T is a linear transformation. (We do not discuss matrices for linear transformations on infinite dimensional spaces.)

EXAMPLE 4. Let $\mathscr{V} = \mathscr{V}_3(\mathfrak{R})$ and $\mathscr{W} = \mathscr{V}_2(\mathfrak{R})$. For each vector $\alpha = (x_1, x_2, x_3)$ in $\mathscr{V}$ we define $\alpha\mathsf{T}$ as the vector $\beta = (x_1, x_2)$ in $\mathscr{W}$. Geometrically T has the effect of mapping each vector $\overrightarrow{OP}$ in space onto its perpendicular projection in the (x_1, x_2) plane.

It is convenient when dealing with a Cartesian space $\mathscr{V} = \mathscr{V}_n(\mathscr{F})$ to select the so-called *natural basis* $\{\varepsilon_1, \cdots, \varepsilon_n\}$ where $\varepsilon_1 = (1, 0, \cdots, 0)$, $\varepsilon_2 = (0, 1, \cdots, 0), \cdots, \varepsilon_n = (0, 0, \cdots, 1)$. Throughout this book we shall assume that this has been done, unless for some particular argument we specify to the contrary.

With this convention we have as the matrix corresponding to T

$$
A = \begin{Vmatrix} 1 & 0 \\ 0 & 1 \\ 0 & 0 \end{Vmatrix}.
$$

EXAMPLE 5. Let $\mathscr{V} = \mathscr{V}_2(\mathfrak{R})$ and $\mathscr{W} = \mathscr{V}_3(\mathfrak{R})$. Define T by the equation $(x_1, x_2)\mathsf{T} = (0, x_1, x_2)$, or in matrix form

$$
A = \begin{Vmatrix} 0 & 1 & 0 \\ 0 & 0 & 1 \end{Vmatrix}.
$$

EXAMPLE 6. Let $\mathscr{F}$ be any field; take $\mathscr{V} = \mathscr{V}_4(\mathscr{F})$ and $\mathscr{W} = \mathscr{V}_3(\mathscr{F})$. For any vector $\alpha = (x_1, x_2, x_3, x_4)$ let $\alpha\mathsf{T}$ be the vector $\beta = (x_1 - x_3, x_2, 0)$. To show that T is a linear transformation we observe that it corresponds to the matrix

$$
A = \begin{Vmatrix} 1 & 0 & 0 \\ 0 & 1 & 0 \\ -1 & 0 & 0 \\ 0 & 0 & 0 \end{Vmatrix}.
$$

Exercises 2.3

Use the natural basis for $\mathscr{V}_n(\mathscr{F})$ in the following exercises.

1. What is the matrix of the transformation which sends (x_1, x_2, x_3, x_4) into

$$
\left(x_1, \frac{x_1 + x_2}{2}, \frac{x_1 - x_2}{2}\right) ?
$$

2. What is the image of the vector α in $\mathscr{V}_3(\mathscr{F})$ under the linear transformation with matrix

$$
\begin{Vmatrix} 2 & 0 & 1 & 0 \\ -1 & 0 & 0 & 3 \\ 0 & 1 & 2 & 4 \end{Vmatrix}
$$

if α equals in turn ε_1, ε_2, ε_3, and $(1, 2, 3)$?

3. What is the matrix of the mapping in ordinary three space which sends each point into its perpendicular projection on the z-axis?

4. Let T be a linear transformation on $\mathscr{V}_2(\mathfrak{Q})$. If $(1, 0)T = (2, -3)$ and $(0, 1)T = (3, 1)$, (a) find $(2, -2)T$, (b) solve the equation $(x, y)T = (2, -2)$, (c) find the matrix for T.

5. Let T be a linear transformation of $\mathscr{V}_2(\mathfrak{Q})$ into $\mathscr{V}_3(\mathfrak{Q})$ for which $(1, 0)T = (2, 3, -2)$, $(1, 1)T = (4, -7, 8)$. (a) What is the matrix for T when the basis $(1, 0)$, $(1, 1)$ is used for $\mathscr{V}_2(\mathfrak{Q})$ and the natural basis for $\mathscr{V}_3(\mathfrak{Q})$? (b) What is the matrix for T relative to the natural bases in both spaces?

6. Find the matrix for the linear transformation T for which $(1, 3)T = (2, 3, 4)$ and $(-2, 5)T = (1, 0, 2)$. Find bases relative to which the matrix of T is

$$\begin{Vmatrix} 1 & 0 & 0 \\ 0 & 1 & 0 \end{Vmatrix}.$$

7. Find the matrix of the linear transformation T that sends $(1, 0, 0)$, $(0, 1, 0)$, $(0, 0, 1)$, respectively, into $(1, -1, 2, 1)$, $(0, 1, 1, 0)$, $(2, 0; 0, 0)$. What is the image of $(2, -1, 1)$ under T? What is the kernel of T?

8. If T is a linear transformation that sends $(1, 0, 0)$, $(0, 1, 0)$, $(0, 0, 1)$, respectively, into $(1, 1, 1)$, $(3, 2, -1)$, $(5, 4, 1)$, find the matrix for T, and find the kernel of T. What is the dimension of the range of T?

9. If T has the matrix

$$A = \begin{Vmatrix} 2 & 1 & 0 & 1 \\ 1 & 1 & 1 & 1 \\ 4 & 3 & 2 & 3 \end{Vmatrix}$$

find $\mathscr{K}(T)$. What is the dimension of $\mathscr{V}_3 T$?

2.4. Multiplication of linear transformations.

Let $\mathscr{V}$, $\mathscr{W}$, and $\mathscr{L}$ be three vector spaces over a field $\mathscr{F}$, let T be a linear transformation of $\mathscr{V}$ into $\mathscr{W}$ and let S be a linear transformation of $\mathscr{W}$ into $\mathscr{L}$. For any vector α in $\mathscr{V}$, $\beta = \alpha T$ is a vector in $\mathscr{W}$. Also $\gamma = \beta S = (\alpha T)S$ is a vector in $\mathscr{L}$; furthermore γ is uniquely determined by α. Thus the iterative process of applying first T and then S to that result defines a mapping of $\mathscr{V}$ into $\mathscr{L}$. We call this mapping the *product* of T and S, and denote it by TS. In symbols

$$(4.1) \qquad \alpha(TS) = (\alpha T)S \qquad \text{(def. of the product } TS).$$

$$\mathscr{V} \xrightarrow{\ T\ } \mathscr{W} \xrightarrow{\ S\ } \mathscr{L}$$

$$\xrightarrow{\qquad TS \qquad}$$

$$\alpha \longrightarrow \beta = \alpha T \longrightarrow \gamma = \beta S$$
$$= \alpha(TS).$$

We illustrate this multiplication using the first example of the preceding section; i.e., rotation in the plane. Let T be a rotation of the plane about the origin through an angle ϕ, and S another rotation through an angle ψ. The net effect of applying first T and then S is to obtain a rotation through a total angle $\phi + \psi$. The rotation is the product TS.

Another illustration can be given using Example 2 of the preceding section. Let T be the scalar transformation on a vector space $\mathscr{V}$ corresponding to the scalar b and S the scalar transformation corresponding to c. Then, if α is in $\mathscr{V}$, $\alpha T = b\alpha$, and $(\alpha T)S = c(\alpha T) = c(b\alpha) = (cb)\alpha$. Thus, since $\alpha(TS)$ is by definition $(\alpha T)S$, we have $\alpha(TS) = (cb)\alpha$, so that TS is also a scalar transformation and corresponds to cb. In this example the product of transformations corresponds to the product of the scalars. In the first example the product of transformations corresponds to the sum of the angles. One might be tempted to call the first the sum of the two transformations. But the sum of two linear transformations will be defined later (Section 2.6) and for two rotations will almost never result in a rotation.

The product of the transformation in Example 4 with that in Example 5 gives a linear transformation on $\mathscr{V}_3(\Re)$. But the product of the transformation in Example 4 with the one in Example 6 is not defined since the range of the former $\mathscr{V}_2(\Re)$ is not contained in the domain $\mathscr{V}_4(\Re)$ of the latter.

MULTIPLICATION CRITERION. *The product of two linear transformations is defined if and only if the range of the first factor is contained in the domain of the second factor. The product (when it is defined) is a mapping of the domain of the first factor into the range of the second factor.*

One case in which multiplication is always possible is when $\mathscr{V} = \mathscr{W} = \mathscr{Z}$. Thus the linear transformations D and T of Example 3 can be multiplied in either order. The product TD is clearly $I_{\mathscr{V}}$. The product DT applied to $f(x)$ gives $f(x) - f(0)$. Hence, TD $\neq$ DT; this illustrates the fact that, unlike multiplication of scalars, multiplication of linear transformations does not satisfy the commutative law.

THEOREM 2.4A. *If the product of two linear transformations is defined then it is a linear transformation.*

Let T and S be linear transformations whose product exists, let b be a scalar, and let α, α_1, α_2 be vectors in the domain of T. Then we have

$$(\alpha_1 + \alpha_2)(TS) = [(\alpha_1 + \alpha_2)T]S \qquad \text{(def. of TS)}$$
$$= [(\alpha_1 T) + (\alpha_2 T)]S \qquad \text{(L1 for T)}$$
$$= (\alpha_1 T)S + (\alpha_2 T)S \qquad \text{(L1 for S)}$$
$$= \alpha_1(TS) + \alpha_2(TS) \qquad \text{(def. of TS)},$$

which checks L1 for TS, and

$$(c\alpha)(\mathsf{TS}) = [(c\alpha)\mathsf{T}]\mathsf{S} \qquad \text{(def. of TS)}$$
$$= [c(\alpha\mathsf{T})]\mathsf{S} \qquad \text{(L2 for T)}$$
$$= c[(\alpha\mathsf{T})\mathsf{S}] \qquad \text{(L2 for S)}$$
$$= c[\alpha(\mathsf{TS})] \qquad \text{(def. of TS)},$$

which checks L2 for TS.

THEOREM 2.4B.   *Let* T, S, *and* R *be three linear transformations such that* TS *and* SR *are defined.   Then* (TS)R *and* T(SR) *are both defined and*

$$(\mathsf{TS})\mathsf{R} = \mathsf{T}(\mathsf{SR}) \qquad (associative\ law\ for\ products).$$

The product TS is a mapping of the domain of T into the range of S. Since SR is defined, the range of S is contained in the domain of R; hence (TS)R is defined.   Next, since TS is defined, T is a mapping *into* the domain of S; and SR is a mapping whose domain is that of S.   Hence the product T(SR) is defined.   Then we have by repeated applications of (4.1)

$$\alpha[(\mathsf{TS})\mathsf{R}] = [\alpha(\mathsf{TS})]\mathsf{R} = [(\alpha\mathsf{T})\mathsf{S}]\mathsf{R}$$

and

$$\alpha[\mathsf{T}(\mathsf{SR})] = (\alpha\mathsf{T})(\mathsf{SR}) = [(\alpha\mathsf{T})\mathsf{S}]\mathsf{R},$$

which checks the associative law for products of linear transformations.

In view of the associative law we can delete the parentheses and write TSR for either product.   More generally, if $\mathsf{T}_1, \cdots, \mathsf{T}_r$ are linear transformations such that $\mathsf{T}_i\mathsf{T}_{i+1}$ is defined ($i = 1, \cdots, r - 1$), then the product $\mathsf{T} = (\cdots((\mathsf{T}_1\mathsf{T}_2)\mathsf{T}_3)\cdots\mathsf{T}_{r-1})\mathsf{T}_r$ is defined.   Moreover, the generalized associative law holds (Theorem 1.2A), and any other way of grouping the factors T_i (provided the same left-to-right order is preserved) will define a product that is equal to T; hence, in this case we are justified in writing merely $\mathsf{T} = \mathsf{T}_1\mathsf{T}_2 \cdots \mathsf{T}_r$.

If, in particular, T is a transformation on a space $\mathscr{V}$ then S = TT is defined, and we write $\mathsf{S} = \mathsf{T}^2$.   Similarly, for any natural number r ($r = 1, 2, \cdots$) we write T^r for the product of r factors T.   We define T^0 to be $\mathsf{I}_{\mathscr{V}}$.

If $\mathscr{V}$ and $\mathscr{W}$ are vector spaces, if T is a linear transformation of $\mathscr{V}$ into $\mathscr{W}$, if S is a linear transformation of $\mathscr{W}$ into $\mathscr{V}$, and if $\mathsf{TS} = \mathsf{I}_{\mathscr{V}}$, we say that S is a *right inverse* for T and that T is a *left inverse* for S.

LEMMA 2.4C.   *If* $\mathsf{TS} = \mathsf{I}_{\mathscr{V}}$, *then the kernel* $\mathscr{K}(\mathsf{T})$ *of* T *consists of the zero vector alone, and the range* $\mathscr{W}\mathsf{S}$ *of* S *is all of* $\mathscr{V}$ (*i.e., the first factor is one-to-one, and the second factor is onto*).   *If* T *has both a left inverse and a right inverse, then they are equal, and* T *is an isomorphism of* $\mathscr{V}$ *onto* $\mathscr{W}$.

For any α in $\mathscr{V}$ we have

$$\alpha = \alpha\mathsf{I}_{\mathscr{V}} = \alpha(\mathsf{TS}) = (\alpha\mathsf{T})\mathsf{S},$$

which shows that $\mathscr{W}\mathsf{S} = \mathscr{V}$; i.e., the second factor is onto.

Next, if $\alpha T = 0_{\mathcal{W}}$, then

$$\alpha = (\alpha T)S = 0_{\mathcal{W}}S = 0_{\mathcal{V}},$$

which shows that $\mathcal{K}(T) = \{0_{\mathcal{V}}\}$. Hence, by Lemma 2.1B, T is an isomorphism.

Finally, if $TS = I_{\mathcal{V}}$ and $S'T = I_{\mathcal{W}}$, then T is both one-to-one and onto. Hence T is an isomorphism of $\mathcal{V}$ onto $\mathcal{W}$; moreover,

$$(4.2) \qquad S = I_{\mathcal{W}}S = (S'T)S = S'(TS) = S'I_{\mathcal{V}} = S'.$$

A linear transformation T of a space $\mathcal{V}$ into a space $\mathcal{W}$ is said to be *nonsingular* if there exists a mapping S of $\mathcal{W}$ into $\mathcal{V}$ such that $TS = I_{\mathcal{V}}$ and $ST = I_{\mathcal{W}}$.

Note that the proof of the equality $S = S'$ in (4.2) does not require that S and S' be linear transformations but merely that they be mappings such that $S'T = I_{\mathcal{W}}$ and $TS = I_{\mathcal{V}}$. Hence, if T is nonsingular the mapping S such that $TS = I_{\mathcal{V}}$ and $ST = I_{\mathcal{W}}$ is unique. We call S the *inverse* of T and denote it by $S = T^{-1}$.

Note that here we do not explicitly require in our definition of inverse that S should be a linear transformation. We now prove that the inverse of a nonsingular linear transformation is in fact a nonsingular linear transformation. Let b be a scalar and β a vector in $\mathcal{W}$. Then we have

$$(b\beta)S = [b(\beta I_{\mathcal{W}})]S = [b(\beta ST)]S = \{b[(\beta S)T]\}S$$
$$= \{[b(\beta S)]T\}S = [b(\beta S)](TS) = b(\beta S)I_{\mathcal{V}} = b(\beta S).$$

which checks L2 for S. The proof of L1 is similar and is left for the reader. The nonsingularity of S follows from the symmetry in S and T of the definition of nonsingularity for T.

Suppose that $\mathcal{V} = \mathcal{W}$, that T is nonsingular, and that r is any natural number. Then we write T^{-r} for $(T^{-1})^r$. It follows from the associative law that T^{-r} is the inverse of T^r and that the ordinary laws of exponents all hold for integer powers of T.

THEOREM 2.4D. *A linear transformation* T *of* $\mathcal{V}$ *into* $\mathcal{W}$ *is nonsingular if and only if* $\mathcal{K}(T) = \{0_{\mathcal{V}}\}$ *and* $\mathcal{V}T = \mathcal{W}$.

According to Lemma 2.1B, if $\mathcal{K}(T) = \{0_{\mathcal{V}}\}$, then T is an isomorphism of $\mathcal{V}$ into $\mathcal{W}$; if also $\mathcal{V}T = \mathcal{W}$, then T is an isomorphism of $\mathcal{V}$ onto $\mathcal{W}$. Hence each vector β in $\mathcal{W}$ is the image αT of exactly one vector α in $\mathcal{V}$. Since β defines α uniquely, we give the mapping $\beta \to \alpha$ the name S and write $\alpha = \beta S$. Now for each β in $\mathcal{W}$ we have $\beta(ST) = (\beta S)T = \alpha T = \beta$; hence $ST = I_{\mathcal{W}}$. Also for each α in $\mathcal{V}$ we have $\alpha(TS) = (\alpha T)S = \beta S = \alpha$; hence $TS = I_{\mathcal{V}}$. Thus T is nonsingular (with $T^{-1} = S$).

If T is nonsingular, it follows from Lemma 2.4C that $\mathcal{K}(T) = \{0_{\mathcal{V}}\}$ and $\mathcal{V}T = \mathcal{W}$.

THEOREM 2.4E.   *Let T be a linear transformation of $\mathcal{V}$ into $\mathcal{W}$, and suppose that* dim $\mathcal{V}$ = dim $\mathcal{W}$ *and is finite. Then T is nonsingular if either $\mathcal{K}(T) = \{0_{\mathcal{V}}\}$ or $\mathcal{V}T = \mathcal{W}$.*

According to Theorem 2.1F

$$\dim \mathcal{V}T + \dim \mathcal{K}(T) = \dim \mathcal{V}.$$

Now, if $\mathcal{V}T = \mathcal{W}$, it follows that $\dim \mathcal{K}(T) = 0$, and therefore $\mathcal{K}(T) = \{0_{\mathcal{V}}\}$, and hence, by Theorem 2.4D, T is nonsingular.   Similarly, if $\mathcal{K}(T) = \{0_{\mathcal{V}}\}$, then $\dim \mathcal{V}T = \dim \mathcal{W}$;   hence $\mathcal{V}T = \mathcal{W}$, and again, by Theorem 2.4D, T is nonsingular.

COROLLARY 2.4F.   *Let T be a linear transformation of $\mathcal{V}$ into $\mathcal{W}$, and suppose that* dim $\mathcal{V}$ = dim $\mathcal{W}$ *and is finite.   Then T is nonsingular if it has either a left inverse or a right inverse.*

This follows at once from the preceding theorem and Lemma 2.4C.

LEMMA 2.4G.   *Suppose that T and S are nonsingular linear transformations and that the domain of S is the range of T.   Then TS is nonsingular and has inverse $S^{-1}T^{-1}$.   The inverse of a product is the product of the inverses in reverse order.*

Let $\mathcal{V}$ = domain T, $\mathcal{W}$ = range T = domain S, and $\mathcal{Z}$ = range S We have

$$(TS)(S^{-1}T^{-1}) = TS(S^{-1}T^{-1}) = T(SS^{-1})T^{-1}$$
$$= T(I_{\mathcal{W}}T^{-1}) = TT^{-1} = I_{\mathcal{V}},$$

and, similarly,

$$(S^{-1}T^{-1})(TS) = I_{\mathcal{Z}};$$

these equalities establish the lemma.

The above proof is a verification of the result stated but gives little indication of the reason for the result.   If a series of knots are made, each on top of the preceding one, then the untying is done in the reverse order; analogously, one can think of the inverse of a product of nonsingular linear transformations as the result of undoing each one starting with the last and proceeding in reverse order.   Another approach to the formula for $(TS)^{-1}$ is to solve the equation $\gamma = \alpha(TS)$ for α.   We first apply S^{-1} to get $\gamma S^{-1} = \alpha(TS)S^{-1} = (\alpha T)(SS^{-1}) = \alpha T I_{\mathcal{W}} = \alpha T$, and then apply T^{-1} to get $\gamma(S^{-1}T^{-1}) = \alpha$.   Then we have $(\alpha(TS))(S^{-1}T^{-1}) = \alpha$.   This shows that $S^{-1}T^{-1}$ is a right inverse for TS; it is then natural to test whether it is also a left inverse.

Exercises 2.4

1. Prove that, if T has an inverse and $T^{-1} = S$, then S has an inverse and $S^{-1} = T$.

2. Prove that, if r is a natural number and T is nonsingular, then $(T^r)^{-1} = T^{-r}$.

3. Prove that, if r, s are integers and T is nonsingular, then $T^r T^s = T^{r+s}$.

4. Let T be a transformation of $\mathscr{V}$ into $\mathscr{W}$, and S a transformation of $\mathscr{W}$ into $\mathscr{Z}$. Prove that $(\mathscr{V}TS) = (\mathscr{V}T)S'$, where S' is the restriction of S to $\mathscr{V}T$.

5. Prove the generalized associative law for products of linear transformations.

6. Show that, if $T = T_1 \cdots T_r$ where $T_1, \cdots, T_r$ are nonsingular, then T is nonsingular, and $T^{-1} = T_r^{-1} \cdots T_1^{-1}$.

7. Complete the proof that the inverse of a nonsingular linear transformation is a linear transformation.

8. Let D and T be the linear transformations defined in Example 3 of the preceding section. Show that D is a right inverse but not a left inverse for T.

2.5. Multiplication of matrices. Now that multiplication of linear transformations has been defined, we wish to use it as a guide for defining multiplication of matrices. For this purpose let $\mathscr{V}$, $\mathscr{W}$, and $\mathscr{Z}$ be three vector spaces over a field $\mathscr{F}$, let T be a linear transformation of $\mathscr{V}$ into $\mathscr{W}$, and let S be a linear transformation of $\mathscr{W}$ into $\mathscr{Z}$. Suppose further that $\mathscr{A} = \{\alpha_1, \cdots, \alpha_v\}$, $\mathscr{B} = \{\beta_1, \cdots, \beta_w\}$, and $\mathscr{C} = \{\gamma_1, \cdots, \gamma_z\}$ are bases for $\mathscr{V}$, $\mathscr{W}$, and $\mathscr{Z}$, respectively, and that relative to these bases T has the matrix A and S has the matrix B.

Consider the matrix $C = \| c_{ij} \|$ of the product transformation $R = TS$ relative to the given bases for $\mathscr{V}$ and $\mathscr{Z}$. We shall find an expression for each c_{ij} in terms of the elements of A and of B. According to formula (2.1) we have the elements a_{ij} of A and b_{ij} of B defined by

$$(5.1) \qquad \alpha_i T = \sum_{v=1}^{w} a_{iv}\beta_v \qquad (i = 1, \cdots, v)$$

and

$$(5.2) \qquad \beta_i S = \sum_{\mu=1}^{z} b_{i\mu}\gamma_\mu \qquad (i = 1, \cdots, w).$$

If we now apply S to both sides of (5.1), substitute from (5.2) on the right-hand side, and rearrange terms using the properties of linear transformations where necessary, we get

$$\alpha_i R = (\alpha_i T)S$$

$$= \left(\sum_{v=1}^{w} a_{iv}\beta_v \right)S$$

$$= \sum_{v=1}^{w} a_{iv}(\beta_v S)$$

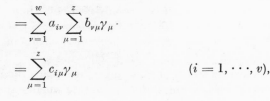

$$= \sum_{\nu=1}^{w} a_{i\nu} \sum_{\mu=1}^{z} b_{\nu\mu}\gamma_{\mu}.$$

$$= \sum_{\mu=1}^{z} c_{i\mu}\gamma_{\mu} \qquad\qquad (i = 1, \cdots, v),$$

where

(5.3) $$c_{ij} = \sum_{\nu=1}^{w} a_{i\nu}b_{\nu j} \qquad (i = 1, \cdots, v; j = 1, \cdots, z)$$

is the coefficient of γ_j in the expression for $\alpha_i \mathsf{R}$; that is, C is the matrix for $\mathsf{R} = \mathsf{TS}$.

We say that the matrix $C = \| c_{ij} \|$ defined by (5.3) is the *product* of the matrices $A = \| a_{ij} \|$ and $B = \| b_{ij} \|$ and write $C = AB$. With this definition for matrix multiplication we have the following theorem.

THEOREM 2.5A. *The matrix of the product of two linear transformations is the product of their matrices; i.e.,* $\| \mathsf{TS} \|_{\mathscr{AC}} = \| \mathsf{T} \|_{\mathscr{AB}} \| \mathsf{S} \|_{\mathscr{BC}}.$

Our definition of matrix product is not complete until we specify exactly when the product AB exists. In the case above where AB was defined we had $\deg_c A = \deg_r B$ since both were equal to the dimension w of $\mathscr{W}$; this is the only requirement in general. We now state the full definition:

DEFINITION OF MATRIX PRODUCT. *Let $\mathscr{F}$ be any field, and let $A = \| a_{ij} \|$ and $B = \| b_{ij} \|$ be any $\mathscr{F}$ matrices. Then the product $AB = C = \| c_{ij} \|$ is defined if and only if $\deg_c A = \deg_r B$. The row degree of the product is equal to the row degree of the left factor, and the column degree of the product is equal to the column degree of the right factor. The elements of the product are given in terms of the elements of the factors by formula (5.3).*

We repeat the existence criterion: *The product of two matrices is defined if and only if the number of columns of the left factor is equal to the number of rows of the right factor.*

We illustrate the situation pictorially using rectangles whose dimensions represent the degrees of the matrices involved in a product.

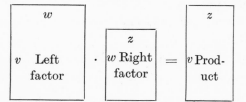

We now examine formula (5.3) a little more closely. Observe that the expression for c_{ij} involves only elements from the ith row of A and from the jth column of B. For this reason we say that matrix multiplication is carried out according to the "row-by-column rule." This rule can be described explicitly in the following way. Rotate the ith row of A clockwise through a right angle, and place the resulting column adjacent to the jth column of B; multiply elements at the same level; then the algebraic sum of the resulting products is c_{ij}. · Thus we write

$$
\begin{array}{ll}
a_{i1} \quad b_{1j} & a_{i1}b_{1j} \\
a_{i2} \quad b_{2j} & a_{i2}b_{2j} \\
\cdots \quad \cdots & \cdots \\
a_{iw} \quad b_{wj} & a_{iw}b_{wj}
\end{array}
$$

$$c_{ij} = a_{i1}b_{1j} + a_{i2}b_{2j} + \cdots + a_{iw}b_{wj}.$$

For matrices whose degrees are not too large a little practice makes it unnecessary to carry out the rule in full detail. However, when the elements of the matrices are numbers with many digits and the degrees are more than two or three, the actual practice of experienced computers is to use something very close to this rule when setting up a problem in matrix multiplication for machine computation.

As an example of matrix multiplication we consider

$$
A = \begin{Vmatrix} 2 & 0 & -2 \\ -1 & 1 & 2 \\ 3 & -1 & 0 \\ 1 & 2 & 1 \end{Vmatrix} \quad \text{and} \quad B = \begin{Vmatrix} 1 & 2 \\ -1 & -3 \\ 0 & 1 \end{Vmatrix}.
$$

Then, for $C = AB$ we have

$$
C = \begin{Vmatrix}
2 \cdot 1 + 0 \cdot (-1) + (-2) \cdot 0 & 2 \cdot 2 + 0 \cdot (-3) + (-2) \cdot 1 \\
-1 \cdot 1 + 1 \cdot (-1) + 2 \cdot 0 & -1 \cdot 2 + 1 \cdot (-3) + 2 \cdot 1 \\
3 \cdot 1 + (-1) \cdot (-1) + 0 \cdot 0 & 3 \cdot 2 + (-1) \cdot (-3) + 0 \cdot 1 \\
1 \cdot 1 + 2 \cdot (-1) + 1 \cdot 0 & 1 \cdot 2 + 2 \cdot (-3) + 1 \cdot 1
\end{Vmatrix} = \begin{Vmatrix} 2 & 2 \\ -2 & -3 \\ 4 & 9 \\ -1 & -3 \end{Vmatrix}.
$$

We observe that for these matrices A and B the product BA does not exist.

THEOREM 2.5B. *If A, B, C are $\mathscr{F}$ matrices such that the products AB and BC are defined, then the products $(AB)C$ and $A(BC)$ are both defined, and, moreover, $(AB)C = A(BC)$ (associative law for products).*

This theorem follows from the corresponding result (Theorem 2.4B) for linear transformations together with Theorem 2.5A; or it can be established directly using formula (5.3). We shall use the first method and leave the second as an exercise for the reader.

Since the products AB and BC are defined we have $\deg_c A = \deg_r B$ and $\deg_c B = \deg_r C$. Now, $\deg_c AB = \deg_c B$, and so the product $(AB)C$ is defined; similarly for $A(BC)$. Now take $\mathscr{V} = \mathscr{V}_v(\mathscr{F})$, $\mathscr{W} = \mathscr{V}_w(\mathscr{F})$, $\mathscr{L} = \mathscr{V}_z(\mathscr{F})$, and $\mathscr{U} = \mathscr{V}_u(\mathscr{F})$, where $v = \deg_r A$, $w = \deg_c A$, $z = \deg_c B$, and $u = \deg_c C$. Then let T be the linear transformation of $\mathscr{V}$ into $\mathscr{W}$ whose matrix (relative to the natural bases) is A; let S be the linear transformation of $\mathscr{W}$ into $\mathscr{L}$ whose matrix is B; and let R be the linear transformation of $\mathscr{L}$ into $\mathscr{U}$ whose matrix is C. Then, by Theorem 2.5A, the matrix of $(\mathsf{TS})\mathsf{R}$ is $(AB)C$, and the matrix of $\mathsf{T}(\mathsf{SR})$ is $A(BC)$. Since multiplication of linear transformations is associative, $(\mathsf{TS})\mathsf{R} = \mathsf{T}(\mathsf{SR})$, and so the corresponding matrices must also be equal, as required.

Just as with products of linear transformations, the associative law for products of matrices allows us to drop parentheses (and other symbols of grouping) from any indicated product of matrices. If $A_1, \cdots, A_r$ are $\mathscr{F}$ matrices, the product $A_1 \cdot \cdots \cdot A_r$ is defined if and only if $\deg_c A_i = \deg_r A_{i+1}$ $(i = 1, \cdots, r - 1)$.

If for two matrices A and B we have $AB = I_v$ where $v = \deg_r A = \deg_c B$, then we say that B is a *right inverse* for A and that A is a *left inverse* for B. A square matrix A of degree v is said to be *nonsingular* if there exists a matrix B, called the *inverse* of A, such that $AB = BA = I_v$. Any matrix that does not have an inverse is said to be *singular*. Note that according to this definition every nonsquare matrix is singular.

LEMMA 2.5C. *If a matrix A has both a left inverse and a right inverse, then they are equal, and A is nonsingular.*

This lemma follows from Lemma 2.4C. We let $\mathscr{V} = \mathscr{V}_v(\mathscr{F})$ and $\mathscr{W} = \mathscr{V}_w(\mathscr{F})$, where $v = \deg_r(A)$ and $w = \deg_c(A)$; and let T be the linear transformation corresponding to A (relative to the natural bases). Then the linear transformations corresponding to the left and right inverses of A will be left and right inverses of T. By the lemma cited, the left and right inverses of T are equal, and so the same holds for those of A. Moreover, T is an isomorphism of $\mathscr{V}$ onto $\mathscr{W}$; hence by Theorem 1.7D we have $v = w$, or, in other words, A is a square matrix. The common left and right inverses of A will then be its inverse so that A is nonsingular. Moreover, it is a consequence of the lemma that, *if A is nonsingular, it has a unique inverse.*

THEOREM 2.5D. *A square matrix is nonsingular if it has either a right or a left inverse.*

This is a translation of Corollary 2.4F into the language of matrices.

For any square matrix A the product $B = AA$ is defined, and we write $B = A^2$. Similarly, for any natural number r we write A^r for the product of r factors A, and we define A^0 to be I_v where v is the degree of A. If, moreover, A is nonsingular, we write A^{-1} for its inverse, and for any natural number r we define A^{-r} to be $(A^{-1})^r$. Then it follows from the associative law that A^{-r} is the inverse of A^r and that the ordinary laws of exponents all hold for integer powers of A.

LEMMA 2.5E. *If A and B are nonsingular matrices of degree n, then $C = AB$ is nonsingular, and $C^{-1} = B^{-1}A^{-1}$.*

This lemma follows at once from Lemma 2.4G or can be proved directly.

Exercises 2.5

In the first five exercises $\mathscr{F}$ is any field,

$$A = \begin{Vmatrix} 1 & 0 & -1 & 2 \\ 1 & 3 & 4 & 1 \\ 2 & -1 & 0 & 1 \end{Vmatrix}, \quad B = \begin{Vmatrix} 3 & 1 & 2 \\ 2 & 0 & 4 \\ -1 & 1 & 1 \\ 0 & 0 & 2 \end{Vmatrix},$$

$$C = \begin{Vmatrix} 1 & -1 & 1 \\ 0 & 1 & 2 \\ 0 & 0 & 1 \end{Vmatrix}, \quad D = \begin{Vmatrix} 1 & 1 & -3 \\ 0 & 1 & -2 \\ 0 & 0 & 1 \end{Vmatrix}, \quad E = \begin{Vmatrix} 1 & 0 & 0 \\ 0 & 1 & 0 \\ 0 & 0 & 1 \end{Vmatrix}.$$

1. Compute AB and BA. Is $AB = BA$; i.e., do A and B commute?

2. Which of the products BC, CB, AC, CA are defined? Compute those that are defined.

3. Show that $EA = A$ and that $BE = B$.

4. (a) Show that $C = D^{-1}$. (b) Find D^{-2}.

5. Show that $(AB)C = A(BC)$.

6. Prove the associative law by the second method mentioned in the proof of Theorem 2.5B.

7. If P and Q are 4-by-4 matrices with
$p_{13} = p_{14} = p_{23} = p_{24} = q_{13} = q_{14} = q_{23} = q_{24} = 0$ and $R = PQ$
show that $r_{13} = r_{14} = r_{23} = r_{24} = 0$.

8. Generalize the result of Exercise 7.

9. Find the form of all 2-by-2 matrices that commute with $\begin{Vmatrix} 1 & 2 \\ 0 & 4 \end{Vmatrix}$.

10. Prove that $\begin{Vmatrix} 1 & 2 \\ 0 & 0 \end{Vmatrix}$ is singular.

11. Find the matrices of the products in both orders of the linear transformations of Examples 4 and 5 of Section 2.3.

12. Show that, if $A = A_1 \cdot \;\cdots\; \cdot A_r$ where $A_1, \cdots, A_r$ are nonsingular, then A is nonsingular and $A^{-1} = A_r^{-1} \cdot \;\cdots\; \cdot A_1^{-1}$.

13. Let T, S be linear transformations mapping $\mathscr{V}_3$ into $\mathscr{V}_2$ and $\mathscr{V}_2$ into $\mathscr{V}_4$, respectively. If, using natural bases throughout, the matrices for T and S are

$$\left\|\begin{array}{rr} 2 & 1 \\ -1 & 0 \\ 3 & 2 \end{array}\right\| \qquad \text{and} \qquad \left\|\begin{array}{rrrr} 2 & 1 & 0 & 3 \\ -1 & 2 & -2 & 1 \end{array}\right\|,$$

what is the matrix for TS?   What is the image of $\left\| \begin{array}{ccc} 1 & 0 & 0 \end{array}\right\|$ under TS?

2.6. Sums and products by scalars.

In the theory of functions the sum f of two functions g, h is defined by $f(x) = g(x) + h(x)$; i.e., the value of f at x is obtained by adding the values of g and h at x. Similarly, if S and T are mappings of a vector space $\mathscr{V}$ into a vector space $\mathscr{W}$, the sum $\mathsf{S} + \mathsf{T}$ is defined by giving the image under $\mathsf{S} + \mathsf{T}$ for every vector α in $\mathscr{V}$ as

$$\alpha(\mathsf{S} + \mathsf{T}) = \alpha\mathsf{S} + \alpha\mathsf{T}.$$

LEMMA 2.6A. *The sum of two linear transformations is a linear transformation.*

We need to prove that

(6.1) $$(\alpha + \beta)(\mathsf{S} + \mathsf{T}) = \alpha(\mathsf{S} + \mathsf{T}) + \beta(\mathsf{S} + \mathsf{T})$$

and

(6.2) $$(c\alpha)(\mathsf{S} + \mathsf{T}) = c(\alpha(\mathsf{S} + \mathsf{T})).$$

Now

$$(\alpha + \beta)(\mathsf{S} + \mathsf{T}) = (\alpha + \beta)\mathsf{S} + (\alpha + \beta)\mathsf{T} \qquad \text{(def.)}$$

$$= \alpha\mathsf{S} + \beta\mathsf{S} + \alpha\mathsf{T} + \beta\mathsf{T}$$

(since S and T are linear transformations)

$$= \alpha\mathsf{S} + \alpha\mathsf{T} + \beta\mathsf{S} + \beta\mathsf{T}$$

$$= \alpha(\mathsf{S} + \mathsf{T}) + \beta(\mathsf{S} + \mathsf{T}).$$

The proof of (6.2) is left as an exercise.

The product of a function $f(x)$ by a scalar (number) c produces the function $cf(x)$. Thus, in particular, the product of a mapping T by a scalar c is the mapping $c\mathsf{T}$ which sends a vector α in $\mathscr{V}$ into $c(\alpha\mathsf{T})$; i.e.,

$$\alpha(c\mathsf{T}) = c(\alpha\mathsf{T}).$$

In particular the scalar transformation (3.1) equals $c\mathsf{I}$.

LEMMA 2.6B. *The product of a linear transformation by a scalar is a linear transformation.*

We must show that

(6.3) $(\alpha + \beta)(c\mathsf{T}) = \alpha(c\mathsf{T}) + \beta(c\mathsf{T})$

and

(6.4) $(b\alpha)(c\mathsf{T}) = b(\alpha(c\mathsf{T})).$

We shall prove the latter and leave the proof of the former as an exercise.

$$(b\alpha)(c\mathsf{T}) = c((b\alpha)\mathsf{T}) \qquad\qquad\qquad\text{(def.)}$$
$$= c(b(\alpha\mathsf{T})) \qquad\qquad\text{(since } \mathsf{T} \text{ is a linear transformation)}$$
$$= (cb)(\alpha\mathsf{T})$$
$$= b(c(\alpha\mathsf{T}))$$
$$= b(\alpha(c\mathsf{T})) \qquad\qquad\qquad\text{(def.).}$$

We have defined for the set of all linear transformations of $\mathscr{V}$ into $\mathscr{W}$ the two operations that occur in a vector space: viz. addition and multiplication by scalars.

THEOREM 2.6C. *Let* $\mathscr{V}$, $\mathscr{W}$ *be vector spaces over a field* $\mathscr{F}$. *The set* $\mathscr{L}$ *of all linear transformations of* $\mathscr{V}$ *into* $\mathscr{W}$ *forms a vector space.*

In the next theorem we shall see that dim $\mathscr{L} = (\dim \mathscr{V})(\dim \mathscr{W})$, provided that both of these dimensions are finite.

The two preceding lemmas take care of the two closure axioms. The zero vector of $\mathscr{L}$ is the *zero mapping*

$$0: \quad \alpha \to \alpha 0 = 0.$$

When more detailed notation is desired we write instead

$$0_{\mathscr{V}\mathscr{W}}: \quad \alpha \to \alpha 0_{\mathscr{V}\mathscr{W}} = 0_{\mathscr{W}}.$$

The negative of a mapping T in $\mathscr{L}$ is $(-1)\mathsf{T}$. The various combinatorial axioms for $\mathscr{L}$ follow from the same axioms in $\mathscr{V}$ and in $\mathscr{W}$. We leave the verification to the reader.

We next define addition of matrices in agreement with addition of mappings. Let $\mathscr{V}$ have the basis $\mathscr{A} = \{\alpha_1, \cdots, \alpha_v\}$, and $\mathscr{W}$ the basis $\mathscr{B} = \{\beta_1, \cdots, \beta_w\}$. Let S and T be linear transformations of $\mathscr{V}$ into $\mathscr{W}$ and let A, B, respectively, be their matrices relative to these bases. Then we define the sum $C = A + B$ to be the matrix of $\mathsf{S} + \mathsf{T}$; i.e., $\| \mathsf{S} \|_{\mathscr{A}\mathscr{B}} + \| \mathsf{T} \|_{\mathscr{A}\mathscr{B}} = \| \mathsf{S} + \mathsf{T} \|_{\mathscr{A}\mathscr{B}}$. We next find a formula for the elements of C in terms of those of A and B.

We have

$$\alpha_i \mathsf{S} = \Sigma\, a_{i\mu}\beta_\mu, \qquad \alpha_i \mathsf{T} = \Sigma\, b_{i\mu}\beta_\mu,$$

and

$$\alpha_i(\mathsf{S} + \mathsf{T}) = \alpha_i\mathsf{S} + \alpha_i\mathsf{T}$$
$$= \Sigma\, a_{i\mu}\beta_\mu + \Sigma\, b_{i\mu}\beta_\mu$$
$$= \Sigma\, (a_{i\mu} + b_{i\mu})\beta_\mu.$$

Hence, if $C = \| c_{ij} \|$, then

(6.5) $$c_{ij} = a_{ij} + b_{ij} \quad (i = 1, \cdots, v; j = 1, \cdots, w).$$

Addition of matrices $A = \| a_{ij} \|$ and $B = \| b_{ij} \|$ is possible if and only if $\deg_r A = \deg_r B$ and $\deg_c A = \deg_c B$. When addition is possible, the sum $C = A + B$ is defined by (6.5). Thus addition of matrices is performed much like addition of vectors in $\mathscr{V}_n(\mathscr{F})$: corresponding components are added.

Similarly, if $D = \| d_{ij} \|$ is the matrix of $c\mathsf{S}$ (relative to the given bases for $\mathscr{V}$ and $\mathscr{W}$), then

(6.6) $$d_{ij} = ca_{ij} \quad (i = 1, \cdots, v; j = 1, \cdots, w),$$

i.e.,

$$c\,\| \,\mathsf{S}\, \|_{\mathscr{A}\mathscr{B}} = \| \,c\mathsf{S}\, \|_{\mathscr{A}\mathscr{B}}.$$

The proof is left as an exercise. Again we see that multiplication of a matrix by a scalar calls for the same operation as in $\mathscr{V}_n(\mathscr{F})$; each component is multiplied by the scalar c.

The set $\mathscr{M}$ of all v-by-w matrices forms a vector space. This can be seen in two ways. First $\mathscr{M}$ is isomorphic to the vector space $\mathscr{L}$ of Theorem 2.6C; in fact, the two vector-space operations in $\mathscr{M}$ were defined so as to be preserved under the 1-to-1 correspondence between $\mathscr{L}$ and $\mathscr{M}$. On the other hand, $\mathscr{M}$ is isomorphic to $\mathscr{V}_{vw}(\mathscr{F})$; the vw elements are merely stacked in v rows instead of being arranged in a single row. Thus $\mathscr{M}$ has the *natural basis* given by the vw matrices E_{ij} $(i = 1, \cdots, v; j = 1, \cdots, w)$, where E_{ij} is the v-by-w matrix with one in position (i, j) and zero everywhere else. Hence the dimension of $\mathscr{M}$ is vw, and $\mathscr{L}$, being isomorphic to $\mathscr{M}$, also has dimension vw.

THEOREM 2.6D. *Let $\mathscr{V}$ and $\mathscr{W}$ be vector spaces with finite dimensions v and w, respectively. Then the set $\mathscr{L}$ of all linear transformations of $\mathscr{V}$ into $\mathscr{W}$ is a vector space of dimension vw.*

The basis of $\mathscr{L}$ corresponding to the natural basis of $\mathscr{M}$ consists of the vw mappings defined by

(6.7) $$\mathsf{U}_{ij}: \quad \alpha_i\mathsf{U}_{ij} = \beta_j;$$
$$\alpha_h\mathsf{U}_{ij} = 0 \qquad \text{if} \quad h \neq i.$$

If $\mathscr{W} = \mathscr{F}$, then $\mathscr{L}$ is called the *dual space* of $\mathscr{V}$ and will be denoted by

$\mathscr{V}^*$. A basis of $\mathscr{F}$, considered as a vector space over $\mathscr{F}$, is the unit element 1. If we suppress the subscript j, then (6.7) becomes

$$\mathsf{U}_i: \quad \alpha_i \mathsf{U}_i = 1;$$
$$\alpha_h \mathsf{U}_i = 0 \qquad \qquad \text{if} \quad h \neq i.$$

The basis $\{\mathsf{U}_1, \cdots, \mathsf{U}_v\}$ of $\mathscr{V}^*$ is said to be the *dual* of the basis $\{\alpha_1, \cdots, \alpha_v\}$ of $\mathscr{V}$. Properties of $\mathscr{V}^*$ are discussed in Section 6.4.

We next connect the "vector operations" of addition and of mutiplication by scalars with the product of linear transformations defined earlier. The equation $c\mathsf{T} = (c\mathsf{I})\mathsf{T}$ where $c\mathsf{I}$ is a scalar linear transformation exhibits one such relationship.

The following theorem establishes the distributive laws which connect products and sums.

THEOREM 2.6E.   *Let $\mathscr{V}, \mathscr{W}$, and $\mathscr{U}$ be vector spaces over a field $\mathscr{F}$; let $\mathsf{T}, \mathsf{T}_1, \mathsf{T}_2$ be linear transformations of $\mathscr{V}$ into $\mathscr{W}$, and $\mathsf{S}, \mathsf{S}_1, \mathsf{S}_2$ be linear transformations of $\mathscr{W}$ into $\mathscr{U}$.   Then*

(D1) $$\mathsf{T}(\mathsf{S}_1 + \mathsf{S}_2) = \mathsf{TS}_1 + \mathsf{TS}_2$$

and

(D2) $$(\mathsf{T}_1 + \mathsf{T}_2)\mathsf{S} = \mathsf{T}_1\mathsf{S} + \mathsf{T}_2\mathsf{S};$$

or, in words, multiplication of linear transformations is distributive on both sides with respect to addition.

Let α be a vector in $\mathscr{V}$.   Then

$$\alpha(\mathsf{T}(\mathsf{S}_1 + \mathsf{S}_2)) = (\alpha\mathsf{T})(\mathsf{S}_1 + \mathsf{S}_2) = (\alpha\mathsf{T})\mathsf{S}_1 + (\alpha\mathsf{T})\mathsf{S}_2$$
$$= \alpha(\mathsf{TS}_1) + \alpha(\mathsf{TS}_2) = \alpha(\mathsf{TS}_1 + \mathsf{TS}_2),$$

which checks D1, and

$$\alpha[(\mathsf{T}_1 + \mathsf{T}_2)\mathsf{S}] = [\alpha(\mathsf{T}_1 + \mathsf{T}_2)]\mathsf{S} = (\alpha\mathsf{T}_1 + \alpha\mathsf{T}_2)\mathsf{S}$$
$$= (\alpha\mathsf{T}_1)\mathsf{S} + (\alpha\mathsf{T}_2)\mathsf{S} = \alpha(\mathsf{T}_1\mathsf{S}) + \alpha(\mathsf{T}_2\mathsf{S}) = \alpha(\mathsf{T}_1\mathsf{S} + \mathsf{T}_2\mathsf{S}),$$

which checks D2.

Notice that, since the commutative law does not hold for multiplication, both distributive laws need to be proved.   In fact, the proof of D1 uses only the definitions of the operations and applies to mappings in general; but the proof of D2 requires that S be a linear transformation.

The distributive laws

(D1) $$A(B + C) = AB + AC,$$

(D2) $$(A + B)C = AC + BC$$

hold for matrices (whenever the sums and products involved are defined). They can be proved directly from the definitions of the matrix operations; they also follow from the distributive laws for linear transformations.

Exercises 2.6

1. Prove (6.2) if S, T are linear transformations.
2. Prove (6.3) if T is a linear transformation.
3. Prove that the set $\mathscr{M}$ of all mappings of a vector space $\mathscr{V}$ into a vector space $\mathscr{W}$ forms a vector space.
4. Prove that the subset $\mathscr{L}$ consisting of all linear transformations of $\mathscr{V}$ into $\mathscr{W}$ is a subspace of $\mathscr{M}$.
5. Prove formula (6.6).
6. Prove that, if T corresponds to a matrix $A = \| a_{ij} \|$ (relative to given bases in $\mathscr{V}$ and in $\mathscr{W}$) and if the U_{ij} are given by (6.7), then $T = \Sigma a_{\lambda\mu} U_{\lambda\mu}$; i.e., $\mathscr{L}$ is dependent on the set of all U_{ij}.
7. Prove that the set of U_{ij} is independent without using the isomorphism between $\mathscr{L}$ and $\mathscr{M}$.
8. Show that, if $\alpha = c_1\alpha_1 + \cdots + c_v\alpha_v$, then $\alpha U_{ij} = c_i\beta_j$.
9. Prove D1 and D2 for matrices directly from the definitions of the matrix operations.
10. Let $A = \left\| \begin{array}{cc} 1 & 2 \\ 0 & 3 \end{array} \right\|$. Show that $AB = BA$ if and only if B can be written in the form $cA + dI_2$ (i.e., B is a linear polynomial in A).
11. In the plane (i.e. $\mathscr{V}_2(\Re)$) let T be the linear transformation which maps each vector into its perpendicular projection on the x_1 axis, and let S be the perpendicular projection on the x_2 axis. Describe $T + S$.

2.7. Sets of linear transformations on a vector space.

Consider a collection of vector spaces over a field $\mathscr{F}$, and let $\mathscr{T}$ be the set of all linear transformations with domain and image space belonging to this collection. The product of any such transformation T by a scalar is always defined and is again such a transformation. Furthermore, the axioms S1, S2, S3, S4, and S5 on multiplication by scalars all hold if the term "vector" is replaced throughout by the term "linear transformation."

The sum $T + S$ of two elements of $\mathscr{T}$ exists if and only if T and S have a common domain and a common image space. When the sum is defined, it is again an element of $\mathscr{T}$, and the axioms A2 and A5 are valid (with "linear transformation" instead of "vector"). Instead of a single zero for $\mathscr{T}$, we have a zero transformation $0_{\mathscr{V}\mathscr{W}}$ for each space $\mathscr{V}$ into each space $\mathscr{W}$. If T is a linear transformation of $\mathscr{V}$ into $\mathscr{W}$, then the equations

$$T + 0_{\mathscr{V}\mathscr{W}} = 0_{\mathscr{V}\mathscr{W}} + T = T$$

and

$$T + (-1)T = (-1)T + T = 0_{\mathscr{V}\mathscr{W}}$$

are the nearest we can come to satisfying axioms A3 and A4.

The product TS is defined if and only if the range of T is contained in the domain of S. We wish to compare multiplication of linear transformations with multiplications of scalars and so recall the field axioms which involve multiplication. Let $\mathscr{M} = \{T, S, \cdots\}$ be a system in which an operation of multiplication, written TS is sometimes defined. We consider the following axioms which may or may not hold in $\mathscr{M}$.

(M1)   Closure: for every T and S in $\mathscr{M}$ there is an element TS of $\mathscr{M}$ called the *product* of T and S.

(M2)   Associativity: $(TS)R = T(SR)$ (whenever either side is defined).

(M3)   Existence of a unit element I: there exists an element I in $\mathscr{M}$ such that $IT = TI = T$ for all T in $\mathscr{M}$.

(M4)   Existence of inverse: for each T in $\mathscr{M}$ there exists an element T^{-1} such that $TT^{-1} = T^{-1}T = I$ (if we also have addition in $\mathscr{M}$, the inverse is required only for $T \neq 0$).

(M5)   Commutativity: for all T and S in $\mathscr{M}$, $TS = ST$.

If $\mathscr{M}$ has both operations of addition and of multiplication we consider also the two distributive laws:

(D1) $T(S + R) = TS + TR$ (whenever either side is defined).

(D2) $(T + S)R = TR + SR$ (whenever either side is defined).

For the set $\mathscr{T}$ introduced at the beginning of this section we have of these axioms only M2, D1, and D2. Instead of M1 we have a criterion for multiplication, however, and, when the product exists, it is again an element of $\mathscr{T}$. Instead of a universal I we have for each vector space $\mathscr{U}$ an identity mapping $I_{\mathscr{U}}$ such that $\alpha I_{\mathscr{U}} = \alpha$ for all α in $\mathscr{U}$. If T is a linear transformation of $\mathscr{V}$ into $\mathscr{W}$, then the equation of M3 has as its nearest counterpart the equation $I_{\mathscr{V}}T = TI_{\mathscr{W}} = T$. Only nonsingular elements have inverses, and even here we have $TT^{-1} = I_{\mathscr{V}}$ and $T^{-1}T = I_{\mathscr{W}}$ instead of the equation of M4. The commutative law M5 is definitely false for linear transformations.

For scalars it is a consequence of the axioms that $a0 = 0a = 0$ for all a. The presence of many zero linear transformations makes such a simple equation impossible for $\mathscr{T}$. Let T be a linear transformation of $\mathscr{V}$ into $\mathscr{W}$, and let $\mathscr{U}$ and $\mathscr{L}$ be any two spaces in our given collection. Then we have $0_{\mathscr{U}\mathscr{V}}T = 0_{\mathscr{U}\mathscr{W}}$ and $T0_{\mathscr{W}\mathscr{L}} = 0_{\mathscr{V}\mathscr{L}}$ which state that a product of linear transformations is zero if either factor is zero.

There is a very important special case in which the situation is simpler: namely the case in which $\mathscr{T}$ is the set of all linear transformations of a single vector space $\mathscr{V}$ into itself. In this case both closure axioms A1 and M1 hold, and we have a unique $0 = 0_{\mathscr{V}\mathscr{V}}$ and a unique $I = I_{\mathscr{V}}$ which satisfy A3 and M3. Thus in $\mathscr{T}$ all five of the axioms of addition hold, all

five of the axioms for multiplication by scalars hold, and we have also
M1, M2, M3, D1, and D2.   (Axioms M4 and M5 still are beyond our reach.)

It is appropriate at this stage to give definitions for some concepts which
are of great importance in mathematics (although they will not all be used
extensively in the present book).

A system $\mathscr{T}$ in which addition is defined is called a *group* if axioms A1,
A2, A3, and A4 hold.   A group in which A5 also holds is said to be a
commutative group (or *abelian group*).   Thus a vector space is a commutative group under the operation of addition.

If multiplication is chosen as the group operation, the group axioms
become M1, M2, M3, and M4.   For example, the nonzero elements of any
field form a group under multiplication.

If in a commutative group $\mathscr{T}$ with operation $+$ we have also a multiplication defined which satisfies axioms M1, M2, D1, and D2, we say that $\mathscr{T}$ is
a *ring*.   A ring in which M3 holds is called a *ring with unity element*, and a
ring in which M5 holds is called a *commutative ring*.   The set of all integers
is an example of a commutative ring with unity element.   The set of all
even integers is an example of a commutative ring without unity
element.

If in a ring $\mathscr{T}$ a multiplication by scalars from a field $\mathscr{F}$ is defined which
satisfies axioms S1, S2, S3, S4, and S5, we say that $\mathscr{T}$ is an *algebra over* $\mathscr{F}$.
Alternatively, we can characterize an algebra as a vector space in which
there is defined a multiplication which satisfies axioms M1, M2, D1, and
D2.   The following theorem is a restatement of much of the discussion of
this section.

THEOREM 2.7A.   *Let $\mathscr{V}$ be a vector space over a field $\mathscr{F}$.   Then the set $\mathscr{T}$
of all linear transformations of $\mathscr{V}$ into itself is an algebra over $\mathscr{F}$.*

The above discussion of the M and D axioms applies also to matrices.
In particular, the set $\mathscr{M} = \mathscr{M}_{vv}(\mathscr{F})$ of all square $\mathscr{F}$ matrices of degree v
satisfies both closure postulates A1 and M1.   For this set we have the
unique zero matrix $0 = 0_{vv}$ and the unique identity matrix $I = I_v$ which
satisfy A3 and M3, and, moreover, we have for all A in $\mathscr{M}$ that $0A = A0 = 0$.
Thus $\mathscr{M}$ is an algebra with unity element;   we call it the *total matrix
algebra of degree v over* $\mathscr{F}$.   It is isomorphic to the set of all linear transformations on a vector space of dimension v.

Since an algebra is also a vector space, the concepts of dimension and
basis are automatically defined for algebras.   Sometimes the term "order"
is used instead of "dimension."   Thus we see that $\mathscr{M}$ is an algebra of order
v^2 and that one basis for $\mathscr{M}$ is the natural basis.   We have already discussed the way in which the E_{hk} combine under addition and under
multiplication by scalars.   We now investigate their properties under

multiplication. As an aid in this we introduce the *Kronecker delta function* δ_{ij} which is defined for all pairs of natural numbers i, j by the equations

(7.1)
$$\begin{cases} \delta_{ii} = 1, \\ \\ \delta_{ij} = 0 \end{cases} \qquad (i \neq j).$$

We observe that, if the ith row of a matrix A is zero (i.e., each element of the row is zero), then the ith row of any product AB is zero: likewise, if the ith column of a matrix B is zero, then the ith column of any product AB is zero. Applying these observations to the product $D = E_{hk}E_{pm}$, we see that the only possible nonzero entry of D is d_{hm}, whence $D = d_{hm}E_{hm}$. Furthermore, in combining the hth row of E_{hk} with the mth column of E_{pm}, we see that d_{hm} is 1 if $k = p$ and is 0 if $k \neq p$. Or, in terms of the delta function, $d_{hm} = \delta_{kp}$. Thus we have

(7.2)
$$E_{hk}E_{pm} = \delta_{kp}E_{hm} \qquad (h, k, p, m = 1, \cdots, v).$$

A formula analogous to this holds for multiplication of rectangular matrices E_{hk}. Before writing it we need a more complete notation. We now denote by $E_{hk}(v, w)$ the v-by-w matrix, all of whose entries are 0 except for a 1 in position h, k. The argument that led to (7.2) then gives

(7.3)
$$E_{hk}(v, w) E_{pm}(w, u) = \delta_{kp}E_{hm}(v, u).$$

Actually, if we assume the distributive laws and the axioms for multiplication by scalars, then formula (7.3) characterizes matrix multiplication. To see this, let $A = \Sigma a_{\lambda\mu} E_{\lambda\mu}(v, w)$ and $B = \Sigma b_{\lambda\mu} E_{\lambda\mu}(w, u)$. (Here we omit the summation indices since they are clear from the context. When the Σ is used without indices we always understand that the summation is over all Greek indices in the expression that follows.) Now

$$AB = (\Sigma a_{\lambda\mu} E_{\lambda\mu}(v, w)(\Sigma b_{\lambda\mu} E_{\lambda\mu}(w, u))$$
$$= \Sigma a_{\lambda\mu} b_{\rho\sigma} E_{\lambda\mu}(v, w) E_{\rho\sigma}(w, u)$$
$$= \Sigma a_{\lambda\mu} b_{\rho\sigma} \delta_{\mu\rho} E_{\lambda\sigma}(v, u).$$

Thus $AB = C = \| c_{ij} \|$ where c_{ij} is the coefficient of $E_{ij}(v, u)$ in this last summation; i.e.,

$$c_{ij} = \Sigma a_{i\mu}b_{\rho j}\delta_{\mu\rho} = \Sigma a_{i\mu}b_{\mu j},$$

since $\delta_{\mu\rho} = 0$ unless $\rho = \mu$. But this result is exactly our original rule for matrix multiplication.

This situation illustrates a general principle in dealing with algebras. If we are given the products of all pairs of basis elements, then all products are determined.

We have seen that the product of two nonsingular matrices of degree v is again a nonsingular matrix of degree v; that the inverse of a nonsingular matrix is again nonsingular; and that $I = I_v$ is nonsingular. Thus the nonsingular elements of $\mathscr{M} = \mathscr{M}_{vv}(\mathscr{F})$ satisfy axioms M1, M4, and M3; clearly the associative law holds for any set of matrix products. Hence we conclude that the set of all nonsingular $\mathscr{F}$ matrices of degree v forms a group under multiplication. It is called the *full linear group of degree v over $\mathscr{F}$* and is usually denoted by $\mathscr{GL}(v, \mathscr{F})$. It is easy to see that this group is not commutative (if $v > 1$). It is isomorphic to the set of all one-to-one linear transformations on a vector space of dimension v.

Exercises 2.7

1. Show that the set of all matrices of the form

$$\left\| \begin{array}{ccc} a_{11} & 0 & 0 \\ a_{21} & a_{22} & 0 \\ a_{31} & a_{32} & a_{33} \end{array} \right\|$$

constitutes an algebra. What is the dimension of this algebra?

2. Show that the set of all matrices of the form

$$\left\| \begin{array}{cccc} 0 & 0 & a_{13} & a_{14} \\ 0 & 0 & a_{23} & a_{24} \\ 0 & 0 & 0 & 0 \\ 0 & 0 & 0 & 0 \end{array} \right\|$$

constitutes an algebra in which every product is zero.

3. Show that the sum of two nonsingular matrices is not necessarily nonsingular.

4. Let A be a square matrix. Show that the set of all polynomials in A constitutes an algebra.

2.8. Submatrices, partitioned matrices.

Let $A = \| a_{ij} \|$ be a v-by-w $\mathscr{F}$ matrix. If we delete r rows and s columns of A, the remaining entries form a $(v - r)$-by-$(w - s)$ matrix called a *submatrix* of A. For example, by deleting the first and third rows and the fourth column of the 4-by-4 matrix

$$A = \left\| \begin{array}{cccc} a_{11} & a_{12} & a_{13} & a_{14} \\ a_{21} & a_{22} & a_{23} & a_{24} \\ a_{31} & a_{32} & a_{33} & a_{34} \\ a_{41} & a_{42} & a_{43} & a_{44} \end{array} \right\| .$$

we obtain the 2-by-3 submatrix

$$B = \begin{Vmatrix} a_{21} & a_{22} & a_{23} \\ a_{41} & a_{42} & a_{43} \end{Vmatrix}.$$

To indicate which rows and columns of A have been deleted we write $B = A(1, 3 \mid 4)$.

More generally, $A(i_1, i_2, \cdots, i_r \mid j_1, j_2, \cdots, j_s)$ denotes the submatrix obtained from A by deleting rows $i_1, i_2, \cdots, i_r$ and columns $j_1, j_2, \cdots, j_s$.

If we prefer to specify a submatrix by indicating which rows and columns have been kept, we use brackets instead of parentheses. Thus in the example above we may write $B = A[2, 4 \mid 1, 2, 3]$. More generally, $A[i_1, i_2, \cdots, i_r \mid j_1, j_2, \cdots, j_s]$ denotes the submatrix obtained from A by deleting all rows except $i_1, i_2, \cdots, i_r$ and all columns except $j_1, j_2, \cdots, j_s$.

Suppose $v = v_1 + v_2$, $w = w_1 + w_2$, and consider the submatrices

$$A_{11} = A[1, \cdots, v_1 \mid 1, \cdots, w_1],$$
$$A_{12} = A[1, \cdots, v_1 \mid w_1 + 1, \cdots, w],$$
$$A_{21} = A[v_1 + 1, \cdots, v \mid 1, \cdots, w_1],$$
$$A_{22} = A[v_1 + 1, \cdots, v \mid w_1 + 1, \cdots, w].$$

We then write

$$A = \begin{Vmatrix} A_{11} & A_{12} \\ A_{21} & A_{22} \end{Vmatrix}$$

and say that A has been partitioned into the submatrices A_{ij} according to the partitions $v = v_1 + v_2$ and $w = w_1 + w_2$ of v and w.

More generally, let $v = v_1 + \cdots + v_r$, $w = w_1 + \cdots + w_s$ be arbitrary partitions of v and w into natural number summands. Let $m_h = v_1 + \cdots + v_h$ $(h = 1, \cdots, r)$, let $n_k = w_1 + \cdots + w_k$ $(k = 1, \cdots, s)$, let $m_0 = n_0 = 0$, and let

$$A_{ij} = A[m_{i-1} + 1, \cdots, m_i \mid n_{j-1} + 1, \cdots, n_j] \, (i = 1, \cdots, r; j = 1, \cdots, s).$$

Then we say that

$$(8.1) \qquad A = \begin{Vmatrix} A_{11} \cdots A_{1j} \cdots A_{1s} \\ \cdot \, \cdots \cdot \, \cdots \cdot \\ A_{i1} \cdots A_{ij} \cdots A_{is} \\ \cdot \, \cdots \cdot \, \cdots \cdot \\ A_{r1} \cdots A_{rj} \cdots A_{rs} \end{Vmatrix}$$

is a *partitioning* of A into the submatrices A_{ij} according to the partitions $v = v_1 + \cdots + v_r$ and $w = w_1 + \cdots + w_s$ of v and w. In the extreme case of a partitioning in which each of the summands v_h and w_k is 1, then the submatrices of the partition reduce to the elements of the matrix: i.e., A_{hk} is the 1-by-1 submatrix whose element is a_{hk}.

The use of partitioned matrices is very helpful in many computations and even in theoretical work. We now discuss the various matrix operations on partitioned matrices. If $A = \| A_{ij} \|$ is partitioned as in (8.1) and c is a scalar, we have

$$cA = \| cA_{ij} \| ;$$

i.e., *to multiply a partitioned matrix by a scalar we multiply each submatrix by that scalar.*

If $B = \| B_{ij} \|$ is a v-by-w matrix partitioned in the same way as A, we have

$$A + B = \| A_{ij} + B_{ij} \| ;$$

i.e., *the sum of two identically partitioned matrices is another matrix with the same partitioning and whose submatrices are the sums of the corresponding submatrices of the summands.*

Next, let v and w be partitioned as above, and let $u = u_1 + \cdots + u_t$ and $p_l = u_1 + \cdots + u_l$ $(l = 1, \cdots, t)$. Let A be given by (8.1), and let B be a w-by-u matrix partitioned according to the given partitions of w and u. We say then that the partitionings of A and B are *conformable.* Then we have

(8.2) $$AB = \left\| \sum_{\mu=1}^{s} A_{i\mu}B_{\mu j} \right\| ;$$

i.e., *the product of two conformably partitioned matrices is a partitioned matrix whose rows are partitioned in the same manner as the rows of the left factor and whose columns are partitioned in the same manner as the columns of the right factor. The submatrices of the product are formed from those of the factors according to the usual row-by-column multiplication rule.* Thus in forming products of partitioned matrices we treat the submatrices as though they were scalars (of course, we must preserve the left-right order of the factors of each summand).

The central idea of the proof of (8.2) which follows is to break the sum for the elements of the product AB into subsums which correspond to elements in the products of various submatrices. For the reader who finds any difficulty in following proofs, such as this one, which involve working with many sets of indices we recommend the selection of definite numerical examples for use in a preliminary following through of the proof. Then after working through the proof for a special case he can return to the study of the general case.

To establish (8.2) we compute the (h, k) element on both sides of the equation.   On the left side we have

(8.3)
$$c_{hk} = \sum_{\lambda=1}^{w} a_{h\lambda} b_{\lambda k}.$$

We now consider the s sums

$$c_{hk}^{(q)} = \sum_{\lambda=n_{q-1}+1}^{n_q} a_{h\lambda} b_{\lambda k} \qquad (q = 1, \cdots, s),$$

and then have from (8.3) that

(8.4)
$$c_{hk} = \sum_{\rho=1}^{s} c_{hk}^{(\rho)}.$$

Now suppose that the hth row of A falls into the submatrices $A_{i1}, \cdots, A_{is}$. Stated analytically, this means that i is defined in terms of h by the condition $m_{i-1} < h \leq m_i$.   Define j similarly in terms of k by the condition $p_{j-1} < k \leq p_j$, and set $h' = h - m_{i-1}$, $k' = k - p_{j-1}$. Then we see that $c_{hk}^{(q)}$ is the element in the position (h', k') of the product $A_{iq}B_{qj}$. Hence, by (8.4), c_{hk} is the (h', k') element of the sum $\sum_{\mu=1}^{s} A_{i\mu}B_{\mu j}$, and therefore c_{hk} is the (h, k) element of the right side of (8.2).   This completes the proof that the multiplication rule (8.2) for partitioned matrices is valid.

Sometimes in partitioning a matrix it is desirable to allow for the possibility that one or more of the integer summands v_i or w_j might be zero. We achieve this goal by generalizing the concept of matrix to allow for matrices in which one degree or both may be zero.   Such a matrix is called a *null matrix*.   A null matrix has no elements in it.   We speak of a matrix with row degree zero as a *null row matrix* (cf. Section 2.9).   Null column matrices are defined analogously.

The significance of partitioned matrices for linear transformations is given in Section 8.8.

Exercises 2.8

1. If

$$A = \begin{Vmatrix} 2 & 1 & 0 & -7 & 6 \\ 3 & 2 & 3 & 1 & 4 \\ 0 & -1 & 2 & 2 & 3 \end{Vmatrix},$$

what is $A(1 \mid 1, 3, 5)$, $A[1 \mid 1, 3, 5]$, $A(1, 2, 3 \mid 1, 3, 5)$?

2. Using the partitioned form, find the product AB if

$$A = \left\| \begin{array}{cc} I_2 & 0 \\ 0 & A_1 \end{array} \right\|, \qquad B = \left\| \begin{array}{ccc} B_1 & 0 & B_2 \\ 0 & I_1 & B_3 \end{array} \right\|,$$

where $A_1 = \| \, 3 \, \|$, $B_1 = \left\| \begin{array}{cc} 1 & 2 \\ 3 & 4 \end{array} \right\|$, $B_2 = \left\| \begin{array}{c} 6 \\ 5 \end{array} \right\|$, $B_3 = \| \, 7 \, \|$.

3. Let A and B be square matrices of degree v, and suppose that each has a rectangular block of zeros in the last r rows and first $v - r$ columns. Show that the sum $A + B$ and the product AB each has a block of zeros in this same position.

4. Show that the set of all square matrices as described in Exercise 3 for fixed v and r forms an algebra.

5. Give a generalization of the preceding exercise.

6. Let P be any square matrix, and let

$$A = \left\| \begin{array}{ccc} P & I & 0 \\ 0 & P & I \\ 0 & 0 & P \end{array} \right\|.$$

Show that

$$A^s = \left\| \begin{array}{ccc} P^s & \binom{s}{1}P^{s-1} & \binom{s}{2}P^{s-2} \\ 0 & P^s & \binom{s}{1}P^{s-1} \\ 0 & 0 & P^s \end{array} \right\| \qquad (s = 1, 2, 3 \cdots)$$

where $\binom{a}{b}$ is the binomial coefficient. Generalize this result.

7. The Kronecker product of two matrices A and B is defined to be the matrix C which has the partitioned form

$$C = \left\| \begin{array}{ccc} a_{11}B & \cdots & a_{1w}B \\ \cdot & \cdots & \cdot \\ a_{v1}B & \cdots & a_{vw}B \end{array} \right\|,$$

and is written as $C = A \times B$. For example, if

$$A = \left\| \begin{array}{ccc} 2 & 1 & 3 \\ 0 & 1 & 2 \end{array} \right\| \qquad \text{and} \qquad B = \left\| \begin{array}{c} 2 \\ 1 \end{array} \right\|,$$

then

$$A \times B = \left\| \begin{array}{ccc} 2B & B & 3B \\ 0 & B & 2B \end{array} \right\| = \left\| \begin{array}{ccc} 4 & 2 & 6 \\ 2 & 1 & 3 \\ 0 & 2 & 4 \\ 0 & 1 & 2 \end{array} \right\|.$$

Find $B \times A$.

8. A function $T: \alpha \to \alpha T$ is said to be *linear* if it satisfies L3.   A function of two vector arguments is said to be *bilinear* if it is linear in each argument separately.   Show that the Kronecker product is a bilinear function of its two factors.

9. Show that $(A_1 \times B_1)(A_2 \times B_2) = (A_1 A_2) \times (B_1 B_2)$.   [We assume here that the row and column degrees are such that the ordinary matrix products $A_1 A_2$ and $B_1 B_2$ are defined.]

10. Show that $A \times (B \times C) = (A \times B) \times C$.

11. Let A and B be square matrices of degree z.   Show that $B \times A$ can be obtained from $A \times B$ by a rearrangement (permutation) of the rows followed by the same rearrangement of the columns.

2.9. Row and column matrices.

A matrix with only one row is called a *row matrix*.   Since there is only one row, we frequently suppress the row index and write

$$K = \| k_j \| = \| k_1 \cdots k_n \|$$

to indicate a row matrix whose column degree is n.   (Throughout the entire book we shall follow the convention that in all matrices i is the row index and j is the column index.)   Sometimes we may use a double subscript having the first subscript 1; e.g., $K = \| k_{1j} \|$.

The set of 1-by-n $\mathscr{F}$ matrices is clearly in one-to-one correspondence with the set of all vectors in $\mathscr{V}_n(\mathscr{F})$ under the mapping T given by

$$T: \quad \alpha = (a_1, \cdots, a_n) \to \alpha T = A = \| a_1 \cdots a_n \|.$$

Let A and B be 1-by-n $\mathscr{F}$ matrices, and let c be a scalar.   Then, in accordance with the definitions of matrix operations, we have

(9.1) $$A + B = \| a_1 + b_1 \cdots a_n + b_n \|$$

and

(9.2) $$cA = \| ca_1 \cdots ca_n \|.$$

We denote by $\mathscr{V}_n^r(\mathscr{F})$ the vector space consisting of all 1-by-n $\mathscr{F}$ matrices and call it the *row space* (of dimension n).   Equations (9.1) and (9.2) show that T is an isomorphism of $\mathscr{V}_n(\mathscr{F})$ onto $\mathscr{V}_n^r(\mathscr{F})$.

Thus $\mathscr{V}_n^r(\mathscr{F})$ can be taken in place of $\mathscr{V}_n(\mathscr{F})$ as the prototype of all n-dimensional vector spaces over $\mathscr{F}$.   The space $\mathscr{V}_n^r(\mathscr{F})$ has a basis given by

$$E_1 = \| 1 \quad 0 \quad 0 \quad \cdots \quad 0 \|,$$

$$E_2 = \| 0 \quad 1 \quad 0 \quad \cdots \quad 0 \|,$$

$$\cdot$$
$$\cdot$$
$$\cdot$$

$$E_n = \| 0 \quad 0 \quad \cdots \quad 0 \quad 1 \|,$$

called the *natural basis* $\mathscr{N}$ for $\mathscr{V}_n{}^r(\mathscr{F})$. The dimension of $\mathscr{V}_n{}^r(\mathscr{F})$ is n. In the expression of any vector $A = \|\, a_1 \cdots a_n \,\|$ in terms of the natural basis the scalar coefficients needed are the elements of A; i.e., $\|\, a_1 \cdots a_n \,\| = a_1 E_1 + \cdots + a_n E_n$. Thus $A = \|\, A \,\|_{\mathscr{N}}$.

One application of matrix multiplication was its relation to products of linear transformations. This fact was used to introduce the matrix product. Our next application is in the actual expression of linear transformations.

THEOREM 2.9A. *If $\mathscr{A} = \{\alpha_1, \cdots, \alpha_v\}$ is a basis of a vector space $\mathscr{V}$ and $\mathscr{B} = \{\beta_1, \cdots, \beta_w\}$ is a basis of $\mathscr{W}$, and T is a linear transformation of $\mathscr{V}$ into $\mathscr{W}$, then, for α in $\mathscr{V}$,*

$$\|\, \alpha\mathsf{T} \,\|_{\mathscr{B}} = \|\, \alpha \,\|_{\mathscr{A}} \,\|\, \mathsf{T} \,\|_{\mathscr{A}\mathscr{B}}.$$

In fact, this is simply a rewriting of (2.8) taking account of (2.3) and (2.5).

COROLLARY 2.9B. *If $\mathscr{V} = \mathscr{V}_v{}^r(\mathscr{F})$ and $\mathscr{W} = \mathscr{V}_w{}^r(\mathscr{F})$, and $\mathscr{M}$ and $\mathscr{N}$ are their natural bases, respectively, and if T is a linear transformation from $\mathscr{V}$ into $\mathscr{W}$, then, for C in $\mathscr{V}_v{}^r(\mathscr{F})$,*

$$C\mathsf{T} = C \,\|\, \mathsf{T} \,\|_{\mathscr{M}\mathscr{N}}.$$

This follows from the theorem since $C\mathsf{T} = \|\, C\mathsf{T} \,\|_{\mathscr{N}}$ and $C = \|\, C \,\|_{\mathscr{M}}$.

Thus every linear transformation between row spaces can be accomplished by matrix multiplication. This result is important since $\mathscr{V}_n{}^r(\mathscr{F})$ is a prototype for all vector spaces of dimension n over $\mathscr{F}$.

The results for row matrices suggest the similar consideration of matrices consisting of only one column, which we call *column matrices*, and of column spaces. We denote by $\mathscr{V}_n{}^c(\mathscr{F})$ the vector space consisting of all n-by-1 $\mathscr{F}$ matrices. We say that the (column) vectors

$$\left\|\begin{matrix} 1 \\ 0 \\ \cdot \\ \cdot \\ \cdot \\ 0 \end{matrix}\right\|, \left\|\begin{matrix} 0 \\ 1 \\ \cdot \\ \cdot \\ \cdot \\ 0 \end{matrix}\right\|, \cdots, \left\|\begin{matrix} 0 \\ 0 \\ \cdot \\ \cdot \\ \cdot \\ 1 \end{matrix}\right\|$$

constitute the *natural basis* for $\mathscr{V}_n{}^c(\mathscr{F})$.

Let $\mathscr{V} = \mathscr{V}_v{}^c(\mathscr{F})$, let $\mathscr{W} = \mathscr{V}_w{}^c(\mathscr{F})$, and let T be a linear transformation of $\mathscr{V}$ into $\mathscr{W}$. Denote by $\alpha_1, \cdots, \alpha_v$ and $\beta_1, \cdots, \beta_w$, respectively, the natural bases for $\mathscr{V}$ and $\mathscr{W}$, and let A be the matrix of T relative to these bases. Thus $A = \| a_{ij} \|$ where $\alpha_i \mathsf{T} = \sum_{\nu=1}^{w} a_{i\nu} \beta_\nu \; (i = 1, \cdots, v)$. The image $Y = X\mathsf{T} = \| y_{i1} \|$ of the column vector $X = \| x_{i1} \|$ is then given by

$$y_{i1} = \sum_{\lambda=1}^{v} x_{\lambda 1} a_{\lambda i} \qquad (i = 1, \cdots, w).$$

We ask if Y can be obtained as a matrix product with X as one factor and the other factor somehow related to A. Since the summation is over the row index of X, we must have X as the second factor. Hence we look for a matrix D such that $Y = DX$. In component form this gives

$$y_{i1} = \sum_{\nu=1}^{v} d_{i\nu} x_{\nu 1} \qquad (i = 1, \cdots, w)$$

where D is a w-by-v $\mathscr{F}$ matrix. Comparing these expressions for y_{i1}, we see that we must have

(9.3) $$d_{ij} = a_{ji} \qquad (i = 1, \cdots, w; j = 1, \cdots, v)$$

and that for this D we do indeed have

(9.4) $$Y = X\mathsf{T} = DX$$

for all X as desired.

Observe that according to (9.3) the ith row of the matrix D is the ith column of A rotated counterclockwise through a right angle and that the jth column of D is the jth row of A rotated clockwise through a right angle.

Let A be any $\mathscr{F}$ matrix. We say that the matrix D defined by (9.3) is the *transpose* of A and write $D = A^{\mathsf{T}}$. We see that, if $D = A^{\mathsf{T}}$, then also $A = D^{\mathsf{T}}$ or in words *any matrix is the transpose of its transpose*. In general, any mapping which twice applied to any object reproduces that object is called an *involution*. Thus transposition of matrices is an involution.

As examples of transposed matrices we have

$$A = \begin{Vmatrix} 3 & 1 & 2 & 0 \\ -1 & 4 & -2 & 6 \\ 0 & 1 & -1 & 2 \end{Vmatrix}, \qquad A^{\mathsf{T}} = \begin{Vmatrix} 3 & -1 & 0 \\ 1 & 4 & 1 \\ 2 & -2 & -1 \\ 0 & 6 & 2 \end{Vmatrix},$$

and

$$A = \left\| \begin{array}{ccc} 2 & 0 & -3 \end{array} \right\|, \qquad A^{\mathsf{T}} = \left\| \begin{array}{c} 2 \\ 0 \\ -3 \end{array} \right\|.$$

Summarizing these results we get the following theorem:

THEOREM 2.9C. *Let $\mathcal{V}$ and $\mathcal{W}$ be column-matrix vector spaces, and let* T *be a linear transformation of $\mathcal{V}$ into $\mathcal{W}$ which has the matrix A relative to the natural bases for $\mathcal{V}$ and $\mathcal{W}$. Then $D = A^{\mathsf{T}}$ is the only matrix that satisfies* (9.4); *i.e.,*

$$(9.5) \qquad Y = X\mathsf{T} = A^{\mathsf{T}}X.$$

THEOREM 2.9D. *Let A and B be $\mathcal{F}$ matrices whose product is defined; then we have*

$$(9.6) \qquad (AB)^{\mathsf{T}} = B^{\mathsf{T}}A^{\mathsf{T}}.$$

More generally, if $A_1, \cdots, A_r$ are matrices for which the product $B = A_1 A_2 \cdots \cdot A_r$ is defined, then

$$(9.7) \qquad B^{\mathsf{T}} = (A_1 A_2 \cdots \cdot A_r)^{\mathsf{T}} = A_r^{\mathsf{T}} \cdots \cdot A_2^{\mathsf{T}} A_1^{\mathsf{T}}.$$

In words, the transpose of a product of matrices is equal to the product of the transposes of the factors in reverse order.

Let $Y = X\mathsf{T}$ and $Z = Y\mathsf{S}$ define linear transformations between column spaces, whose matrices are A and B, respectively, and let $C = AB$ be the matrix of $\mathsf{R} = \mathsf{TS}$. Then by (9.5) we have $Y = X\mathsf{T} = A^{\mathsf{T}}X$, $Z = Y\mathsf{S} = B^{\mathsf{T}}Y$, and $X(\mathsf{TS}) = C^{\mathsf{T}}X$. But we have also

$$Z = X(\mathsf{TS}) = (X\mathsf{T})\mathsf{S} = Y\mathsf{S} = B^{\mathsf{T}}Y = B^{\mathsf{T}}(A^{\mathsf{T}}X).$$

By the associative law for matrix multiplication we then get $Z = X(\mathsf{TS}) = (B^{\mathsf{T}}A^{\mathsf{T}})X$, whence it follows from the uniqueness of the solution C^{T} that $B^{\mathsf{T}}A^{\mathsf{T}} = C^{\mathsf{T}} = (AB)^{\mathsf{T}}$ as claimed. It is also easy to establish this result by direct appeal to the definitions of matrix multiplication and transpose. However, we feel that the proof as given is preferable.

We establish formula (9.7) by induction on the number of factors. It is trivially true for $r = 1$, and we have just proved it for $r = 2$. Now suppose it already is established for $r - 1$ factors and set $C = A_2 \cdots A_r$. Then $B = A_1 C$, so that $B^{\mathsf{T}} = C^{\mathsf{T}} A_1^{\mathsf{T}} = (A_r^{\mathsf{T}} \cdots \cdot A_2^{\mathsf{T}})A_1^{\mathsf{T}}$. The formula for r factors now follows from the associative law for matrix multiplication.

COROLLARY 2.9E. *If A is a nonsingular matrix with inverse B, then A^T is nonsingular with inverse B^T; i.e., the inverse of the transpose is the transpose of the inverse.*

For, if $AB = BA = I$, then $(AB)^\mathsf{T} = (BA)^\mathsf{T} = I^\mathsf{T} = I$, and from (9.6) we get $B^\mathsf{T}A^\mathsf{T} = A^\mathsf{T}B^\mathsf{T} = I$ as claimed.

Exercises 2.9

1. Prove that $(AB)^\mathsf{T} = B^\mathsf{T}A^\mathsf{T}$ by direct use of the formula for matrix multiplication.

2. Prove that $A \to A^\mathsf{T}$ is an isomorphism of $\mathscr{V}_n{}^r(\mathscr{F})$ onto $\mathscr{V}_n{}^c(\mathscr{F})$.

3. Let X be a 1-by-v row vector, let A be a v-by-w matrix, and let Y be a w-by-1 column vector. Show that $XAY = Y^\mathsf{T}A^\mathsf{T}X^\mathsf{T}$.

4. Prove that, if $\mathscr{N}$ is the natural basis of $\mathscr{V}_n{}^c(\mathscr{F})$ and if A is in $\mathscr{V}_n{}^c(\mathscr{F})$, then $\| A \|_{\mathscr{N}} = A^\mathsf{T}$. Use this result and Theorem 2.9D to prove Theorem 2.9C.

5. Let X be a vector in $\mathscr{V}_n{}^r(\mathfrak{R})$. Show that XX^T is a non-negative scalar which is zero only if $X = 0$.

6. Let X and Y be vectors in $V_n{}^r(\mathscr{F})$. Show that $XY^\mathsf{T} = YX^\mathsf{T}$.

Chapter 3

Systems of
Linear Equations

We have seen in the first two chapters that systems of linear equations occupy an important place in the theory of vector spaces and linear transformations. In this chapter we give a constructive method for solution of linear systems. Our treatment is complete so far as the theory is concerned and provides an algebraic basis for an understanding of modern computational procedures for handling large-scale linear systems (a topic that is not considered in this book). The problem is first put into matrix form, and the solution is given in terms of matrix concepts such as rank, row space, column space, row kernel, column kernel.

3.1. Rank; row and column spaces of a matrix. Let T be a linear transformation of $\mathscr{V}_v{}^r(\mathscr{F})$ into $\mathscr{V}_w{}^r(\mathscr{F})$; let A be the matrix of T with respect to the natural bases. Then the row

$$A_h = \| \, a_{h1} \cdots a_{hw} \|$$

of A is precisely the image $E_h\mathsf{T}$ of the basis vector E_h ($h = 1, \cdots, v$) (see Section 2.2). Thus the range $\mathscr{V}\mathsf{T}$ of T is spanned by the rows of A;

$$\mathscr{V}\mathsf{T} = \langle A_1, \cdots, A_v \rangle.$$

It is called the *row space* of A and is denoted by $\mathscr{R}(A)$; $\mathscr{R}(A) = \mathscr{V}\mathsf{T}$.

LEMMA 3.1A. *Let A be a v-by-w matrix, and let T be the linear transformation of $\mathscr{V}_v{}^r(\mathscr{F})$ into $\mathscr{V}_w{}^r(\mathscr{F})$ whose matrix relative to the natural bases is A; then $\mathscr{R}(A) = \mathscr{V}\mathsf{T}$.*

Similarly, the columns

$$A^k = \left\| \begin{array}{c} a_{1k} \\ a_{2k} \\ \cdots \\ a_{vk} \end{array} \right\| \qquad\qquad (k = 1, \cdots, w)$$

of A span a subspace $\mathscr{C}(A)$ of $\mathscr{V}_v{}^c(\mathscr{F})$ called the *column space of A*.

73

THEOREM 3.1B. *The dimension of the row space of any matrix is equal to the dimension of its column space.*

This common dimension is called the *rank* of the matrix. The rank of a matrix A will be denoted by $r(A)$.

Let $r = \dim \mathscr{R}(A)$, $r' = \dim \mathscr{C}(A)$. We first prove that $r' \leq r$. This is trivial if $r = v$. If $r < v$, we consider initially the case in which the first r rows of A span $\mathscr{R}(A)$. Let $A^{k_1}, \cdots, A^{k_s}$ be any set of s columns of A; then, if we can show that this set is dependent whenever $s > r$, it will follow that $r' \leq r$.

This set will be dependent if the vector equation

$$(1.1) \qquad x_1 A^{k_1} + \cdots + x_s A^{k_s} = 0$$

has a nontrivial solution. This vector equation is equivalent to the following system of v scalar equations:

$$(1.2) \qquad a_{hk_1} x_1 + \cdots + a_{hk_s} x_s = 0 \qquad (h = 1, \cdots, v).$$

We are assuming that $s > r$. Then, by the fundamental theorem on linear equations (Theorem 1.5E), the first r of the v equations of (1.2) have a nontrivial solution $c_1, \cdots, c_s$; i.e.,

$$(1.3) \qquad a_{hk_1} c_1 + \cdots + a_{hk_s} c_s = 0 \qquad (h = 1, \cdots, r).$$

Let

$$(1.4) \qquad d_h = a_{hk_1} c_1 + \cdots + a_{hk_s} c_s \qquad (h = 1, \cdots, v).$$

We have $d_h = 0 \ (h = 1, \cdots, r)$ from (1.3). We shall prove that $c_1, \cdots, c_s$ is a solution of (1.2); i.e., that $d_h = 0$ also for $h > r$.

Since $A_1, \cdots, A_r$ span $\mathscr{R}(A)$, there exist scalars b_{ij} for which

$$(1.5) \qquad A_h = \sum_{\lambda=1}^{r} b_{h\lambda} A_\lambda \qquad (h = r + 1, \cdots, v);$$

or, in terms of elements of A,

$$(1.6) \qquad a_{hj} = \sum_{\lambda=1}^{r} b_{h\lambda} a_{\lambda j} \qquad (h = r + 1, \cdots, v; j = 1, \cdots, w).$$

If we use (1.6) for $j = k_1, \cdots, k_s$, we get

$$
\begin{aligned}
d_h &= \sum_{\lambda=1}^{r} b_{h\lambda} a_{\lambda k_1} c_1 + \cdots + \sum_{\lambda=1}^{r} b_{h\lambda} a_{\lambda k_s} c_s \\
(1.7) \qquad &= \sum_{\lambda=1}^{r} b_{h\lambda} (a_{\lambda k_1} c_1 + \cdots + a_{\lambda k_s} c_s) \\
&= \sum_{\lambda=1}^{r} b_{h\lambda} d_\lambda = 0 \qquad (h = r + 1, \cdots, v),
\end{aligned}
$$

since $d_1 = \cdots = d_r = 0$. Equations (1.3) and (1.7) show that $c_1, \cdots, c_s$ is a nontrivial solution of (1.2) and therefore of (1.1).

Next, suppose that the first r rows of A do not span $\mathscr{R}(A)$. Then we can proceed in either of two ways. We could choose an independent set $A_{h_1}, \cdots, A_{h_r}$ which does span $\mathscr{R}(A)$, express the remaining A_h as linear combinations of these, and continue exactly as above but with slightly more complicated notation. The second way is to make use of the concept of isomorphism. Let $h_1, \cdots, h_v$ be any *permutation* (rearrangement) of $1, \cdots, v$, and consider the mapping T

$$(1.8) \qquad \begin{Vmatrix} c_1 \\ \cdot \\ \cdot \\ \cdot \\ \cdot \\ c_v \end{Vmatrix} \rightarrow \begin{Vmatrix} c_{h_1} \\ \cdot \\ \cdot \\ \cdot \\ \cdot \\ c_{h_v} \end{Vmatrix} = \begin{Vmatrix} c_1 \\ \cdot \\ \cdot \\ \cdot \\ \cdot \\ c_v \end{Vmatrix} \mathsf{T}$$

of $\mathscr{V}_v^c(\mathscr{F})$ into itself. This mapping T is readily seen to be an isomorphism of $\mathscr{V}_v^c(\mathscr{F})$ onto itself. Let A' be the v-by-w matrix whose ith row is the h_ith row of A $(i = 1, \cdots, v)$. Then $\mathscr{R}(A) = \mathscr{R}(A')$ and T maps $\mathscr{C}(A)$ isomorphically onto $\mathscr{C}(A')$. Hence $r = \dim \mathscr{R}(A) = \dim \mathscr{R}(A')$ and $r' = \dim \mathscr{C}(A) = \dim \mathscr{C}(A')$. We may choose a permutation such that the first r rows of A' span $\mathscr{R}(A)$. Then, since A' comes under the case already treated, we conclude that $r' \leq r$.

The reverse inequality $r \leq r'$ follows from the symmetry of the situation. For we have proved that, given any matrix B, $\dim \mathscr{C}(B) \leq \dim \mathscr{R}(B)$. Apply this to $B = A^{\mathsf{T}}$. The column space of B consists of the transposes of the vectors of the row space of A. Since transposition is an isomorphism of $\mathscr{V}_v^r(\mathscr{F})$ onto $\mathscr{V}_v^c(\mathscr{F})$, we conclude that $\dim \mathscr{C}(B) = \dim \mathscr{R}(A) = r$. Similarly $\dim \mathscr{R}(B) = r'$. Hence $r \leq r'$; this inequality together with $r' \leq r$ gives $r' = r$ and completes the proof of the theorem.

Hereafter we use $\mathscr{V}_v$ for $\mathscr{V}_v(\mathscr{F})$, $\mathscr{V}_v^r$ for $\mathscr{V}_v^r(\mathscr{F})$, and $\mathscr{V}_v^c$ for $\mathscr{V}_v^c(\mathscr{F})$ unless we wish to call attention to the field $\mathscr{F}$ being used.

THEOREM 3.1C. *The rank of a product AB of matrices A, B cannot exceed the rank of either factor.*

Suppose A is v-by-w and B is w-by-z. Let T be the linear transformation corresponding to A using the natural bases of $\mathscr{V}_v^r$ and $\mathscr{V}_w^r$, and let S similarly correspond to B using the natural bases $\mathscr{V}_w^r$ and $\mathscr{V}_z^r$. The theorem states that $\dim \mathscr{R}(AB)$ does not exceed either $\dim \mathscr{R}(A)$ or $\dim \mathscr{R}(B)$. According to Lemma 3.1A, this is equivalent to showing that $\dim \mathscr{V}_v^r(\mathsf{TS})$ does not exceed either $\dim \mathscr{V}_v^r \mathsf{T}$ or $\dim \mathscr{V}_w^r \mathsf{S}$. Now $\mathscr{V}_v^r \mathsf{T} \subseteq \mathscr{V}_w^r$; hence $\mathscr{V}_v^r(\mathsf{TS}) = (\mathscr{V}_v^r \mathsf{T})\mathsf{S} \subseteq \mathscr{V}_w^r \mathsf{S}$ and $\dim \mathscr{V}_v^r(\mathsf{TS}) \leq$

dim $\mathcal{V}_w{}^r S$. On the other hand, by Corollary 2.1E, dim $\mathcal{V}_v{}^r(TS) =$ dim $(\mathcal{V}_v{}^r T)S \leq$ dim $\mathcal{V}_v{}^r T$.

COROLLARY 3.1D. *If one factor of a product AB is nonsingular, then the rank of the product is equal to the rank of the other factor.*

We have already proved that rank $AB \leq$ rank A. If B is nonsingular, then we have $A = (AB)B^{-1}$, and so by the theorem just proved rank $A \leq$ rank AB. Hence, if the second factor is nonsingular, the rank of the product is equal to that of the first factor. The proof is similar in case the first factor is nonsingular.

COROLLARY 3.1E. *If P and Q are nonsingular matrices, then rank $PAQ =$ rank A.*

THEOREM 3.1F. *A square matrix is nonsingular if and only if its rank is equal to its degree.*

Let $A = \| a_{ij} \|$ be a v-by-v matrix and T be the linear transformation of $\mathcal{V}_v{}^r$ into itself which has matrix A relative to the natural basis. Suppose that rank $A = v$. Then $\mathcal{V}T = \mathcal{R}(A) = \mathcal{V}_v{}^r$, and hence, by Theorem 2.4E, T is nonsingular. Let B be the matrix for T^{-1}. Then $BA = AB = I$, so that A is nonsingular with inverse B. The converse follows from Corollary 3.1C; the details are left as an exercise.

THEOREM 3.1G. *The rank of a matrix is equal to the degree of its largest nonsingular submatrix.*

If a matrix A has rank r, suppose that $\{A_{i_1}, \cdots, A_{i_r}\}$ is a basis for $\mathcal{R}(A)$. Then $B = A[i_1, \cdots, i_r \,|\, 1, \cdots, w]$ has rank r, and hence there exists an independent set $\{B^{j_1}, \cdots, B^{j_r}\}$ of columns of B. Hence the square submatrix $C = A[i_1, \cdots, i_r \,|\, j_1, \cdots, j_r]$ has degree r and rank r, and so from Theorem 3.1F is nonsingular. On the other hand, no square submatrix of degree exceeding r can be nonsingular, for if so we could reverse the above argument and show that the corresponding rows of A would span a space of dimension exceeding r.

THEOREM 3.1H. *Let A be a matrix whose elements lie in a field $\mathscr{F}$, and suppose that $\mathscr{F}'$ is a field that contains $\mathscr{F}$. Then the rank of A is the same whether A is regarded as an $\mathscr{F}$ matrix or as an $\mathscr{F}'$ matrix.*

Suppose that A has rank r over $\mathscr{F}$ and rank r' over $\mathscr{F}'$. Then $r' \leq r$ since, if a set of rows with entries in $\mathscr{F}$ is independent over $\mathscr{F}'$, it is a fortiori independent over $\mathscr{F}$.

Next, let C be a square $\mathscr{F}$ matrix whose $\mathscr{F}$ rank is equal to its degree. According to Theorem 3.1F, C is nonsingular, and its inverse C^{-1} is also an $\mathscr{F}$ matrix. Moreover, the existence of C^{-1} shows that C has $\mathscr{F}'$ rank equal to its degree. This proves that a nonsingular matrix remains nonsingular when the scalar domain is enlarged from $\mathscr{F}$ to $\mathscr{F}'$. The theorem now follows from Theorem 3.1G since there is a nonsingular submatrix C of A with degree r, and hence $r' \geq r$; finally $r' = r$.

THEOREM 3.1I. *Let A and B be two matrices with sum C. Then* rank $C \leq$ rank A + rank B.

Since $C = A + B$, the row space $\mathscr{R}(C)$ is contained in $\mathscr{R}(A) + \mathscr{R}(B)$. Now, by Theorem 1.9A,

$$\dim (\mathscr{R}(A) + \mathscr{R}(B)) \leq \dim \mathscr{R}(A) + \dim \mathscr{R}(B),$$

and hence

$$\text{rank } C \leq \dim (\mathscr{R}(A) + \mathscr{R}(B)) \leq \text{rank } A + \text{rank } B.$$

COROLLARY 3.1J. *Let A and B be two matrices with sum C. Then* rank $C \geq |$ rank A − rank $B |$.

We first observe that $r(B) = r(-B)$. Then $r(A) \leq r(A + B) + r(-B)$ $= r(C) + r(B)$; hence $r(C) \geq r(A) - r(B)$. Similarly, $r(C) \geq r(B) - r(A)$.

Exercises 3.1

1. Find the rank of the matrix $\begin{Vmatrix} 1 & 0 & 0 & 0 \\ 0 & 1 & 0 & 0 \\ 0 & 0 & 1 & 1 \end{Vmatrix}$.

2. Show that a product of two square matrices is nonsingular if and only if each factor is nonsingular.

3. Find a basis of $\mathscr{R}(A)$ if $A = \begin{Vmatrix} 2 & 1 & 0 & -1 \\ 1 & -2 & 1 & 2 \\ 5 & 0 & 1 & 0 \end{Vmatrix}$.

4. Which of the following matrices has the same row space as $A = \begin{Vmatrix} 1 & 0 \\ 0 & 1 \end{Vmatrix}$:

$$\begin{Vmatrix} 2 & 1 \\ 0 & 0 \end{Vmatrix}, \begin{Vmatrix} 1 & 0 \\ 0 & -1 \end{Vmatrix}, \begin{Vmatrix} 1 & 0 & 0 \\ 0 & 1 & 0 \\ 0 & 0 & 1 \end{Vmatrix}, \begin{Vmatrix} 1 & 2 \\ -1 & 1 \\ 2 & 1 \end{Vmatrix}, \begin{Vmatrix} 1 & 0 \\ 1 & 1 \end{Vmatrix}?$$

5. Complete the proof of Theorem 3.1B for the case when the first r rows of A are not independent, using the first method suggested.

6. Prove that $r(A) = r(-A)$.

7. Using transposes give an alternative proof for the second part of the proof of Theorem 3.1C.

8. Let A be a v-by-w matrix, and let T' be the linear transformation of $\mathscr{V}_w{}^c$ into $\mathscr{V}_v{}^c$ whose matrix relative to the natural bases is A^T. Show that $\mathscr{C}(A) = \mathscr{V}_w{}^c \mathsf{T}'$.

9. Let A, B, and C be matrices with $AB = C$. Show that $\mathscr{C}(C) \subseteq \mathscr{C}(A)$.

3.2. Systems of linear homogeneous equations. Let

$$a_{11}x_1 + a_{12}x_2 + \cdots + a_{1w}x_w = 0,$$
$$a_{21}x_1 + a_{22}x_2 + \cdots + a_{2w}x_w = 0,$$
$$\cdot \quad \cdot \quad \cdot \quad \cdot \cdots \cdot \quad \cdot \cdot \cdot,$$
$$a_{v1}x_1 + a_{v2}x_2 + \cdots + a_{vw}x_w = 0,$$

or more briefly

$$(2.1) \qquad \sum_{\lambda=1}^{w} a_{i\lambda}x_\lambda = 0 \qquad\qquad (i = 1, \cdots, v)$$

be a system of simultaneous equations with coefficients in a field $\mathscr{F}$. We can designate the system (2.1) by its *matrix of coefficients* $A = \| a_{ij} \|$ and accordingly speak of the system with matrix A, or, for short, of the system $\mathscr{L}(A)$.

The system $\mathscr{L}(A)$ can be expressed compactly using matrix multiplication as

$$(2.2) \qquad\qquad AX = 0.$$

Here 0 is the zero vector in $\mathscr{V}_v{}^c$, and the solution $X = \| x_i \|$ is to be found in $\mathscr{V}_w{}^c$. This supersedes our earlier convention by which we consider solutions as w-tuples. Thus the set of all solutions of the system $\mathscr{L}(A)$ is henceforth interpreted as a subspace of $\mathscr{V}_w{}^c$ rather than of $\mathscr{V}_w$ (cf. Section 1.4). We call this subspace given by (2.2) the *column kernel* of A and denote it by $\mathscr{K}^c(A)$. The *row kernel* $\mathscr{K}^r(A)$ of A is defined analogously as the subspace of $\mathscr{V}_v{}^r$ of all solutions Y of $YA = 0$.

Since the solution of the system (2.1) is the column kernel of the coefficient matrix A, we now establish some properties of row and column kernels and their connections with row and column spaces.

THEOREM 3.2A. *Let A be a v-by-w $\mathscr{F}$ matrix of rank r. Then the space $\mathscr{K}^c(A)$ of all solutions X of $AX = 0$ has dimension $w - r$ and the space $\mathscr{K}^r(A)$ of all solutions Y of $YA = 0$ has dimension $v - r$.*

Consider the linear transformation T of $\mathscr{V}_v{}^r$ into $\mathscr{V}_w{}^r$ whose matrix relative to the natural bases is A; i.e.

$$\mathsf{T}: \ Y \to YA = Y\mathsf{T}.$$

According to Lemma 3.1A the range of T is $\mathscr{R}(A)$; clearly the kernel of T is the row kernel of A; i.e., $\mathscr{K}(\mathsf{T}) = \mathscr{K}^r(A)$. Now, by Theorem 2.1F we have

$$\text{dim kernel } \mathsf{T} = \text{dim domain } \mathsf{T} - \text{dim range } \mathsf{T};$$

or in terms of A

$$\dim \mathscr{K}^r(A) = \dim \mathscr{V}_v^{\,r} - \dim \mathscr{R}(A).$$

But dim $\mathscr{R}(A) = r$ by definition of rank; hence

$$\dim \mathscr{K}^r(A) = v - r.$$

Consideration of the linear transformation

$$\mathsf{T}': \quad X \to AX$$

shows similarly that dim $\mathscr{K}^c(A) = \dim \mathscr{W}_w^{\,r} - \dim \mathscr{C}(A) = w - r$, since, by Theorem 3.1B, dim $\mathscr{C}(A) = \dim \mathscr{R}(A) = r$.

This theorem states that a linear homogeneous system with w unknowns and matrix of rank r has a set of $w - r$ linearly independent solutions, and thus gives much more precise information than the fundamental theorem on linear equations (Theorem 1.5E) which merely guarantees a nontrivial solution when $v < w$.

LEMMA 3.2B. *If A, B are matrices and $AB = 0$, then $\mathscr{K}^c(A) \supseteq \mathscr{C}(B)$ and $\mathscr{R}(A) \subseteq \mathscr{K}^r(B)$.*

For, if $AB = 0$, then $\Sigma a_{i\lambda} b_{\lambda j} = 0$; i.e., $AB^j = 0$, where B^j is the jth column of B; hence B^j is in $\mathscr{K}^c(A)$. Since every vector of the spanning set $B^1, B^2, \cdots$ of $\mathscr{C}(B)$ is in $\mathscr{K}^c(A)$, it follows that $\mathscr{C}(B) \subseteq \mathscr{K}^c(A)$. The other part of the lemma can be proved similarly or by using transposes.

The problem of solving a system of linear equations with matrix of coefficients A is considered to be completed when a spanning set (or better, a basis) of $\mathscr{K}^c(A)$ has been obtained. If these vectors are made the columns of a matrix B, then $AB = 0$. On the other hand, if $AB = 0$, and dim $\mathscr{C}(B) = \dim \mathscr{K}^c(A)$, it follows from Lemma 3.2B that the columns of B will span $\mathscr{K}^c(A)$; i.e., $\mathscr{C}(B) = \mathscr{K}^c(A)$. By Theorem 3.2A, dim $\mathscr{K}^c(A) = \deg_c A - \operatorname{rank} A$, and hence $\mathscr{C}(B) = \mathscr{K}^c(A)$ if rank $B = \deg_c A - \operatorname{rank} A$.

These considerations lead to the following definition. An ordered pair (A, B) of matrices is said to be an *apolar pair* if

(2.3)
$$AB = 0,$$

$$\operatorname{rank} A + \operatorname{rank} B = \deg_c A \ (= \deg_r B).$$

THEOREM 3.2C.   *The following statements are equivalent:*

(i) (A, B) *is an apolar pair,*

(ii) $\mathscr{K}^c(A) = \mathscr{C}(B)$,

(iii) $\mathscr{R}(A) = \mathscr{K}^r(B)$.

The discussion which led to the definition of apolar pair shows that (i) implies (ii), and a similar argument shows that (i) implies (iii).

Next suppose that $\mathscr{K}^c(A) = \mathscr{C}(B)$. Then $AB = 0$, and, according to Theorem 3.2A, rank $B = \dim \mathscr{C}(B) = \dim \mathscr{K}^c(A) = \deg_c A - \text{rank } A$. Therefore (A, B) is an apolar pair. This shows that (ii) implies (i).

Similarly, if $\mathscr{R}(A) = \mathscr{K}^r(B)$, then $AB = 0$, and (cf. Theorem 3.2A) rank $A = \dim \mathscr{R}(A) = \dim \mathscr{K}^r(B) = \deg_r B - \text{rank } B$, and again (A, B) is an apolar pair. Therefore (iii) implies (i).

Finally, since statements (ii) and (iii) are each equivalent to (i), they are equivalent to each other.

We next take another look at the relationships between the system (2.1) and its coefficient matrix A. If $A_i = \| a_{i1} \cdots a_{iw} \|$ is the ith row of A, then the ith equation $L_i = L_i(x_1, \cdots, x_w) = a_{i1}x_1 + \cdots + a_{iw}x_w = 0$ can be written in matrix form as $A_i X = 0$. The usual operations of forming a linear combination of equations leads to a new equation whose coefficients form a matrix in the row space of A. Instead of using the equations it is more convenient to deal with their (row) matrices of coefficients. This transition from equation to matrix is justified formally by the fact that the mapping $\sum_{\lambda=1}^{w} b_\lambda x_\lambda \to \| b_1 \cdots b_w \|$ is an isomorphism of $\mathscr{L}_w(\mathscr{F})$ into $\mathscr{V}_w{}^r$. Under this isomorphism the left-hand member $L_i = \sum_{\lambda=1}^{w} a_{i\lambda}x_\lambda$ of the ith equation is mapped into the ith row A_i of A, and the subspace of $\mathscr{L}_w(\mathscr{F})$ spanned by $\{L_1, \cdots, L_v\}$ is mapped into the row space $\mathscr{R}(A)$ of A.

We now have direct interpretations in the theory of linear equations for both the row space and the column kernel of a matrix. The problem of solving a system $\mathscr{L}(A)$ has been reduced to the problem of finding a matrix B apolar to A. The existence of such a matrix B follows from Theorem 3.2C, since we need only take B a matrix whose columns span the column kernel of A. On the other hand, if B is apolar to A, then $\mathscr{R}(A) = \mathscr{K}^r(B)$. Therefore the only equations satisfied by the columns of B are those whose left-hand members lie in $\langle L_1, \cdots, L_v \rangle$.

We are now in a position to prove a statement made in Section 1.10 about double description. Let $\mathscr{W}$ be any subspace of $\mathscr{V}_w{}^r$. Then $\mathscr{W}$ has a finite spanning set, say $\{A_1, \cdots, A_v\}$, and so $\mathscr{W}$ is the row space of the v-by-w matrix A whose rows are $A_1, \cdots, A_v$. Now let B be a matrix whose columns span the column kernel of A. Then $\mathscr{W}$ is the row kernel of B. This proves that there exists a double description for $\mathscr{W}$. The following theorems summarize these results.

THEOREM 3.2D. *Let $\mathscr{W}$ be any subspace of $\mathscr{V}_w{}^c$. Then there exist matrices A and B such that $\mathscr{W}$ is the row space of A and is also the row kernel of B. Moreover, (A, B) is then an apolar pair.*

THEOREM 3.2E. *Given any matrix A, there exists a matrix B such that (A, B) is an apolar pair.*

The actual construction of the second member B of an apolar pair (A, B) is, of course, exactly the same as the problem of finding a set of vectors which span the space of all solutions of the system $\mathscr{L}(A)$.

Exercises 3.2

1. Show that a matrix A has a right inverse only if $\mathscr{K}^r(A) = 0$.
2. Show that a matrix A has a right inverse only if its rank equals its row degree.
3. State several necessary conditions for a matrix A to have a left inverse.
4. Prove that, if A_0 is in $\mathscr{R}(A)$, then $A_0{}^\mathsf{T}$ is in $\mathscr{C}(A^\mathsf{T})$.
5. Prove the second part of Lemma 3.2B using transposes.
6. Prove that, if (A, B) is an apolar pair, then so is $(B^\mathsf{T}, A^\mathsf{T})$.
7. Show that the dimension of the space of solutions of a system of linear homogeneous equations equals the number of unknowns minus the rank of the coefficient matrix.
8. A v-by-w matrix A has rank r. Give a geometric interpretation for each of $w, r, v - r, w - r$.
9. Find a matrix apolar to I_3.

10. Let $A = \left\| \begin{array}{ccc} 2 & -3 & 1 \\ 4 & -1 & -3 \end{array} \right\|$, $B = \left\| \begin{array}{c} 1 \\ 1 \\ 1 \end{array} \right\|$. Show that (A, B) is an apolar pair.

11. Let $A = \left\| \begin{array}{cc} 2 & -3 \\ 4 & -6 \end{array} \right\|$. Find matrices B and C such that (C, A) and (A, B) are both apolar pairs.

12. Let $A = \left\| \begin{array}{ccc} 2 & 1 & 5 \\ 1 & -2 & 0 \\ 0 & 1 & 1 \\ -1 & 2 & 0 \end{array} \right\|$. Find a matrix B for which (A, B) is an apolar pair.

3.3. Elementary transformations. Most methods of solution for linear systems are based on the idea of "equivalence." If A and A' are matrices with the same number of columns, we say that the systems $\mathscr{L}(A)$ and $\mathscr{L}(A')$ are *equivalent* if every solution of each system is a solution of the other system. The following theorem states three obvious properties of equivalence.

THEOREM 3.3A. *(a) Any system is equivalent to itself; (b) if $\mathscr{L}(A)$ is equivalent to $\mathscr{L}(A')$, then $\mathscr{L}(A')$ is equivalent to $\mathscr{L}(A)$; (c) if $\mathscr{L}(A)$ is equivalent to $\mathscr{L}(A')$ and if $\mathscr{L}(A')$ is equivalent to $\mathscr{L}(A'')$, then $\mathscr{L}(A)$ is equivalent to $\mathscr{L}(A'')$.*

THEOREM 3.3B. *Let A and A' be two matrices. Then the following statements are all logically equivalent:*

(i) $\mathscr{L}(A)$ *is equivalent to* $\mathscr{L}(A')$,

(ii) $\mathscr{R}(A) = \mathscr{R}(A')$,

(iii) $\mathscr{K}^c(A) = \mathscr{K}^c(A')$.

Since $\mathscr{K}^c(A)$ is the space of solutions of the system $\mathscr{L}(A)$, the equivalence of (i) and (iii) is immediate. Next, suppose that $\mathscr{K}^c(A) = \mathscr{K}^c(A')$, and let B be a matrix apolar to A (the existence of B is stated in Theorem 3.2E). Then, by Theorem 3.2C B is also apolar to A' and $\mathscr{R}(A') = \mathscr{K}^r(B) = \mathscr{R}(A)$; thus (iii) implies (ii). Finally, if $\mathscr{R}(A) = \mathscr{R}(A') = \mathscr{K}^r(B)$, then $\mathscr{K}^c(A) = \mathscr{K}^c(A') = \mathscr{C}(B)$.

For purposes of illustration we consider the system

$$(3.1)\quad \begin{aligned} 2x_2 - 4x_3 \qquad + 3x_6 - 7x_7 + 7x_8 &= 0, \\ x_2 - 2x_3 + x_4 + x_6 \qquad + 2x_8 &= 0, \\ -x_2 + 2x_3 + 2x_4 + x_6 \qquad - 3x_8 &= 0, \\ x_4 - x_6 + 5x_7 - 2x_8 &= 0. \end{aligned}$$

After interchanging the first two equations we obtain a new system consisting of the same equations in a different order. The new system obviously has the same solutions as the former system.

If instead of interchanging the first two equations we had kept the first, second, and fourth equations and had added the second equation to the third, we would have

$$\begin{aligned} 2x_2 - 4x_3 \qquad + 3x_6 - 7x_7 + 7x_8 &= 0, \\ x_2 - 2x_3 + x_4 + x_6 \qquad + 2x_8 &= 0, \\ 3x_4 + 2x_6 \qquad - x_8 &= 0, \\ x_4 - x_6 + 5x_7 - 2x_8 &= 0. \end{aligned}$$

This system is also equivalent to (3.1). Next we add to the first equation
−2 times the second equation and keep the last three equations as before;
we follow this by interchanging the first two equations and obtain an
equivalent system

$$
\begin{aligned}
x_2 - 2x_3 + x_4 + x_6 \qquad\quad + 2x_8 &= 0, \\
- 2x_4 + x_6 - 7x_7 + 3x_8 &= 0, \\
3x_4 + 2x_6 \qquad\quad - x_8 &= 0, \\
x_4 - x_6 + 5x_7 - 2x_8 &= 0.
\end{aligned}
$$

Ultimately we can arrive at the equivalent system

$$
(3.2) \qquad
\begin{aligned}
x_2 - 2x_3 \qquad\qquad + x_7 + 2x_8 &= 0, \\
x_4 \qquad\quad + 2x_7 - x_8 &= 0, \\
x_6 - 3x_7 + x_8 &= 0, \\
0 &= 0,
\end{aligned}
$$

which has matrix

$$
(3.3) \qquad C =
\begin{Vmatrix}
0 & 1 & -2 & 0 & 0 & 0 & 1 & 2 \\
0 & 0 & 0 & 1 & 0 & 0 & 2 & -1 \\
0 & 0 & 0 & 0 & 0 & 1 & -3 & 1 \\
0 & 0 & 0 & 0 & 0 & 0 & 0 & 0
\end{Vmatrix}.
$$

The system $\mathscr{L}(H)$ where H is the matrix

$$
(3.4) \qquad H =
\begin{Vmatrix}
0 & 0 & 0 & 0 & 0 & 0 & 0 & 0 \\
0 & 1 & -2 & 0 & 0 & 0 & 1 & 2 \\
0 & 0 & 0 & 0 & 0 & 0 & 0 & 0 \\
0 & 0 & 0 & 1 & 0 & 0 & 2 & -1 \\
0 & 0 & 0 & 0 & 0 & 0 & 0 & 0 \\
0 & 0 & 0 & 0 & 0 & 1 & -3 & 1 \\
0 & 0 & 0 & 0 & 0 & 0 & 0 & 0 \\
0 & 0 & 0 & 0 & 0 & 0 & 0 & 0
\end{Vmatrix}
$$

is equivalent to (3.1), since $\mathscr{L}(H)$ can be obtained from (3.2) by adding four new equations with zero coefficients.　The importance of the matrix H will be seen in Section 3.5 where Hermite matrices are defined.

This step-by-step passage from

$$(3.5) \qquad A = \begin{Vmatrix} 0 & 2 & -4 & 0 & 0 & 3 & -7 & 7 \\ 0 & 1 & -2 & 1 & 0 & 1 & 0 & 2 \\ 0 & -1 & 2 & 2 & 0 & 1 & 0 & -3 \\ 0 & 0 & 0 & 1 & 0 & -1 & 5 & -2 \end{Vmatrix}$$

to C to H is typical of the general case.

Given a system $\mathscr{L}(A)$, one can obtain an equivalent system $\mathscr{L}(B)$ by any of the following simple operations (called *elementary operations*):

R_{ih}:　　　　　　Interchange the ith and hth equations.

$R_i(c)$:　　　　　　Multiply the ith equation by a nonzero scalar c.

$R_i(c, h)$, $i \neq h$:　Add c times the hth equation to the ith equation.

R_+:　　　　　　　Append an equation all of whose coefficients are zero.

R_-:　　　　　　　Delete the last equation if all of its coefficients are zero.

In fact, these are the operations usually employed in solving a system $\mathscr{L}(A)$ by elimination.　The first three types do not change the number of equations; they are called *proper* elementary transformations, and the remaining two are said to be *improper*.

THEOREM 3.3C.　*If $\mathscr{L}(B)$ is obtained from $\mathscr{L}(A)$ by any sequence of elementary operations, then $\mathscr{L}(B)$ is equivalent to $\mathscr{L}(A)$.*

It is easy to see that, if the system $\mathscr{L}(B)$ is obtained from $\mathscr{L}(A)$ by applying any of these operations, then $\mathscr{L}(B)$ must include among its solutions all the solutions of $\mathscr{L}(A)$. We show this first for the case $R_i(1, h)$ and next for R_+; the proof of the others is left as an exercise.　If $\mathscr{L}(B) = \mathscr{L}(A)R_i(1, h)$ then all those equations of $\mathscr{L}(B)$ except the ith are equations of $\mathscr{L}(A)$ and hence will be satisfied by solutions of $\mathscr{L}(A)$. The ith equation is

$$\sum_{\lambda=1}^{w} b_{i\lambda}x_\lambda = \sum_{\lambda=1}^{w} (a_{i\lambda} + a_{h\lambda})x_\lambda$$
$$= \sum_{\lambda=1}^{w} a_{i\lambda}x_\lambda + \sum_{\lambda=1}^{w} a_{h\lambda}x_\lambda,$$

and its right-hand member is 0 for solutions of $\mathscr{L}(A)$.

Also in case $\mathscr{L}(B) = \mathscr{L}(A)\,\mathsf{R}_+$, then all equations of $\mathscr{L}(B)$ except the last are satisfied by all solutions of $\mathscr{L}(A)$. But the last equation with coefficients all zero holds when any set of values is substituted for the unknowns.

To prove that the system $\mathscr{L}(B)$ is equivalent to $\mathscr{L}(A)$, it remains to show conversely that the solutions of $\mathscr{L}(A)$ include all the solutions of, $\mathscr{L}(B)$. For this purpose it is sufficient to show that each elementary operation R has an inverse R^{-1} which is itself an elementary operation. These inverses are

$$(3.6) \quad \begin{aligned} &\mathsf{R}_{ih}{}^{-1} = \mathsf{R}_{hi}, \quad \mathsf{R}_i(c)^{-1} = \mathsf{R}_i(1/c), \quad \mathsf{R}_i(c,\,h)^{-1} = \mathsf{R}_i(-c,\,h), \\ &\qquad\qquad \mathsf{R}_+{}^{-1} = \mathsf{R}_-, \quad \mathsf{R}_-{}^{-1} = \mathsf{R}_+. \end{aligned}$$

[The statement $\mathsf{R}_-{}^{-1} = \mathsf{R}_+$ must be interpreted in light of the fact that the domain of R_- is the range of R_+ and is the set of all systems $\mathscr{L}(A)$ in which the last row of A is zero. Hence, it is not true that the product $\mathsf{R}_-\mathsf{R}_+$ is the identity operator on all systems $\mathscr{L}(A)$.]

This shows that $\mathscr{L}(B)$ is equivalent to $\mathscr{L}(A)$ if it can be obtained from $\mathscr{L}(A)$ by a sequence of length one. The case of sequences of arbitrary length now follows from Theorem 3.3A.

For some purposes it is convenient to replace the elementary operations on systems of equations by operations on matrices. If in the definitions of the elementary operations we replace the word "equation" by "row" and the word "coefficient" by "element," we obtain operations on matrices to which we give the name *elementary row transformations*, and for which we retain the same symbols R_{ih}, $\mathsf{R}_i(c)$, $\mathsf{R}_i(c,\,h)$, R_+, R_-. For example, $A\,\mathsf{R}_{ih}$ is the matrix obtained from A by interchanging the ith and hth rows of A. Thus, if R is any one of these, then the equations $\mathscr{L}(A)\mathsf{R} = \mathscr{L}(B)$ and $A\mathsf{R} = B$ are equivalent. As before we call the first three types *proper* and the remaining two *improper*.

Exercises 3.3

1. Let $A = \begin{Vmatrix} 1 & 2 & 3 & 4 \\ -1 & 1 & 0 & 2 \\ 3 & 1 & 1 & 1 \end{Vmatrix}$. Find $A\,\mathsf{R}_{13}$, $A\,\mathsf{R}_2(3)$, $A\,\mathsf{R}_3(-3,\,1)$, $A\,\mathsf{R}_{13}\mathsf{R}_1(-2,\,3)$.

2. Prove (a) $\mathsf{R}_{13}\mathsf{R}_{32} = \mathsf{R}_{12}\mathsf{R}_{13}$; (b) $\mathsf{R}_{13}\mathsf{R}_1(c) = \mathsf{R}_3(c)\mathsf{R}_{13}$. Generalize these results.

3. (a) Prove that one type of the proper elementary transformations can be effected by a sequence of proper elementary transformations of the other two types. (b) Show that this is not true for one of the other proper elementary transformations.

3.4. Row-echelon matrices. The matrix C of the system (3.2) can be obtained from the matrix of the system (3.1) by a sequence of proper elementary row transformations; viz., those corresponding to the operations given at the beginning of the preceding section. In this section we shall give a general result (Theorem 3.4B) along these same lines.

Let $B = \| \, b_1 \cdots b_w \, \|$ be a nonzero vector in $\mathscr{V}_w{}^r$. We say that B has *spread* h if $b_1 = \cdots = b_{h-1} = 0$ and $b_h \neq 0$. Thus $\| \, 0 \quad 0 \quad 4 \quad 2 \, \|$ has spread 3. The nonzero rows of the matrix C of (3.3) have spreads 2, 4, 6. We do not define spread for the zero vector.

A vector $B = \| \, b_1 \cdots b_w \, \|$ with spread h is said to be *monic* if $b_h = 1$. For example, each of the nonzero rows of C is monic.

The matrix C is also an example of a row echelon matrix. A matrix $D = \| \, d_{ij} \, \|$ is said to be a *row-echelon matrix* if

(i) The nonzero rows (if any) occur first.

(ii) If e_i is the spread of the ith row then $e_1 < e_2 < \cdots < e_r$, where r is the number of nonzero rows.

(iii) Each nonzero row is monic; i.e., $d_{ie_i} = 1$ ($i = 1, \cdots, r$).

(iv) $d_{ie_j} = 0$ ($i \neq j$).

The spreads $e_1, \cdots, e_r$ are called the *indices* of D.

LEMMA 3.4A. *Let $D = \| \, d_{ij} \, \|$ be an echelon matrix with r nonzero rows. Then $r = \operatorname{rank} D$.*

Since D has only r nonzero rows, we have $\operatorname{rank} D \leqq r$. On the other hand, the columns with indices $e_1, \cdots, e_r$ are

$$
\begin{Vmatrix} 1 \\ 0 \\ \\ \\ \cdot \\ \cdot \\ \cdot \\ 0 \end{Vmatrix}, \quad
\begin{Vmatrix} 0 \\ 1 \\ 0 \\ \\ \cdot \\ \cdot \\ \\ 0 \end{Vmatrix}, \quad \cdots, \quad
\begin{Vmatrix} 0 \\ \cdot \\ \cdot \\ \cdot \\ 0 \\ 1 \\ 0 \\ \cdot \end{Vmatrix},
$$

and these are clearly independent; hence $\operatorname{rank} D \geqq r$. We conclude from the two inequalities that $\operatorname{rank} D = r$.

THEOREM 3.4B. *Let A be a v-by-w matrix. Then there exists a sequence of proper elementary row transformations leading from A to a row-echelon matrix D.*

The proof is by induction on the row degree of A. First let A have a single row. If $A = 0$, then A is a row-echelon matrix. Otherwise let e be the index of the first column having a nonzero element a_{1e}; i.e., the spread of A. Application of $R_1(1/a_{1e})$ replaces this element by 1 and yields a matrix in row-echelon form and with a single index $e_1 = e$.

Suppose now that A has v rows. We assume that the result is true for matrices having less than v rows. Let e be the index of the first nonzero column of A; i.e., the smallest spread of the rows of A. Then there is a nonzero element a_{ie} in A. First apply $R_i(1/a_{ie})$ to make this element 1, and then use R_{i1} to send its row into the first. Call the resulting matrix B; for it $b_{1e} = 1$. The sequence of transformations $R_h(-b_{he}, 1)$ for $h = 2, 3, \cdots, v$ gives a new matrix C having the same first row as B, having $c_{he} = 0$ $(h = 2, \cdots, v)$, and having its jth column zero for all $j < e$.

Let C' be the matrix made up of the last $v - 1$ rows of C. Then, by our induction hypothesis, C' can be sent into a row-echelon matrix D' by a sequence of proper elementary row transformations. A similar sequence of proper elementary row transformations will send C into the matrix

$$C'' = \left\| \begin{array}{c} C_1 \\ \\ D' \end{array} \right\|,$$

where C_1 is the first row of C. Suppose that $e_2, \cdots, e_r$ are the indices of D'. Then, if $c_{1e_2} = \cdots = c_{1e_r} = 0$, C'' is a row-echelon matrix; and, in any case, application of $R_1(-c_{1e_2}, 2), \cdots, R_1(-c_{1e_r}, r)$ to C'' leads to a row-echelon matrix

$$D = \left\| \begin{array}{c} D_1 \\ \\ D' \end{array} \right\|$$

having indices $e_1 = e, e_2, \cdots, e_r$.

Although this proof was by induction, there is implicit in it a constructive method for passing from A to D. The reduction from A to C' (i.e., from row degree v to row degree $v - 1$) can be iterated to obtain a matrix G satisfying the first three conditions in the definition of a row-echelon matrix. To obtain D from G we follow the process employed in passing from C'' to D; first we use the sequence of operations $R_h(-c_{he_r}, r)$ $(h = 1, \cdots, r - 1)$ to get the necessary zeros in the e_rth column. This done, we subtract suitable multiples of the $(r - 1)$th row from higher rows to get the proper zeros in the e_{r-1}th column. Note that these operations do not disturb the zeros already obtained in the e_rth column. We continue in this fashion a column at a time until we reach a row-echelon matrix.

This method of passing from A to D is the basic process underlying systematic solution of systems of linear equations. In the present book we do not discuss the variants of this process which make it into a practical computational operation.

In Section 3.5 we shall show that the matrix D of Theorem 3.4B is uniquely determined by A.

Exercises 3.4

Find a row-echelon matrix obtained from each of the following matrices by a sequence of proper elementary row transformations. List the (echelon) indices in each case.

1. $\begin{Vmatrix} 1 & -1 & 2 \\ 2 & 1 & 1 \end{Vmatrix}.$

2. $\begin{Vmatrix} 1 & 2 & 3 & 0 & 0 \\ 0 & 1 & 2 & 3 & 0 \\ 0 & 0 & 1 & 2 & 3 \end{Vmatrix}.$

3. $\begin{Vmatrix} 0 & 2 & -4 & 0 & 0 & 3 & -7 & 7 \\ 0 & 1 & -2 & 1 & 0 & 1 & 0 & 2 \\ 0 & -1 & 2 & 2 & 0 & 1 & 0 & -3 \\ 0 & 0 & 0 & 1 & 0 & -1 & 5 & 2 \end{Vmatrix}.$

4. $\begin{Vmatrix} 0 & 0 & 0 & 0 & -3 \\ 0 & 2 & 2 & 10 & 4 \\ 0 & 1 & -1 & 1 & -1 \\ 0 & 4 & -3 & 6 & 87 \end{Vmatrix}.$

5. $\begin{Vmatrix} 2 & -4 & 1 & 3 & -5 & -8 \\ 3 & -6 & -1 & 2 & -5 & -7 \\ 1 & -2 & 1 & 1 & 0 & -3 \\ 2 & -4 & -1 & 4 & -12 & -10 \end{Vmatrix}.$

6. $\begin{Vmatrix} 2 & -1 & 0 \\ 3 & 2 & -2 \\ -7 & -7 & 6 \\ 6 & -4 & 5 \end{Vmatrix}.$

7. $\begin{Vmatrix} 3.21 & 2.14 & 7.96 & -3.13 \\ 4.36 & -1.03 & 0.07 & 2.44 \\ 1.72 & 3.46 & -2.88 & 1.03 \end{Vmatrix}.$

3.5. Triangular and Hermite matrices.   We discuss in this section some special types of bases and spanning sets for subspaces of $\mathcal{V}_w{}^r$. These results are important even aside from their immediate application to the solution of equations.

An ordered set $\mathcal{S} = \{A_1, \cdots, A_w\}$ of w vectors in $\mathcal{V}_w{}^r$ is said to be *triangular* if for each h either $A_h = 0$ or A_h has spread h. The set $\{\| \; 0 \quad 0 \quad 0 \; \|, \; \| \; 0 \quad -3 \quad 6 \; \|, \; \| \; 0 \quad 0 \quad 2 \; \|\}$ is triangular. A square matrix is said to be *upper-triangular* if all of its entries below the diagonal are zero (a *lower-triangular* matrix is one with only zeros above the diagonal).   For example,

$$\left\| \begin{array}{ccc} 0 & 0 & 0 \\ 0 & -3 & 6 \\ 0 & 0 & 2 \end{array} \right\|$$

is an upper-triangular matrix.   In general, to each triangular set $\mathcal{S}$ there corresponds an upper-triangular matrix A whose hth row is

$$A_h \qquad\qquad (h = 1, \cdots, w).$$

The matrix H of (3.4) is upper-triangular.   Obviously $\mathcal{R}(H) = \mathcal{R}(C)$ where C is given by (3.3) since they have the same nonzero rows.   Furthermore, since the system $\mathcal{L}(C)$ is equivalent to $\mathcal{L}(A)$ [of (3.1)], $\mathcal{R}(A) = \mathcal{R}(C)$ (by Theorem 3.3B).   Hence $\mathcal{R}(A)$ has a triangular spanning set; viz., the rows of H.

LEMMA 3.5A.   *Every subspace of $\mathcal{V}_w{}^r$ has a triangular spanning set.*
Let $\mathcal{W}$ be a subspace of $\mathcal{V}_w{}^r$, and let $\mathcal{S}$ be a finite spanning set for $\mathcal{W}$. Let A be the matrix whose rows comprise the vectors of $\mathcal{S}$.   Then there exists a row-echelon matrix D such that $\mathcal{R}(D) = \mathcal{R}(A)$.   Let the indices of D be $e_1, \cdots, e_r$.   If there are r nonzero rows in D, we adjoin or delete zero rows, using R_+ or R_- until there are $w - r$ zero rows.   Finally with the use of interchanges R_{ih} we obtain an upper-triangular matrix T by successive interchanges of rows; i.e., by applying $\mathsf{R}_{re_r}, \mathsf{R}_{r-1,e_{r-1}}, \cdots, \mathsf{R}_{1e_1}$ in the order listed.

A triangular set is said to be *monic* if each nonzero vector in it is monic. It follows readily from Theorem 3.4B that *every subspace of $\mathcal{V}_w{}^r$ has a monic triangular spanning set*.

A monic triangular set $\mathcal{T} = \{H_1, \cdots, H_w\}$ is said to be a *Hermite set* provided that, when $H_i \neq 0$, then the ith component of each vector H_h ($h \neq i$) is zero.   For example, $\| \; 0 \quad 0 \quad 0 \quad 0 \; \|$, $\| \; 0 \quad 1 \quad 0 \quad 7 \; \|$,

$\| \; 0 \quad 0 \quad 1 \quad 6 \; \|$, $\| \; 0 \quad 0 \quad 0 \quad 0 \; \|$ is a Hermite set. The rows of the matrix H of (3.4) constitute a Hermite set.

COROLLARY 3.5B. *Every subspace of $\mathscr{V}_w^{\,r}$ has a Hermite spanning set.*
The triangular spanning set obtained in the proof of Lemma 3.5A is actually a Hermite spanning set.

We shall subsequently prove the uniqueness of a Hermite spanning set (Theorem 3.5E).

Let $\mathscr{E} = \{e_1, \cdots, e_r\}$, $e_1 < \cdots < e_r$ be the ordered set of all spreads of vectors in $\mathscr{W}$. We call $\mathscr{E}$ the set of *indices* of $\mathscr{W}$. The following result implies that, if D is a row-echelon matrix, the indices of $\mathscr{R}(D)$ are the same as the indices of D.

THEOREM 3.5C. *Let $\mathscr{W}$ be a subspace of $\mathscr{V}_w^{\,r}$, let $\mathscr{E} = \{e_1, \cdots, e_r\}$ be the indices of $\mathscr{W}$, and let $\mathscr{S} = \{A_1, \cdots, A_w\}$ be a triangular spanning set for $\mathscr{W}$. Then* (i) *the nonzero vectors of $\mathscr{S}$ are independent;* (ii) $A_h \neq 0$ *if and only if h is an index of $\mathscr{W}$; and* (iii) $\dim \mathscr{W} = r$.

Let $B = \| \, b_1, \cdots, b_w \, \|$ be any nontrivial combination of vectors of $\mathscr{S}$. Then we can find nonzero scalars $c_1, \cdots, c_s$ such that

$$B = c_1 A_{h_1} + \cdots + c_s A_{h_s},$$

where $A_{h_1}, \cdots, A_{h_s}$ are nonzero vectors in $\mathscr{S}$ and $h_1 < \cdots < h_s$. Now $b_1 = \cdots = b_{h_1 - 1} = 0$ since each A_{h_i} has spread at least h_1. Also b_{h_1} equals c_1 times the (nonzero) h_1th component of A_{h_1} since the h_1th components of $A_{h_2}, \cdots, A_{h_s}$ are all zero. Hence B is a nonzero vector of spread $h = h_1$. This shows that the nonzero vectors of $\mathscr{S}$ are independent [i.e., statement (i)] and also shows that, if h is an index of $\mathscr{W}$, then $A_h \neq 0$. If h is not an index of $\mathscr{W}$, then $A_h = 0$, since no vector in $\mathscr{W}$ has spread h. This proves (ii), and shows that $\mathscr{S}$ has exactly r nonzero elements; by (i) these are independent. It follows that the nonzero elements of $\mathscr{S}$ are a basis for $\mathscr{W}$ and hence that $\dim \mathscr{W} = r$.

LEMMA 3.5D. *If $H_{e_1}, \cdots, H_{e_r}$ are the nonzero vectors of a Hermite set, then*

$$c_1 H_{e_1} + \cdots + c_r H_{e_r} = \| \, \cdots \, c_1 \, \cdots \, c_r \, \cdots \, \|,$$

where c_i is the e_ith component $(i = 1, \cdots, r)$.
The proof is left to the reader.

THEOREM 3.5E. *Every subspace has a unique Hermite spanning set.*

We have already established the existence of a Hermite spanning set $\mathscr{T}$; we now establish the uniqueness of $\mathscr{T}$. Let $\mathscr{T} = \{H_1, \cdots, H_w\}$ and $\mathscr{S} = \{K_1, \cdots, K_w\}$ be two Hermite spanning sets for $\mathscr{W}$. According to Theorem 3.5C, the nonzero vectors of $\mathscr{T}$ and of $\mathscr{S}$ are precisely those whose subscripts are indices. Now consider the expression

$$K_{e_h} = c_1 H_{e_1} + \cdots + c_r H_{e_r}$$

of K_{e_h} in terms of the nonzero vectors of $\mathscr{T}$. According to Lemma 3.5D, the e_ith component of the right-hand side is c_i ($i = 1, \cdots, r$), but, since $\mathscr{S}$ is a Hermite set, the e_ith component of the left-hand side is zero for each $c \neq h$ and is 1 for $i = h$. Hence $c_h = 1$ and $c_i = 0$ ($i \neq h$). Therefore $K_{e_h} = H_{e_h}$ ($h = 1, \cdots, r$), and so $\mathscr{S} = \mathscr{T}$ as claimed.

An upper-triangular matrix H is said to be a *Hermite matrix* if every nonzero row has a 1 on the diagonal and if whenever a 1 appears on the diagonal it is the only nonzero element in its column. The indices of the nonzero rows of H are called the *indices* of H. Clearly, *H is a Hermite matrix if and only if its rows form a Hermite set.*

THEOREM 3.5F. *Let $\mathscr{W}$ be a subspace of $\mathscr{V}_w{}^r$. Then there exists a unique Hermite matrix H whose row space is $\mathscr{W}$. Moreover, the indices of H are the indices of $\mathscr{W}$.*

This theorem is a direct translation of Theorem 3.5E into matrix language.

THEOREM 3.5G. *Let A be any matrix. Then there exists a unique Hermite matrix H with the same row space as A, and there exists a unique row-echelon matrix D with the same row space as A and the same row degree as A. The matrix D can be obtained from A by a sequence of proper elementary row operations, and the matrix H can be obtained from A by a sequence of elementary row operations.*

We say that H and D, respectively, are the Hermite and row-echelon matrices *related* to A.

The existence and uniqueness of H follow from Theorem 3.5F if we take $\mathscr{W} = \mathscr{R}(A)$. The existence of D and the fact that D can be obtained from A by proper elementary row operations were established in Theorem 3.4B. The uniqueness of D follows from that of H since the nonzero rows of D are just those of H and the number of zero rows in D is $\deg_r A$ — rank A. Finally, it is easy to see that we can go from D to H by a sequence of transformations of types R_+, R_-, and R_{ih} (cf. the proof of Lemma 3.5A).

Exercises 3.5

1. Find a triangular spanning set for the row space $\mathscr{W}$ of the matrix

$$A = \begin{Vmatrix} 1 & 2 & 4 & 0 & 1 \\ 1 & 1 & 1 & -1 & 0 \\ 0 & 1 & 3 & 2 & 1 \\ 1 & 1 & 1 & 1 & 1 \end{Vmatrix}.$$

What are the indices of $\mathscr{W}$?

2. Give an example of an upper-triangular matrix whose rows are not a triangular set.

3. Find a Hermite spanning set for the row space of each of the following triangular matrices.

$$B = \begin{Vmatrix} 1 & 2 & 3 & 4 & 5 & 6 \\ 0 & 0 & 0 & 0 & 0 & 0 \\ 0 & 0 & 1 & 2 & 3 & 4 \\ 0 & 0 & 0 & 0 & 0 & 0 \\ 0 & 0 & 0 & 0 & 1 & 2 \\ 0 & 0 & 0 & 0 & 0 & 0 \end{Vmatrix}, \quad C = \begin{Vmatrix} 2 & 1 & 3 & 1 & 4 & 6 \\ 0 & 0 & 0 & 0 & 0 & 0 \\ 0 & 0 & 1 & 2 & 1 & -1 \\ 0 & 0 & 0 & 0 & 0 & 0 \\ 0 & 0 & 0 & 0 & 3 & 6 \\ 0 & 0 & 0 & 0 & 0 & 2 \end{Vmatrix}.$$

4. Let

$$B_1 = \begin{Vmatrix} 2 & 1 & 1 & -1 \\ 0 & 1 & 1 & 1 \end{Vmatrix}, \quad B_2 = \begin{Vmatrix} 3 & 1 & 0 & 1 \\ 2 & 1 & -1 & 1 \\ 5 & 2 & -1 & 0 \end{Vmatrix}, \quad B_3 = \begin{Vmatrix} 0 & 1 & 1 & 1 \\ 0 & 0 & 1 & 2 \\ 0 & 3 & 6 & 9 \end{Vmatrix},$$

and find Hermite matrices H_1, H_2, H_3 such that $\mathscr{R}(B_i) = \mathscr{R}(H_i)$ $(i = 1, 2, 3)$.

5. Compute directly the square of each of the Hermite matrices obtained in Exercise 4.

6. Find the Hermite matrix whose row space is $\mathscr{V}_w{}^r$.

7. Show that the product of two upper-triangular matrices is upper-triangular.

8. Let $\mathscr{U}$ and $\mathscr{W}$ be subspaces of $\mathscr{V}_w{}^r$, and suppose that $\mathscr{U} \subseteq \mathscr{W}$. Show then that every index of $\mathscr{U}$ is also an index of $\mathscr{W}$.

9. Let $\mathscr{U}$ and $\mathscr{W}$ be subspaces of $\mathscr{V}_w{}^r$, and let $\mathscr{L} = \mathscr{U} + \mathscr{W}$. Show that $\mathscr{L}$ may have indices which are not indices of $\mathscr{U}$ or of $\mathscr{W}$. (Hint: consider the case $w = 2$.)

10. Find the Hermite matrices related to the matrices given in Exercises 3.4.
11. Let D be a 3-by-4 echelon matrix of rank 3. What are the possible forms for D?

3.6. Properties of Hermite matrices.

A nonzero matrix that is equal to its square is said to be *idempotent*. The following lemma shows that *every nonzero Hermite matrix is idempotent*.

LEMMA 3.6A. *If H is a Hermite matrix, then $H^2 = H$.*

Suppose $H = \| h_{ij} \|$ and $H^2 = \| k_{ij} \|$; then $k_{ij} = \sum_{\lambda=1}^{w} h_{i\lambda} h_{\lambda j}$. If i is not an index of H, then $h_{i\lambda} = 0$ $(\lambda = 1, \cdots, w)$, and hence $k_{ij} = 0 = h_{ij}$. Next suppose that i is an index of H. Then, if λ is not an index of H, $h_{\lambda j} = 0$; and if λ is an index of H, then either $\lambda = i$ and $h_{i\lambda} = h_{ii} = 1$ or $\lambda \neq i$ and $h_{i\lambda} = 0$. Therefore the only possible nonvanishing product $h_{i\lambda} h_{\lambda j}$ in the sum for k_{ij} is $h_{ii} h_{ij} = h_{ij}$. Thus $k_{ij} = h_{ij}$ when i is an index of H; hence $H = H^2$.

THEOREM 3.6B. *If H is a Hermite matrix of degree w, then $(H, I_w - H)$ is an apolar pair.*

We have from the preceding lemma that $H(I_w - H) = H - H^2 = 0$. Hence the matrices H and $I_w - H$ will be an apolar pair if the sum of their ranks is w. Let $e_1, \cdots, e_r$ be the indices of H. Then, by Theorem 3.5C, H has rank r. Now, if e is an index of H the eth column of H is the same as the eth column of I_w. Hence $I_w - H$ has at most $w - r$ nonzero columns and hence rank $(I_w - H) \leq w - r$. But, by Corollary 3.1J, rank $(I_w - H) \geq |\operatorname{rank} I_w - \operatorname{rank} H| = w - r$. These two inequalities show that rank $(I_w - H) = w - r$.

THEOREM 3.6C. *Let A be a v-by-w matrix, and let H be the Hermite matrix whose row space is the same as that of A. Then the nonzero columns of $I_w - H$ are a basis for the set of all solutions of the system of linear homogeneous equations with matrix A.*

Since $\mathscr{R}(H) = \mathscr{R}(A)$, it follows from Theorem 3.3B that the solution space $\mathscr{K}^c(A)$ for the system $\mathscr{L}(A)$ is equal to $\mathscr{K}^c(H)$. But, since H and $I_w - H$ are an apolar pair, $\mathscr{C}(I_w - H) = \mathscr{K}^c(H) = \mathscr{K}^c(A)$ (by Theorem 3.2C) as claimed. In the proof of Theorem 3.6B we saw that rank $I_w - H = w - r =$ number of nonzero columns in $I_w - H$. Hence the nonzero columns of $I_w - H$ are a basis for $\mathscr{C}(I_w - H) = \mathscr{K}^c(A)$.

Exercises 3.6

1. Find bases for the column kernels of the matrices B and C of Exercise 3.5.3.
2. Solve $\mathscr{L}(B_1)$, $\mathscr{L}(B_2)$, $\mathscr{L}(B_3)$, where B_1, B_2, B_3 are given in Exercise 3.5.4.

3. Let H and K be Hermite matrices which commute (i.e., $HK = KH$). Show then that HK and $H + K - HK$ are also Hermite matrices. Show more-over that $\mathscr{R}(H) \cap \mathscr{R}(K) = \mathscr{R}(HK)$ and $\mathscr{R}(H) + \mathscr{R}(K) = \mathscr{R}(H + K - HK)$.

4. Prove rank $(I_w - H) = w - $ rank H for a Hermite matrix H by showing that the nonzero columns are independent.

5. Solve the system $AX = 0$ where A is in turn each of the matrices given in Exercises 3.4.

3.7. Elementary matrices.

The elementary row transformations introduced in Section 3.3 can be described by matrix multiplication.

LEMMA 3.7A. *To every elementary row transformation* R *there corresponds a matrix* F *such that, if* B *is obtained from* A *by application of* R, *then*

$$B = FA; \quad i.e., \quad A\,\mathsf{R} = FA.$$

Thus elementary operations on a system correspond to premultiplication of the matrix of the system by an appropriate matrix.

If the lemma is true, then by taking $A = I$ we find that $B = FI = F$; i.e., *F is the matrix obtained by applying* R *to* I.

We designate by F_{ih}, $F_i(c)$, $F_i(c, h)$, F_+, respectively, the matrices obtained by applying R_{ih}, $\mathsf{R}_i(c)$, $\mathsf{R}_i(c, h)$, R_+. We then have

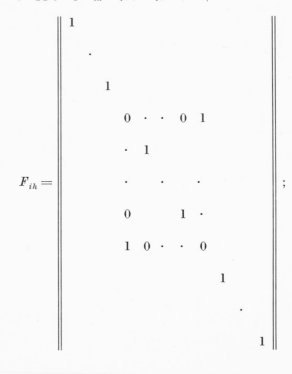

here the 0's on the diagonal occur only in rows i and h, and the only 1's off the diagonal are at positions (i, h) and (h, i).   Next

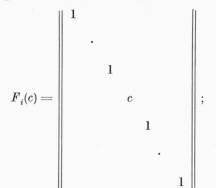

$$F_i(c) =$$

the element c occurs in the ith row, and all elements not on the diagonal are 0.   Next

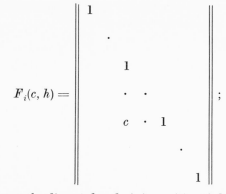

$$F_i(c, h) =$$

where 1's appear on the diagonal and c is in position (i, h), all other elements being 0.

Finally,

$$F_+ =$$

$(v + 1$ rows$)$;

i.e., F_+ is I_v with a row of zeros appended.

We cannot apply R_- to I_v but

$$F_- = \left\| \begin{array}{ccc} 1 & & 0 \\ & \cdot & \cdot \\ & \cdot & \cdot \\ & \cdot & \cdot \\ & 1 & 0 \end{array} \right\| \qquad (v - 1 \text{ rows}),$$

and F_- is obtained by deleting the last row from I_v.

To prove the lemma merely apply R to A, and compare the result with the matrix product FA, in each of the five cases. The details are left as an exercise.

The matrices F_{ih}, $F_i(c)$, $F_i(c, h)$ are called *elementary matrices*. Notice that the matrices of the improper elementary row transformations are not included by this definition. The elementary matrices are square matrices whose degree equals the row degree of the matrix to which the corresponding elementary row operation is being applied. The next lemma follows by direct computation or from (3.6).

LEMMA 3.7B.   *Elementary matrices are nonsingular. The inverse of an elementary matrix is also an elementary matrix;*

$$F_{ih}^{-1} = F_{hi}; \quad F_i(c)^{-1} = F_i(1/c); \quad F_i(c, h)^{-1} = F_i(-c, h).$$

When the degrees permit multiplication, $F_- F_+ = I$. Although $F_+ F_- \neq I$, it is true that, if A has final row zero, then $F_+ F_- A = A$. Hence these two types of matrices are almost inverses of each other. We call F_+ and F_- *improper elementary matrices*.

THEOREM 3.7C.   *Let A be a v-by-w matrix. Then there exist matrices P and Q such that $\dot{H} = PA$, and $A = QH$, where H is the Hermite matrix with the same row space as A. Also there exists a nonsingular matrix R such that $D = RA$ where D is the row-echelon matrix related to A.*

Let $R_1, \cdots, R_k$ be the elementary operations which lead from A to H (cf. Theorem 3.5G), and let F_i be the matrix corresponding to R_i ($i = 1, \cdots, k$). Then it follows from Lemma 3.7A that $H = F_k(\cdots (F_1 A) \cdots)$, and hence that $H = PA$ where $P = F_k \cdots F_1$. Next we let $F'_i = F_i^{-1}$ if F_i is nonsingular, and, if $F_i = F_+$ or F_-, we let $F'_i = F_-$ or F_+, respectively. Then $Q = F'_1 \cdots F'_k$ satisfies the condition of the theorem.

A similar argument shows that $D = RA$ where R is a product of elementary matrices. But, since each elementary matrix is nonsingular (3.7B), any product of elementary matrices is nonsingular. This completes the proof of Theorem 3.7C and also establishes the "if" part of the following theorem.

THEOREM 3.7D. *A matrix A is nonsingular if and only if it is a product of elementary matrices.*

Suppose that A is nonsingular, and let $D = F_k \cdots F_1 A$ be the related row-echelon matrix. Since D is a product of nonsingular matrices, it is itself nonsingular. But a nonsingular row-echelon matrix must be the identity matrix since it is square and has no zero rows. Hence $F_k \cdots F_1 A = I$; finally $A = F_1^{-1} \cdots F_k^{-1}$ is a product of elementary matrices.

The following computing scheme is convenient for determining D and R at the same time. Consider the partitioned matrix $A' = \| \; A \quad I_v \; \|$. If P is any matrix of degree v, we have

$$PA' = \| \; PA \quad PI_v \; \| = \| \; PA \quad P \; \|.$$

If, in particular, $P = F_r \cdots F_1$ is a product of elementary matrices, we can calculate both PA and P by applying the corresponding elementary row operations to A'. If we carry out (proper) elementary row operations on A' until A is replaced by D and I by R then the equation

$$PA' = \| \; PA \quad P \; \| = \| \; D \quad R \; \|$$

shows that $P = R$ and $D = RA$.

We illustrate this computing scheme for the matrix

$$A = \left\|\begin{array}{cccc} 1 & 1 & 2 & 3 \\ 2 & 0 & 1 & 1 \\ -1 & 1 & 2 & 1 \end{array}\right\|.$$

Then

$$A' = \left\|\begin{array}{ccccccc} 1 & 1 & 2 & 3 & 1 & 0 & 0 \\ 2 & 0 & 1 & 1 & 0 & 1 & 0 \\ -1 & 1 & 2 & 1 & 0 & 0 & 1 \end{array}\right\|,$$

and we proceed step by step through the matrices

$$\left\|\begin{array}{ccccccc} 1 & 1 & 2 & 3 & 1 & 0 & 0 \\ 0 & -2 & -3 & -5 & -2 & 1 & 0 \\ -1 & 1 & 2 & 1 & 0 & 0 & 1 \end{array}\right\|, \qquad \left\|\begin{array}{ccccccc} 1 & 1 & 2 & 3 & 1 & 0 & 0 \\ 0 & -2 & -3 & -5 & -2 & 1 & 0 \\ 0 & 2 & 4 & 4 & 1 & 0 & 1 \end{array}\right\|,$$

$$\left\|\begin{array}{ccccccc} 1 & 1 & 2 & 3 & 1 & 0 & 0 \\ 0 & 1 & \frac{3}{2} & \frac{5}{2} & 1 & -\frac{1}{2} & 0 \\ 0 & 2 & 4 & 4 & 1 & 0 & 1 \end{array}\right\|, \qquad \left\|\begin{array}{ccccccc} 1 & 1 & 2 & 3 & 1 & 0 & 0 \\ 0 & 1 & \frac{3}{2} & \frac{5}{2} & 1 & -\frac{1}{2} & 0 \\ 0 & 0 & 1 & -1 & -1 & 1 & 1 \end{array}\right\|,$$

$$\left\|\begin{array}{ccccccc} 1 & 0 & \frac{1}{2} & \frac{1}{2} & 0 & \frac{1}{2} & 0 \\ 0 & 1 & \frac{3}{2} & \frac{5}{2} & 1 & -\frac{1}{2} & 0 \\ 0 & 0 & 1 & -1 & -1 & 1 & 1 \end{array}\right\|, \qquad \left\|\begin{array}{ccccccc} 1 & 0 & \frac{1}{2} & \frac{1}{2} & 0 & \frac{1}{2} & 0 \\ 0 & 1 & 0 & 4 & \frac{5}{2} & -2 & -\frac{3}{2} \\ 0 & 0 & 1 & -1 & -1 & 1 & 1 \end{array}\right\|,$$

$$\left\|\begin{array}{ccccccc} 1 & 0 & 0 & 1 & \frac{1}{2} & 0 & -\frac{1}{2} \\ 0 & 1 & 0 & 4 & \frac{5}{2} & -2 & -\frac{3}{2} \\ 0 & 0 & 1 & -1 & -1 & 1 & 1 \end{array}\right\|.$$

From this we get

$$D = \left\|\begin{array}{cccc} 1 & 0 & 0 & 1 \\ 0 & 1 & 0 & 4 \\ 0 & 0 & 1 & -1 \end{array}\right\| \quad \text{and} \quad R = \frac{1}{2} \left\|\begin{array}{ccc} 1 & 0 & -1 \\ 5 & -4 & -3 \\ -2 & 2 & 2 \end{array}\right\|.$$

The numerical accuracy of the process can be checked by comparing the product RA with D.

The computing scheme suggested above for finding D and R is especially handy for computing inverses.   For, if A is nonsingular we have $D = I_v$, and hence

$$RA' = \parallel RA \quad R \parallel = \parallel I_v \quad R \parallel .$$

But now, from $RA = I_v$, we conclude $R = A^{-1}$.   An illustration of this is given by the preceding example if we let $B = A(\mid 4)$ and delete the fourth column throughout.   Then the R obtained there is B^{-1}.

THEOREM 3.7E.   *Two systems $\mathscr{L}(A)$ and $\mathscr{L}(A')$ are equivalent if and only if there exist matrices P and Q such that $A' = PA$ and $A = QA'$.*

If $A' = PA$ and $AX = 0$, then $A'X = (PA)X = P(AX) = 0$;   hence $\mathscr{K}^c(A) \subseteq \mathscr{K}^c(A')$.   If, in addition, $A = QA'$, then $\mathscr{K}^c(A') \subseteq \mathscr{K}^c(A)$, and hence $\mathscr{K}^c(A') = \mathscr{K}^c(A)$.

The converse is a ready consequence of Theorem 3.7C; the details of its proof are left as an exercise.

THEOREM 3.7F.   *Let A and A' be v-by-w matrices.   Then the systems $\mathscr{L}(A)$ and $\mathscr{L}(A')$ are equivalent if and only if there exists a nonsingular matrix P such that $A' = PA$.*

The proof is left as an exercise.

Two matrices A and A' are said to be *row-equivalent* if they have the same row degree and if their row spaces are equal.   The following theorem is a collection of numerous results proved in this chapter.

THEOREM 3.7G.   *The following statements are logically equivalent:*

(i) A *is row-equivalent to* A'.

(ii)   *There exists a nonsingular matrix P such that* $A' = PA$.

(iii)   *There exists a sequence $F_1, \cdots, F_h$ of elementary matrices such that* $A' = F_h \cdots F_1 A$.

(iv) A *and* A' *are related to the same row-echelon matrix* D.

(v)   *Row degree A = row degree A', and $\mathscr{L}(A)$ is equivalent to $\mathscr{L}(A')$.*

(vi)   *Row degree A = row degree A', and $\mathscr{K}^c(A) = \mathscr{K}^c(A')$.*

(vii)   *Row degree A = row degree A', and A and A' are related to the same Hermite matrix H.*

Exercises 3.7

1. For the matrix

$$A = \left\| \begin{array}{cccc} 2 & -1 & 3 & -1 \\ -2 & 1 & 2 & 2 \\ 4 & -2 & 11 & -1 \end{array} \right\|$$

find (a) a basis for the row space, (b) the rank, (c) the row-echelon form, (d) a basis for the column kernel, (e) a set of equations for the column kernel, (f) a set of equations defining the row space.

2. Do the same for the matrix

$$\left\| \begin{array}{ccccc} 1 & 1 & 1 & 1 & -4 \\ 27 & 9 & 3 & 1 & 10 \\ 125 & 25 & 5 & 1 & 84 \end{array} \right\|.$$

3. Find the inverse of the matrix

$$\left\| \begin{array}{ccc} 2 & 1 & 3 \\ -1 & 0 & 4 \\ 1 & 1 & 2 \end{array} \right\|.$$

4. Find the inverse of the matrix

$$\left\| \begin{array}{cccc} 2 & -1 & 0 & 1 \\ 0 & 1 & 3 & -2 \\ 1 & -2 & 1 & 0 \\ 0 & 4 & 6 & -1 \end{array} \right\|.$$

5. Find the inverse of the matrix

$$\left\| \begin{array}{cccc} 2 & 1 & 0 & 0 \\ 1 & 2 & 1 & 0 \\ 0 & 1 & 2 & 1 \\ 0 & 0 & 1 & 2 \end{array} \right\|.$$

6. Express each of the matrices in the preceding three exercises as a product of elementary matrices.

7. Find a nonsingular matrix P for which PA is in row-echelon form where

$$A = \left\| \begin{array}{cccc} 2 & 1 & 2 & 1 \\ 1 & 2 & 1 & -1 \\ 3 & 4 & 1 & 2 \end{array} \right\|.$$

8. Do Exercise 7 if

$$A = \left\| \begin{array}{ccccc} 2 & 3 & 2 & 1 & 0 \\ 1 & -1 & 3 & 2 & 1 \\ 3 & 2 & 5 & -1 & 2 \\ 1 & 4 & -1 & -3 & 1 \end{array} \right\|.$$

9. Do Exercise 7 if

$$A = \begin{Vmatrix} 1 & 1 & 1 & 1 & 1 \\ 1 & 2 & 4 & 8 & 3 \\ 1 & 3 & 9 & 27 & 5 \\ 1 & 4 & 16 & 64 & 7 \end{Vmatrix}.$$

Use this result to find an inverse for $A(|5)$.

10. Let $\mathcal{U}_1 = \mathcal{R}(A_1)$ and $\mathcal{U}_2 = \mathcal{R}(A_2)$ where

$$A_1 = \begin{Vmatrix} 1 & 2 & 1 & -1 & 1 \\ 2 & 1 & 3 & 4 & 1 \end{Vmatrix} \quad \text{and} \quad A_2 = \begin{Vmatrix} 3 & 1 & 2 & 1 & 1 \\ 1 & 0 & 1 & 1 & 2 \\ 3 & 3 & 4 & 3 & 2 \end{Vmatrix}.$$

Find bases for $\mathcal{U}_3 = \mathcal{U}_1 \cap \mathcal{U}_2$ and $\mathcal{U}_4 = \mathcal{U}_1 + \mathcal{U}_2$. Find a matrix B_i for which $\mathcal{U}_i = \mathcal{K}^r(B_i)$ $(i = 1, 2, 3, 4)$.

3.8. Equivalence of matrices. Our emphasis until now has been on row operations, row spaces, column kernels, and multiplication on the left by elementary matrices. One might expect a dual theory with emphasis on column operations, column spaces, row kernels, and multiplication on the right by elementary matrices. The operation of transposition provides a ready means of passing from rows to columns and accordingly from the row-space theory to a column-space theory.

If R is an elementary row transformation, we define a corresponding *elementary column transformation* C by the statement that C applied to matrix A yields the matrix B if R applied to A^T yields B^T. Thus, for example, if $R = R_{ih}$, then $C = C_{ih}$ is the operation that interchanges the ith and hth columns. Similarly, $C_i(c)$ and $C_i(c, h)$ correspond, respectively, to $R_i(c)$ and $R_i(c, h)$.

LEMMA 3.8A. *To every elementary column transformation C on a v-by-w matrix A, there corresponds a matrix, which is, indeed, the transpose of the matrix F for the corresponding elementary row transformation, such that, if $B = AC$, then $B = AF^T$. The matrix F^T can be obtained by applying C to I_w; i.e., $F^T = I_w C$.*

By definition of C we have $AC = B$ if and only if $A^T R = B^T$; i.e., if $FA^T = B^T$. But then $B = (B^T)^T = (FA^T)^T = AF^T$; this establishes the lemma.

It is easy to verify that

$$F_{ih}{}^T = F_{ih},$$
$$F_i(c)^T = F_i(c),$$
$$F_i(c, h)^T = F_h(c, i).$$

Hence the matrices needed to effect elementary column transformations are also elementary transformation matrices. What determines whether a row or column transformation is being carried out is not the appearance of the elementary transformation matrix but whether it is being premultiplied or postmultiplied.

A matrix A is in *column-echelon form* if A^T is in row-echelon form.

Improper column transformations C_+, C_- have a definition which parallels that for rows. As is to be expected, the matrix which on *post*multiplication of a given matrix effects an improper column transformation is the transpose of the corresponding improper row-transformation matrix.

Since the theory of column spaces is entirely analogous to the theory of row spaces, we do not develop it here. Instead we consider what can be done using both row and column operations.

LEMMA 3.8B. *If* R *is a row transformation and* C *a column transformation, then* RC = CR.

Let F_1, F_2 be the matrices corresponding to R, C, respectively. Then

$$A(\mathsf{RC}) = (A\mathsf{R})\mathsf{C} = (F_1 A)F_2$$

and

$$A(\mathsf{CR}) = (A\mathsf{C})\mathsf{R} = F_1(A F_2).$$

The lemma now follows from the associative law for matrix multiplication.

This lemma justifies the terminology "apply R and C simultaneously to A" which will be used later.

A matrix A is said to be *equivalent* to a matrix B, written $A \overset{\mathrm{E}}{=} B$, if B can be obtained from A by a sequence of (proper) elementary row and column transformations.

THEOREM 3.8C. *For any matrix* A, $A \overset{\mathrm{E}}{=} A$. *If* $A \overset{\mathrm{E}}{=} B$, *then* $B \overset{\mathrm{E}}{=} A$. *If* $A \overset{\mathrm{E}}{=} B$ *and* $B \overset{\mathrm{E}}{=} C$, *then* $A \overset{\mathrm{E}}{=} C$.

The proof is left as an exercise.

THEOREM 3.8D. *Two matrices* A *and* B *are equivalent if and only if there exist nonsingular matrices* P *and* Q *such that* $B = PAQ$.

Suppose that B is equivalent to A. Then according to Lemma 3.8B we may interchange row and column operations so that all of the row operations come first and then all of the column operations. Thus we have

(8.1) $B = A \mathsf{R}_1 \cdots \mathsf{R}_s \mathsf{C}_1 \cdots \mathsf{C}_t,$

where the R_i are elementary row operations and the C_j are elementary column operations. Let F_i be the matrix for R_i and F'_j the matrix for C_j ($i = 1, \cdots, s$; $j = 1, \cdots, t$). Then $B = PAQ$ where $P = F_s \cdots F_1$ and $Q = F'_1 \cdots F'_t$. Since P and Q are products of elementary matrices, they are nonsingular.

Conversely, if $B = PAQ$ where P and Q are nonsingular, then by Theorem 3.7D there exist elementary matrices $F_1, \cdots, F_s, F'_1, \cdots, F'_t$ such that $P = F_s \cdots F_1$ and $Q = F'_1 \cdots F'_t$. Then, if R_i and C_j correspond to F_i and F'_j $(i = 1, \cdots, s; j = 1, \cdots, t)$, we have (8.1) and hence $B \overset{\mathrm{E}}{=} A$.

THEOREM 3.8E. *Every matrix A is equivalent to a unique matrix C having the form*

$$C = \left\| \begin{array}{cc} I_r & 0 \\ 0 & 0 \end{array} \right\|,$$

where r is the rank of A.

It is understood here that, if $r = 0$, then C is the v-by-w zero matrix. Also, if r equals v, the number of rows in C, then the two zero matrices at the bottom do not actually appear; similarly for the two zero matrices on the right in C when $r = w$ (i.e these are null matrices).

We first establish the existence of C. If A is the zero matrix then it already has the form of C. Otherwise choose a nonzero element a_{ij}. Apply R_{1i} and then C_{1j} to bring it into the upper left corner. Next use $\mathsf{R}_1(1/a_{ij})$ to change it to 1. Then employ elementary row transformations $\mathsf{R}_i(c,1)$ to make the rest of the first column all zero, and similarly employ column transformations $\mathsf{C}_i(c,1)$ to obtain zeros throughout the rest of the first row. We now have a matrix in the form

$$\left\| \begin{array}{cc} 1 & 0 \\ 0 & A' \end{array} \right\|,$$

where the 0 in the upper right corner is a zero row matrix and the 0 in the lower left corner is a zero column matrix.

Repeat the process, concentrating on the elements of A'. Any elementary operations performed on the last $v - 1$ rows or last $v - 1$ columns will not change the first row or column. Thus, if $A' \neq 0$, we get a matrix having the form

$$\left\| \begin{array}{ccccc} 1 & 0 & 0 & \cdots & 0 \\ 0 & 1 & 0 & \cdots & 0 \\ 0 & 0 & * & \cdots & * \\ \cdot & \cdot & \cdot & \cdots & \cdot \\ 0 & 0 & * & \cdots & * \end{array} \right\|$$

The process is repeated until the matrix C is obtained. Matrices P, Q for which $C = PAQ$ will be given by $P = F_s \cdots F_1$, where F_i is the matrix corresponding to the ith elementary row operation R_i used, and $Q = F'_1 \cdots F'_t$, where F'_j is the matrix corresponding to the jth elementary column transformation C_j applied.

Now according to Corollary 3.1E the matrices A and $C = PAQ$ have the same rank; the rank of C is clearly r; hence $r = \operatorname{rank} A$. Since C is defined by rank A, $\deg_r A$, and $\deg_c A$, there can be only one matrix C equivalent to A.

THEOREM 3.8F. *Suppose that two matrices A and B have equal row degrees and equal column degrees. Then A is equivalent to B if and only if* rank $A =$ rank B.

If rank $A =$ rank B, then A and B are equivalent to the same matrix C, and hence, by Theorem 3.8C, A is equivalent to B. Conversely the equality rank $A =$ rank B follows from Corollary 3.1E.

The matrix equation

$$(8.2) \qquad \begin{Vmatrix} P & 0 \\ 0 & I \end{Vmatrix} \begin{Vmatrix} A & I_v \\ I_w & 0 \end{Vmatrix} \begin{Vmatrix} Q & 0 \\ 0 & I \end{Vmatrix} = \begin{Vmatrix} PAQ & P \\ Q & 0 \end{Vmatrix}$$

can be used as a computing form if one wishes to keep a record of the matrices P and Q used to get from A to any equivalent matrix $B = PAQ$.

There are many sequences of elementary transformations which lead

from A to $C = \begin{Vmatrix} I_r & 0 \\ 0 & 0 \end{Vmatrix}$. Likewise the matrices P and Q are not uniquely

determined by A and C.

If A is nonsingular, then by taking $P = A^{-1}$ and $Q = I$ we have $PAQ = I$, and hence $A \overset{\mathrm{E}}{=} I$. But in carrying out a reduction of A to I both row and column transformations can be used. If this is done, the inverse A^{-1} of A is given by

$$(8.3) \qquad\qquad A^{-1} = QP,$$

instead of being simply P as when row transformations alone are used. The proof of this formula is left as an exercise. In actually finding A^{-1} it may sometimes be faster to apply both row and column transformations and then use (8.3).

Exercises 3.8

1. Prove Theorem 3.8C.

2. Find a matrix having the form $C = \left\| \begin{matrix} I_r & 0 \\ 0 & 0 \end{matrix} \right\|$ equivalent to

(a)
$$A = \left\| \begin{matrix} 0 & 3 & 2 \\ -1 & -2 & 2 \end{matrix} \right\|,$$

(b)
$$A = \left\| \begin{matrix} 0 & 1 & -2 \\ 2 & 1 & 3 \\ -1 & 0 & 4 \end{matrix} \right\|,$$

(c)
$$A = \left\| \begin{matrix} 2 & 1 & 0 & -1 \\ 1 & -2 & 1 & 2 \\ 5 & 0 & 1 & 0 \end{matrix} \right\|.$$

3. Find nonsingular matrices P, Q for which $C = PAQ$ where C and A are given in Exercise 2.

4. (a) Prove formula (8.3).   (b) Apply it to find the inverse of A given by Exercise 2(b).

5. Two matrices A and B are said to be *improperly equivalent* if they have the same rank.   Show that A is improperly equivalent to B if and only if there exist matrices P_1, Q_1, P_2, Q_2 such that $B = P_1AQ_1$ and $A = P_2BQ_2$.

6. Let $A = \left\| \begin{matrix} 3 & 0 & 1 & 2 \\ -1 & 5 & 4 & -1 \\ 5 & -10 & -7 & 4 \end{matrix} \right\|$.   Find the rank r of A, and find

nonsingular matrices P, Q for which $PAQ = \left\| \begin{matrix} I_r & 0 \\ 0 & 0 \end{matrix} \right\|$.

7. Do Exercise 6 for $A = \left\| \begin{matrix} 4 & -1 & 1 \\ 2 & -3 & 5 \\ 1 & 1 & -2 \\ 5 & 0 & 1 \end{matrix} \right\|.$

8. Do Exercise 6 for $A = \left\| \begin{matrix} 2 & 1 & -1 & 2 \\ 1 & -2 & 1 & -3 \\ 4 & -3 & 1 & -4 \end{matrix} \right\|.$

9. Do Exercise 6 for $A = \left\Vert \begin{array}{ccc} 0 & 2 & -5 \\ 9 & -1 & 7 \\ 16 & 2 & 3 \\ -12 & -2 & -1 \end{array} \right\Vert .$

10. Let A and B be two matrices. Show that there exist elementary matrices, $F_1, \cdots, F_r, F'_1, \cdots, F'_s$, each of the type F_{ih} (i.e. each F_j, F_j' is obtained by interchange of two rows of the identity matrix) such that

(∗) $$B \times A = F_r \cdots F_1(A \times B)F'_1 \cdots F'_s.$$

Show that (∗) holds with the same F_j, F'_j for every pair of matrices A', B' having the same degrees, respectively, as A and B. (See Exercise 7 of Section 2.8 for definition of $A \times B$.)

11. If A and B are square matrices (not necessarily of the same degree), show that (∗) holds with $s = r$ and $F'_j = F_j$ $(j = 1, \cdots, r)$.

3.9. Nonhomogeneous linear equations. Let

(9.1) $$\sum_{\lambda=1}^{w} a_{i\lambda}x_\lambda = b_i \qquad\qquad (i = 1, \cdots, v)$$

be a system of v simultaneous nonhomogeneous linear equations in the w unknowns $x_1, \cdots, x_w$. In matrix form these equations become

(9.2) $$AX = B,$$

where $B = \Vert b_i \Vert$ is the v-by-1 column vector made up of the right-hand sides, where $X = \Vert x_i \Vert$ is the w-by-1 column vector made up of the unknowns, and where $A = \Vert a_{ij} \Vert$ is the v-by-w matrix of coefficients. Suppose that $X^{(1)} = \Vert x_i^{(1)} \Vert$ and $X^{(2)} = \Vert x_i^{(2)} \Vert$ are two solutions of (9.2). Then we have

(9.3) $$A(X^{(2)} - X^{(1)}) = AX^{(2)} - AX^{(1)} = B - B = 0,$$

and hence the difference $Y = X^{(2)} - X^{(1)}$ is a solution of the homogeneous system

(9.4) $$AX = 0.$$

Conversely, if $X^{(1)}$ is any solution of (9.2) and Y is any solution of (9.4), then $X^{(2)} = X^{(1)} + Y$ is a solution of (9.2), since

$$AX^{(2)} = A(X^{(1)} + Y) = AX^{(1)} + AY = B + 0 = B.$$

Summarizing these results in slightly different language, we have the following theorem:

THEOREM 3.9A.   *Let A be a v-by-w matrix, let B be a column vector with v rows, and let $\mathscr{S}$ be the set of all solutions of the equation $AX = B$.   Then either* (i) $\mathscr{S}$ *is empty or* (ii) $\mathscr{S}$ *is the set of all vectors of the form $X = X^{(1)} + Y$ where $X^{(1)}$ is a fixed element of $\mathscr{S}$ and Y belongs to $\mathscr{K}^c(A)$.*

In case (ii) we can write $\mathscr{S} = X^{(1)} + \mathscr{K}^c(A)$.

The special case $w = 3$ admits an interpretation in familiar geometric terms.   Suppose that the matrix A has rank 1 so that $\mathscr{K}^c(A)$ has dimension 2 (cf. Theorem 3.2A).   Then $\mathscr{K}^c(A)$ can be interpreted as a plane passing through the origin, and $\mathscr{S}$ is the unique plane parallel to $\mathscr{K}^c(A)$ which contains the points whose coordinates are the entries of $X^{(1)}$.

This theorem reduces the whole problem of solving a system of nonhomogeneous linear equations to the following questions: Under what circumstances is there a solution, and how can one solution be found?

We answer the first question in terms of the matrix

$$(9.5) \qquad\qquad A^* = \| \ A \quad B \ \|$$

called the *augmented matrix* of the system (9.1).

THEOREM 3.9B.   *A nonhomogeneous system of linear equations has a solution if and only if the rank of its coefficient matrix is equal to the rank of its augmented matrix.*

Equation (9.2) can be written in the form

$$(9.6) \qquad\qquad A^{(1)}x_1 + \cdots + A^{(w)}x_w = B,$$

where $A^{(j)}$ is the jth column of A ($j = 1, \cdots, w$).   This shows that (9.1) has a solution if and only if B is in the column space of A.   Now, if B is dependent on the columns of A, then A and A^* have the same column space and therefore the same rank.   On the other hand, if rank $A^* >$ rank A, then $\mathscr{C}(A^*) \supset \mathscr{C}(A)$; this in turn implies that B is not in $\mathscr{C}(A)$ and hence that (9.1) has no solution.

This theorem tells us when a solution exists, i.e. when the equations are *consistent*, but gives no construction for a solution.

Suppose that D is the echelon matrix related to A, let P be a nonsingular matrix such that $PA = D$, and set

$$(9.7) \qquad\qquad D^* = PA^* = \| \ PA \quad PB \ \| = \| \ D \quad F \ \|.$$

Then (9.1) is equivalent to

$$(9.8) \qquad\qquad DX = F.$$

Suppose that the indices of D are $e_1, \cdots, e_r$. Then, unless the elements $f_{r+1}, \cdots, f_v$ of F are all 0, we have rank $A^* = $ rank $D^* = 1 + $ rank A, and hence (9.2) has no solution. (A slight modification of the present argument would give a new proof of Theorem 3.9B.) If $f_{r+1} = \cdots = f_v = 0$, then $x_h = 0$ for h not an index of D and $x_{e_i} = f_i$ $(i = 1, \cdots, r)$ is seen to be a solution of (9.8) and therefore also of (9.1).

This result can be put into a neater form if we insert zero rows in D^* so as to obtain

$$(9.9) \qquad\qquad H^* = \| \; H \quad G \; \|,$$

where H is a Hermite matrix. Theorems 3.9A and 3.6C yield the next result.

THEOREM 3.9C. *If the system* (9.1) *is consistent, every solution has the form* $Y + G$ *where* G *is given by* (9.9) *and* Y *is a linear combination of the columns of* $I_w - H$.

These theorems show how to test for consistency and to solve a nonhomogeneous system within the framework of our theory for the homogeneous case.

Exercises 3.9

1. For the system of equations

$$\begin{aligned}
2x - 3y + z &= -1, \\
x + 2y - 2z &= -1, \\
4x + y - 3z &= -3, \\
x - 5y + 3z &= 0,
\end{aligned}$$

do solutions exist? If so find them.

2. Find all polynomials $f(x) = a_0 x^3 + a_1 x^2 + a_2 x + a_3$ with real coefficients for which $f(1) = -2, f(2) = 2$, and $f(3) = 14$.

3. Let $AX = B$ be a nonhomogeneous system with nonsingular coefficient matrix A. Prove that its solution is $X = A^{-1}B$.

4. Solve the system

$$\begin{aligned}
2x - 3y - 2z + v + w &= 1, \\
x + y \qquad + 2v \qquad &= -3, \\
3y - 4z + 3v + 2w &= 0.
\end{aligned}$$

5. Find all solutions X of the matrix equation $AX = K$ where

$$A = \left\| \begin{array}{cccc} 2 & 1 & -1 & 2 \\ 1 & -2 & 1 & -3 \\ 4 & -3 & 1 & -4 \end{array} \right\|, \qquad K = \left\| \begin{array}{c} -1 \\ 3 \\ 5 \end{array} \right\|.$$

6. Do Exercise 5 if

$$A = \begin{Vmatrix} 4 & -1 & 1 \\ 2 & -3 & 5 \\ 1 & 1 & -2 \\ 5 & 0 & -1 \end{Vmatrix}, \qquad K = \begin{Vmatrix} 5 \\ 1 \\ 2 \\ 2 \end{Vmatrix}.$$

7. Does the vector $\begin{Vmatrix} 1 & 2 & -3 & 4 \end{Vmatrix}$ lie in the row space of the matrix

$$A = \begin{Vmatrix} 2 & 1 & -2 & 1 \\ 1 & -2 & 3 & 1 \\ 1 & 8 & -13 & -1 \end{Vmatrix} ?$$

8. Let $A = \begin{Vmatrix} 2 & 1 & 3 & 2 \\ 1 & -1 & 2 & -2 \\ 3 & 0 & 1 & 3 \end{Vmatrix}$. Which, if any, of the following vectors

lie in the row space of A:

$$K^{(1)} = \begin{Vmatrix} 1 & 0 & 1 & 1 \end{Vmatrix}, \qquad K^{(2)} = \begin{Vmatrix} 2 & 0 & 2 & 1 \end{Vmatrix},$$

$$K^{(3)} = \begin{Vmatrix} 5 & 1 & 8 & 2 \end{Vmatrix} ?$$

9. Show how the theory of apolar matrices can be used in the solution of Exercise 8.

| # Determinants

4.1. Definition of determinant. Determinants, which we now introduce, can be given a central role in the development of matrix theory. We have chosen instead to use other tools in treating such concepts as rank, systems of linear equations, and singularity. In the present chapter we shall first define and develop properties of determinants and then study some applications to matrix theory and related topics.

Determinants are scalars associated with square matrices. We denote the determinant of A by any one of the symbols $\det A$, $|A|$, $|a_{ij}|$, $\det \| a_{ij} \|$,

$$
\begin{vmatrix}
a_{11} \cdots a_{1n} \\
\cdot \; \cdots \; \cdot \\
a_{n1} \cdots a_{nn}
\end{vmatrix},
$$

or $D(A)$. We sometimes abbreviate $D(A)$ to D. If A has degree n, we say that $D(A)$ is a determinant of *order n*.

There are several equivalent ways to define an nth-order determinant; of these we choose an inductive definition. If $n = 1$, i.e., $A = \| a_{11} \|$, we set $D = \det A = a_{11}$ (i.e., the determinant of a scalar is the scalar itself). If $n > 1$, we suppose that determinants of orders less than n have already been defined and set (cf. Section 2.8)

$$
(1.1) \qquad\qquad D = \det A = \sum_{\nu=1}^{n} (-1)^{1+\nu} a_{1\nu} \det A(1 \mid \nu).
$$

When the limits of summation are obvious from the context, the symbol $\sum_{\nu=1}^{n}$ is sometimes replaced by $\sum_{\nu}$. If in addition it is also clear what the summation index is, a further abbreviation to Σ is sometimes made. In this book the symbol Σ means sum over each Greek index. (Indeed every summation index in this book is Greek, and Greek indices are used in no other way than as summation indices.) Thus (1.1) may be written

$$D = \Sigma \, (-1)^{1+\nu} a_{1\nu} \det A(1 \mid \nu).$$

In particular, for $n = 2$ we have

$$\begin{vmatrix} a_{11} & a_{12} \\ a_{21} & a_{22} \end{vmatrix} = (-1)^{1+1} a_{11} \det A(1 \mid 1) + (-1)^{1+2} a_{12} \det A(1 \mid 2)$$
$$= \qquad a_{11} a_{22} \qquad - \qquad a_{12} a_{21} \, ,$$

and for $n = 3$ we have

$$\begin{vmatrix} a_{11} & a_{12} & a_{13} \\ a_{21} & a_{22} & a_{23} \\ a_{31} & a_{32} & a_{33} \end{vmatrix} = a_{11} \begin{vmatrix} a_{22} & a_{23} \\ a_{32} & a_{33} \end{vmatrix} - a_{12} \begin{vmatrix} a_{21} & a_{23} \\ a_{31} & a_{33} \end{vmatrix} + a_{13} \begin{vmatrix} a_{21} & a_{22} \\ a_{31} & a_{32} \end{vmatrix}.$$

If we try to apply formula (1.1) for $n = 1$, we run into the undefined symbol $\det A(1 \mid 1)$ where $A(1 \mid 1)$ is the square null matrix. Since our definition of determinant does not cover null matrices (i.e., determinants of order 0), we are at liberty to define them any way we wish; it turns out to be convenient to define $\det B = 1$ for the square null matrix. An immediate advantage of this definition is that with it formula (1.1) is valid even for $n = 1$; moreover, with this convention determinants of order zero can be dropped from any product in which they appear.

In the definition of D as presented in (1.1), special attention is given to the first row of the matrix A, and we call (1.1) the *expansion* of D according to the first row of A. The following theorem shows that D can be expanded according to any row or column of A.

THEOREM 4.1A. *Let* $A = \| \, a_{ij} \, \|$ *be a square matrix of degree n, let*
$$D_i = \Sigma \, (-1)^{i+\nu} a_{i\nu} \det A(i \mid \nu) \qquad (i = 1, \cdots, n),$$
and let
$$D'_j = \Sigma \, (-1)^{\mu+j} a_{\mu j} \det A(\mu \mid j) \qquad (j = 1, \cdots, n).$$
Then $D_i = D'_j = D$ *for all i and all j.*

The theorem is trivially true for $n = 1$ since there are only D_1 and D'_1 to consider, and each of these is just a_{11}. We proceed by induction, taking as our induction hypothesis that the theorem is true for all matrices of degree $r < n$, and show then that it is true for $r = n$. We consider any two indices i and j and show that $D_i = D'_j$.

Let $\mathscr{S}$ be a set of natural numbers. Then we denote by $\varepsilon(n; \mathscr{S})$ the number of members of $\mathscr{S}$ that are less than n. We call $\varepsilon(n; \mathscr{S})$ the *inversion* function. If the elements of $\mathscr{S}$ are $p_1, \cdots, p_s$, we also write $\varepsilon(n; \mathscr{S}) = \varepsilon(n; p_1, \cdots, p_s)$. Thus $\varepsilon(5; 4, 1, 7, 8, 6) = 2$, and $\varepsilon(2; 3) = 0$.

We use the inversion function as an aid in comparing the position of an element in a matrix with its position in a submatrix.

LEMMA 4.1B. *Let* $B = \| b_{ij} \|$ *be any* $\mathscr{F}$ *matrix, and let* $C = \| c_{ij} \|$ *be the submatrix* $B(i_1, \cdots, i_r \mid j_1, \cdots, j_s)$ *obtained by deleting rows* $i_1, \cdots, i_r$ *and columns* $j_1, \cdots, j_s$ *from* B. *Suppose that neither the ith row nor the jth column are among those deleted. Then* $b_{ij} = c_{hk}$ *where*

$$h = i - \varepsilon(i; i_1, \cdots, i_r) \qquad and \qquad k = j - \varepsilon(j; j_1, \cdots, j_s)$$

Proof of lemma. By definition of the matrix C the position in it of the ith row of B is the number of nondeleted rows among the first i rows of B. But this is clearly i minus the number of rows among the first i that were deleted. But, since the ith row was not deleted, this number is given by $h = i - \varepsilon$, where $\varepsilon = \varepsilon(i; i_1, \cdots, i_r)$ is the number of deleted rows whose indices are less than i. The same argument applies to the column indices.

We return now to the proof that $D_i = D'_j$. The term $(-1)^{i+j} a_{ij} \det A(i \mid j)$ is common to the sums that define D_i and D'_j:

(1.2) $D_i = (-1)^{i+j} a_{ij} \det A(i \mid j) + \displaystyle\sum_{\nu \neq j} (-1)^{i+\nu} a_{i\nu} \det A(i \mid \nu),$

(1.3) $D'_j = (-1)^{i+j} a_{ij} \det A(i \mid j) + \displaystyle\sum_{\mu \neq i} (-1)^{\mu+j} a_{\mu j} \det A(\mu \mid j).$

Here the symbol $\displaystyle\sum_{\mu \neq j}$ means the sum over all natural numbers except j in the range $1, \cdots, n$. Each factor $\det A(h \mid k)$ in these sums is a determinant of order $n - 1$. For each of them the induction hypothesis applies; hence each can be expanded according to any row or column. In the sum for D_i for each $k \neq j$ we expand $\det A(i \mid k)$ according to the column which is made up of elements of the jth column of A and thus obtain altogether $(n - 1)^2$ terms. We shall show that these terms are exactly the same (and with the same signs) as those that occur when each of the factors $\det A(h \mid j)$ for $h \neq i$ in D'_j is expanded according to the row which comes from the ith row of A.

Thus suppose $k \neq j$; then the column of $A(i \mid k)$ which is composed of elements of the jth column of A has index $j - \varepsilon(j; k)$. Similarly elements of the hth row of A appear in the row $A(i \mid k)$ whose index is $h - \varepsilon(h; i)$. Now according to our induction hypothesis the theorem is correct for the $(n - 1)$-rowed matrix $A(i \mid k)$, and hence we have

(1.4) $\det A(i \mid k) = \displaystyle\sum_{\mu \neq i} (-1)^{\mu - \varepsilon(\mu; i) + j - \varepsilon(j; k)} a_{\mu j} \det A(i, \mu \mid k, j).$

The $n - 1$ numbers $\mu - \varepsilon(\mu; i)$ are of course just $1, 2, \cdots, n - 1$; thus (1.4) is the expansion of $\det A(i \mid k)$ according to the column $j - \varepsilon(j; k)$.

Similarly, for $h \neq i$ we may expand $\det A(h \mid j)$ according to the row that contains elements of the ith row of A, i.e., according to the row $i - \varepsilon(i; h)$, and we get

(1.5) $\qquad \det A(h \mid j) = \sum_{\nu \neq j} (-1)^{i - \varepsilon(i; h) + \nu - \varepsilon(\nu; j)} a_{i\nu} \det A(h, i \mid j, \nu).$

Now substitute (1.4) and (1.5) in the expressions (1.2) and (1.3), respectively, and obtain

(1.6) $\quad D_i = (-1)^{i+j} a_{ij} \det A(i \mid j)$

$\qquad + \sum_{\nu \neq j} (-1)^{i+\nu} a_{i\nu} \sum_{\mu \neq i} (-1)^{\mu - \varepsilon(\mu; i) + j - \varepsilon(j; \nu)} a_{\mu j} \det A(i, \mu \mid \nu, j)$

and

(1.7) $\quad D'_j = (-1)^{i+j} a_{ij} \det A(i \mid j)$

$\qquad + \sum_{\mu \neq i} (-1)^{\mu+j} a_{\mu j} \sum_{\nu \neq j} (-1)^{i - \varepsilon(i, \mu) + \nu - \varepsilon(\nu; j)} a_{i\nu} \det A(\mu, i \mid j, \nu).$

Note that $A(h, i \mid j, k) = A(i, h \mid k, j)$. Now for any $h \neq i$, $k \neq j$ the coefficients of $\det A(i, h \mid k, j)$ in (1.6) and (1.7) are identical save for the factors

$\qquad (-1)^{-\varepsilon(h; i) - \varepsilon(j; k)}$ in (1.6) $\qquad$ and $\qquad (-1)^{-\varepsilon(i; h) - \varepsilon(k; j)}$ in (1.7).

The identities $\varepsilon(k; j) + \varepsilon(j; k) = 1$ and $\varepsilon(h; i) + \varepsilon(i; h) = 1$ show that these factors are equal. Therefore the double sums in (1.6) and (1.7) are equal; the remaining term is $(-1)^{i+j} a_{ij} \det A(i \mid j)$ in both (1.6) and (1.7); hence $D_i = D'_j$.

Now, by definition $D = D_1$; from the result above with $i = 1$ we get $D = D_1 = D'_j$ for each j; and finally $D_i = D'_j = D_1 = D$ for each i and each j.

The theorem just proved will be our basic tool in the development of the theory of determinants. There are other properties that are more useful for evaluating determinants in practice. In the following sections we shall develop some of these properties of determinants. However, we are already in a position to evaluate quickly the determinant of a triangular matrix.

THEOREM 4.1C. *Let $A = \| a_{ij} \|$ be a triangular matrix, where, say, $a_{ij} = 0$ if $i > j$ $(i, j = 1, \cdots, n)$. Then $\det A = a_{11} a_{22} \cdots a_{nn}$; i.e., the determinant of triangular matrix is the product of the elements on the diagonal.*

The theorem is trivially true for degree 1. Take as an induction hypothesis that it is true for all degrees less than n. Now apply Theorem 4.1A to expand $\det A$ according to the nth row of A. Since $a_{nj} = 0$ for $j < n$ (if A is upper-triangular), we have

$\det A = \Sigma(-1)^{n+\nu} a_{n\nu} \det A(n \mid \nu) = (-1)^{n+n} a_{nn} \det A(n \mid n) = a_{nn} \det A(n \mid n).$

By our induction hypothesis, the determinant of the $(n-1)$-rowed diagonal matrix $A(n \mid n)$ is $a_{11}a_{22} \cdots a_{n-1,n-1}$; we substitute this in the formula above and get $\det A = a_{11}a_{22} \cdots a_{nn}$ as contended.

COROLLARY 4.1D. *The determinant of a diagonal matrix is the product of the elements on the diagonal.*

COROLLARY 4.1E. *The determinant of the scalar matrix cI_n is c^n. In particular, $\det I_n = 1$.*

Exercises 4.1

Evaluate:

1.
$$\det \begin{Vmatrix} 2 & 0 & 0 & 0 \\ 17 & -3 & 0 & 0 \\ 136 & -61 & 6 & 0 \\ -73 & 18 & 9 & 2 \end{Vmatrix}.$$

2.
$$\det \begin{Vmatrix} 1 & 2 & 0 & 0 \\ 0 & 3 & 4 & 0 \\ 0 & 0 & 5 & 6 \\ 1 & 2 & 3 & 4 \end{Vmatrix}.$$

[Hint: expand according to the last row.]

3.
$$\det \begin{Vmatrix} x & -1 & 0 & 0 \\ 0 & x & -1 & 0 \\ 0 & 0 & x & -1 \\ -2 & -3 & -4 & -5 \end{Vmatrix}.$$

4.
$$\det \begin{Vmatrix} 3 & 13 \\ -7 & 5 \end{Vmatrix}.$$

5.
$$\det \begin{Vmatrix} 3 & 8 & -2 \\ -6 & -1 & 4 \\ 2 & 2 & 1 \end{Vmatrix}.$$

6.
$$\det \begin{Vmatrix} -1 & 2 & 5 & -6 \\ 3 & 3 & -2 & 4 \\ 7 & 1 & 9 & -2 \\ 4 & 6 & 1 & 8 \end{Vmatrix}.$$

7.
$$\det \begin{Vmatrix} 0 & 0 & 0 & -6 \\ 0 & 0 & -2 & 4 \\ 0 & 1 & 9 & -2 \\ 4 & 6 & 1 & 8 \end{Vmatrix}.$$

4.2. Basic properties of determinants. Evaluation of determinants by means of the definition (1.1) is practical only for small orders n. In practice, auxiliary methods are usually employed whenever the order is greater than three. The present section is devoted to setting up some theorems which facilitate evaluation of determinants. We give especial attention to the use of elementary transformations in determinant theory.

To simplify reference to them we state a string of theorems in this section and then give the proofs in the following section. In all of these theorems $A = \| a_{ij} \|$ denotes a matrix of degree n.

THEOREM 4.2A. *The determinant of a matrix is equal to the determinant of its transpose; i.e.,* $\det A = \det A^\mathsf{T}$.

Suppose we have established some theorem on determinants in which the rows of the matrix play some special role. Then Theorem 4.2A guarantees the validity of the analogous theorem on determinants in which the roles of row and column are reversed.

THEOREM 4.2B. *If all the elements of any column (or of any row) of A are zero, then* $\det A = 0$.

THEOREM 4.2C. *If two matrices A and B are identical save for one column, then* $\det A + \det B = \det C$ *where C is the same as A and B except for the given column, and it is the sum of the corresponding columns of A and B. In symbols*

$$
\begin{vmatrix} c_{11} \cdots a_{1j} \cdots c_{1n} \\ \cdot \ \cdots \ \cdot \ \cdots \ \cdot \\ c_{n1} \cdots a_{nj} \cdots b_{nn} \end{vmatrix}
+
\begin{vmatrix} c_{11} \cdots b_{1j} \cdots c_{1n} \\ \cdot \ \cdots \ \cdot \ \cdots \ \cdot \\ c_{n1} \cdots b_{nj} \cdots c_{nn} \end{vmatrix}
=
\begin{vmatrix} c_{11} \cdots a_{1j} + b_{1j} \cdots c_{1n} \\ \cdot \ \cdots \ \cdot \ \cdots \ \cdot \\ c_{n1} \cdots a_{nj} + b_{nj} \cdots c_{nn} \end{vmatrix}.
$$

(The analogous result holds for rows.)

This theorem is a special case of the following one.

THEOREM 4.2D. *If $A, \cdots, B, C$ are matrices such that the jth column of C is the sum of the jth columns of $A, \cdots, B$ and if for $h \neq j$ the hth columns of $A, \cdots, B$ are identical with the hth column of C, then*

$$\det C = \det A + \cdots + \det B.$$

(The analogous result holds for rows.)

THEOREM 4.2E. *If two columns (or two rows) of A are proportional, then* $\det A = 0$.

COROLLARY 4.2F. *If two columns (or two rows) of A are equal, then* $\det A = 0$.

We recall (see Sections 3.7 and 3.8) that elementary row operations can be effected by multiplication on the left by an elementary matrix and that elementary column operations can be effected by multiplication on the right by an elementary matrix. The following theorem is stated in the notation of the sections cited.

THEOREM 4.2G.

(2.1) $$\det A = -\det (F_{ih}A) = -\det (AF_{jk}),$$

(2.2) $$\det A = \frac{1}{c} \det (F_i(c)A) = \frac{1}{c} \det (AF_j(c)),$$

(2.3) $$\det A = \det (F_i(c, h)A) = \det (AF_k(c, j)).$$

The three formulas describe, respectively, the effects of elementary transformations of types 1, 2, and 3.

COROLLARY 4.2H. *For the determinants of the elementary matrices we have*
$$\det F_{ih} = -1, \qquad \det F_i(c) = c, \qquad \det F_i(c, h) = 1.$$

The following example shows how Theorems 4.2G and 4.1A can be used in evaluating determinants. Let

$$A = \begin{Vmatrix} 4 & 3 & 2 & -2 \\ 2 & 1 & 3 & 1 \\ 3 & 2 & 1 & 5 \\ -3 & 6 & -1 & 4 \end{Vmatrix}.$$

Then by three consecutive applications of (2.3) all with $k = 2$ and with $j = 1$, $c = -2$; $j = 3$, $c = -3$; $j = 4$, $c = -1$, respectively, we have

$$\det A = \begin{vmatrix} -2 & 3 & 2 & -2 \\ 0 & 1 & 3 & 1 \\ -1 & 2 & 1 & 5 \\ -15 & 6 & -1 & 4 \end{vmatrix} = \begin{vmatrix} -2 & 3 & -7 & -2 \\ 0 & 1 & 0 & 1 \\ -1 & 2 & -5 & 5 \\ -15 & 6 & -19 & 4 \end{vmatrix} = \begin{vmatrix} -2 & 3 & -7 & -5 \\ 0 & 1 & 0 & 0 \\ -1 & 2 & -5 & 3 \\ -15 & 6 & -19 & -2 \end{vmatrix}.$$

Next apply Theorem 4.1A, and expand according to the second row and obtain

$$\det A = (-1)^{2+1} \cdot 0 \det A(2 \mid 1) + (-1)^{2+2} \cdot 1 \det A(2 \mid 2)$$
$$+ (-1)^{2+3} \cdot 0 \det A(2 \mid 3) + (-1)^{2+4} \cdot 0 \det A(2 \mid 4)$$

$$= \det A(2 \mid 2) = \begin{vmatrix} -2 & -7 & -5 \\ -1 & -5 & 3 \\ -15 & -19 & -2 \end{vmatrix}.$$

(The terms having a zero factor are written down here to emphasize the application of Theorem 4.1A; in practice, only the nonzero terms are written.) We have now reduced the initial determinant of order four to one of order three. We can repeat the process to arrive at a determinant of order two. This time we add multiples of the second row to the first and third rows to obtain

$$\det A = \begin{vmatrix} 0 & 3 & -11 \\ -1 & -5 & 3 \\ -15 & -19 & -2 \end{vmatrix} = \begin{vmatrix} 0 & 3 & -11 \\ -1 & -5 & 3 \\ 0 & 56 & -47 \end{vmatrix} = (-1)^{2+1}(-1) \begin{vmatrix} 3 & -11 \\ 56 & -47 \end{vmatrix}$$

$$= -3 \cdot 47 + 11 \cdot 56 = 475.$$

A general procedure for reduction from order n to order $n - 1$ is now clear. We first apply elementary transformations of type 3 until some row or column has all but one of its elements equal to zero, and then expand the determinant of the resulting matrix according to the given row or column.

Exercises 4.2

Evaluate the following determinants

1.
$$\det \begin{Vmatrix} 1 & 1 & 1 & 1 \\ 1 & 2 & 3 & 4 \\ 1 & 4 & 9 & 16 \\ 1 & 8 & 27 & 64 \end{Vmatrix}.$$

2.
$$\det \begin{Vmatrix} x-1 & 1 & 0 \\ 2 & x-3 & 1 \\ 1 & 0 & x+1 \end{Vmatrix}.$$

3.
$$\det \begin{Vmatrix} 2 & 3 & -2 & 4 \\ 6 & 2 & 3 & -2 \\ 5 & -3 & 2 & 0 \\ -2 & 3 & 5 & 7 \end{Vmatrix}.$$

4.
$$\det \begin{Vmatrix} 2 & 3 & 2 & 3 \\ 3 & 2 & 3 & 2 \\ 4 & 5 & 4 & 5 \\ 5 & 4 & 5 & 4 \end{Vmatrix}.$$

5.
$$\det \begin{Vmatrix} 1 & 2 & 3 & 4 & 5 \\ 2 & 3 & 4 & 5 & 1 \\ 3 & 4 & 5 & 1 & 2 \\ 4 & 5 & 1 & 2 & 3 \\ 5 & 1 & 2 & 3 & 4 \end{Vmatrix}.$$

6.
$$\det \begin{Vmatrix} 1 & 0 & 1 & 2 & -2 \\ 2 & 3 & 3 & 1 & 0 \\ 2 & -1 & 0 & 1 & 3 \\ -3 & 2 & 2 & 0 & 3 \\ 0 & 1 & 2 & 3 & 1 \end{Vmatrix}.$$

4.3. Proofs of the properties of determinants. All of the theorems are obvious for $n = 1$ and $n = 2$. The main tools which we shall use in their proof are induction on the order n and the fundamental expansion of Theorem 4.1A.

Proof of Theorem 4.2A *(by induction on n)*. Let $B = A^\mathsf{T}$. By Theorem 4.1A (for the first column)

$$(3.1) \qquad \det B = \begin{vmatrix} a_{11} & a_{21} & \cdots & a_{n1} \\ a_{12} & a_{22} & \cdots & a_{n2} \\ & & \cdots & \\ a_{1n} & a_{2n} & \cdots & a_{nn} \end{vmatrix} = (-1)^{1+\nu} a_{1\nu} \det B(\nu \mid 1).$$

Observe that $B(h \mid 1) = A(1 \mid h)^\mathsf{T}$, and so by our induction hypothesis $\det B(h \mid 1) = \det A(1 \mid h)$. Substitute this in the summation on the right-hand side of (3.1), and it becomes $\det A$ expanded according to the first row; hence, $\det B = \det A$.

Proof of Theorem 4.2B. Theorem 4.2B follows immediately from Theorem 4.1A if we expand according to the zero column (or row).

Proof of Theorem 4.2D. Since $A, \cdots, B, C$ are identical except for the jth column, $A(i \mid j) = \cdots = B(i \mid j) = C(i \mid j)$ $(i = 1, \cdots, n)$. Therefore we have

$$\det A + \cdots + \det B$$

$$= \Sigma(-1)^{\mu+j} a_{\mu j} \det A(\mu \mid j) + \cdots + (-1)^{\mu+j} b_{\mu j} \det B(\mu \mid j)$$

$$= \Sigma(-1)^{\mu+j}(a_{\mu j} + \cdots + b_{\mu j}) \det C(\mu \mid j)$$

$$= \Sigma(-1)^{\mu+j} c_{\mu j} \det C(\mu \mid j)$$

$$= \det C.$$

Proof of Theorem 4.2E *(by induction on n)*. Suppose that $n > 2$ and that the jth and kth columns are proportional. Expand $\det A$ by any third column h (there is such a column since $n > 2$). Now each submatrix $A(i \mid h)$ has a pair of proportional columns, and so by our induction hypothesis $\det A(i \mid h) = 0$ $(i = 1, \cdots, n)$. Finally then $\det A = 0$ since each term in its expansion is zero.

Corollary 4.2F is a special case of Theorem 4.2E.

Proof of formula (2.1). Let $B = A F_{jk}$ $(j < k)$, and let C be identical with A except in the jth and kth columns which shall each be the sum of the jth and kth columns of A. Then $\det C = 0$ by Corollary 4.2F. Now by two applications of Theorem 4.2D we have

$$
0 = \det C = \begin{vmatrix} \cdots & a_{1j} & \cdots & a_{1j} & \cdots \\ \cdots & \cdot & \cdots & \cdot & \cdots \\ \cdots & a_{nj} & \cdots & a_{nj} & \cdots \end{vmatrix} + \begin{vmatrix} \cdots & a_{1j} & \cdots & a_{1k} & \cdots \\ \cdots & \cdot & \cdots & \cdot & \cdots \\ \cdots & a_{nj} & \cdots & a_{nk} & \cdots \end{vmatrix}
$$

$$
+ \begin{vmatrix} \cdots & a_{1k} & \cdots & a_{1j} & \cdots \\ \cdots & \cdot & \cdots & \cdot & \cdots \\ \cdots & a_{nk} & \cdots & a_{nj} & \cdots \end{vmatrix} + \begin{vmatrix} \cdots & a_{1k} & \cdots & a_{1k} & \cdots \\ \cdots & \cdot & \cdots & \cdot & \cdots \\ \cdots & a_{nk} & \cdots & a_{nk} & \cdots \end{vmatrix}
$$

$$
= 0 + \det A + \det B + 0.
$$

(The jth and kth columns are indicated; all other columns are the same as in A.) Hence $\det A = -\det B = -\det (AF_{jk})$. The remaining equality in (2.1) follows from Theorem 4.2A (and the results of Section 3.8 above).

Proof of formula (2.2). Let $B = AF_j(c)$; then

$$
\det B = \begin{vmatrix} a_{11} & \cdots & ca_{1j} & \cdots & a_{1n} \\ \cdot & \cdots & \cdot & \cdots & \cdot \\ a_{n1} & \cdots & ca_{nj} & \cdots & a_{nn} \end{vmatrix} = \Sigma(-1)^{\mu+j}(ca_{\mu j}) \det A(\mu \mid j)
$$

$$
= c\Sigma(-1)^{\mu+j}a_{\mu j} \det A(\mu \mid j) = c \det A.
$$

Here we use the fact that $A(i \mid j) = B(i \mid j)$ $(i = 1, \cdots, n)$. Now divide by the nonzero scalar c, and we get one of the equalities in (2.2); the other then follows from Theorem 4.2A.

Proof of formula (2.3). Let $B = AF_k(c, j)$. Then by Theorems 4.2D and 4.2E we have

$$
\det B = \begin{vmatrix} \cdots & a_{1j} + ca_{1k} & \cdots & a_{1k} & \cdots \\ \cdots & \cdot & \cdots & \cdot & \cdots \\ \cdots & a_{nj} + ca_{nk} & \cdots & a_{nk} & \cdots \end{vmatrix} = \begin{vmatrix} \cdots & a_{1j} & \cdots & a_{1k} & \cdots \\ \cdots & \cdot & \cdots & \cdot & \cdots \\ \cdots & a_{nj} & \cdots & a_{nk} & \cdots \end{vmatrix}
$$

$$
+ \begin{vmatrix} \cdots & ca_{1k} & \cdots & a_{1k} & \cdots \\ \cdots & \cdot & \cdots & \cdot & \cdots \\ \cdots & ca_{nk} & \cdots & a_{nk} & \cdots \end{vmatrix} = \det A + 0.
$$

(Here the jth and kth columns are indicated; all other columns are the same as in A.) The remaining equality in (2.3) follows from Theorem 4.2A.

Proof of Corollary 4.2H. This corollary is the special case $A = I$ of Theorem 4.2G, and follows from the fact that $\det I = 1$.

1. Prove that

$$
\det \begin{Vmatrix} 1 & 1 & 1 & 1 \\ x_1 & x_2 & x_3 & x_4 \\ x_1{}^2 & x_2{}^2 & x_3{}^2 & x_4{}^2 \\ x_1{}^3 & x_2{}^3 & x_3{}^3 & x_4{}^3 \end{Vmatrix} = \prod_{i<j} (x_j - x_i).
$$

Here the product is over the six pairs (i, j) with $1 \leq i < j \leq 4$. [Hint: subtract the first column from each of the later ones, expand according to the first row, take out a common factor $(x_j - x_1)$ from the jth column $(j = 2, 3, 4)$, and then subtract x_1 times each row from the one below beginning at the bottom and working up to the top. This sets the stage for an induction argument.]

2. Prove that

$$
\det \begin{Vmatrix} 1 & \cdots & 1 \\ x_1 & \cdots & x_n \\ \cdot & \cdots & \cdot \\ x_1{}^{n-1} & \cdots & x_n{}^{n-1} \end{Vmatrix} = \prod_{i<j} (x_j - x_i).
$$

3. Prove that, if $a_{ij} = i^{j-1} (i, j = 1, \cdots, n)$, then $\| a_{ij} \|$ is nonsingular.

4. Prove, using Theorem 4.1A, that if two adjacent rows of A are interchanged then the determinant changes sign.

5. Let A and B be 3-by-3 matrices. Then show that $\det (A + B) = \Sigma \det M$ where the sum is over the $2^3 = 8$ matrices M having the property that for $j = 1, 2, 3$, the jth column of M is either the jth column of A or the jth column of B.

6. Give generalizations of the result of the preceding exercise (a) to the case of arbitrary square matrices A and B, (b) to the case of more than two summands.

7. Let $A = \| a_{ij} \|$ be an n-by-n matrix with $a_{nn} \neq 0$, let $B = \| b_{ij} \|$ where

$$
b_{ij} = \begin{vmatrix} a_{ij} & a_{in} \\ a_{nj} & a_{nn} \end{vmatrix} (i, j = 1, \cdots, n - 1). \quad \text{Show that } \det A = \frac{1}{a_{nn}{}^{n-2}} \det B.
$$

(This formula is known as Chio's Condensation.)

8. Use the formula of Exercise 7 to evaluate the determinants in Exercises 3 and 4 of Section 4.2.

4.4. Classical definition of determinant; Laplace Expansion by minors.

Let A be any matrix, square or not, and let B be any square submatrix of A. Then we call $\det B$ a *minor* of A. If B has degree r, we say that $\det B$ is a *minor* of order r. Theorem 4.1A shows that, if A is square, then $\det A$ is a sum of products each of the form $(\pm 1) \cdot$ (a minor of order 1) $\cdot$ (a minor of order $n - 1$). We wish to generalize this to expansions by minors of various orders.   The method will involve repeated applications of Theorem 4.1A.

We first give several definitions.   Let A be any matrix, square or not. Then we say that the submatrices $A(i_1, \cdots, i_r \mid j_1, \cdots, j_s)$ and $A[i_1, \cdots, i_r \mid j_1, \cdots, j_s]$ are *complementary*.   If B and C are complementary square submatrices of a square matrix A, then we say that det B and det C are *complementary minors*.   The term complementary is justified by the observation that, if B is any submatrix of a matrix A then it has a unique complementary submatrix C, and, moreover, B is the complement of its complement.   If B is the square submatrix of degree zero, we say that its complement is A itself, and conversely call B the complement of A.

Now let A be a square matrix of degree n, and apply Theorem 4.1A to A and its submatrices k times, taking in turn $i = n, i = n - 1, \cdots, i = n - k + 1$.   We have

$$\det A = \sum_{\nu_n} (-1)^{n + \nu_n} a_{n\nu_n} \det A(n \mid \nu_n)$$

$$= \sum_{\nu_n} (-1)^{n + \nu_n} a_{n\nu_n} \sum_{\nu_{n-1} \neq \nu_n} (-1)^{n - 1 + \nu_{n-1} - \varepsilon(\nu_{n-1}; \nu_n)} a_{n-1, \nu_{n-1}}$$
$$\cdot \det A(n, n - 1 \mid \nu_n, \nu_{n-1})$$

$$= \sum_{\nu_n, \nu_{n-1}, \nu_{n-2}} (-1)^{e_1 + e_2 + e_3} a_{n\nu_n} a_{n-1, \nu_{n-1}} a_{n-2, \nu_{n-2}}$$
$$\cdot \det A(n, n - 1, n - 2 \mid \nu_n, \nu_{n-1}, \nu_{n-2}),$$

where $e_1 = n + (n - 1) + (n - 2)$, $e_2 = \nu_n + \nu_{n-1} + \nu_{n-2}$, $e_3 = -\varepsilon(\nu_{n-1}; \nu_n) - \varepsilon(\nu_{n-2}; \nu_n, \nu_{n-1})$, and the summation is over all possible choices for ν_n, ν_{n-1}, ν_{n-2} in the range from 1 to n subject to the sole condition that no two shall be equal in any one term.   (Hence there will be $n(n - 1)(n - 2)$ summands; in the language of elementary algebra the sum is over all permutations of the n integers $1, \cdots, n$ taken three at a time.)

Continuing the iteration up to k steps, we get

$$\det A = \sum_{\nu_n, \nu_{n-1}, \cdots, \nu_k} (-1)^{e_1 + e_2 + e_3} a_{n\nu_n} a_{n-1, \nu_{n-1}} \cdots a_{n-k+1, \nu_{n-k+1}}$$
$$\text{(4.1)} \qquad \cdot \det A(n, n - 1, \cdots, n - k + 1 \mid \nu_n, \nu_{n-1}, \cdots, \nu_{n-k+1}),$$

where $e_1 = n + (n-1) + \cdots + (n-k+1)$, $e_2 = \nu_n + \nu_{n-1} + \cdots + \nu_{n-k+1}$, $e_3 = -\varepsilon(\nu_{n-1}; \nu_n) - \varepsilon(\nu_{n-2}; \nu_n, \nu_{n-1}) - \cdots - \varepsilon(\nu_{n-k+1}; \nu_n, \cdots, \nu_{n-k+2})$, and the summation is over all permutations of $\nu_n, \nu_{n-1}, \cdots, \nu_{n-k+1}$ from the set $1, \cdots, n$ (i.e., over all choices of the k numbers ν_j subject to the condition that no two are equal in any one term).   There are $n(n - 1) \cdots (n - k + 1)$ summands.

We first consider the case $n = k$. By virtue of the agreement of our definition for determinants of null matrices with formula (1.1) for determinants of order one, we see that the appearance of the null matrices $A(n, \cdots, 1 \mid \nu_n, \cdots, \nu_1)$ does not affect the validity of formula (4.1). In this case the summation is over the $n!$ permutations $\nu_n, \cdots, \nu_1$ of $1, \cdots, n$. But then $\nu_n + \cdots + \nu_1 = n + \cdots + 1$, so that $e_1 = e_2$. Hence the factor $(-1)^{e_1 + e_2}$ can be dropped.

For any sequence $\nu_1, \cdots, \nu_n$ of distinct integers we say that $\sigma(\nu_1, \cdots, \nu_n) = \varepsilon(\nu_{n-1}; \nu_n) + \varepsilon(\nu_{n-2}; \nu_n, \nu_{n-1}) + \cdots + \varepsilon(\nu_j; \nu_n, \cdots, \nu_{j+1}) + \cdots + \varepsilon(\nu_1; \nu_n, \cdots, \nu_2)$ is the number of *inversions* of the given sequence. We can regard $\sigma(\nu_1, \cdots, \nu_n)$ as the number of interchanges of pairs ν_j, ν_k required to restore $\nu_1, \cdots, \nu_n$ to their natural order when the interchanges are made in the following sequence. We first obtain increasing order for ν_{n-1} and ν_n by $\varepsilon(\nu_{n-1}; \nu_n)$ interchanges; this is accomplished by interchanging ν_{n-1} and ν_n if $\nu_{n-1} > \nu_n$ and otherwise leaving them unchanged. Next we get $\nu_{n-2}, \nu_{n-1}, \nu_n$ in increasing order by $\varepsilon(\nu_{n-2}; \nu_n, \nu_{n-1})$ further interchanges. After the kth stage we have $\nu_{n-k+1}, \cdots, \nu_n$ arranged in increasing order and the $(k + 1)$th stage puts $\nu_{n-k}, \cdots, \nu_n$ in increasing order with $\varepsilon(\nu_{n-k}; \nu_n, \cdots, \nu_{n-k+1})$ further interchanges.

Note that in the case $n = k$ above we have $e_3 = -\sigma(\nu_1, \cdots, \nu_n)$. Hence if we now set $\pi(\nu_1, \cdots, \nu_n) = (-1)^{\sigma(\nu_1, \cdots, \nu_n)}$, we can collect the above results together in the following theorem which embodies the classical definition of determinant.

THEOREM 4.4A.   *For any square matrix A,*

$$(4.2) \qquad \det A = \Sigma \pi(\nu_1, \cdots, \nu_n) a_{1\nu_1} \cdots a_{n\nu_n}$$

where the sum is over all permutations $\nu_1, \cdots, \nu_n$ of $1, \cdots, n$ and $\pi(\nu_1, \cdots, \nu_n)$ is $+1$ or -1 according as the sequence $\nu_1, \cdots, \nu_n$ has an even number or an odd number of inversions.

The analogous result for permutations on the row indices is

$$(4.2') \qquad \det A = \Sigma \pi(\mu_1, \cdots, \mu_n) a_{\mu_1 1} \cdots a_{\mu_n n}.$$

We now return to formula (4.1) for $k < n$ and obtain another important theorem. Choose k indices $j_1 < \cdots < j_{k-1} < j_k$ from the set $1, \cdots, n$. Then for each of the $k!$ permutations $\nu_{n-k+1}, \cdots, \nu_n$ of $j_1, \cdots, j_k$ we have $A(n, \cdots, n - k + 1 \mid j_1, \cdots, j_k) = A(n, \cdots, n - k + 1 \mid \nu_{n-k+1}, \cdots, \nu_n)$. Each of the corresponding $k!$ terms in the summation will have $\det A(n, \cdots, n - k + 1 \mid \nu_{n-k+1}, \cdots, \nu_n)$ as a factor, and for each of these terms $e_2 = j_1 + \cdots + j_k$. Thus in (4.1) the coefficient of

$\det A(n, \cdots, n-k+1 \mid j_1, \cdots, j_k)$ is the product of $(-1)^{e_1+e_2}$ with

(4.3) $$\Sigma(-1)^{e_3} a_{n-k+1, \nu_{n-k+1}} \cdots a_{n\nu_n},$$

where the summation is over all permutations $\nu_{n-k+1}, \cdots, \nu_n$ of $j_1, \cdots, j_k$. Set $b_{ih} = a_{n-k+i, j_h}$ $(i, h = 1, \cdots, k)$, and let $B = \| b_{ih} \|$. Apart from sign the terms in the summation (4.3) are exactly those that occur in $\det B$ when expanded according to (4.2). We contend that the signs agree also. For consider any permutation $\nu_{n-k+1}, \cdots, \nu_n$ of $j_1, \cdots, j_k$, and suppose that $\nu_{n-k+i} = j_{\lambda_i}$ $(i = 1, \cdots, k)$. Then $a_{n-k+1, \nu_{n-k+1}} = b_{i\lambda_i}$ $(i = 1, \cdots, k)$. Since the j's are in increasing order, we see that $\nu_i > \nu_h$ if and only if $\lambda_i > \lambda_h$; hence e_3 in (4.3) is exactly the number of inversions in the sequence $\lambda_1, \cdots, \lambda_k$, and so $(-1)^{e_3} = \pi(\lambda_1, \cdots, \lambda_k)$ as claimed. This completes the proof that the expression in (4.3) is $\det B$. We note that $B = A[n-k+1, \cdots, n \mid j_1, \cdots, j_k]$.

Now return to formula (4.1). With each sequence $\nu_{n-k+1}, \cdots, \nu_n$ we can associate the unique ordered sequence $1 \leq \mu_1 < \cdots < \mu_k \leq n$ obtained by rearranging its terms. Each such ordered sequence $\{\mu_i\}$ will be associated with $k!$ of the sequences $\{\nu_i\}$. We have just proved that for a given ordered sequence $\{\mu_i\}$ the sum of the $k!$ terms of (4.1) belonging to the associated sequences $\{\nu_i\}$ is

$$(-1)^{e_1+e_2} \det A(n-k+1, \cdots, n \mid \mu_1, \cdots, \mu_k) \det A[n-k+1, \cdots, n \mid \mu_1, \cdots, \mu_k].$$

We will get all of (4.1) by summing this expression over all solutions of $1 \leq \mu_1 < \cdots < \mu_k \leq n$. This establishes the special case $h_1, \cdots, h_k = n-k+1, \cdots, n$ of the following theorem.

THEOREM 4.4B. (*Laplace Expansion*). *Let A be any square matrix; let $h_1, \cdots, h_k$ be k natural numbers such that $h_1 < h_2 < \cdots < h_k \leq n$. Then*

(4.4)
$$\det A = \Sigma(-1)^{h_1 + \cdots + h_k + \nu_1 + \cdots + \nu_k} \det A(h_1, \cdots, h_k \mid \nu_1, \cdots, \nu_k)$$
$$\cdot \det A[h_1, \cdots, h_k \mid \nu_1, \cdots, \nu_k],$$

where the summation is over all solutions of $1 \leq \nu_1 < \nu_2 < \cdots < \nu_k \leq n$. (The analogous expansion for columns also holds.)

Before proving the theorem we paraphrase it. Select any set of k rows from a square matrix A. Then $\det A$ is a sum of the form $\Sigma \pm BB'$ where B is a minor of A and B' is its complementary minor, and the summation is over all minors B of order k which can be formed from the given k rows, and the sign is given by (4.4).

We base the proof on the special case already obtained. Let $h_{k+1}, \cdots, h_n$ $(h_{k+1} < \cdots < h_n)$ be the natural numbers remaining in the set

$1, \cdots, n$ after removing $h_1, \cdots, h_k$, and set $B = \| b_{ij} \|$ where $b_{n-k+i,j} = a_{h_i j}$ $(i = 1, \cdots, k; j = 1, \cdots, n)$ and $b_{ij} = a_{h_{k+i} j}$ $(i = 1, \cdots, n - k; j = 1, \cdots, n)$. Then by the special case of the Laplace Expansion already proved

$$(4.5) \qquad \begin{aligned} \det B = \Sigma(-1)^{e_1+e_2} \det A(h_1, \cdots, h_k \mid v_1, \cdots, v_k) \\ \cdot \det A[h_1, \cdots, h_k \mid v_1, \cdots, v_k], \end{aligned}$$

where $e_1 = (n - k + 1) + \cdots + n$ and $e_2 = v_1 + \cdots + v_k$.

We know from formula (2.1) that $\det A = \pm \det B$, the sign depending on how many interchanges of rows are made in getting from A to B. It requires $n - h_k$ interchanges to move the h_kth row successively past the rows below it and into the last row; likewise it takes $(n - 1) - h_{k-1}$ interchanges to move the h_{k-1}th row down to the $(n - 1)$th row. Proceeding thus, we see that it takes in all $n + (n - 1) + \cdots + (n - k + 1) - h_k - h_{k-1} - \cdots - h_1$ interchanges to get from A to B. Thus

$$(4.6) \qquad \det A = (-1)^{e_1 + h_1 + \cdots + h_k} \det B.$$

Now substitute (4.5) in (4.6), and remove the factor $(-1)^{e_1+e_1} = 1$. The formula thus obtained is precisely (4.4).

The Laplace Expansion is especially useful in dealing with partitioned matrices having large blocks of zeros. For example, let

$$A = \left\| \begin{matrix} B & 0 \\ D & C \end{matrix} \right\|,$$

where A, B, and C are all square and B has degree k (D need not be square). Then any minor of order k formed from the first k rows of A is zero if its contains any column beyond the kth column. Thus the Laplace Expansion for $\det A$ according to the first k rows has only the single possibly nonzero term

$$(-1)^{1+2+\cdots+k+1+2+\cdots+k} (\det B)(\det C),$$

and so $\det A = (\det B)(\det C)$.

Exercises 4.4

1. What sign is associated with each of the following terms in the expansion of $\det \| a_{ij} \|$:

(a) $a_{43} \, a_{12} \, a_{21} \, a_{34}$,

(b) $a_{32} \, a_{15} \, a_{53} \, a_{24} \, a_{41}$,

(c) $a_{24} \, a_{66} \, a_{35} \, a_{42} \, a_{13} \, a_{51}$?

2. Evaluate the following determinant using the Laplace expansion on the first two columns:

$$\begin{vmatrix} 3 & -2 & 0 & 0 \\ 1 & 4 & 2 & 1 \\ 7 & 3 & 0 & 6 \\ -2 & -1 & 2 & 3 \end{vmatrix}.$$

3. Find det A if

$$A = \begin{Vmatrix} 0 & x-1 & 0 & 1 \\ 0 & 2 & 0 & -1 \\ 1 & 2 & x-1 & 1 \\ 2 & z & x & y \end{Vmatrix}.$$

4. Let $A = \begin{Vmatrix} B & 0 \\ D & C \end{Vmatrix}$ be a square matrix of degree v with a t-by-s 0 matrix in the upper right-hand corner. Show that det $A = 0$ if $s + t > v$.

4.5. Determinants of products of square matrices; determinantal criterion for rank.

We know from Theorem 4.2C that there is no simple connection between the determinant of a sum of two matrices and the determinants of the summands. The following theorem shows that we are more fortunate with products.

THEOREM 4.5A. *Let A and B be square matrices of degree n. Then* det $(AB) = ($det $A)($det $B)$.

The proof of this theorem will be completed after the next two lemmas.

It follows from Theorem 4.2G and Corollary 4.2H that this theorem is correct if either factor is an elementary matrix. More generally, if A is a product of elementary matrices, say $A = F_1 F_2 \cdots F_r$, then

$$\det (AB) = \det (F_1(F_2 \cdots F_r B)) = (\det F_1)(\det (F_2 \cdots F_r B))$$

$$= \cdots = (\det F_1)(\det F_2) \cdots (\det F_r)(\det B).$$

The special case $B = I_n$ of this formula shows that det $A = ($det $F_1)($det $F_2) \cdots ($det $F_r)$ and, in particular, det $A \neq 0$. Moreover, for B arbitrary we have det $(AB) = ($det $A)($det $B)$ provided that A is a product of elementary matrices. But (cf. Theorem 3.7D) a matrix is a product of elementary matrices if and only if it is nonsingular. Thus we have proved the following lemma.

LEMMA 4.5B. *Suppose that A is nonsingular. Then (a) det $A \neq 0$ and (b)* det $(AB) = ($det $A)($det $B)$.

Next suppose that a square matrix B is singular. Then we can find a nonsingular matrix A such that the product $C = AB$ is a Hermite matrix. Since B is singular, C will have at least one row of zeros. Now by Theorem 4.2B and Lemma 4.5B we have $0 = \det C = \det AB = (\det A)(\det B)$, and therefore $\det B = 0$. This result together with the preceding lemma establishes the following lemma.

LEMMA 4.5C. *A square matrix B is singular if and only if $\det B = 0$.*

Since a product of two square matrices is singular if either factor is singular (see Section 3.1), we see from this lemma that $\det AB = 0$ if either A or B is singular, and hence $\det (AB) = (\det A)(\det B)$ if either factor is singular.

This result together with Lemma 4.5B gives Theorem 4.5A in all cases.

THEOREM 4.5D. *Let A be a martix of degree n, and let c be a scalar. Then* $\det (cA) = c^n \det A$.

We have $cA = c(I_n A) = (cI_n)A$. Hence, $\det (cA) = (\det (cI_n))(\det A) = c^n \det A$ (cf. Corollary 4.1D).

We can use the above results to get a new method for characterizing the rank of a matrix.

THEOREM 4.5E. *Let $A = \| a_{ij} \|$ be a v-by-w $\mathscr{F}$ matrix. Let $s(A)$ be the largest integer for which there exists a square submatrix B of degree $s(A)$ such that $\det B \neq 0$. Then $s(A)$ is equal to the rank of A.*

This theorem follows at once from Theorem 3.1G and Lemma 4.5C.

Exercises 4.5

1. Find the maximum possible rank for a 7-by-10 matrix having a 4-by-7 zero submatrix.

2. Give a generalization of the preceding exercise.

3. Use determinants to compute the rank of the matrix

$$A = \left\| \begin{array}{rrr} 3 & 1 & 2 \\ 2 & 3 & -2 \\ -3 & -8 & 8 \end{array} \right\|.$$

4. Find those values of x for which

$$A = \left\| \begin{array}{cc} x+1 & 2 \\ 4 & x-1 \end{array} \right\|$$

is singular.

5. Let $A = \left\|\begin{matrix} 2 & 1 & 3 \\ 0 & 1 & 2 \\ 0 & 0 & -2 \end{matrix}\right\|$. Find those values of x for which $xI - A$ is singular.

6. Do Exercise 5 if $A = \left\|\begin{matrix} -1 & 4 & -1 \\ 0 & 2 & 0 \\ 2 & -3 & 0 \end{matrix}\right\|$.

4.6. Determinants of products of rectangular matrices. Suppose that $A = \| a_{ij} \|$ is a v-by-w matrix and that $B = \| b_{ij} \|$ is a w-by-v matrix. Then the product $C = AB$ is square of degree v. Since the rank of a product cannot exceed that of either factor, C will be singular if $v > w$, and in this case it follows from Lemma 4.5C that $\det AB = 0$. The main result of the present section is a theorem that provides a means of evaluating $\det AB$ in case $v \leqq w$. The proofs will be based on the results of Sections 4.2 and 4.4 and so will provide incidentally a proof of Theorem 4.5A which does not make use of our previous work on row equivalence of matrices.

THEOREM 4.6A. *Let $A = \| a_{ij} \|$ be a v-by-w $\mathscr{F}$ matrix, let $B = \| b_{ij} \|$ be w-by-v $\mathscr{F}$ matrix, and suppose that $v \leqq w$. Then*

$$(6.1) \quad \det AB = \Sigma \det A[1, \cdots, v \mid \mu_1, \cdots, \mu_v] \det B[\mu_1, \cdots, \mu_v \mid 1, \cdots, v],$$

where the sum is over all solutions of $1 \leqq \mu_1 < \cdots < \mu_v \leqq w$.

In words, $\det AB$ is the sum of all products of the form $\det A' \det B'$ where A' is a square submatrix of A of degree v, and B' is the square submatrix of B of degree v which is obtained by keeping the rows of B whose indices are the same as the indices of those columns of A which are kept to give A'. Of course, if $v = w$, there is just one term, and Theorem 4.6A reduces to Theorem 4.5A.

Let $AB = C = \| c_{ij} \| = \| \Sigma a_{ir}b_{\lambda j} \|$. For each j, the jth column of C is the sum of the w column matrices $\| a_{ir}b_{rj} \|$ $(r = 1, \cdots, w)$. Hence, by repeated applications of Theorem 4.2C we get

$$\det C = \Sigma \det \| a_{i\lambda_h}b_{\lambda_h j} \|,$$

where the summation is over the w^v solutions of $1 \leqq \lambda_h \leqq w$ $(h = 1, \cdots, v)$.

Next apply formula (2.2) to each column, and we get

$$(6.2) \qquad \det C = \Sigma \det \| a_{i\lambda_h} \| \cdot b_{\lambda_1 1} \cdots b_{\lambda_v v},$$

where the summation still includes w^v terms. However, any of the terms for which two λ_h are equal will be zero since it has as a factor the determinant of a matrix with two equal columns (Corollary 4.2F). Thus we restrict the summation to all permutations of $1, \cdots, w$ taken v at a time. We now follow the method used in the proof of Theorem 4.4B. Let $\mu_1, \cdots, \mu_v$ be a solution of $1 \leq \mu_1 < \cdots < \mu_v \leq w$. Then exactly $v!$ of the permutations $\{\lambda_h\}$ are permutations of the given ordered subset $\mu_1, \cdots, \mu_v$. Furthermore, if $\{\lambda_h\}$ is a permutation of $\mu_1, \cdots, \mu_v$, then it follows from formula (2.1) that $\det \| a_{i\lambda_h} \| = \pi(\lambda_1, \cdots, \lambda_v) \det \| a_{i\mu_h} \|$. Hence, the $v!$ terms of (6.2) associated with a given ordered set $\mu_1, \cdots, \mu_v$ give

$$(6.3) \qquad (\det \| a_{i\mu_h} \|)(\Sigma \pi(\lambda_1, \cdots, \lambda_v) b_{\lambda_1 1} \cdots b_{\lambda_v v}),$$

where the summation is over all permutations $\{\lambda_h\}$ of $\mu_1, \cdots, \mu_v$. But, according to formula (4.2'), the second factor in (6.3) is $\det \| b_{\mu_h j} \|$. Now, since $\| a_{i\mu_h} \| = A[1, \cdots, v \mid \mu_1, \cdots, \mu_v]$ and $\| b_{\mu_h j} \| = B[\mu_1, \cdots, \mu_v \mid 1, \cdots, v]$, we can write the product in (6.3) as

$$(6.4) \qquad \det A[1, \cdots, v \mid \mu_1, \cdots, \mu_v] \det B[\mu_1, \cdots, \mu_v \mid 1, \cdots, v].$$

The theorem now follows when we substitute (6.4) in (6.2) and observe that the summation over all permutations $\{\lambda_h\}$ is then replaced by the summation over all solutions $\{\mu_h\}$ of $1 \leq \mu_1 < \cdots < \mu_v \leq w$.

This theorem has many important applications. We first use it to get a new proof of Theorem 4.5E. This new proof is based on the following lemma, with notation as in the statement of Theorem 4.5E.

LEMMA 4.6B. *Let A and B be two matrices for which the product AB is defined. Then $s(AB) \leq \min \{s(A), s(B)\}$.*

Let $C = AB$, and let $C' = C[i_1, \cdots, i_s \mid j_1, \cdots, j_s]$ be a square submatrix of degree s of C. Then according to the rules of matrix multiplication $C' = A'B'$, where $A' = A[i_1, \cdots, i_s \mid 1, \cdots, w]$ and $B' = B[1, \cdots, w \mid j_1, \cdots, j_s]$ (w being the column degree of A).

Suppose that $s > s(A)$. Then each s-rowed square submatrix of A and therefore also of A' has zero determinant, and so by Theorem 4.6A we conclude that $\det C' = 0$. Hence, $s(C) \leq s(A)$. Similarly $s(C) \leq s(B)$.

COROLLARY 4.6C. *Let A be a v-by-w matrix, and let P and Q be nonsingular square matrices of degrees v and w, respectively. Then $s(A) = s(PAQ)$.*

By the lemma $s(PAQ) \leqq s(A)$. On the other hand, $A = P^{-1}(PAQ)Q^{-1}$, so that $s(A) \leqq s(PAQ)$. Hence $s(A) = s(PAQ)$ as claimed.

Now, according to Theorem 3.8E there exist nonsingular matrices P and Q such that

$$PAQ = B = \left\| \begin{matrix} I_r & 0 \\ 0 & 0 \end{matrix} \right\|,$$

where $r = \text{rank } A$. It is obvious that $s(B) = r$. But by the corollary $r = s(B) = s(PAQ) = s(A)$; this establishes Theorem 4.5E. Note that this also gives a new proof that a square matrix is singular if and only if its determinant is zero.

Another application of Theorem 4.6A is given in the following theorem:

THEOREM 4.6D.   *Let A be a v-by-w matrix where $v \leqq w$.   Then $\det AA^\mathsf{T}$ is a sum of squares.*

Let $B = A^\mathsf{T}$.   Then $A[1, \cdots, v \mid \mu_1, \cdots, \mu_v]^\mathsf{T} = B[\mu_1, \cdots, \mu_v \mid 1, \cdots, v]$ and so by Theorem 4.2A each summand in formula (6.1) is a square. Indeed we have

$$\det AA^\mathsf{T} = \Sigma \ (\det A[1, \cdots, v \mid \mu_1, \cdots, \mu_v])^2,$$

[the summation has the same range as the one in (6.1)].

Exercise 4.6

1. Let C be a real m-by-n matrix of rank m.   Show that $C' = C^\mathsf{T}(CC^\mathsf{T})^{-1}$ is a right inverse for C, and that $C = [(C')^\mathsf{T}C']^{-1}(C')^\mathsf{T}$. Show that C' is the only right inverse for C whose transpose $(C')^\mathsf{T}$ has the same row space as C.

(T. N. E. Greville)

4.7. Adjoints and inverses of square matrices; Cramer's Rule.

Suppose that $A = \| a_{ij} \|$ is a square matrix of degree v. Let $b_{ij} = (-1)^{i+j} \det A (j \mid i)$ $(i, j = 1, \cdots, v)$. We say that $B = \| b_{ij} \|$ is the *adjoint* of A, sometimes written as $B = \text{adj } A$.

THEOREM 4.7A.   *For any square matrix A of degree v, $A \, (\text{adj } A) = (\text{adj } A)A = (\det A)I$, or in terms of the elements*

$$\Sigma(-1)^{j+\lambda}a_{i\lambda} \det A(j \mid \lambda) = \Sigma(-1)^{\mu+i} \det A(\mu \mid i)a_{\mu j}$$
$$= \delta_{ij} \det A \qquad (i, j = 1, \cdots, v).$$

Let $B = \text{adj } A$ and let $AB = C = \| c_{ij} \|$. Then $c_{ij} = \Sigma a_{i\lambda}b_{\lambda j} = \Sigma a_{i\lambda}(-1)^{j+\lambda} \det A(j \mid \lambda)$ $(i, j = 1, \cdots, v)$. If $i = j$, it follows from Theorem 4.1A that $c_{ii} = \det A$. Next suppose that $i \neq j$, and let A_{ij}

be the matrix obtained from A by replacing the jth row of A by the ith row of A. Then $A_{ij}(j \mid h) = A(j \mid h)$ $(h = 1, \cdots, v)$, and det $A_{ij} = 0$ (since A_{ij} has two identical rows). Now we have

$$0 = \det A_{ij} = \Sigma(-1)^{j+\lambda}a_{i\lambda} \det A_{ij}(j \mid \lambda) = \Sigma(-1)^{j+\lambda}a_{i\lambda} A(j \mid \lambda) = c_{ij}.$$

This establishes the equality $A(\text{adj } A) = (\det A)I_v$. The proof that $(\text{adj } A)A = (\det A)I_v$ is similar, and we omit it.

$\times$**Theorem 4.7B.** *Let A be a nonsingular matrix of degree v. Then $A^{-1} = (1/\det A) \text{adj } A$.*

This is an immediate consequence of the preceding theorem. Note that the (i, j) entry of A^{-1} is $(-1)^{i+j} \det A(j \mid i)/\det A$. This result is actually more important for theoretical purposes than as a practical method for computing A^{-1}.

Theorem 4.7C. *Let A be a square matrix of degree v. Then the rank of adj A is v, 1, or 0 according as the rank of A is v, $v - 1$, or less than $v - 1$.*

It follows from Theorem 4.7A that adj A has rank v if A has rank v, and it follows from the definition of the adjoint that adj $A = 0$ (and hence has rank 0) if A has rank less than $v - 1$. Suppose next that rank $A = v - 1$. Then according to Theorem 4.5E at least one element of adj A is different from zero, and so rank $(\text{adj } A) \geq 1$. To see that the rank of adj A is at most one we consider the matrix equation $AX = 0$, where X is a v-by-1 matrix. According to Theorem 3.2A the set of solutions forms a vector space of dimension $v - (v - 1) = 1$. Let Y be a particular nonzero solution. Then any other solution is a scalar multiple of Y. Now from Theorem 4.7A we have $A(\text{adj } A)=(\det A)I_v=0$. Thus every column of adj A is a solution of $AX = 0$, and hence the maximum number of independent columns of adj A is one; i.e., $r(\text{adj } A)\leq 1$. It follows that $r(\text{adj } A)$ is exactly one.

Theorem 4.7D. *(Cramer's Rule).* *Let $A = \| a_{ij} \|$ be a square $\mathscr{F}$ matrix of degree v, let $K = \| k_i \|$ be a v-by-1 $\mathscr{F}$ matrix, and let A_i $(i=1, \cdots, v)$ be the matrix obtained from A by substituting K for the ith column of A. Then, if $\det A \neq 0$, the equation $AX = K$ has the unique solution*

$$(7.1) \qquad X = \| x_i \| = \| (\det A_i)/\det A \|.$$

If $\det A = 0$, then the equation has either no solution or infinitely many solutions according as the ranks of A and the augmented matrix $B = \| A \ K \|$ are unequal or equal.

The last part of the theorem is merely a restatement of Theorem 3.9B; hence, we need only consider the case $\det A \neq 0$; i.e., A is nonsingular. If $AX = K$, then, on premultiplying both sides by A^{-1}, we find that

$X = A^{-1}K$. Furthermore $X = A^{-1}K$ is a solution of $AX = K$ since $A(A^{-1}K) = K$. This establishes the uniqueness and existence of a solution of $AX = K$. To complete the proof of the theorem we need only show that the right-hand term in (7.1) is equal to $A^{-1}K$. To see this we observe that since A_i agrees with A aside from the ith column we have det $A_i = \sum (-1)^{\nu+i}k_\nu$ det $A(\nu \mid i)$ which is also the element in the ith row of the product (adj $A)K$. Dividing through by det A and using Theorem 4.7B, we then get $\| (\det A_i)/\det A \| = A^{-1}K$ as claimed.

COROLLARY 4.7E.   *Let A be a square $\mathscr{F}$ matrix of degree v. Then the system of homogeneous linear equations with matrix A has a nontrivial solution if and only if* det $A = 0$.

By Cramer's Rule $AX = 0$ has only the trivial solution $X = 0$ if det $A \neq 0$. On the other hand, if det $A = 0$, the rank of A is less than the number of unknowns, and so there is a nontrivial solution (see Theorem 3.2A).

Exercises 4.7

1. Compute the inverse of each of the following matrices :

$$
(a) \quad \begin{Vmatrix} 2 & 3 & -1 \\ -2 & 6 & 4 \\ 3 & 0 & 1 \end{Vmatrix}, \qquad (b) \quad \begin{Vmatrix} 2 & 6 & 3 & 1 \\ 0 & 3 & 0 & 7 \\ 0 & 0 & 1 & -3 \\ 0 & 0 & 0 & -2 \end{Vmatrix}.
$$

(i) by means of the adjoint, (ii) by means of row transformations as suggested in the paragraphs preceding Theorem 3.7E.

2. Solve using Cramer's Rule:

(a) $x_1 + x_2 + x_3 = 2,$

$4x_1 + 2x_2 + x_3 = 8,$

$x_1 - x_2 + x_3 = -4;$

(b) $x_1 + x_2 + x_3 = 0,$

$9x_1 + 3x_2 + x_3 = 12,$

$6x_1 + 3x_2 + 2x_3 = 5.$

Chapter 5

Equivalence Relations and Canonical Forms

In Chapter 2 we saw that relative to fixed bases each linear transformation corresponds to a unique matrix; this matrix might be regarded as the "analytic expression" for the linear transformation much as we speak of an "equation" for a curve. In the present chapter we consider what happens to the matrices when the bases are changed. The terms "alias" and "alibi" are utilized to help describe the situation. We introduce several relations between matrices and by abstraction from them arrive at the concepts of equivalence relation, partition, and canonical form. Finally some fundamental results on similarity of matrices are presented.

5.1. Equivalence relations. We recall (see Appendix II) that a relation between two sets $\mathscr{M}$ and $\mathscr{N}$ is a subset $\mathscr{R}$ of the Cartesian product $\mathscr{M} \times \mathscr{N}$; i.e., $\mathscr{R}$ is a set of ordered pairs (A, B) with A in $\mathscr{M}$ and B in $\mathscr{N}$. If (A, B) is one of the ordered pairs in $\mathscr{R}$, we write $A \mathscr{R} B$ (read "A is in the relation $\mathscr{R}$ to B"). We are now interested in the special case $\mathscr{N} = \mathscr{M}$ and then speak of (binary) relations on $\mathscr{M}$.

For example, row equivalence is a relation on the set of all matrices over a given field. We have no special symbol for this relation and have written "A is row-equivalent to B" in place of "$A \mathscr{R} B$." For equivalence of matrices we introduced the notation $A \overset{\text{E}}{=} B$, and thus may speak of the relation $\overset{\text{E}}{=}$.

A binary relation $\mathscr{R}$ on a set $\mathscr{M}$ is said to be an *equivalence relation* if it satisfies the following conditions:

	(i)	For all A in $\mathscr{M}$, $A \mathscr{R} A$	(reflexivity),
(1.1)	(ii)	If $A \mathscr{R} B$, then $B \mathscr{R} A$	(symmetry),
	(iii)	If $A \mathscr{R} B$ and $B \mathscr{R} C$, then $A \mathscr{R} C$	(transitivity).

All of the relations discussed above are equivalence relations; this has been proved in Theorems 3.3A, 3.7G, and 3.8C. The relation $\leq$ on the set of real numbers is not an equivalence relation since it fails to satisfy (ii). It is easy to construct relations that satisfy none of the conditions (i), (ii), (iii).

Let $\mathscr{R}$ be an equivalence relation on a set $\mathscr{M}$, and let A be an element of $\mathscr{M}$. We denote by $[A]$ the set of all elements B for which $A \mathscr{R} B$, and call $[A]$ an *equivalence class*.

LEMMA 5.1A. *Let $\mathscr{R}$ be an equivalence relation on a set $\mathscr{M}$. Then we have* (I) *Every element A in $\mathscr{M}$ lies in at least one equivalence class, and* (II) *No element lies in two distinct equivalence classes.*

By (1.1i), if A is in $\mathscr{M}$, then $A \mathscr{R} A$, and so A is in $[A]$; this proves I. Next, suppose that C is in $[A]$ and C is in $[B]$; i.e., $A \mathscr{R} C$ and $B \mathscr{R} C$. Let D be in $[B]$; i.e., $B \mathscr{R} D$. From (1.1ii) we have $C \mathscr{R} B$, and then from (1.1iii) and $A \mathscr{R} C$, $C \mathscr{R} B$, $B \mathscr{R} D$ we have $A \mathscr{R} D$. This means that every element D of $[B]$ also lies in $[A]$, or $[A]$ contains $[B]$. Similarly $[B]$ contains $[A]$; hence $[A] = [B]$; this establishes II.

A collection $\mathscr{C} = \{\mathscr{N}, \mathscr{P}, \cdots\}$ of subsets of a set $\mathscr{M}$ is said to be a *partition* of $\mathscr{M}$ if it satisfies the following conditions:

(1.2)

    I Each element A in $\mathscr{M}$ lies in at least one subset $\mathscr{P}$ of the collection $\mathscr{C}$.

    II No element of $\mathscr{M}$ lies in two distinct subsets of the collection $\mathscr{C}$.

By the lemma above, every equivalence relation on a set $\mathscr{M}$ defines a partition of $\mathscr{M}$, the subsets of the partition being the equivalence classes. The converse is given by the next lemma.

LEMMA 5.1B. *Let $\mathscr{C}$ be a partition of $\mathscr{M}$ into subsets $\mathscr{N}$, $\mathscr{P}$, $\cdots$, and define the binary relation $\mathscr{R}$ by the condition $A \mathscr{R} B$ if and only if there exists a subset $\mathscr{P}$ of the collection $\mathscr{C}$ of which both A and B are members. Then $\mathscr{R}$ is an equivalence relation on $\mathscr{M}$.*

First, we observe that (i) follows from I and that (ii) is a consequence of the symmetry of A and B in the definition of $\mathscr{R}$. Next suppose that A and B belong to $\mathscr{N}$ and that B and C belong to $\mathscr{P}$. Then, by II, $\mathscr{N} = \mathscr{P}$ and so $A \mathscr{R} C$; this checks (iii).

COROLLARY 5.1C. *The mapping from $\mathscr{C}$ to $\mathscr{R}$ described in Lemma 5.1B is a one-to-one correspondence of the set of all partitions $\mathscr{C}$ of $\mathscr{M}$ onto the set of all equivalence relations $\mathscr{R}$ on $\mathscr{M}$ and is the inverse of the mapping described in Lemma 5.1A.*

A binary operation on a set is a function that assigns to each ordered pair from the set a unique element of the set. We frequently wish to define operations on equivalence classes using properties of the elements of the equivalence classes.   The following theorem gives a condition under which this can be done.

THEOREM 5.1D.   *Let $\mathscr{R}$ be an equivalence relation on a set $\mathscr{M} = \{A, B, \cdots\}$, and suppose that $\odot$ is a binary operation on $\mathscr{M}$.   The association $[A] \odot [B] = [A \odot B]$ is a binary operation on the set of equivalence classes if and only if $A \mathscr{R} A'$ and $B \mathscr{R} B'$ imply $(A \odot B)\mathscr{R}(A' \odot B')$.*

If $\mathscr{R}$ and $\odot$ satisfy the hypotheses of this theorem, we say that $\mathscr{R}$ has the *substitution property relative to* $\odot$.

What one needs to prove is that the association is well-defined, i.e., does not depend for its value on what representatives A, B are chosen.   The proof of this theorem is left as an exercise.

Exercises 5.1

1. Give examples of relations which satisfy (*a*) (i), (ii) but not (iii); (*b*) (i), (iii) but not (ii); (*c*) (ii), (iii) but not (i); (*d*) none of (i), (ii), (iii).

2. Give a proof for Theorem 5.1D.

3. Let m be a nonzero integer.   Two integers a, b are said to be *congruent modulo m* if $a - b$ is divisible by m; we write $a \equiv b \pmod{m}$.   Prove that congruence modulo m is an equivalence relation.

4. Let $\mathscr{W}$ be a subspace of a vector space $\mathscr{V}$.   Two vectors α, β are said to be *congruent modulo $\mathscr{W}$* if $\alpha - \beta$ is in $\mathscr{W}$; we write $\alpha \equiv \beta \pmod{\mathscr{W}}$.   Prove that congruence modulo $\mathscr{W}$ is an equivalence relation.

5. Show that congruence modulo m has the substitution property relative to $+$ and $\cdot$, and give related definitions for addition and multiplication for the equivalence classes.

6. Prove that the set of equivalence classes of the integers modulo m, with addition and multiplication defined as in the preceding exercise, is a ring.

7. Let $\mathscr{W}$ be a subspace of a vector space $\mathscr{V}$.   If $\alpha \equiv \beta \pmod{\mathscr{W}}$, show that $c\alpha \equiv c\beta \pmod{\mathscr{W}}$.   If also $\gamma \equiv \delta \pmod{\mathscr{W}}$, show that $\alpha + \gamma \equiv \beta + \delta \pmod{\mathscr{W}}$.

8. Show that addition of equivalence classes modulo $\mathscr{W}$ defined as $[\alpha] + [\gamma] = [\alpha + \gamma]$ and the multiplication by a scalar defined as $c[\alpha] = [c\alpha]$ are operations.   Finally show that the set of equivalence classes modulo $\mathscr{W}$ forms a vector space; it is called the *quotient space* of $\mathscr{V}$ by $\mathscr{W}$ and is designated by $\mathscr{V}/\mathscr{W}$.

9. Prove that, if $\{\alpha_1, \cdots, \alpha_v\}$ is a basis of $\mathscr{V}$, where $\{\alpha_1, \cdots, \alpha_r\}$ is a basis of $\mathscr{W}$, then $\{[\alpha_{r+1}], \cdots, [\alpha_v]\}$ is a basis of $\mathscr{V}/\mathscr{W}$.

10. Show that equivalence of matrices does not have the substitution property relative to matrix addition.

11. Find some further examples of equivalence relations and operations for which the substitution property does not hold.

5.2. Canonical forms and invariants.

The work in many of the preceding sections can be summarized under the heading of determining various conditions under which two objects A and B will lie in the same equivalence class, and of determining in each equivalence class some special unique member whose form is especially convenient in studying properties of the whole equivalence class. This is true of the Hermite matrix H for improper row equivalence, the row-echelon matrix D for row equivalence,

and the matrix $\left\| \begin{matrix} I_r & 0 \\ 0 & 0 \end{matrix} \right\|$ for equivalence. Such a selection of one

member from each class is said to provide a *canonical form* for the given equivalence relation, and the selected element is called the *canonical form* for all the members of its equivalence class. Once a canonical form has been determined for an equivalence relation, one can check $A \mathcal{R} B$ by seeing if A and B have the same canonical form.

Although from the strictly formal point of view a canonical form is a mapping which assigns to each equivalence class one of its members, an additional feature frequently found in a presentation of canonical forms is a systematic method for passing from an element A to the canonical form C equivalent to A. We have seen this in the cases mentioned above.

Sometimes the term "canonical form" is used even if there are several members selected from each equivalence class. In such cases the members selected will usually differ only in some minor point, and the equivalence of the selected members will be obvious. A more accurate term for this case is "normal form."

Consider the relation $\overset{\mathrm{E}}{=}$. If two matrices A and B belong to the same equivalence class, we must have

$$
\begin{aligned}
\deg_r (A) &= \deg_r (B) &&\text{(row degrees equal)}, \\
\deg_c (A) &= \deg_c (B) &&\text{(column degrees equal)}, \\
\operatorname{rank} A &= \operatorname{rank} B &&\text{(ranks equal)}.
\end{aligned}
$$

(2.1)

The quantities $\deg_r(A)$, $\deg_c(A)$, and rank A are accordingly said to be *invariants* for the relation $\overset{\mathrm{E}}{=}$. In general, if $f: A \to f(A)$ is any function on the elements of a set $\mathcal{M}$ and if $\mathcal{R}$ is an equivalence relation on $\mathcal{M}$, we say that the function f *is an invariant for the relation* $\mathcal{R}$ if $f(A) = f(B)$ whenever $A \mathcal{R} B$.

In geometry, congruence is an example of an equivalence relation. If two circles are congruent, they have the same radius; if two parabolas are congruent, the distance from focus to vertex (focal radius) is the same in both; if two triangles are congruent, corresponding angles are equal. These quantities are accordingly invariants for congruence. Also in geometry similarity is an example of an equivalence relation. Radius and focal radius are not invariants for this relation, but the angles of a triangle are still invariants.

It is clear from the definition of an invariant f that $f(A) \neq f(B)$ implies that A and B lie in different equivalence classes.   We are interested also in the converse problem: Does $f(A) = f(B)$ imply $A \mathscr{R} B$?   In the examples above, equality of radii or of focal radii do indeed imply congruence, but equality of rank is not sufficient to guarantee $A \overset{\text{E}}{\equiv} B$.

In some cases equality of several invariants may be needed to guarantee equivalence.   Thus the three equalities in (2.1) are sufficient conditions for $A \overset{\text{E}}{\equiv} B$ (cf. Theorem 3.8F).

In general, a set $f, g, \cdots$ of invariants for a relation $\mathscr{R}$ is said to be *complete* if $f(A) = f(B)$, $g(A) = g(B), \cdots$ implies $A \mathscr{R} B$.   Thus the radius is a complete set of invariants for circles under congruence, and row degree, column degree, and rank are a complete set of invariants for the relation $\overset{\text{E}}{\equiv}$.   Given any relation, an important problem is to find a complete set of invariants.   We have solved this problem for equivalence, row equivalence, and improper row equivalence, and shall consider it in coming chapters for other important equivalence relations.

If we have a canonical form for a relation $\mathscr{R}$, say $f(A)$ is the canonical form for A, then $f(A)$ is a complete set of invariants for $\mathscr{R}$.   A canonical form is especially effective when it can be constructed in terms of invariants which have a simple direct meaning for each element A of $\mathscr{M}$; e.g., rank, row degree, and column degree for equivalence of matrices.

Exercises 5.2

1. Give a complete set of invariants for triangles under congruence.

2. Show that $A + C$ and $B^2 - 4AC$ are invariants for loci

$$Ax^2 + Bxy + Cy^2 + Dx + Ey + F = 0$$

under translation and rotation of coordinate axes.   Discuss the geometric significance of these invariants.

3. Find canonical forms for equations of second degree in x and y under translations and rotations of coordinate axes.

4. Find the canonical forms for the matrix

$$A = \left\| \begin{array}{cccc} 2 & 0 & -1 & 3 \\ 1 & 0 & 2 & 5 \\ 1 & 0 & 7 & 12 \end{array} \right\|$$

relative to equivalence, row equivalence, and improper row equivalence, respectively.

5.3. Alias and alibi.   The parabola $16x^2 + 24xy + 9y^2 - 15x + 20y = 0$ is congruent to the parabola $y^2 = x$ as one can demonstrate by use of the substitution

(3.1)
$$\begin{cases} x = \tfrac{3}{5}x' + \tfrac{4}{5}y', \\[2mm] y = \tfrac{4}{5}x' + \tfrac{3}{5}y', \end{cases} \quad \text{or} \quad \begin{cases} x' = \tfrac{3}{5}x - \tfrac{4}{5}y, \\[2mm] y' = \tfrac{4}{5}x + \tfrac{3}{5}y. \end{cases}$$

These equations can be interpreted in either of two ways: first, as representing a rotation about the origin in which the point with coordinates (x, y) is mapped into the point with coordinates (x', y') and hence as a rotation which sends the first parabola into congruence with the second parabola; second, as representing a change of coordinates (via rotation of axes) under which the point with coordinates (x, y) is given new coordinates (x', y') and under which the old equation $16x^2 + 24xy + 9y^2 - 15x + 20y = 0$ is replaced by the new equation $y'^2 = x'$. The words *alibi* (the point has changed its position) and *alias* (the point has changed its name) are used to refer to these two interpretations of equations such as (3.1) and also in the analogous situation in the theory of vector spaces.

We can regard a linear transformation T of a vector space $\mathscr{V}$ into itself as a process of moving vectors into new position. If $\mathscr{S} = \{\alpha_1, \cdots, \alpha_v\}$ is a basis for $\mathscr{V}$ and T has matrix $C = \| c_{ij} \|$ relative to $\mathscr{S}$, we have seen (cf. Theorem 2.9A) that, if

$$(3.2) \qquad \alpha = a_1\alpha_1 + \cdots + a_v\alpha_v,$$

then $\alpha\mathsf{T} = \beta = b_1\alpha_1 + \cdots + b_v\alpha_v$ where

$$(3.3) \qquad \| b_j \| = \| a_j \| \, \| c_{ij} \|.$$

Here we might say that $\| b_j \|$ is the alibi for $\| a_j \|$.

The corresponding alias problem is handled by the following theorem.

THEOREM 5.3A. *Let $\mathscr{V}$ be a vector space with bases $\mathscr{S} = \{\alpha_1, \cdots, \alpha_v\}$ and $\mathscr{S}' = \{\alpha'_1, \cdots, \alpha'_v\}$; let $P = \| p_{ij} \|$ be the matrix whose ith row is $\| \alpha'_i \|_{\mathscr{S}}$; let $P' = \| p_{ij'} \|$ be the matrix whose ith row is $\| \alpha_i \|_{\mathscr{S}'}$ $(i = 1, \cdots, v)$. Then P is a nonsingular matrix with inverse P'. Moreover, for each vector α we have*

$$\| \alpha \|_{\mathscr{S}'} = \| \alpha \|_{\mathscr{S}} P' \qquad and \qquad \| \alpha \|_{\mathscr{S}} = \| \alpha \|_{\mathscr{S}'} P.$$

If $\alpha = \Sigma a_\lambda \alpha_\lambda = \Sigma a'_\lambda \alpha'_\lambda$ then $\| \alpha \|_{\mathscr{S}} = \| a_j \|$, $\| \alpha \|_{\mathscr{S}'} = \| a'_j \|$, and the above equations become

$$(3.4) \qquad \| a'_j \| = \| a_j \| P' \qquad and \qquad \| a_j \| = \| a'_j \| P.$$

By our hypotheses on P and P' we have

$$(3.5) \qquad a'_i = \sum_{\lambda=1}^{v} p_{i\lambda}\alpha_\lambda \qquad\qquad (i = 1, \cdots, v),$$

$$(3.6) \qquad \alpha_i = \sum_{\lambda=1}^{v} p'_{i\lambda}\alpha'_\lambda \qquad\qquad (i = 1, \cdots, v).$$

If we substitute (3.5) in (3.6) we get

$$\alpha_i = \sum_{\lambda=1}^{v} p'_{i\lambda} \sum_{\mu=1}^{v} p_{\lambda\mu}\alpha_\mu$$

$$= \sum_{\mu=1}^{v} \left(\sum_{\lambda=1}^{v} p'_{i\lambda}p_{\lambda\mu} \right)\alpha_\mu \qquad (i=1,\cdots,v).$$

Since $\mathscr{S}$ is a basis we must have

$$(3.7) \qquad \sum_{\lambda=1}^{v} p'_{i\lambda}p_{\lambda j} = \begin{cases} 1 & \text{if} \quad i=j \\ 0 & \text{if} \quad i \neq j \end{cases} \qquad (i,j=1,\cdots,v),$$

or, in matrix terms, $P'P = I$; i.e., P' is a left inverse for P. It follows from Theorem 2.5D that $PP' = I$, i.e., that P is nonsingular and has P' as its inverse. This result could also be obtained by substituting (3.6) in (3.5).

We now compute the alias of α; i.e., $\| \alpha \|_{\mathscr{S}'}$. We have

$$\alpha = \sum a_\lambda \alpha_\lambda$$

$$= \sum_\lambda a_\lambda \sum_\mu p'_{\lambda\mu}\alpha'_\mu$$

$$= \sum_\mu \left(\sum_\lambda a_\lambda p'_{\lambda\mu} \right) \alpha'_\mu = \sum_\mu a'_\mu \alpha'_\mu,$$

which gives $\| \alpha \|_{\mathscr{S}'} = \| \alpha \|_{\mathscr{S}} P'$.

We can paraphrase this result by the statement that the new or alias coordinates are obtained by multiplying the row matrix of old coordinates on the right by the matrix which describes the old basis in terms of the new one.

In general, a major application of alias methods lies in the solution of alibi problems. This is illustrated by the example at the beginning of this section in which we solved an alibi problem (congruence) by alias methods (change of coordinates).

In the next section we apply this idea to problems arising in the theory of vector spaces and base this application on the close formal resemblance of equations (3.3) and (3.4).

We note one important distinction between alias and alibi. Whereas in the alias case the matrix P must be nonsingular, there is no such restriction on C in the alibi case. However, this restriction applies if we wish to solve an alibi problem by alias methods.

Exercises 5.3

1. Let $\mathscr{V} = \mathscr{V}_3$, $\mathscr{S} = \{(1, 0, 0), \quad (0, 1, 0), \quad (0, 0, 1)\}$ and $\mathscr{S}' = \{(1, 1, 1), (1, -1, 1), (-1, 1, 1)\}$. Find the $\mathscr{S}'$ coordinates of the following vectors: $\beta_1 = (2, 1, -1)$, $\beta_2 = (1, 4, 3)$, $\beta = (y_1, y_2, y_3)$.

2. Let $\mathscr{V} = \mathscr{V}_2$, $\mathscr{S} = \{(1, 0), (0, 1)\}$ and $\mathscr{S}' = \{\alpha'_1, \alpha'_2\}$. Determine α'_1 and α'_2 so that $(2, 1) = \alpha'_1 + \alpha'_2$ and $(-1, 3) = \alpha'_1 - 2\alpha'_2$, and then find the $\mathscr{S}'$ coordinates of $(1, 1)$.

3. Show that the formula of Theorem 5.3A is a special case of the formula of Theorem 2.9A. (Hint: show that $P' = \| I_{\mathscr{V}} \| \mathscr{S}\mathscr{S}'$.)

4. Let $\mathscr{V} = \mathscr{V}_4{}^r$, let $\mathscr{S}$ be the natural basis $\{\varepsilon_1, \varepsilon_2, \varepsilon_3, \varepsilon_4\}$, and let $\mathscr{S}' = \{\alpha_1, \alpha_2, \alpha_3, \alpha_4\}$ where α_i is the ith row of the matrix

$$
A = \left\|
\begin{array}{cccc}
3 & 1 & 1 & 0 \\
-1 & 2 & 0 & 1 \\
1 & 1 & 1 & 1 \\
-1 & -1 & 1 & 1
\end{array}
\right\|.
$$

Find the matrix B whose ith row gives the $\mathscr{S}'$ coordinates of ε_i.

5. Let $X = \| x_1 x_2 x_3 x_4 \|$. With bases as in Exercise 4 find a matrix Q for which $X' = XQ$ provides the $\mathscr{S}'$ coordinates of X.

5.4. Change of basis.

Let $\mathscr{V}$ and $\mathscr{W}$ be two vector spaces with bases $\mathscr{S} = \{\alpha_1, \cdots, \alpha_v\}$ and $\mathscr{T} = \{\beta_1, \cdots, \beta_w\}$, respectively. Relative to these bases each linear transformation T of $\mathscr{V}$ into $\mathscr{W}$ is characterized by a matrix $A = \| \mathsf{T} \| \mathscr{S}\mathscr{T}$. A second pair of bases $\mathscr{S}' = \{\alpha'_1, \cdots, \alpha'_v\}$ and $\mathscr{T}' = \{\beta'_1, \cdots, \beta'_w\}$ will assign a second matrix $A' = \| \mathsf{T} \| \mathscr{S}'\mathscr{T}'$, to T. We wish to study the connection between the two matrices A and A'.

Let P and $P^{-1} = P'$ be determined from $\mathscr{S}$ and $\mathscr{S}'$ as in the preceding section, and let $Q = \| q_{ij} \|$ and $Q^{-1} = \| q'_{ij} \|$ be the corresponding matrices for $\mathscr{T}$ and $\mathscr{T}'$; i.e.,

$$
\beta'_i = \sum_{v=1}^{w} q_{iv}\beta_v \qquad (i = 1, \cdots, w),
$$

and

$$
\beta_i = \sum_{v=1}^{w} q'_{iv}\beta'_v \qquad (i = 1, \cdots, w).
$$

Now consider the matrix A' of the linear transformation T. By the definition of A' we have

(4.1) $$
\alpha'_i\mathsf{T} = \sum_{v=1}^{w} a'_{iv}\beta'_v \qquad (i = 1, \cdots, v).
$$

On the other hand, we have

$$\alpha'_i \mathsf{T} = \left(\sum_{\mu=1}^{v} p_{i\mu}\alpha_\mu \right)\mathsf{T} = \sum_{\mu=1}^{v} p_{i\mu} \sum_{\lambda=1}^{w} a_{\mu\lambda}\beta_\lambda$$

$$= \sum_{\mu=1}^{v} p_{i\mu} \sum_{\lambda=1}^{w} a_{\mu\lambda} \sum_{v=1}^{w} q'_{\lambda v}\beta'_v$$

$$= \sum_{v=1}^{w} \left(\sum_{\mu=1}^{v} \sum_{\lambda=1}^{w} p_{i\mu}a_{\mu\lambda}q'_{\lambda v} \right) \beta'_v.$$

Hence,

$$(4.2) \qquad a'_{ij} = \sum_{\mu=1}^{v} \sum_{\lambda=1}^{w} p_{i\mu}a_{\mu\lambda}q'_{\lambda j},$$

or in matrix form

$$(4.3) \qquad\qquad A' = PAQ^{-1}.$$

LEMMA 5.4A.   *Let $\mathscr{V}$ be a vector space, let $\mathscr{S} = \{\alpha_1, \cdots, \alpha_v\}$ and $\mathscr{S}' = \{\alpha'_1, \cdots, \alpha'_v\}$ be two bases of $\mathscr{V}$, and let $\mathscr{W}$ be a vector space with bases $\mathscr{T} = \{\beta_1, \cdots, \beta_w\}$ and $\mathscr{T}' = \{\beta'_1, \cdots, \beta'_w\}$. If T is a linear transformation of $\mathscr{V}$ into $\mathscr{W}$, then*

$$\|\mathsf{T}\|_{\mathscr{S}'\mathscr{T}'} = P\|\mathsf{T}\|_{\mathscr{S}\mathscr{T}}Q^{-1},$$

where

$$P = \left\|\begin{array}{c} \|\alpha'_1\|_{\mathscr{S}} \\ \cdot \\ \cdot \\ \cdot \\ \|\alpha'_v\|_{\mathscr{S}} \end{array}\right\| \qquad and \qquad Q^{-1} = \left\|\begin{array}{c} \|\beta_1\|_{\mathscr{T}'} \\ \cdot \\ \cdot \\ \cdot \\ \|\beta_w\|_{\mathscr{T}'} \end{array}\right\|.$$

Thus, if A is one matrix for a linear transformation T, then by a suitable choice of basis elements we can replace A by any matrix A' equivalent to A.   In particular, we can obtain $A' = C$ where $C = \left\|\begin{array}{cc} I_r & 0 \\ 0 & 0 \end{array}\right\|$ (Theorem 3.8E).

Use of the matrix C is especially convenient if we are interested in the range and kernel of T. For suppose that $\{\alpha_1, \cdots, \alpha_r, \cdots, \alpha_v\}$ and $\{\beta_1, \cdots, \beta_r, \cdots, \beta_w\}$ are bases relative to which T has matrix C.   Then

$$(4.4) \qquad \begin{array}{ll} \alpha_i\mathsf{T} = \beta_i & (i = 1, \cdots, r), \\ \alpha_i\mathsf{T} = 0 & (i = r+1, \cdots, v). \end{array}$$

From this it follows that $\{\beta_1, \cdots, \beta_r\}$ is a basis for the range of T and that $\{\alpha_{r+1}, \cdots, \alpha_v\}$ is a basis for the kernel of T.

The fact that every linear transformation T can be represented by a matrix C in this form was essentially established in the proof of Theorem 2.1F.

THEOREM 5.4B. *Two matrices A and A' are equivalent if and only if they both correspond to the same linear transformation* T.

This follows immediately from equation (4.3) and the definition of equivalence. This theorem illustrates the use of alias methods in an alibi situation.

Next, let T be a linear transformation of $\mathscr{V}$ into $\mathscr{W}$, and let A and A' be computed as above except that just one basis is used for $\mathscr{W}$ (i.e., $Q = I$). Then $A' = PA$. Hence two matrices are row-equivalent if and only if they correspond to the same linear transformation T with·respect to a common basis in the range of T.

Exercises 5.4

1. Show that Lemma 5.4A follows from Theorem 2.5A. (Hint: show that $P = \|\ I_{\mathscr{V}}\ \|_{\mathscr{S}'\mathscr{S}}$, and $Q^{-1} = \|\ I_{\mathscr{W}}\ \|_{\mathscr{T}\mathscr{T}'}$. Then

$$\|\ \mathsf{T}\ \|_{\mathscr{S}'\mathscr{T}'} = \|\ I_{\mathscr{V}}\ \|_{\mathscr{S}'\mathscr{S}}\ \|\ \mathsf{T}\ \|_{\mathscr{S}\mathscr{T}}\ \|\ I_{\mathscr{W}}\ \|_{\mathscr{T}\mathscr{T}'}$$

since $\mathsf{T} = I_{\mathscr{V}}\mathsf{T}I_{\mathscr{W}}$.)

2. Let $\mathscr{V} = \mathscr{V}_2{}^r$, let $\mathscr{W} = \mathscr{V}_3{}^r$, and let $\mathscr{S} = \{\alpha_1, \alpha_2\}$ and $\mathscr{T} = \{\beta_1, \beta_2, \beta_3\}$ be the natural bases for $\mathscr{V}$ and $\mathscr{W}$, respectively. Let $\mathscr{S}'$ and $\mathscr{T}'$ be bases for $\mathscr{V}$ and $\mathscr{W}$ whose elements are the rows of the matrices

$$P = \left\|\begin{array}{rr} 1 & 2 \\ -1 & -3 \end{array}\right\|, \qquad Q = \left\|\begin{array}{rrr} 0 & 1 & 1 \\ 1 & -1 & -2 \\ 1 & -1 & -1 \end{array}\right\|,$$

respectively. Let T be a linear transformation of $\mathscr{V}$ into $\mathscr{W}$ for which

$$\|\ \mathsf{T}\ \|_{\mathscr{S}\mathscr{T}} = \left\|\begin{array}{rrr} 2 & 1 & -3 \\ 1 & -3 & 1 \end{array}\right\|.$$

Find $\|\ \mathsf{T}\ \|_{\mathscr{S}'\mathscr{T}'}$.

3. With the same notation as in Exercise 2 let R be a linear transformation on $\mathscr{W}$ such that

$$\|\ \mathsf{R}\ \|_{\mathscr{T}\mathscr{T}} = \left\|\begin{array}{rrr} 1 & -1 & 2 \\ -2 & 3 & 5 \\ 2 & 1 & -1 \end{array}\right\|.$$

Find $\|\ \mathsf{R}\ \|_{\mathscr{T}'\mathscr{T}'}$ and $\|\ \mathsf{T}\mathsf{R}\ \|_{\mathscr{S}'\mathscr{T}'}$.

5.5. Similarity of matrices; eigenvalues. The special case $\mathscr{V} = \mathscr{W}$, i.e., of a linear transformation T on $\mathscr{V}$, is important. We then choose the same bases for $\mathscr{V}$ and $\mathscr{W}$, i.e., $\alpha_i = \beta_i$ $(i = 1, \cdots, v)$, and $\alpha'_i = \beta'_i$ $(i = 1, \cdots, v)$, and equation (4.3) then specializes to

(5.1) $$A' = PAP^{-1}.$$

Two matrices A and A' are said to be *similar*, written $A \sim A'$, if there exists a nonsingular matrix P such that (5.1) holds. Here, of course, all the matrices are square. Clearly similar matrices are equivalent, but the converse does not hold. The following theorem is an immediate consequence of (5.1).

THEOREM 5.5A. *Let A and A' be square matrices both of degree v, and let $\mathscr{V}$ be a vector space of dimension v. Then $A \sim A'$ if and only if there exists a linear transformation T on $\mathscr{V}$ which has A as its matrix relative to one basis for $\mathscr{V}$ and which has A' as its matrix relative to another basis for $\mathscr{V}$.*

It is easy to verify that similarity of matrices is an equivalence relation. The determination of a complete set of invariants for similarity is postponed until Chapter 10. However, there is one special case of considerable importance which we can treat now, and its treatment serves as a good introduction to the general case.

The preceding theorem indicates the possibility that linear transformations can play an important role in the study of similarity of matrices. We proceed to take advantage of this possibility.

Let $\mathscr{V}$ be a vector space, and let T be a linear transformation on $\mathscr{V}$. A nonzero vector α is said to be an *eigenvector* for T if there exists a scalar λ, called an *eigenvalue*, for T such that

(5.2) $$\alpha\mathsf{T} = \lambda\alpha.$$

(We use the Greek letter λ for a scalar in this instance to conform with the custom firmly established in the literature on eigenvalues. The terms *characteristic root*, *latent root*, *secular value* are synonyms for eigenvalue, with corresponding terminology for eigenvectors.)

LEMMA 5.5B. *Let T be a linear transformation on a vector space $\mathscr{V}$ of dimension v, and let $\mathscr{S} = \{\alpha_1, \cdots, \alpha_v\}$ be a basis for $\mathscr{V}$. Then*

$$A = \| \mathsf{T} \|_{\mathscr{S}\mathscr{S}}$$

is a diagonal matrix if and only if each vector in $\mathscr{S}$ is an eigenvector.

Suppose that α_i is an eigenvector, say $\alpha_i\mathsf{T} = \lambda_i\alpha_i$. Then by formula (2.2.9) the ith row of A is $\| 0 \cdots \lambda_i \cdots 0 \|$: i.e., has zeros everywhere except for λ_i in the ith column. This shows that A is diagonal if $\mathscr{S}$ consists entirely of eigenvectors.

Conversely, if A is diagonal, say

$$A = \| a_{ij} \| = \begin{Vmatrix} \lambda_1 & & 0 \\ & \cdot & \\ & & \cdot \\ 0 & & \lambda_v \end{Vmatrix},$$

then $\alpha_i \mathsf{T} = \Sigma a_{i\mu}\alpha_\mu = a_{ii}\alpha_i = \lambda_i \alpha_i$ $(i = 1, \cdots, v)$, and so each element of $\mathscr{S}$ is an eigenvector.

LEMMA 5.5C.   *Let $\mathscr{S}$ be any set of eigenvectors for T, no two of which correspond to the same eigenvalue.   Then $\mathscr{S}$ is independent.*

Suppose that $\mathscr{S}$ is dependent.   Then there exists a minimal dependent subset $\mathscr{S}' = \{\beta_1, \cdots, \beta_r\}$ of $\mathscr{S}$; let

$$(5.3) \qquad\qquad 0 = c_1\beta_1 + \cdots + c_r\beta_r$$

be a nontrivial dependence relation on $\mathscr{S}'$.   Since each $\beta_i \neq 0$, $r > 1$. Now apply T to both sides of (5.3); this gives

$$0\mathsf{T} = c_1\beta_1\mathsf{T} + \cdots + c_r\beta_r\mathsf{T}$$

or

$$(5.4) \qquad\qquad 0 = \lambda_1 c_1\beta_1 + \cdots \lambda_r c_r\beta_r,$$

where λ_i is the eigenvalue corresponding to β_i $(i = 1, \cdots, r)$.   Next multiply (5.3) by $-\lambda_r$, and add the result to (5.4); this gives

$$(5.5) \qquad 0 = (\lambda_1 - \lambda_r)c_1\beta_1 + \cdots + (\lambda_{r-1} - \lambda_r)c_{r-1}\beta_{r-1}.$$

None of the c_i can be zero, for then $\mathscr{S}'$ would not be a minimal dependent set.   Hence, since $r > 1$ and since $\lambda_1 \neq \lambda_r$, equation (5.5) is a nontrivial dependence relation on $\beta_1, \cdots, \beta_{r-1}$; this contradicts the assumption that $\mathscr{S}'$ is a minimal dependent set.   Since $\mathscr{S}$ can have no minimal dependent subset, it is, therefore, an independent set as claimed.

THEOREM 5.5D.   *Let T be a linear transformation on a space $\mathscr{V}$ of finite dimension v.   Then T has at most v distinct eigenvalues.   Moreover, if T has v distinct eigenvalues $\lambda_1, \cdots, \lambda_v$ and if β_i is an eigenvector belonging to λ_i $(i = 1, \cdots, v)$, then the set $\mathscr{S} = \{\beta_1, \cdots, \beta_v\}$ is a basis for $\mathscr{V}$ relative to which T has the diagonal matrix*

$$B = \begin{Vmatrix} \lambda_1 & & 0 \\ & \cdot & \\ & & \cdot \\ & & \cdot \\ 0 & & \lambda_v \end{Vmatrix}.$$

All of the statements follow at once from the preceding lemmas.

Thus far we have not discussed any method for finding eigenvalues and eigenvectors. To determine the solutions of (5.2) we reformulate the problem in matrix language. Let $\mathscr{S} = \{\alpha_1, \cdots, \alpha_v\}$ be any basis for $\mathscr{V}$, and let A be the corresponding matrix for the linear transformation T. If we set $\alpha = x_1\alpha_1 + \cdots + x_v\alpha_v$, then equation (5.2) is equivalent to the matrix equation

$$(5.6) \qquad XA = \lambda X = X(\lambda I),$$

where $X = \| x_j \|$ is the row matrix whose entries are the coordinates of α; i.e., $X = \| \alpha \|_{\mathscr{S}}$. This equation is equivalent to

$$(5.7) \qquad X(\lambda I - A) = 0.$$

We recall from the theory of kernels as developed in Chapters 3 and 4 that equation (5.7) has a nonzero solution X if and only if the matrix $\lambda I - A$ is singular; i.e., if det $(\lambda I - A) = 0$. We call the polynomial $f(x) =$ det $(xI - A)$ the *characteristic function* of the matrix A. Note that the degree of $f(x)$ equals the number of rows of A, and this equals dim $\mathscr{V}$. We call $f(x) = 0$ the *characteristic equation* of A. Its roots are the eigenvalues of T and are also called the eigenvalues of A. A row vector X that satisfies (5.6) is said to be an *eigenvector* of A (corresponding to the eigenvalue λ).

If A is similar to B, then they both have the same eigenvalues, viz., the eigenvalues of a linear transformation for which both are matrices (with respect to appropriate bases of $\mathscr{V}$). Thus their characteristic equations have the same roots; actually they have the same characteristic equations.

LEMMA 5.5E. *If $A \sim B$, then A and B have the same characteristic function and the same set of eigenvalues.*

If $A \sim B$, then there is a nonsingular matrix P such that $B = PAP^{-1}$. But then the characteristic function of B is

$$\left|xI - B\right| = \left|xPIP^{-1} - PAP^{-1}\right| = \left|P(xI - A)P^{-1}\right| = \left|P\right|\left|xI - A\right|\left|P^{-1}\right|$$
$$= \left|PP^{-1}\right|\left|xI - A\right| = \left|xI - A\right|,$$

which is the characteristic function of A.

Although the sets of eigenvalues are the same, this will ordinarily not be true of the eigenvectors, for, if x is an eigenvector of A belonging to the eigenvalue λ, then $Y = XP^{-1}$ is a corresponding eigenvector for B.

Since all matrices corresponding to a given linear transformation T are similar and have the same characteristic function $f(x)$, this function $f(x)$ is uniquely determined by T. We call it the *characteristic function* of T.

THEOREM 5.5F. *Let A be a matrix of degree v with v distinct eigenvalues. Then $A \sim B$ if and only if A and B have the same characteristic function.*

The "if" part of the theorem follows from Theorem 5.5D and the fact that similarity is an equivalence relation; the "only if" part follows from Lemma 5.5E.

This is the special case for which we promised to give a complete set of invariants for similarity. We give an example at the end of the section which shows that equality of the sets of eigenvalues is not always a sufficient condition for similarity. We observe that in the special case the diagonal matrices play the role of a canonical form.

We now give some examples. Take $\mathscr{V} = \mathscr{V}_2{}^r$ and let T have the

matrix $A = \left\|\begin{array}{rr} 1 & 1 \\ -2 & 4 \end{array}\right\|$ with respect to the natural basis $\|\ 1 \quad 0\ \|$, $\|\ 0 \quad 1\ \|$. An eigenvector $\|\ x_1 \quad x_2\ \|$ satisfies the equation

$$\|\ x_1 \quad x_2\ \| \left\|\begin{array}{rr} 1 & 1 \\ -2 & 4 \end{array}\right\| = \lambda\ \|\ x_1 \quad x_2\ \|$$

for an appropriate value of λ. This equation is equivalent to the system

$$x_1 - 2x_2 = \lambda x_1,$$
$$x_1 + 4x_2 = \lambda x_2,$$

or to

(5.8)
$$(\lambda - 1)x_1 + 2x_2 = 0,$$
$$-x_1 + (\lambda - 4)x_2 = 0.$$

The system has a nontrivial solution if its determinant

$$\left|\begin{array}{cc} \lambda-1 & 2 \\ -1 & \lambda-4 \end{array}\right| = \left|\begin{array}{cc} \lambda-1 & -1 \\ 2 & \lambda-4 \end{array}\right|$$

is 0. This gives $\lambda^2 - 5\lambda + 6 = 0$ and the eigenvalues are $\lambda = 2, 3$. For $\lambda = 2$, the matrix of coefficients of (5.8) is

$$\left\|\begin{array}{rr} 1 & 2 \\ -1 & -2 \end{array}\right\|.$$

A nontrivial solution of (5.8) is given by $\|\ -2 \quad 1\ \|$. Hence $\|\ -2 \quad 1\ \|$ is an eigenvector corresponding to the eigenvalue 2. Of course, any multiple of $\|\ -2 \quad 1\ \|$ is also an eigenvector.

Similarly, the eigenvector $\|\ 1 \quad -1\ \|$ belongs to the eigenvalue 3.

Now, according to Theorem 5.5D we have

$$A = \left\| \begin{array}{cc} 1 & 1 \\ -2 & 4 \end{array} \right\| \sim \left\| \begin{array}{cc} 2 & 0 \\ 0 & 3 \end{array} \right\| = B;$$

i.e., there is a matrix P such that $B = PAP^{-1}$. This matrix P can be taken as the matrix of the transformation which expresses the new basis of $\mathscr{V}$ in terms of the old basis. In this case of distinct eigenvalues this matrix is composed simply of the eigenvectors, i e.,

$$P = \left\| \begin{array}{cc} -2 & 1 \\ 1 & -1 \end{array} \right\|.$$

As a second example consider the matrices

$$A_1 = \left\| \begin{array}{cc} 2 & 0 \\ 1 & 2 \end{array} \right\| \quad \text{and} \quad A_2 = \left\| \begin{array}{cc} 2 & 0 \\ 0 & 2 \end{array} \right\|.$$

Both A_1 and A_2 have the characteristic function $f(x) = (x - 2)^2$, and hence only the one eigenvalue 2. However, A_1 and A_2 are not similar since the only eigenvectors for A_1 are of the form $\| c \quad 0 \|$ whereas every vector in $\mathscr{V}_2{}^r$ is an eigenvector for A_2. Note also that A_1 is not similar to any diagonal matrix.

Exercises 5.5

1. Let A_1 and A_2 be two matrices each of whose eigenvectors span $\mathscr{V}_n{}^r$. Show that $A_1 \sim A_2$ if and only if the two matrices have the same characteristic function.

2. Let λ be an eigenvalue of the matrix A of degree v, and let $B = \lambda I - A$ have rank $v - 1$. Show that $\alpha = \| a_1 \cdots a_v \|$. where $a_i = (-1)^i \det B(i \mid 1)$, is an eigenvector corresponding to λ if $\det B(i \mid j) \neq 0$ for some j.

3. Find the eigenvalues and a corresponding set of eigenvectors for

$$A = \left\| \begin{array}{cc} 1 & 3 \\ 0 & 2 \end{array} \right\|.$$

4. Find a matrix P such that $B = PAP^{-1}$, where B is diagonal and

$$A = \left\| \begin{array}{cc} 1 & 3 \\ 0 & 2 \end{array} \right\|.$$

5. Prove that, if $B = PAP^{-1}$ and x is an eigenvector of A, then $Y = XP^{-1}$ is an eigenvector of B.

6. Prove that, if λ is an eigenvalue of A, then λ^2 is an eigenvalue of A^2.

7. If A and B are square matrices of degree n, show that AB and BA have the same eigenvalues. (Hint: consider the sums of the powers of the eigenvalues.)

8. If A and B are rectangular matrices such that AB and BA are defined, show that AB and BA have the same nonzero eigenvalues.

9. If α is an eigenvector of the restriction of T to a subspace, show that α is an eigenvector of T.

10. Let A be a square matrix of degree n with distinct eigenvalues $\lambda_1, \cdots, \lambda_n$. Prove that the cofactors of a row of $\lambda_i I - A$ are the components of an eigenvector corresponding to the eigenvalue λ_i.

11. Let D be a diagonal matrix and let $f(x) = a_0 + a_1 x + a_2 x^2 + \cdots$ be its characteristic function. Prove that $a_0 I + a_1 D + a_2 D^2 + \cdots = 0$. This is a special case of the Cayley-Hamilton Theorem (Theorem 10.3C).

12. Let A have characteristic function $a_0 + a_1 x + \cdots$. Show that, if A is similar to a diagonal matrix, then $a_0 I + a_1 A + \cdots = 0$.

13. Find a diagonal matrix similar to $\begin{Vmatrix} 3 & -5 \\ -4 & 6 \end{Vmatrix}$.

14. Find all eigenvectors for the matrix $\begin{Vmatrix} 3 & 1 & 1 \\ 0 & -2 & 1 \\ 0 & 0 & 2 \end{Vmatrix}$.

15. A 4-by-4 matrix A has eigenvalues $\{2, 0, 1, -1\}$. Find a diagonal matrix similar to A. Find a nondiagonal matrix similar to A.

16. Let A and B be square matrices (not necessarily of the same degree). Show that $A \times B$ is similar to $B \times A$. (Hint: see Exercise 11 of Section 3.8.)

5.6. Equivalence and similarity of linear transformations.

The concepts of equivalence and similarity can be defined for linear transformations. We first consider equivalence.

Let $\mathcal{V}, \mathcal{V}', \mathcal{W}, \mathcal{W}'$ be vector spaces, let T be a linear transformation of $\mathcal{V}$ into $\mathcal{W}$, and let T' be a linear transformation of $\mathcal{V}'$ into $\mathcal{W}'$. Then we say that T *is equivalent to* T' (written $\mathsf{T} \overset{E}{=} \mathsf{T}'$) if there exist isomorphisms R and S of $\mathcal{V}$ onto $\mathcal{V}'$ and $\mathcal{W}$ onto $\mathcal{W}'$, respectively, such that

(6.1) $$\mathsf{R}\mathsf{T}' = \mathsf{T}\mathsf{S},$$

or, equivalently, such that

(6.2) $$\mathsf{T}' = \mathsf{R}^{-1}\mathsf{T}\mathsf{S}.$$

Observe that $\mathsf{R}\mathsf{T}'$ and $\mathsf{T}\mathsf{S}$ are both mappings of $\mathcal{V}$ into $\mathcal{W}'$ so that equality in (6.1) is possible. The following diagram helps to motivate formula (6.1):

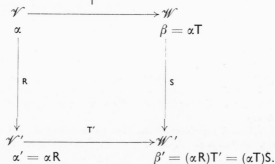

Formula (6.2) establishes the analogy between equivalence for matrices and equivalence for linear transformations.   This is, however, more than an analogy, since by means of it we can apply the results for equivalence of matrices to get the full theory of equivalence for linear transformations.

THEOREM 5.6A. *Let* $\mathscr{V}$, $\mathscr{V}'$, $\mathscr{W}$, $\mathscr{W}'$ *be vector spaces, let* T *be a linear transformation of* $\mathscr{V}$ *into* $\mathscr{W}$, *and let* T' *be a linear transformation of* $\mathscr{V}'$ *into* $\mathscr{W}'$. *Then* T *is equivalent to* T' *if and only if* (i) dim $\mathscr{V}$ = dim $\mathscr{V}'$, (ii) dim $\mathscr{W}$ = dim $\mathscr{W}'$, *and* (iii) dim $\mathscr{V}$T = dim $\mathscr{V}'$T'.

First suppose T $\overset{\mathrm{E}}{=}$ T'. Then, since R and S are isomorphisms onto, dim $\mathscr{V}$ = dim $\mathscr{V}'$ and dim $\mathscr{W}$ = dim $\mathscr{W}'$. Next from (6.1) we have $\mathscr{V}$TS = $\mathscr{V}$RT' = $\mathscr{V}'$T' and then, since dimension is unchanged under an isomorphism, we have dim $\mathscr{V}$T = dim ($\mathscr{V}$T)S = dim $\mathscr{V}'$T'.

Conversely, suppose that (i), (ii), and (iii) hold, and let A, A' be any matrices for T, T', respectively.   From (iii) we get rank A = rank A', and from (i) and (ii) we get row degree A = row degree A' and column degree A = column degree A'.   It now follows from Theorem 3.8F that A is equivalent to A'.   But by the definition of equivalence there exist nonsingular matrices P and Q such that $PAQ = A'$ or $P^{-1}A' = AQ$. Then let R be the linear transformation of $\mathscr{V}$ into $\mathscr{V}'$ whose matrix (relative to the bases already selected to define A and A') is P^{-1}, and let S be the linear transformation of $\mathscr{W}$ into $\mathscr{W}'$ whose matrix is Q.   Since P^{-1} and Q are nonsingular, R and S are isomorphisms onto, and the equation $P^{-1}A' = AQ$ implies RT' = TS.   Hence T' is equivalent to T.

[Alternatively, we can establish the "if" part of the theorem without recourse to matrices in the following manner: First apply the construction which yields formula (4.4) for both T and T'; and next define R and S explicitly by the conditions α_iR = α'_i $(i = 1, \cdots, v)$, β_iS = β'_i $(i = 1, \cdots, w)$.   Equation (6.1) then follows immediately.]

We next introduce the concept of similarity of linear transformations. Let $\mathscr{V}$ and $\mathscr{V}'$ be vector spaces, and let T and T' be linear transformations on $\mathscr{V}$ and $\mathscr{V}'$, respectively.   We say that T' is *similar* to T (written T' $\sim$ T) if there exists an isomorphism R of $\mathscr{V}$ onto $\mathscr{V}'$ such that

$$RT' = TR$$

or equivalently such that
(6.3) $$T' = R^{-1}TR.$$

THEOREM 5.6B.   *Let* $\mathscr{V}$ *and* $\mathscr{V}'$ *be vector spaces, let* T *and* T' *be linear transformations on* $\mathscr{V}$ *and* $\mathscr{V}'$, *respectively; and let* A *and* A', *respectively, be any matrices for* T *and* T'.   *Then* T $\sim$ T' *if and only if* $A \sim A'$.

This theorem follows from the parallelism of formulas (5.1) and (6.3). For the "if" part we have only to take R as the isomorphism whose matrix is P^{-1}, and for the "only if" part let P be the matrix of R^{-1}.

Chapter 6 | Functions of Vectors

A function of v variables $x_1, \cdots, x_v$ can be considered as a function of the vector $X = \| x_1 \cdots x_v \|$ in $\mathscr{V}_v^{\,r}(\mathscr{F})$. The linear form $a_1x_1 + \cdots + a_vx_v$ and the quadratic form $a_{11}x_1^{\,2} + a_{12}x_1x_2 + \cdots + a_{vv}x_v^{\,2}$ are two important examples. We shall discuss these and also functions of two sets of variables $x_1, \cdots, x_v$ and $y_1, \cdots, y_w$ which we shall consider to be functions of the two vectors $X = \| x_1 \cdots x_v \|$ in $\mathscr{V}_v^{\,r}$ and $Y = \| y_1 \cdots y_w \|$ in $\mathscr{V}_w^{\,r}$. More generally we will treat the theory of certain types of functions of vectors in vector spaces $\mathscr{V}, \mathscr{W}, \cdots$ over $\mathscr{F}$.

An important instance of such functions is given by determinant functions, and their connection with determinants is discussed. For the real and complex fields we give a more complete development of the theory of quadratic and related functions than is possible for arbitrary fields.

6.1. Bilinear forms. Let $X = \| x_1 \cdots x_v \|$ and $Y = \| y_1 \cdots y_w \|$ be row vectors, and let $C = \| c_{ij} \|$ be a v-by-w matrix. The product

$$(1.1) \qquad f(X, Y) = XCY^\mathsf{T} = \sum_{\lambda=1}^{v} \sum_{\mu=1}^{w} x_\lambda c_{\lambda\mu} y_\mu$$

is called a *bilinear form* in the two sets of variables $x_1, \cdots, x_v$ and $y_1, \cdots, y_w$. The term "bilinear" is justified by the fact that f is linear in both X and Y; viz.,

$$f(cX, Y) = cf(X, Y) = f(X, cY),$$

$$f(X_1 + X_2, Y) = f(X_1, Y) + f(X_2, Y),$$

$$f(X, Y_1 + Y_2) = f(X, Y_1) + f(X, Y_2).$$

We call C the *matrix of the form* f. If f is a bilinear form, the matrix C is uniquely determined since $f(E_i, E'_j) = c_{ij}$, where $\{E_1, \cdots, E_v\}$ and

$\{E'_1, \cdots, E'_w\}$ are the natural bases of $\mathscr{V}_v{}^r(\mathscr{F})$ and $\mathscr{V}_w{}^r(\mathscr{F})$, respectively.

Each nonsingular matrix $P = \| p_{ij} \|$ of degree v defines a *reversible linear substitution*

$$(1.2) \qquad x_j = \sum_{\lambda=1}^{v} x'_\lambda p_{\lambda j} \quad (j = 1, \cdots, v), \qquad \text{or} \qquad X = X'P,$$

which expresses the *old* variables x_j in terms of the *new* variables x'_j. The term reversible is justified by the equation $X' = XP^{-1}$ which is a consequence of (1.2). Let $Q = \| q_{ij} \|$ define a reversible linear substitution on the y_j;

$$(1.3) \qquad y_j = \sum_{\mu=1}^{w} y'_\mu q_{\mu j} \quad (j = 1, \cdots, w) \qquad \text{or} \qquad Y = Y'Q.$$

Under these substitutions $f(X, Y)$ is sent into the new bilinear form $f'(X', Y')$ defined by $f'(X', Y') = f(X'P, Y'Q)$ or in matrix form

$$(1.4) \qquad f'(X', Y') = (X'P)C(Y'Q)^\mathsf{T} = X'(PCQ^\mathsf{T})Y'^\mathsf{T},$$

which shows that $C' = PCQ^\mathsf{T}$ is the matrix for the new form f'.

A bilinear form f is said to be *equivalent* to a bilinear form f', written $f \overset{\mathrm{E}}{=} f'$, if f' can be obtained from f by reversible linear substitutions on the variables.

LEMMA 6.1A. *Equivalence of bilinear forms is an equivalence relation.*

To see that $f \overset{\mathrm{E}}{=} f$, we need only take $P = I_v$ and $Q = I_w$. If the substitutions (1.2) and (1.3) give $f \overset{\mathrm{E}}{=} f'$ then the inverse substitutions $X' = XP^{-1}$ and $Y' = YQ^{-1}$ show that $f' \overset{\mathrm{E}}{=} f$. Finally, if $f \overset{\mathrm{E}}{=} f'$ and $f' \overset{\mathrm{E}}{=} f''$ where, say, $X = X'P_1, X' = X''P_2,\ Y = Y'Q_1,\ Y' = Y''Q_2$, then the equations $X = X''(P_2 P_1)$ and $Y = Y''(Q_2 Q_1)$ show that $f \overset{\mathrm{E}}{=} f''$.

THEOREM 6.1B. *Two bilinear forms f and f' are equivalent if and only if their matrices C and C' are equivalent.*

This theorem is an immediate consequence of formula (1.4).

We define the rank of a bilinear form to be the rank of its matrix.

THEOREM 6.1C. *Two bilinear forms $f(X, Y)$ and $f'(X', Y')$ are equivalent if and only if all of the following conditions hold* (i) rank $f =$ rank f', (ii) *number of $x_j =$ number of x'_j, and* (iii) *number of $y_j =$ number of y'_j. Any form of rank r is equivalent to the form*

$$(1.5) \qquad f(X, Y) = x_1 y_1 + \cdots + x_r y_r.$$

The first statement follows immediately from Theorems 6.1B and 3.8F.

The second part follows from the fact that every v-by-w matrix C is equivalent to a matrix

$$E = \left\| \begin{array}{cc} I_r & 0 \\ 0 & 0 \end{array} \right\|$$

(Theorem 3.8F), which is the matrix of the form (1.5).

In (1.5) we regard the variables $x_{r+1}, \cdots, x_v$ and $y_{r+1}, \cdots, y_w$ as appearing with zero coefficients.

Next, we turn to the case where the vectors X and Y belong to the same space $\mathscr{V}_v^r$ and where we require that whatever substitution is carried out on the x_j shall also be carried out on the y_j: i.e., $P = Q$. Corresponding forms in this case are said to be *congruent*, and likewise two square matrices C and C' are said to be *congruent* if there exists a nonsingular matrix P such that

$$(1.6) \qquad\qquad C' = PCP^\mathsf{T}.$$

Clearly, both congruence of forms and congruence of matrices are equivalence relations, and two forms are congruent if and only if their matrices are congruent.

Interest in congruence is focused on two special cases: the *symmetric* case $f(X, Y) = f(Y, X)$ and the *skew-symmetric* case $f(X, Y) = -f(Y, X)$. We observe that $f(Y, X) = YCX^\mathsf{T}$, but since a scalar is its own transpose this gives $f(X, Y) = (YCX^\mathsf{T})^\mathsf{T} = XC^\mathsf{T}Y^\mathsf{T}$. Because the matrix of f is unique, we see that the form f is symmetric if and only if

$$(1.7) \qquad\qquad C^\mathsf{T} = C,$$

and f is skew-symmetric if and only if

$$(1.8) \qquad\qquad C^\mathsf{T} = -C.$$

Matrices that satisfy (1.7) or (1.8), respectively, are called *symmetric* or *skew-symmetric*. Note that $(P^\mathsf{T}CP)^\mathsf{T} = P^\mathsf{T}C^\mathsf{T}P$, so that, if C is symmetric (or skew-symmetric), so is every matrix congruent to C.

Suppose $C' = PCP^\mathsf{T}$ where P is nonsingular. If $P = F_s \cdots F_1$ is a factorization of P into a product of elementary matrices, then $P^\mathsf{T} = F_1^\mathsf{T} \cdots F_s^\mathsf{T}$, so that

$$(1.9) \qquad C' = F_s(\cdots(F_2(F_1CF_1^\mathsf{T})F_2^\mathsf{T})\cdots)F_s^\mathsf{T}.$$

When we first introduced elementary column transformations, we proved (Lemma 3.8A) that, if R is an elementary row operation whose application can be described by left multiplication by the matrix F, then right multiplication by F^T yields the same result as applying the corresponding elementary column transformation. Thus from (1.9) we see that C' is obtained from C by a sequence of s steps, each step consisting of applying an elementary row transformation and the corresponding elementary column transformation.

Exercises 6.1

1. Are the following two bilinear forms in x_1, x_2, x_3, x_4 and y_1, y_2, y_3 equivalent:

$$2x_1y_1 - 3x_1y_2 + x_2y_3 - x_4y_3,$$
$$x_2y_1 - x_1y_2 + 2x_3y_2 + 3x_3y_3 - 2x_4y_3 \ ?$$

2. For each of the forms f in Exercise 1 find substitutions on x and y which change f into the canonical form (1.5).

3. Give linear mappings that reduce the bilinear form $2x_1y_1 + x_1y_2 - 2x_1y_3 + 3x_1y_4 + 3x_2y_1 - 2x_2y_2 + 2x_2y_4 + 7x_3y_2 - 6x_3y_3 + 5x_3y_4$ to the canonical form (1.5).

4. Consider the bilinear form XCY^T where

$$C = \left\|\ \begin{array}{rrrr} 2 & 1 & -3 & 0 \\ 1 & 2 & 0 & 1 \\ -1 & -1 & 1 & 0 \end{array}\ \right\|.$$

Find substitutions $X = X'P$ and $Y = Y'Q$ such that the equivalent form in the primed variables is in canonical form.

5. Prove that every square matrix is the sum of a symmetric and a skew-symmetric matrix.

6.2. Canonical forms for skew-symmetric and symmetric matrices.

We now apply the approach indicated by formula (1.9) to find invariants and to obtain canonical forms for skew-symmetric and symmetric matrices. The treatment which follows and also certain of the results are not valid for fields of characteristic 2. The skew-symmetric case is simpler, and for it a canonical form is obtained; we treat it first.

Let $C = \|\ c_{ij}\ \|$ be a skew-symmetric matrix. Since $c_{ij} = -c_{ji}$, we have in particular $c_{ii} = -c_{ii}$ or *each diagonal element of a skew-symmetric matrix is* 0. (This last result is false for $\mathscr{F}$ of characteristic 2.)

If $C = 0$, then C is already in the canonical form [described by (2.1) below]. Otherwise there is a $c_{ij} \neq 0$ $(i \neq j)$. This element is sent into position $(2, 1)$ by applying R_{i2}, C_{i2} and R_{j1}, C_{j1}, unless $j = 2$. In this case R_{i1}, C_{i1} send c_{ji} into position $(2, 1)$ and $c_{ji} = -c_{ij} \neq 0$. Hence we can assume $c_{21} \neq 0$. By applying $R_2(1/c_{21})$, $C_2(1/c_{21})$, we obtain 1 in position $(2,1)$ and -1 in $(1, 2)$.

Our matrix now has the form

$$C' = \left\|\ \begin{array}{cccccc} 0 & -1 & -c'_{31} & \cdots & -c'_{v1} \\ 1 & 0 & -c'_{32} & \cdots & -c'_{v2} \\ c'_{31} & c'_{32} & 0 & \cdots & \\ \cdot & \cdot & \cdot & \cdots & \cdot \\ c'_{v1} & c'_{v2} & & & 0 \end{array}\ \right\|.$$

The transformations $R_i(-c'_{i1}, 2)$, $C_i(-c'_{i1}, 2)$ replace c'_{i1} by 0 $(i = 3, \cdots, v)$ and do not change the elements

$$\begin{Vmatrix} 0 & -1 \\ 1 & 0 \end{Vmatrix}$$

in the upper left hand corner.   We now have a matrix

$$C'' = \begin{Vmatrix} 0 & -1 & 0 & \cdots & 0 \\ 1 & 0 & -c''_{32} & \cdots & -c''_{v2} \\ 0 & c''_{32} & 0 & & \\ \cdot & \cdot & \cdot & \cdots & \cdot \\ 0 & c''_{v2} & & & 0 \end{Vmatrix}.$$

We apply $R_i(c''_{i2}, 1)$, $C_i(c''_{i2}, 1)$ to replace c''_{i2} by 0 $(i = 3, \cdots, v)$. This does not alter the first column or row because of the 0 in position $(1, 1)$. Our new matrix C''' is congruent to C and has the form

$$C''' = \begin{Vmatrix} 0 & -1 & 0 & \cdots & 0 \\ 1 & 0 & 0 & \cdots & 0 \\ \cdot & \cdot & & & \\ & & & C_1 & \\ 0 & 0 & & & \end{Vmatrix},$$

where C_1 is a skew-symmetric matrix of degree $v - 2$.

If $C_1 = 0$, C''' is in the canonical form.   Otherwise the entire process is repeated on C_1 to obtain a matrix

$$C''''_1 = \begin{Vmatrix} 0 & -1 & 0 & \cdots & 0 \\ 1 & 0 & 0 & \cdots & 0 \\ 0 & 0 & & & \\ \cdot & \cdot & & C_2 & \\ 0 & 0 & & & \end{Vmatrix}$$

of degree $v - 2$ which is congruent to C_1.   When we apply transformations, corresponding to those which sent C_1 into C'''_1, to the last $v - 2$ rows and columns of C''', we obtain

$$D = \begin{Vmatrix} 0 & -1 & 0 & \cdots & 0 \\ 1 & 0 & 0 & \cdots & 0 \\ 0 & 0 & & & \\ \cdot & \cdot & & & \\ & & & C'''_1 & \\ 0 & 0 & & & \end{Vmatrix}$$

The elements in either the first two rows or first two columns are unaltered because of the 0's in positions $(i, 1)$, $(i, 2)$, $(1, j)$ and $(2, j)$ $(i, j = 3, \cdots, v)$.

Now

$$D = \begin{Vmatrix} 0 & -1 & & & \\ 1 & 0 & & & \\ & & 0 & -1 & \\ & & 1 & 0 & \\ & & & & C_2 \end{Vmatrix}$$

The entire process is repeated on C_2, unless $C_2 = 0$, and an induction argument gives the following theorem.

THEOREM 6.2A. *Let C be a skew-symmetric matrix of rank r and degree v. Then r is divisible by 2, say $r = 2s$, and C is congruent to the matrix*

$$(2.1) \quad H_{s,v} = \begin{Vmatrix} 0 & -1 & & & & & & & \\ 1 & 0 & & & & & & & \\ & & 0 & -1 & & & & & \\ & & 1 & 0 & & & & & \\ & & & & \cdot & & & & \\ & & & & & \cdot & & & \\ & & & & & & 0 & -1 & \\ & & & & & & 1 & 0 & \\ & & & & & & & & 0 \\ & & & & & & & & \cdot \\ & & & & & & & & \cdot \\ & & & & & & & & 0 \end{Vmatrix}$$

where there are s blocks $\begin{Vmatrix} 0 & -1 \\ 1 & 0 \end{Vmatrix}$ *along the diagonal, and all other entries of $H_{s,v}$ are zero.*

COROLLARY 6.2B. *Two skew-symmetric matrices of equal degree are congruent if and only if their ranks are equal.*

If C is congruent to C' we must have rank $C = $ rank C' since congruence is a special case of equivalence. Conversely, if rank $C = $ rank $C' = 2s$, both are congruent to $H_{s,v}$, and hence to each other.

Another canonical form is given by

$$(2.2) \qquad H'_{s,v} = \begin{Vmatrix} 0 & -I_s & 0 \\ I_s & 0 & 0 \\ 0 & 0 & 0 \end{Vmatrix}.$$

It can be obtained from $H_{s,v}$ by transformations of type R_{hi} and C_{hi}.

The case of symmetric matrices is more complicated, and we obtain only partial analogs to the preceding theorem and its corollary.

Suppose that C is a symmetric matrix of degree v and rank r. If $r = 0$, then $C = 0$. and there is no problem. Next suppose $r \neq 0$. Then if any diagonal element c_{ii} of C is not zero, we can interchange the 1st and ith rows and the 1st and ith columns to get a congruent matrix C' with $c'_{11} \neq 0$. If every diagonal element is zero, but $c_{ij} = c_{ji} \neq 0$ where, say, $i > j$, then add the ith row to the jth row and the ith column to the jth column and we get a new matrix whose (j, j) entry is $2c_{ij}$, which puts us in the case already treated. We see that in every case a nonzero symmetric matrix C is congruent to a symmetric matrix C' with $c'_{11} \neq 0$.

Now add suitable multiples of the first row of C' to the later rows and the same multiples of the first column to the later columns, and we arrive at a matrix C'' congruent to C which has the form

$$(2.3) \qquad C'' = \begin{Vmatrix} d_1 & 0 & \cdots & 0 \\ 0 & & & \\ \cdot & & C''^* & \\ \cdot & & & \\ \cdot & & & \end{Vmatrix},$$

where C''^* is symmetric, and $d_1 \neq 0$.

Next, following the line of argument developed in the skew-symmetric case, we repeat the above process on C''^*; and then an induction argument gives the following theorem.

THEOREM 6.2C. *Let C be a symmetric matrix of degree v and rank r.*

Then there exist nonzero scalars $d_1, \cdots, d_r$ such that C is congruent to the diagonal matrix

$$(2.4) \qquad D = \left\|\begin{array}{cccccccc} d_1 & & & & & & & \\ & \cdot & & & & & & \\ & & \cdot & & & & & \\ & & & \cdot & & & & \\ & & & & d_r & & & \\ & & & & & 0 & & \\ & & & & & & \cdot & \\ & & & & & & & \cdot \\ & & & & & & & & \cdot \\ & & & & & & & & & 0 \end{array}\right\|$$

It is in the theory of congruence that we reach for the first time in our development a place where the nature of the field of scalars is really important. We now consider in turn the cases where this field is $\mathfrak{C}$ and $\mathfrak{R}$.

THEOREM 6.2D. *Let C be a symmetric matrix over the field $\mathfrak{C}$ of complex numbers. Then C is congruent to the matrix*

$$(2.5) \qquad E_{r,v} = \left\|\begin{array}{cc} I_r & 0 \\ 0 & 0 \end{array}\right\|$$

where r is the rank of C. Two symmetric $\mathfrak{C}$ matrices of equal degree are congruent if and only if they have the same rank.

Let $P = \left\|\begin{array}{cccccc} p_1 & & & & & \\ & \cdot & & & & \\ & & \cdot & & & \\ & & & p_r & & \\ & & & & \cdot & \\ & & & & & p_v \end{array}\right\|$ be a diagonal matrix with $p_i{}^2 = \dfrac{1}{d_i}$

$(i = 1, \cdots, r)$ and $p_{r+1} = \cdots = p_v = 1$.   Then $P = P^\mathsf{T}$ and $PDP^\mathsf{T} = E_{r,v}$.

THEOREM 6.2E. *Let C be a symmetric matrix over the field $\mathfrak{R}$ of real numbers. Then C is congruent to a matrix*

$$(2.6) \qquad E_{r,t,v} = \left\|\begin{array}{ccc} I_t & 0 & 0 \\ 0 & -I_{r-t} & 0 \\ 0 & 0 & 0 \end{array}\right\|.$$

We proceed almost as before.   Suppose that D has t positive and $r - t$ negative entries $(0 \leq t \leq r)$.   We then interchange rows and colums until we obtain a congruent diagonal matrix D' with $d'_1, \cdots, d'_t$ positive and $d'_{t+1}, \cdots, d'_r$ negative.   Then take p as the diagonal matrix with $p_i^2 = 1/d_i$ $(i = 1, \cdots, t)$, $p_1^2 = -1/d'_i$ $(i = t+1, \cdots, r)$, $p_i = 1 (i = r+1, \cdots, v)$ and then have $PD'P^\mathsf{T} = E_{r,t,v}$.

In Section 6.6 we shall prove that C is congruent to at most one matrix $E_{r,t,v}$; i.e., that (2.6) is a canonical form for congruence of real symmetric matrices.

The problem of congruence over the field $\mathfrak{Q}$ belongs to the theory of numbers, and its treatment is beyond the scope of this text.

Exercises 6.2

1. Find matrices $H_{s,v}$ and $H'_{s,v}$ congruent to

$$\begin{Vmatrix} 0 & 3 & 0 & -1 & 0 \\ -3 & 0 & 2 & 1 & -1 \\ 0 & -2 & 0 & 1 & -2 \\ 1 & -1 & -1 & 0 & 2 \\ 0 & 1 & 2 & -2 & 0 \end{Vmatrix}.$$

2. Find a diagonal matrix congruent to

$$\begin{Vmatrix} 0 & 1 & 0 & 2 \\ 1 & 0 & 2 & -2 \\ 0 & 2 & 0 & 3 \\ 2 & -2 & 3 & 0 \end{Vmatrix}.$$

3. Find a matrix $E_{r,t,v}$ congruent to the real matrix of Exercise 2.

4. What matrix in canonical form is congruent to

$$\begin{Vmatrix} 0 & -2 & 1 & 0 \\ 2 & 0 & 3 & 4 \\ -1 & -3 & 0 & -5 \\ 0 & -4 & 5 & 0 \end{Vmatrix}?$$

5. Find a quadratic form without cross-products which is equivalent to

$$x_1^2 + 4x_1x_2 - 2x_1x_3 + 2x_2^2 + 3x_2x_3.$$

6. Prove that congruence of matrices is an equivalence relation.

7. Prove that, if A is symmetric of degree v and if $A(I - A) = 0$, then $r(A) + r(I - A) = v$.

8. Let A be a 5-rowed skew-symmetric matrix with a nonsingular square submatrix of degree three. Show that A has rank 4.

9. (a) Let A be a real symmetric matrix. Show that the diagonal elements of A^2 cannot all be zero unless $A = 0$. (b) Show that this is not true for complex symmetric matrices. (c) Show that the conclusion in part (a) is also valid for real skew-symmetric matrices.

6.3. Quadratic forms. Let $x_1, \cdots, x_v$ be variables in a field $\mathscr{F}$ (of characteristic $\neq 2$). A homogeneous polynomial $q(x_1, \cdots, x_v)$ of degree 2 with coefficients in $\mathscr{F}$ is called a *quadratic form* in $\mathscr{F}$. For example, $q(x_1, x_2) = ax_1^2 + bx_1x_2 + cx_2^2$ is a quadratic form in the 2 variables x_1, x_2.

If $f(X, Y)$ is a bilinear form in $x_1, \cdots, x_v$ and $y_1, \cdots, y_v$, then on setting $x_i = y_i$ $(i = 1, \cdots, v)$ we obtain a quadratic form $f(X, X)$. However, there are many bilinear forms so related to each quadratic form. The bilinear forms with matrices

$$(3.1) \quad \left\| \begin{matrix} a & b \\ 0 & c \end{matrix} \right\|, \quad \left\| \begin{matrix} a & 0 \\ b & c \end{matrix} \right\|, \quad \left\| \begin{matrix} a & 100 \\ b - 100 & c \end{matrix} \right\|, \quad \left\| \begin{matrix} a & \tfrac{1}{2}b \\ \tfrac{1}{2}b & c \end{matrix} \right\|$$

all correspond to $q(x_1, x_2) = ax_1^2 + bx_1x_2 + cx_2^2$. For various reasons (e.g., application of theorems on symmetric matrices and congruence, also see polar form below) the symmetric matrix is preferred.

If we denote by c_{ii} the coefficient of x_i^2 and by $2c_{ij}$ the coefficient of x_ix_j where $i \neq j$, we see that

$$(3.2) \quad q(x_1, \cdots, x_v) = XCX^\mathsf{T} = \sum_{\lambda, \mu = 1}^{v} x_\lambda c_{\lambda\mu} x_\mu,$$

where $C = \| c_{ij} \|$ is symmetric. Thus each quadratic form defines a unique symmetric matrix.

Conversely, if $C = \| c_{ij} \|$ is a symmetric matrix of degree v, then (3.2) defines a quadratic form $q(x_1, \cdots, x_v)$. Clearly, the mapping $q \to C$ is a one-to-one correspondence of the set of all quadratic forms onto the set of all symmetric matrices.

Two quadratic forms $q(X) = q(x_1, \cdots, x_v)$ and $q'(X) = q'(x_1, \cdots, x_v)$ are said to be *equivalent* if there exists a reversible linear substitution $X = X'P$ such that $q(X) = q'(X')$. Reference to formulas (1.1), (1.4), and (3.2) shows that q is equivalent to q' if and only if C is congruent to C'. Hence the whole theory of equivalence of quadratic forms can be directly deduced from the theory of congruence of matrices. We define *rank* $r(q)$ for a form

q to be that of its matrix C. Thus *two complex quadratic forms (in the same number of variables) are equivalent if and only if they have the same rank.*

A symmetric matrix C defines both the quadratic form $q(X) = XCX^\mathsf{T}$ and the symmetric bilinear form $f(X, Y) = XCY^\mathsf{T}$. Clearly $f(X, X) = q(X)$. We call $f(X, Y)$ the *polar* form of $q(x)$. The algebraic identity

$$(3.3) \qquad q(X + tY) = q(X) + 2tf(X, Y) + t^2q(Y)$$

obtained by direct substitution in (3.2) and use of the fact that $f(X, Y) = f(Y, X)$ provides a means of defining the polar form without the use of matrices. The polar form is important in the geometry of conics and quadrics.

The reduction process which sends a symmetric matrix into a congruent diagonal matrix is closely related to the process of completing the square used in college algebra and analytic geometry. For example, the form $3x_1{}^2 + 2x_1x_2 + 2x_2{}^2$ can be written $3(x_1 + \frac{1}{3}x_2)^2 + \frac{5}{3}x_2{}^2$ and so the matrix

$$C = \left\| \begin{array}{cc} 3 & 1 \\ 1 & 2 \end{array} \right\| \text{ is congruent to the diagonal matrix } \left\| \begin{array}{cc} 3 & 0 \\ 0 & \frac{5}{3} \end{array} \right\|.$$

The quadratic form $4x_1x_2$ illustrates the case of a symmetric matrix

$$C = \left\| \begin{array}{cc} 0 & 2 \\ 2 & 0 \end{array} \right\| \text{ with only zero entries on the diagonal. The identity}$$

$4x_1x_2 = (x_1+x_2)^2 - (x_1-x_2)^2$ shows that C is congruent to $C' = \left\| \begin{array}{cc} 1 & 0 \\ 0 & -1 \end{array} \right\|.$

Exercises 6.3

1. Express the following real quadratic forms as sums of multiples of squares.
   (a) $x_1{}^2 + 6x_2{}^2 + 8x_3{}^2 - 2x_1x_2 - 4x_1x_3 + 2x_2x_3$.
   (b) $2x_1x_3 - 4x_2x_3 + 2x_1x_2$.
2. Show that, if $A = \| a_{ij} \|$ is the matrix of a quadratic form q, then

$$a_{ij} = \frac{1}{2} \frac{\partial^2 q}{\partial x_i \, \partial x_j}.$$

3. Show that the polar form of a quadratic form q is given by

$$\frac{1}{2} \sum_i y_i \frac{\partial q}{\partial x_i}.$$

4. Show that a complex quadratic form is the product of two linear forms if and only if its matrix has rank less than 3.

5. Let $C = \left\| \begin{array}{ccc} 1 & 2 & -2 \\ 2 & 2 & 0 \\ -2 & 0 & 5 \end{array} \right\|$. Show that the locus $XCX^\mathsf{T} = 0$ is a

quadratic cone. Show that $Y = \| \begin{array}{ccc} 1 & -1 & 1 \end{array} \|$ is a "point" on this cone, and show that $XCY^\mathsf{T} = 0$ is the equation of the tangent plane at the point Y. If Z is a point not on the cone, give an interpretation to the locus $XCZ^\mathsf{T} = 0$.

6.4. Bilinear functions; dual spaces. In the preceding chapters we have developed a theory of linear transformations from a vector space $\mathscr{V}$ into a vector space $\mathscr{W}$. In this section we give attention to the important special case when $\mathscr{W}$ is of dimension one; i.e., when $\mathscr{W}$ is the scalar field $\mathscr{F}$ considered as a vector space over itself.

A mapping

$$(4.1) \qquad \lambda: \quad \alpha \to \alpha\lambda = a$$

of $\mathscr{V}$ into $\mathscr{F}$ is said to be a *scalar function on* $\mathscr{V}$. A scalar function is said to be linear if it is a linear transformation, i.e. (cf. Section 2.1), if for all vectors α_1, α_2 in $\mathscr{V}$ and all scalars c_1, c_2 in $\mathscr{F}$

$$(4.2) \qquad (c_1\alpha_1 + c_2\alpha_2)\lambda = c_1(\alpha_1\lambda) + c_2(\alpha_2\lambda).$$

According to Theorem 2.6D the set of all linear scalar functions on $\mathscr{V}$ is a vector space of dimension $v = \dim \mathscr{V}$. This space is called the *dual space* of $\mathscr{V}$ and will be denoted by $\mathscr{V}^*$.

Thus λ is both a linear transformation and a vector. Since we wish to stress its properties as a vector, we have employed for it the notation of a vector rather than that of a linear transformation.

Let α be in $\mathscr{V}$ and λ in $\mathscr{V}^*$; then $\alpha\lambda$ is a scalar. Thus $\alpha\lambda$ gives a function

$$(4.3) \qquad \mathsf{M}: \quad (\alpha, \lambda) \to \alpha\lambda = (\alpha, \lambda)\mathsf{M}$$

on the Cartesian product (see Appendix II) $\mathscr{V} \times \mathscr{V}^*$ of all pairs (α, λ) with α in $\mathscr{V}$, λ in $\mathscr{V}^*$ into the scalar field $\mathscr{F}$. Let c_1 and c_2 be scalars. If λ is fixed then M is linear in its first argument α; i.e.,

$$(c_1\alpha_1 + c_2\alpha_2, \lambda)\mathsf{M} = (c_1\alpha_1 + c_2\alpha_2)\lambda = c_1(\alpha_1\lambda) + c_2(\alpha_2\lambda)$$
$$= c_1((\alpha_1, \lambda)\mathsf{M}) + c_2((\alpha_2, \lambda)\mathsf{M});$$

and, if α is fixed, then M is linear in λ; i.e.,

$$(\alpha, c_1\lambda_1 + c_2\lambda_2)\mathsf{M} = \alpha(c_1\lambda_1 + c_2\lambda_2) = c_1(\alpha\lambda_1) + c_2(\alpha\lambda_2)$$
$$= c_1((\alpha, \lambda_1)\mathsf{M}) + c_2((\alpha, \lambda_2)\mathsf{M}).$$

We extend these notions to the concept of a bilinear function. Let $\mathcal{V}$, $\mathcal{W}$, $\mathcal{Z}$ be vector spaces over a common scalar field $\mathcal{F}$. A mapping

$$(4.4) \qquad\qquad M: \quad (\alpha, \beta) \rightarrow (\alpha, \beta)M = \gamma$$

of $\mathcal{V} \times \mathcal{W}$ into $\mathcal{Z}$ is said to be *linear over* $\mathcal{V}$ if, for all scalars c_1, c_2, and for all vectors α_1, α_2 in $\mathcal{V}$ and β in $\mathcal{W}$ we have

$$(4.5) \qquad (c_1\alpha_1 + c_2\alpha_2, \beta)M = c_1((\alpha_1, \beta)M) + c_2((\alpha_2, \beta)M);$$

M is said to be *linear over* $\mathcal{W}$ if for all scalars c_1, c_2 and for all vectors α in $\mathcal{V}$ and β_1, β_2 in $\mathcal{W}$ we have

$$(4.6) \qquad (\alpha, c_1\beta_1 + c_2\beta_2)M = c_1((\alpha, \beta_1)M) + c_2((\alpha, \beta_2)M).$$

We say that M is a *bilinear function* if it is linear over both $\mathcal{V}$ and $\mathcal{W}$.

A function M of $\mathcal{V} \times \mathcal{W}$ into $\mathcal{Z}$ is called a *vector function* of two vector arguments. If $\mathcal{Z} = \mathcal{F}$, then M is called a *scalar function* of two vector arguments. If M satisfies (4.5) and (4.6), we call it a *bilinear vector function* (or a *bilinear scalar function* if $\mathcal{Z}$ has dimension one). The function M given by (4.3) is a bilinear scalar function. Another example is the inner product defined in the following way. If $\mathcal{V} = \mathcal{W} = \mathcal{V}_v{}^r$ and $A = \| a_1 \cdots a_v \|$, $B = \| b_1 \cdots b_v \|$ are row vectors, the *inner product* of A and B is

$$(4.7) \qquad\qquad AB^\mathsf{T} = a_1 b_1 + \cdots + a_v b_v.$$

Bilinear forms, discussed in Section 6.1, can be considered as bilinear scalar functions on $\mathcal{V}_v{}^r \times \mathcal{V}_w{}^r$.

If $\mathcal{V}$, $\mathcal{W}$ are two vector spaces, a bilinear scalar function M on $\mathcal{V} \times \mathcal{W}$ is said to be *nonsingular* if

$$(4.8)
\begin{aligned}
&(\alpha, \beta)M = 0 \quad \textit{for all } \beta \textit{ in } \mathcal{W} \textit{ implies} \quad \alpha = 0, \quad \textit{and} \\
&(\alpha, \beta)M = 0 \quad \textit{for all } \alpha \textit{ in } \mathcal{V} \textit{ implies} \quad \beta = 0.
\end{aligned}$$

LEMMA 6.4A. *The mapping* M: $(\alpha, \lambda) \rightarrow (\alpha, \lambda)M = \alpha\lambda$ *on* $\mathcal{V} \times \mathcal{V}^*$ *is a nonsingular bilinear scalar function.*

Let $\mathcal{S} = \{\alpha_1, \cdots, \alpha_v\}$ be a basis for $\mathcal{V}$, and let $\alpha = c_1\alpha_1 + \cdots + c_v\alpha_v$ be a nonzero vector in $\mathcal{V}$, say $c_h \neq 0$. Then the linear transformation λ_h of $\mathcal{V}$ into $\mathcal{F}$ whose matrix relative to $\mathcal{S}$ is $E_h = \| \delta_{hj} \|$ sends α into c_h. Hence $\alpha\lambda = 0$ for all λ in $\mathcal{V}^*$ implies $\alpha = 0$. Conversely, the equation $\alpha\lambda = 0$ for all α in $\mathcal{V}$ requires $\lambda = 0$ by definition of the zero function.

We now give a justification of the term "dual space" by showing that there is a natural way of identifying $\mathcal{V}$ with the dual space $(\mathcal{V}^*)^*$ of $\mathcal{V}^*$. For fixed α in $\mathcal{V}$ the "product" $\alpha\lambda$ can be interpreted as a linear scalar function on $\mathscr{V}^*$; we designate this element of $(\mathscr{V}^*)^*$ by S_α. Since each λ is a linear function, it follows that

$$S_{\alpha_1+\alpha_2} = S_{\alpha_1} + S_{\alpha_2} \quad \text{and} \quad S_{c\alpha} = cS_\alpha.$$

Now, the nonsingularity of M requires that $S_\alpha = 0$ if and only if $\alpha = 0$. This proves that the mapping

$$S: \quad \alpha \rightarrow S_\alpha$$

is an isomorphism of $\mathscr{V}$ into $(\mathscr{V}^*)^*$. However, according to Theorem 2.6D

$$\dim (\mathscr{V}^*)^* = \dim \mathscr{V}^* = \dim \mathscr{V};$$

hence, S is an isomorphism of $\mathscr{V}$ onto $(\mathscr{V}^*)^*$.

It is sometimes convenient to identify α with S_α, and hence $\mathscr{V}$ with $(\mathscr{V}^*)^*$. When this is done, we have the symmetric situation: $\mathscr{V}^*$ is the space of all linear scalar functions on $\mathscr{V}$, and $\mathscr{V}$ is the space of all linear scalar functions on $\mathscr{V}^*$.

We next turn to a further consideration of nonsingular bilinear scalar functions which leads to a more general definition of dual spaces.

LEMMA 6.4B. *Let $\mathscr{V}$ and $\mathscr{W}$ be finite dimensional vector spaces, and let* $M: (\alpha, \beta) \rightarrow (\alpha, \beta)M$ *be a nonsingular bilinear scalar function on $\mathscr{V} \times \mathscr{W}$. Then* $\dim \mathscr{V} = \dim \mathscr{W}$. *Moreover, for fixed β in $\mathscr{W}$ the mapping* $M_\beta: \alpha \rightarrow \alpha M_\beta = (\alpha, \beta)M$ *is a linear scalar function on $\mathscr{V}$, and the correspondence $\beta \rightarrow M_\beta$ is an isomorphism of $\mathscr{W}$ onto the dual space $\mathscr{V}^*$ of $\mathscr{V}$.*

The linearity of M in its first argument α shows that each mapping M_β is a linear scalar function on $\mathscr{V}$. The linearity of M in its second argument β shows that $M_{c_1\beta_1+c_2\beta_2} = c_1 M_{\beta_1} + c_2 M_{\beta_2}$, so that the correspondence $\beta \rightarrow M_\beta$ is a linear transformation of $\mathscr{W}$ into $\mathscr{V}^*$. From the nonsingularity of M we conclude that M_β is the zero mapping if and only if $\beta = 0$. Hence the given correspondence is an isomorphism of $\mathscr{W}$ into $\mathscr{V}^*$, and it will be an isomorphism onto $\mathscr{V}^*$ if $\dim \mathscr{W} = \dim \mathscr{V}^*$. But, since $\dim \mathscr{V}^* = \dim \mathscr{V}$, all that remains is to prove that $\dim \mathscr{V} = \dim \mathscr{W}$.

To do this we begin by selecting a basis $\{\alpha_1, \cdots, \alpha_v\}$ for $\mathscr{V}$ and a basis $\{\beta_1, \cdots, \beta_w\}$ for $\mathscr{W}$. Let $C = \| c_{ij} \|$ be the v-by-w matrix defined by $c_{ij} = (\alpha_i, \beta_j)M$ $(i = 1, \cdots, v;\ j = 1, \cdots, w)$. Let $\alpha = a_1\alpha_1 + \cdots + a_v\alpha_v$ and $\beta = b_1\beta_1 + \cdots + b_w\beta_w$. Then we have

$$(4.9) \qquad (\alpha, \beta)\, M = \sum_{\lambda=1}^{v} a_\lambda \left(\sum_{\mu=1}^{w} c_{\lambda\mu} b_\mu \right).$$

Now, if $v < w$ the system of equations $\Sigma c_{i\mu} b_\mu = 0$ $(i = 1, \cdots, v)$ has a nontrivial solution $b_1, \cdots, b_w$, and hence for the corresponding $\beta \neq 0$ we $(\alpha, \beta)M = 0$ for all α in $\mathscr{V}$ contrary to (4.8). Hence $v \geq w$. Similarly $w \leq v$, and hence $v = w$.

By reversing the roles of $\mathscr{V}$ and $\mathscr{W}$ we see from this lemma that $\mathscr{V}$ is isomorphic to $\mathscr{W}^*$. We now are justified in the following extension of our initial definition of dual spaces. If M is a nonsingular bilinear scalar function on two spaces $\mathscr{V}$ and $\mathscr{W}$, we say that $\mathscr{V}$ and $\mathscr{W}$ are *dual relative to* M.

THEOREM 6.4C. *Let* T *be a linear transformation on a vector space* $\mathscr{V}$, *and let* $\mathscr{V}^*$ *be the dual space of* $\mathscr{V}$. *Then there exists a unique linear transformation* T* *on* $\mathscr{V}^*$ *with the property that*

(4.10) $$(\alpha T)\lambda = \alpha(\lambda T^*)$$

for all α *in* $\mathscr{V}$ *and* λ *in* $\mathscr{V}^*$.

We call T* the *conjugate* (or *adjoint*) of T.

We begin the proof by observing that, for fixed λ in $\mathscr{V}^*$, $T\lambda$ is a linear scalar function on $\mathscr{V}$, and hence there exists a unique vector λ' in $\mathscr{V}^*$ such that $T\lambda = \lambda'$. This enables us to define a mapping T* on $\mathscr{V}^*$ by the formula $\lambda T^* = \lambda'$. Clearly T* satisfies (4.10), and it follows from the uniqueness of λ' that T* is the only mapping that satisfies (4.10). Finally it follows from the linearity of the product $T\lambda$ in its second factor that T* is a linear transformation.

Exercises 6.4

1. Let $\mathscr{V}$, $\mathscr{W}$, $\mathscr{Z}$ be vector spaces over the same field $\mathscr{F}$. Prove that the set of all vector functions on $\mathscr{V} \times \mathscr{W}$ into $\mathscr{Z}$ is a vector space.

2. Show that the set of all bilinear vector functions on $\mathscr{V} \times \mathscr{W}$ into $\mathscr{Z}$ is a subspace of the space defined in the previous exercise. What is the dimension of this subspace?

3. Give a generalization of Exercise 1 to vector functions (with r arguments) on $\mathscr{V}_1 \times \cdots \times \mathscr{V}_r$ into $\mathscr{Z}$.

4. A vector function on $\mathscr{V}_1 \times \cdots \times \mathscr{V}_r$ is said to be *multilinear* if it is linear in each argument. Show that the set of all multilinear vector functions is a subspace of the set of all vector functions with r arguments, and find the dimension of this subspace.

5. Let
$$C = \begin{Vmatrix} 2 & 1 & 3 \\ 1 & 0 & 1 \end{Vmatrix}, \quad \text{let} \quad \mathscr{V} = \mathscr{V}_2{}^r \quad \text{and} \quad \mathscr{W} = \mathscr{V}_3{}^r. \quad \text{Show that}$$

$(A, B) \to ACB^\mathsf{T}$ is a bilinear scalar function on $\mathscr{V} \times \mathscr{W}$. Show that this function is singular.

6.5. Bilinear scalar functions and matrices; dualities. Let $\mathscr{V}$ and $\mathscr{W}$

be finite dimensional vector spaces, and let M: $(\alpha, \beta) \to (\alpha, \beta)M$ be a bilinear scalar function on $\mathscr{V}$ and $\mathscr{W}$. Choose a basis $\mathscr{S} = \{\alpha_1, \cdots, \alpha_v\}$ for $\mathscr{V}$ and a basis $\mathscr{T} = \{\beta_1, \cdots, \beta_w\}$ for $\mathscr{W}$. Then for $\alpha = a_1\alpha_1 + \cdots + a_v\alpha_v$ and $\beta = b_1\beta_1 + \cdots + b_w\beta_w$, we have

$$
\begin{aligned}
(\alpha, \beta)\mathsf{M} &= \left(\sum_{\lambda=1}^{v} a_\lambda\alpha_\lambda, \beta \right) \mathsf{M} \\
&= \sum_{\lambda=1}^{v} a_\lambda((\alpha_\lambda, \beta)\mathsf{M}) \\
(5.1) \qquad &= \sum_{\lambda=1}^{v} a_\lambda((\alpha_\lambda, \Sigma b_\mu\beta_\mu)\mathsf{M}) \\
&= \sum_{\lambda=1}^{v} \sum_{\mu=1}^{w} a_\lambda b_\mu((\alpha_\lambda, \beta_\mu)\mathsf{M}) \\
&= \sum_{\lambda=1}^{v} \sum_{\mu=1}^{w} a_\lambda b_\mu c_{\lambda\mu},
\end{aligned}
$$

where

$$(5.2) \qquad c_{ij} = (\alpha_i, \beta_j)\mathsf{M} \qquad (i = 1, \cdots, v; \; j = 1, \cdots, w).$$

Thus M is completely described by the matrix $C = \| c_{ij} \|$ once the bases for $\mathscr{V}$ and $\mathscr{W}$ are given; and it follows from (5.2) that the matrix C is uniquely determined by M. Formula (5.1) can be expressed compactly in matrix form as

$$(5.3) \qquad (\alpha, \beta)\mathsf{M} = ACB^\mathsf{T}$$

where A is the row matrix $\| a_j \| = \| \alpha \|_{\mathscr{S}}$ and B is the row matrix $\| b_j \| = \| \beta \|_{\mathscr{T}}$. Conversely, to every v-by-w matrix $C = \| c_{ij} \|$, for given bases of $\mathscr{V}$ and $\mathscr{W}$, there corresponds a bilinear scalar function defined by (5.1).

We next consider the effect on C of a change of bases in $\mathscr{V}$ and $\mathscr{W}$. Suppose that $\alpha'_1, \cdots, \alpha'_v$ is a second basis for $\mathscr{V}$ where

$$(5.4) \qquad \alpha'_i = \sum_{\lambda=1}^{v} p_{i\lambda}\alpha_\lambda \qquad (i = 1, \cdots, v)$$

and the matrix $P = \| p_{ij} \|$ has the inverse $P^{-1} = \| p'_{ij} \|$. A vector α in $\mathscr{V}$ can be written both in the form $a_1\alpha_1 + \cdots + a_v\alpha_v$ and in the form $a'_1\alpha'_1 + \cdots + a'_v\alpha'_v$. According to Theorem 5.3A these two sets of "coordinates" for α are connected by the equations

$$(5.5) \qquad A' = AP^{-1} \qquad \text{or} \qquad A = A'P.$$

Similarly, if a second basis $\beta'_1, \cdots, \beta'_w$ for $\mathscr{W}$ is defined by a matrix Q, we have

(5.6) $$B' = BQ^{-1} \qquad \text{or} \qquad B = B'Q,$$

and hence

(5.7) $$(\alpha, \beta)\mathsf{M} = ACB^\mathsf{T} = (A'P)C(Q^\mathsf{T}B'^\mathsf{T}) = A'C'B'^\mathsf{T},$$

where

(5.8) $$C' = PCQ^\mathsf{T}.$$

This result should be compared with Lemma 5.4A, which described the effect of change of basis on the matrix of a linear transformation. Matrices play two roles in the theory of vector spaces: first as analytic formulations of linear transformations, and second as analytic expressions for bilinear functions. The shift from Q^{-1} in Lemma 5.4A to Q^T in (5.8) is typical of the transition from the first role to the second.

Returning to (5.8), we observe that P and Q^T are arbitrary nonsingular matrices and hence C can be replaced by any matrix C' equivalent to C. In particular, by a proper initial choice of bases we may assume that

(5.9) $$C = \left\| \begin{matrix} I_r & 0 \\ 0 & 0 \end{matrix} \right\|.$$

In other words the *degrees v, w and the rank $r = r(C)$ are a complete set of invariants* for the class of matrices which correspond to the given bilinear scalar function M.

Note that then (5.1) takes the especially simple form

(5.10) $$(\alpha, \beta)\mathsf{M} = a_1 b_1 + \cdots + a_r b_r.$$

We can use (5.10) to show that for a fixed M the dimension of the space of all linear scalar functions

$$\mathsf{M}_\beta: \quad \alpha \to \alpha\mathsf{M}_\beta = (\alpha, \beta)\mathsf{M}$$

on $\mathscr{V}$ is equal to the rank of any matrix C for M. Let $\beta = b_1\beta_1 + \cdots + b_w\beta_w$. From the linearity of M in its second argument we have

$$\mathsf{M}_\beta = b_1\mathsf{M}_{\beta_1} + \cdots + b_w\mathsf{M}_{\beta_w}.$$

Comparing with (5.10) we see that $\alpha\mathsf{M}_{\beta_i} = a_i$ $(i = 1, \cdots, r)$ and $\alpha\mathsf{M}_{\beta_i} = 0$ $(i = r + 1, \cdots, w)$. Hence, $\mathsf{M}_{\beta_1}, \cdots, \mathsf{M}_{\beta_r}$ form a basis for the space of all M_β. The symmetry of M in its two arguments shows that r is also the dimension of the space of all mappings M^α defined by

$$\mathsf{M}^\alpha: \quad \beta \to \beta\mathsf{M}^\alpha = (\alpha, \beta)\mathsf{M}.$$

We call this common dimension the *rank* of M, and denote it by $r(\mathsf{M})$. We summarize the above results in the following theorem:

THEOREM 6.5A. *Let* M *be a bilinear scalar function of two finite dimensional spaces* $\mathscr{V}$ *and* $\mathscr{W}$. *Then there exist bases in* $\mathscr{V}$ *and* $\mathscr{W}$ *such that for all* α *in* $\mathscr{V}$ *and* β *in* $\mathscr{W}$ *we have*

$$(\alpha, \beta)\mathsf{M} = a_1 b_1 + \cdots + a_r b_r,$$

where r *is the rank of* M. *The rank of* M *can be characterized in any one of the following three ways* (i) $r(\mathsf{M}) = r(C)$ *where* C *is any matrix corresponding to* M, (ii) $r(\mathsf{M}) = \dim \{\mathsf{M}_\beta\}$, *and* (iii) $r(\mathsf{M}) = \dim \{\mathsf{M}^\alpha\}$.

One consequence of this theorem is that M is nonsingular if and only if rank $\mathsf{M} = \dim \mathscr{V} = \dim \mathscr{W}$. Moreover, if M is nonsingular, (5.10) becomes

(5.11) $(\alpha, \beta)\mathsf{M} = a_1 b_1 + \cdots + a_v b_v = AIB^\mathsf{T} = AB^\mathsf{T}.$

This formula shows that the spaces $\mathscr{V} = \mathscr{V}_v{}^r$ and $\mathscr{W} = \mathscr{V}_v{}^c$ are dual relative to the function M defined by $(A, B)\mathsf{M} = AB$ where A is in $\mathscr{V}$, B is in $\mathscr{W}$ and the product AB is the ordinary matrix product. Indeed this example can be taken as a prototype of dual spaces.

For A and B both in $\mathscr{V}_v{}^r$ the product AB^T is sometimes called simply the *scalar product* of A and B.

Next suppose that $\mathscr{V}$ and $\mathscr{W}$ are dual spaces relative to a nonsingular bilinear scalar function M. If $\mathscr{S}$ is any subset of $\mathscr{V}$, we define the *annihilator* of $\mathscr{S}$ relative to M to be the set of all β in $\mathscr{W}$ such that $(\alpha, \beta)\mathsf{M} = 0$ for all α in $\mathscr{S}$. We denote this set by $\mathscr{A}_\mathsf{M}(\mathscr{S})$. Similarly if $\mathscr{R}$ is a subset of $\mathscr{W}$ we denote by $\mathscr{A}^\mathsf{M}(\mathscr{R})$ the set of all α in $\mathscr{V}$ such that $(\alpha, \beta)\mathsf{M} = 0$ for all β in $\mathscr{R}$.

LEMMA 6.5B. *Let* $\mathscr{S}$ *and* $\mathscr{R}$ *be subsets of* $\mathscr{V}$ *and* $\mathscr{W}$, *respectively. Then* (i) $\mathscr{A}_\mathsf{M}(\mathscr{S})$ *and* $\mathscr{A}^\mathsf{M}(\mathscr{R})$ *are subspaces,* (ii) $\dim \mathscr{A}_\mathsf{M}(\mathscr{S}) + \dim \langle \mathscr{S} \rangle = \dim \mathscr{V}$, *and* (iii) $\mathscr{A}^\mathsf{M}(\mathscr{A}_\mathsf{M}(\mathscr{S})) = \langle \mathscr{S} \rangle$.

Statement (i) follows from the linearity of M in its two arguments.

Next suppose that $\alpha_1, \cdots, \alpha_v$ is any basis for $\mathscr{V}$ and $\beta_1, \cdots, \beta_v$ is any basis for $\mathscr{W}$, and let $C = \| c_{ij} \|$ be the corresponding matrix for M. If we choose a new basis for $\mathscr{W}$ (leaving the one for $\mathscr{V}$ unchanged), the new matrix C' for M has the form $C' = CQ^\mathsf{T}$ [see formula (5.8)]. Now choose $Q^\mathsf{T} = C^{-1}$ and we have $C' = I$. This shows that for nonsingular M we can obtain I as corresponding matrix even subject to the restriction that some fixed basis is assigned in advance for one of the spaces $\mathscr{V}$ and $\mathscr{W}$.

Now, choose a maximal set $\{\alpha_1, \cdots, \alpha_s\}$ of independent vectors in $\mathscr{S}$ (i.e., a basis for $\langle \mathscr{S} \rangle$ made up of vectors belonging to $\mathscr{S}$), and extend this into a basis $\{\alpha_1, \cdots, \alpha_v\}$ for $\mathscr{V}$. Next choose a basis $\{\beta_1, \cdots, \beta_v\}$ for $\mathscr{W}$ so that M has I for its matrix. Since every vector in $\mathscr{S}$ is dependent on $\{\alpha_1, \cdots, \alpha_s\}$, a vector $\beta = b_1 \beta_1 + \cdots + b_v \beta_v$ in $\mathscr{W}$ will belong to $\mathscr{A}_\mathsf{M}(\mathscr{S})$

if and only if $(\alpha_i, \beta)M = b_i = 0$ $(i = 1, \cdots, s)$. Hence $\mathscr{A}_M(\mathscr{S}) = \langle \beta_{s+1}, \cdots, \beta_v \rangle$ has dimension $v - s$; this establishes (ii).

Finally, a vector $\alpha = a_1\alpha_1 + \cdots + a_v\alpha_v$ in $\mathscr{V}$ belongs to $\mathscr{A}^M(\mathscr{A}_M(\mathscr{S}))$ if and only if $(\alpha, \beta_j)M = a_j = 0$ $(j = s + 1, \cdots, v)$; i.e., if and only if α is dependent on $\{\alpha_1, \cdots, \alpha_s\}$. This establishes (iii).

We call the mapping $\mathscr{V}' \rightarrow \mathscr{A}_M(\mathscr{V}')$ (defined for all subspaces $\mathscr{V}'$ of $\mathscr{V}$) together with the reverse mapping $\mathscr{W}' \rightarrow \mathscr{A}^M(\mathscr{W}')$ (defined for all subspaces $\mathscr{W}'$ of $\mathscr{W}$) a *duality*. Each nonsingular bilinear scalar function defines a duality. The terms *correlation* and *polarity* are sometimes used for duality. Suppose that $\mathscr{V}_1$ and $\mathscr{V}_2$ are subspaces of $\mathscr{V}$ with $\mathscr{V}_1 \subseteq \mathscr{V}_2$, and let $\mathscr{W}_i = \mathscr{A}_M(\mathscr{V}_i)$ $(i = 1, 2)$. Then from Lemma 6.5B we see that $\mathscr{V}_i = \mathscr{A}^M(\mathscr{W}_i)$ $(i = 1, 2)$, and, moreover, $\mathscr{W}_1 \supseteq \mathscr{W}_2$; i.e., *a duality inverts inclusion*. In particular, $\mathscr{A}_M(\mathscr{V}) = \{0\}$ and $\mathscr{A}_M(\{0\}) = \mathscr{W}$.

LEMMA 6.5C. *If* $\mathscr{V}_1 \subseteq \mathscr{V}_2$, *then* $\mathscr{A}_M(\mathscr{V}_1) \supseteq \mathscr{A}_M(\mathscr{V}_2)$, *and, if* $\mathscr{W}_1 \subseteq \mathscr{W}_2$ *then* $\mathscr{A}^M(\mathscr{W}_1) \supseteq \mathscr{A}^M(\mathscr{W}_2)$.

We illustrate the concept of duality with the case when $\mathscr{V}$ and $\mathscr{W}$ are both three-dimensional vector spaces. Then the annihilator of a line (through the origin) in $\mathscr{V}$ is a plane (through the origin) in $\mathscr{W}$, and the annihilator of a plane in $\mathscr{V}$ is a line in $\mathscr{W}$. The duality in this case is closely related to duality in plane projective geometry, as can be seen by interpreting each one-dimensional subspace in $\mathscr{V}$ as a point in a projective plane.

Exercises 6.5

1. Let $\mathscr{V}$ and $\mathscr{V}^*$ be dual spaces, and suppose that $\mathscr{S} = \{\alpha_1, \cdots, \alpha_v\}$ and $\mathscr{S}^* = \{\lambda_1, \cdots, \lambda_v\}$ are bases for $\mathscr{V}$ and $\mathscr{V}^*$ such that, if $\alpha = x_1\alpha_1 + \cdots x_v\alpha_v$ and $\lambda = y_1\lambda_1 + \cdots + y_v\lambda_v$, then $\alpha\lambda = x_1y_1 + \cdots + x_vy_v$ [cf. (5.11)]. Let T be a linear transformation on $\mathscr{V}$ and let T* be a linear transformation on $\mathscr{V}^*$. Then show that T* is the conjugate of T if and only if $\| T \|_{\mathscr{S}\mathscr{S}} = (\| T^* \|_{\mathscr{S}^*\mathscr{S}^*})^T$.

2. Show if we identify $\mathscr{V}^{**}$ with $\mathscr{V}$ that $(T^*)^* = T$. Give two proofs, one based on formula (4.10) and the other based on Exercise 1.

6.6. Quadratic functions.

A bilinear scalar function M on $\mathscr{V} \times \mathscr{V}$ is said to be *symmetric* if

$$(6.1) \qquad (\alpha, \beta)M = (\beta, \alpha)M$$

for all α, β in $\mathscr{V}$. If M is a symmetric bilinear scalar function then the function Q defined by

$$(6.2) \qquad \alpha Q = (\alpha, \alpha)M$$

is said to be a *quadratic function* on $\mathscr{V}$. One can calculate M in terms of Q by the formula

$$(6.3) \qquad (\alpha, \beta)M = \tfrac{1}{2}[(\alpha + \beta)Q - \alpha Q - \beta Q].$$

Moreover, it is easy to show that a function Q is quadratic if and only if the right-hand side of (6.3) is a symmetric bilinear scalar function.

Let $\mathscr{S} = \{\alpha_1, \cdots, \alpha_v\}$ be a basis for $\mathscr{V}$, and let $C = \| c_{ij} \|$ be the matrix for M relative to this basis [cf. (5.3)]. Then, since $\mathscr{V} = \mathscr{W}$, (5.3) becomes

$$(6.4) \qquad \alpha Q = \| \alpha \|_{\mathscr{S}} \, C \, \| \alpha \|_{\mathscr{S}}^{\mathsf{T}}.$$

If $\| \alpha \|_{\mathscr{S}} = \| x_1 \cdots x_v \|$, then $\alpha Q = q(x_1, \cdots, x_v)$ is a quadratic form in $x_1, \cdots, x_v$; thus we see that quadratic forms provide analytic descriptions for quadratic functions. If $\mathscr{S}' = \{\alpha'_1, \cdots, \alpha'_v\}$ is a second basis for $\mathscr{V}$, then according to (5.8), C is replaced by $C' = PCP^{\mathsf{T}}$, where P is the matrix for which $\| \alpha \|_{\mathscr{S}} = \| \alpha \|_{\mathscr{S}'} P$. Moreover, $q(x_1, \cdots, x_v) = q'(x'_1, \cdots, x'_v)$ where $\| \alpha \|_{\mathscr{S}'} = \| x'_1 \cdots x'_v \|$ and q' has matrix C'. Thus we see that *two quadratic forms can be the analytic expressions of the same quadratic function if and only if they are equivalent.* Similarly, *two symmetric matrices correspond to the same quadratic function if and only if they are congruent.* It follows from this remark and Theorem 6.2C that, if Q is a quadratic function on $\mathscr{V}$, then there exists a basis relative to which the matrix corresponding to Q is diagonal.

For the rest of this section we assume that $\mathscr{F}$ is the real field $\mathfrak{R}$. In this case, it follows from Theorem 6.2E that by suitable choice of basis we may suppose that a given quadratic function Q has matrix

$$E_{r,t,v} = \left\| \begin{array}{ccc} I_t & 0 & 0 \\ 0 & -I_{r-t} & 0 \\ 0 & 0 & 0 \end{array} \right\|.$$

A quadratic function Q is said to be *positive definite* on a subspace $\mathscr{W}$ of $\mathscr{V}$ if $\alpha Q > 0$ for all nonzero vectors α in $\mathscr{W}$; Q is said to be *positive semidefinite* on $\mathscr{W}$ if $\alpha Q \geq 0$ for all α in $\mathscr{W}$. In particular, if Q has the matrix $I_v = E_{v,v,v}$, then Q is positive definite on $\mathscr{V}$; we shall soon prove a converse result.

We define *negative definite* and *negative semidefinite* by changing $>, \geq$ to $<, \leq$, respectively, in the definitions above.

Let $p(Q)$ denote the largest dimension for subspaces on which Q is positive definite; and, similarly, let $n(Q)$ be the largest dimension for subspaces on which Q is negative definite.

LEMMA 6.6A. *Let Q have matrix $E_{r,t,v}$; then $p(Q) = t$ and $n(Q) = r - t$.*

Let $\{\alpha_1, \cdots, \alpha_v\}$ be a basis for $\mathscr{V}$ relative to which Q has matrix $E_{r,t,v}$. Then Q is positive definite on $\mathscr{U}_1 = \langle \alpha_1, \cdots, \alpha_t \rangle$, and Q is negative semidefinite on $\mathscr{U}_2 = \langle \alpha_{t+1}, \cdots, \alpha_v \rangle$. This shows, in particular, that $t \leq p(Q)$. Next suppose that Q is positive definite on a subspace $\mathscr{W}$. Then

$\mathscr{W} \cap \mathscr{U}_2 = \{0\}$ since for any nonzero vector in this intersection we must have Q both positive and nonpositive. Hence, by Theorem 1.9A,

$$\dim \mathscr{W} + \dim \mathscr{U}_2 = \dim (\mathscr{W} + \mathscr{U}_2) \leqq \dim \mathscr{V} = v,$$

and so

$$\dim \mathscr{W} \leqq v - \dim \mathscr{U}_2 \leqq v - (v - t) = t.$$

This shows that $p(Q)$ cannot exceed t, and hence $p(Q) = t$. The equality $n(Q) = r - t$ follows by applying this first result to $-Q$.

COROLLARY 6.6B. *The integers* r, t, v *are uniquely determined by* Q, *and hence* Q *has only one corresponding matrix* $E_{r,t,v}$.

Next let A be any real symmetric matrix, suppose that A is congruent to $E_{r, t, v}$, say $E_{r, t, v} = PAP^\mathsf{T}$, and suppose that Q is a quadratic function on $\mathscr{V}$ with matrix A relative to some basis. Then, since Q has matrix $E_{r, t, v}$ relative to an appropriate basis for $\mathscr{V}$, we conclude that $p(Q) = t$ and $n(Q) = r - t$. It follows that the integers $p(Q)$ and $n(Q)$ are uniquely defined by A; we denote them, respectively, by $p(A)$ and $n(A)$. Moreover, if A and A' are congruent then $p(A) = p(A')$ and $n(A) = n(A')$, since congruent matrices correspond to the same quadratic function. Combining these results with Theorem 6.2E, we get the following theorem.

THEOREM 6.6C. *Every real symmetric matrix* A *is congruent to a unique matrix* $E_{r, t, v}$; *namely that one for which* $t = p(A)$, $r = p(A) + n(A)$, *and* $v = \deg A$. *Two real symmetric matrices* A *and* A' *of equal degree* v *are congruent if and only if* $r(A) = r(A')$ *and* $p(A) = p(A')$.

The difference $s(A) = p(A) - n(A)$ is called the *signature* of A. It follows from Theorem 6.6C that rank, signature, and degree are a complete set of invariants for congruence of real symmetric matrices.

A real symmetric matrix A of degree v is called *positive definite* if it is the matrix of a quadratic function that is positive definite on a space $\mathscr{V}$ of dimension v. Positive semidefinite, negative definite, and negative semidefinite matrices are defined analogously.

It follows that a real symmetric matrix A is positive definite if and only if $p(A) = v$; A is positive semidefinite if and only if $n(A) = 0$. The only matrices $E_{r, t, v}$ that are positive definite are those for which $r = t = v$; i.e., the identity matrices I_v.

THEOREM 6.6D. *A real symmetric matrix* A *is positive definite if and only if* $A = PP^\mathsf{T}$ *where* P *is nonsingular.*

If A is positive definite, it is congruent to the identity matrix; i.e., $A = PI_v P^\mathsf{T} = PP^\mathsf{T}$ where P is nonsingular. Conversely, if P is nonsingular, then $A = PP^\mathsf{T} = PI_v P^\mathsf{T}$ is positive definite since it is congruent to I_v.

COROLLARY 6.6E. *The determinant of a positive definite matrix is positive.*

For, if $A = PP^\mathsf{T}$, then $\det A = (\det P)^2$ is positive.

LEMMA 6.6F. *If A is congruent to A', then $\det A$ and $\det A'$ have the same sign or are both zero.*

For, if $A' = PAP^\mathsf{T}$, then $\det A = (\det A')(\det P)^2$.

A square submatrix B of a square matrix A is said to be *principal* if its diagonal is part of the diagonal of A. If B is a principal submatrix of A, we call $\det B$ a *principal minor* of A. For example, if $A = I$, the principal minors of A are all 1 whereas all other minors are 0.

THEOREM 6.6G. *A real symmetric matrix A of degree v is positive definite if and only if the v principal minors $\det A[1 \mid 1]$, $\det A[1, 2 \mid 1, 2]$, $\cdots$, $\det A[1, 2, \cdots v \mid 1, 2, \cdots v]$ are all positive.*

Let A be the matrix of the quadratic function $\mathbf{Q}$ on a v-dimensional vector space $\mathscr{V}$ relative to a given basis $\{\alpha_1, \cdots \alpha_v\}$. Let $\mathbf{Q}'$ be the restriction of $\mathbf{Q}$ to the w-dimensional subspace $\mathscr{W} = \langle \alpha_1, \cdots, \alpha_w \rangle$. Then $\mathbf{Q}'$ has matrix $A_w = A[1 \cdots, w \mid 1, \cdots, w]$ relative to the basis $\{\alpha_1 \cdots, \alpha_w\}$ for $\mathscr{W}$. Its determinant must be positive by Corollary 6.6E.

Conversely, suppose that $\det A_1, \cdots, \det A_v$ are all positive. We shall complete the proof of the theorem with the help of Lemma 6.6F by showing that $p(A) = v$. Clearly, A_1 is positive definite. We take as an induction hypothesis that A_s is positive definite for a given s less than v. Let $\mathbf{Q}_{s+1}$ be a quadratic function with matrix A_{s+1}. Since A_s is positive definite, $p(\mathbf{Q}_{s+1}) = s$ or $p(\mathbf{Q}_{s+1}) = s + 1$. But, if $p(\mathbf{Q}_{s+1}) = s$, then either (i) $n(\mathbf{Q}_{s+1}) = 1$, $r(\mathbf{Q}_{s+1}) = s + 1$ and therefore $\det A_{s+1}$ has the same sign as $\det E_{s+1, s, s+1}$, namely -1, or (ii) $n(\mathbf{Q}_{s+1}) = 0$, $r(\mathbf{Q}_{s+1}) = s$ and therefore $\det A_{s+1} = \det E_{s, s, s+1} = 0$. Both of these conclusions contradict our hypothesis $\det A_{s+1} > 0$ and hence we cannot have $p(\mathbf{Q}_{s+1}) = s$. We conclude that $p(\mathbf{Q}_{s+1}) = s + 1$; i.e., $\mathbf{Q}_{s+1}$ and A_{s+1} are positive definite. This completes the induction.

Exercises 6.6

1. Prove that a function $\mathbf{Q}$ is quadratic if and only if the right-hand side of (6.3) is a symmetric bilinear function.

2. Find the rank and signature of the following quadratic forms:

(a) $x_1{}^2 + 6x_2{}^2 + 8x_3{}^2 - 2x_1x_2 - 4x_1x_3 + 2x_2x_3$,

(b) $2x_1x_3 - 4x_2x_3 + 2x_1x_2$.

3. Prove that a real symmetric matrix A of degree v is positive definite if and only if $p(A) = v$, and that A is positive semidefinite if and only if $p(A) = \operatorname{rank} A$.

4. State and prove analogous conditions that A should be negative definite or negative semidefinite.

5. Show that a matrix A is positive semidefinite if and only if there exists a square matrix C such that $A = CC^\mathsf{T}$.

6. Show that, if a matrix A of degree v and rank r is semidefinite, then there exists a v-by-r matrix B such that $A = BB^\mathsf{T}$.

7. Let $A = PP^\mathsf{T}$ where P is nonsingular. Show by use of Theorem 4.6D that each principal minor of A is positive.

8. Give an example of a symmetric matrix A that has a positive determinant but is not positive definite.

9. Find $r(\mathbf{Q})$ and $p(\mathbf{Q})$ if $\mathbf{Q} = 4x^2 + 5y^2 - 6xy + 2xz - 2xw - 8yz - 2zw$.

10. Which of the following quadratic forms are equivalent:

$$\mathbf{Q}_1 = 2x_1^2 + 5x_2^2 + 3x_3^2 - 4x_1x_2 - 2x_2x_3,$$
$$\mathbf{Q}_2 = 3x_1^2 + 2x_2^2 - 2x_3^2 + 4x_1x_2 + 2x_2x_3,$$
$$\mathbf{Q}_3 = 2x_1^2 + 5x_2^2 + 10x_3^2 - 2x_1x_2 - 14x_2x_3 + 4x_1x_3,$$

(a) if $\mathscr{F} = \mathfrak{R}$, (b) if $\mathscr{F} = \mathfrak{C}$?

11. Is the quadratic form $x_1^2 + x_2^2 - x_3^2$ equivalent to $y_1y_2 - y_3^2$ if (a) $\mathscr{F} = \mathfrak{C}$, (b) $\mathscr{F} = \mathfrak{R}$, (c) $\mathscr{F} = \mathfrak{Q}$.?

12. Use *two* methods to determine whether $21x^2 + 8y^2 + 20z^2 - 52xy + 92xz - 32yz$ is positive definite.

13. Show that the quadratic form $-6x^2 - 10xy + 2xz - 4xw + 56y^2 + 8yz + 22yw + 2zw + 4w^2$ is not semidefinite.

6.7. Hermitian functions.

In this section we consider only vector spaces over the complex field $\mathfrak{C}$. A vector function $\alpha \to \beta = \alpha\mathsf{M}$ is said to be *semilinear* if

(7.1) $$(\alpha_1 + \alpha_2)\mathsf{M} = \alpha_1\mathsf{M} + \alpha_2\mathsf{M}$$

and

(7.2) $$(c\alpha)\mathsf{M} = \bar{c}(\alpha\mathsf{M}),$$

where $\bar{c}$ means complex conjugate of c. Let $\mathscr{V}$ be a $\mathfrak{C}$ space, and consider a scalar function H: $(\alpha, \beta) \to (\alpha, \beta)\mathsf{H}$ on $\mathscr{V} \times \mathscr{V}$; H is said to be a *Hermitian function* if

(7.3)
     (i) H is linear in its first argument,

     (ii) H is semilinear in its second argument,

     (iii) $(\alpha, \beta)\mathsf{H} = c$ implies $(\beta, \alpha)\mathsf{H} = \bar{c}$,

Suppose that $\mathscr{V}$ is finite-dimensional with basis $\{\alpha_1, \cdots, \alpha_v\}$, and let $H = \| h_{ij} \|$ where $h_{ij} = (\alpha_i, \alpha_j)\mathsf{H}$ $(i, j = 1, \cdots, v)$. It follows from (7.3iii) that $\bar{h}_{ji} = h_{ij}$ $(i, j = 1, \cdots, v)$. This can be expressed by the matrix equation $H = H^*$ where $*$ denotes conjugate transpose; i.e., if $C = \| c_{ij} \|$, then C^* is the matrix whose (i, j) entry is $\bar{c}_{ji}$. A matrix A is said to be *Hermitian* if $A^* = A$. Moreover, if $\alpha = x_1\alpha_1 + \cdots + x_v\alpha_v$, and $\beta = y_1\alpha_1 + \cdots + y_v\alpha_v$, we have from (7.1), (7.2), and (7.3i and ii) that

(7.4) $$(\alpha, \beta)\mathsf{H} = XHY^*$$

where X and Y are the row matrices $\| x_j \|$ and $\| y_j \|$.

We consider the right-hand side of (7.4) as the analytic expression of the function H. We call XHY^* a *Hermitian form*. An example of a Hermitian form is

$$XHY^* = 2x_1\bar{y}_1 + (1 + i)x_1\bar{y}_2 + (1 - i)x_2\bar{y}_1,$$

where

$$H = \left\| \begin{matrix} 2 & 1 + i \\ 1 - i & 0 \end{matrix} \right\|.$$

The * mapping on matrices has much the same properties as transpose. We state the following properties and leave the proofs to the reader.

(7.5)

    (i) $(A^*)^* = A$ for all matrices A.

    (ii) $(A + B)^* = A^* + B^*$.

    (iii) $(AB)^* = B^*A^*$.

    (iv) $c^* = \bar{c}$ if c is a scalar.

Since $c = XHY^*$ is a scalar, we have

$$\bar{c} = (XHY^*)^* = (Y^*)^*H^*X^* = YHX^*,$$

as required by (7.3iii).

A change of basis with matrix P will give new coordinate matrices X', Y' to α, β where $X = X'P$, $Y = Y'P$. Then, since $Y^* = P^*Y'^*$, we have $(\alpha, \beta)H = XHY^* = X'PHP^*Y'^*$, so that the new matrix H' for H is given by

(7.6) $$H' = PHP^*.$$

Note that $H'^* = (PHP^*)^* = P^{**}H^*P^* = PHP^* = H'$, and so H' is again a Hermitian matrix.

A matrix C' is said to be *conjunctive* to the matrix C if there exists a nonsingular matrix P such that $C' = PCP^*$. Clearly conjunction is an equivalence relation, and we conclude from (7.6) that *two Hermitian matrices are conjunctive if and only if they correspond to the same Hermitian function* H *relative to two bases for* $\mathscr{V}$.

We can also regard the relation $X = X'P$ as a linear transformation $\alpha = \alpha'\mathsf{T}$ on $\mathscr{V}$ which sends the vector α with coordinate matrix X' into the vector α' with coordinate matrix Y', and hence the Hermitian function H: $(\alpha, \beta) \to (\alpha, \beta)$H into the new Hermitian function H': $(\alpha', \beta') \to (\alpha', \beta')$H' $= (\alpha, \beta)$H.

In matrix form this becomes

(7.7) $$(\alpha', \beta')\mathsf{H'} = (\alpha, \beta)\mathsf{H} = XHY^* = X'PHP^*Y'^*$$

and hence $H' = PHP^*$ is the matrix for the new form H' (still relative to the initial basis $\{\alpha_1, \cdots, \alpha_v\}$ for $\mathscr{V}$). We say the Hermitian functions H and H' are *equivalent* if there exists a nonsingular linear transformation T on $\mathscr{V}$ such that

$$(7.8) \qquad\qquad (\alpha\mathsf{T}, \beta\mathsf{T})\mathsf{H} = (\alpha, \beta)\mathsf{H}'.$$

In view of the formulas (7.6) and (7.7) we see that *two Hermitian functions are equivalent if and only if their matrices are conjunctive.*

If F is an elementary matrix, then FHF^* is obtained from H by carrying out an elementary row operation on H followed by the complex conjugate of the corresponding elementary column operation (the complex conjugates of C_{ih}, $\mathsf{C}_i(c, h)$, $\mathsf{C}_i(c)$ are C_{ih}, $\mathsf{C}_i(\bar{c}, h)$, $\mathsf{C}_i(\bar{c})$, respectively). If P is a product of elementary matrices, we can determine PHP^* by a sequence of steps of this kind. Now starting with any Hermitian matrix H we can proceed by analogy with the treatment for symmetric matrices and obtain a diagonal matrix D conjunctive to H, where

$$(7.9) \qquad D = \left\|\begin{array}{cccccc} d_{11} & & & & & \\ & \ddots & & & & \\ & & d_{rr} & & & \\ & & & 0 & & \\ & & & & \ddots & \\ & & & & & 0 \end{array}\right\| ;$$

here $r = \operatorname{rank} H$.

Since D is Hermitian, its diagonal elements $d_{ii} = \bar{d}_{ii}$ are real. Just as in the real case we can now reduce each positive d_{ii} to $+1$ and each negative d_{ii} to -1 and then get H conjunctive to a matrix

$$(7.10) \qquad E_{r,\,t,\,v} = \left\|\begin{array}{ccc} I_t & 0 & 0 \\ 0 & -I_{r-t} & 0 \\ 0 & 0 & 0 \end{array}\right\|.$$

The analogy with the real symmetric case is completed by once again introducing the idea of signature $s = 2t - r$ and proving its invariance under conjunction. This can be summarized in the following theorem.

THEOREM 6.7A. *Two Hermitian matrices H and H' are conjunctive if and only if* (i) degree $H =$ degree H', (ii) rank $H =$ rank H'; *and* (iii) signature $H =$ signature H'. *Moreover any Hermitian matrix H is conjunctive to a unique matrix* $E_{r,\,t,\,v}$ *of the form* (7.10).

A matrix J such that $J^* = -J$ is called *skew-Hermitian*; likewise a function S on $\mathscr{V} \times \mathscr{V}$ which satisfies (7.3i), (7.3ii), and

(7.11)   if $(\alpha, \beta)\mathsf{H} = c$,   then $(\beta, \alpha)\mathsf{H} = -\bar{c}$

is called *skew-Hermitian*. Note that, if J is a skew-Hermitian matrix, then iJ and $-iJ$ are Hermitian matrices. Moreover, $i(-iJ) = J$. Thus we can get a full theory for skew-Hermitian matrices from that for Hermitian matrices, by first treating $H = -iJ$ and then multiplying by i. The canonical form (7.10) is replaced by

$$
(7.12) \qquad\qquad iE_{r,\,t,\,v} =
\begin{Vmatrix}
iI_t & 0 & 0 \\
0 & -iI_{r-t} & 0 \\
0 & 0 & 0
\end{Vmatrix} .
$$

Exercises 6.7

1. Translate Theorem 6.7A into a statement about Hermitian functions.
2. Determine whether the Hermitian forms

$$2x_1\bar{x}_1 + 3ix_1\bar{x}_2 - 3i\bar{x}_1 x_2 - x_2\bar{x}_2,$$
$$(2 + i)x_1\bar{x}_2 + (2 - i)\bar{x}_1 x_2$$

are equivalent.

3. Prove that every complex square matrix is the sum of a Hermitian and a skew-Hermitian matrix.
4. Show that a real symmetric matrix is Hermitian and a real skew-symmetric matrix is skew-Hermitian.
5. A matrix is said to be *normal* if $AA^* = A^*A$. Show that the following matrices are normal: real symmetric, real skew-symmetric, Hermitian, skew-Hermitian.
6. Justify the equations in (7.5).
7. Give the details in the proof that any Hermitian matrix can be reduced to the form (7.10).
8. Prove that the signature of a Hermitian form is invariant under conjunction.

6.8. Determinants as multilinear functions.

Let $\mathscr{V}$ be a vector space of dimension v over any field $\mathscr{F}$. A multilinear function (for definition see the exercises for Section 6.4) is said to be *scalar* if its values are scalars. A multilinear scalar function

(8.1) $\mathsf{D}\colon\ (\alpha_1, \cdots, \alpha_w) \to (\alpha_1, \cdots, \alpha_w)\mathsf{D}$

on $\mathscr{V} \times \cdots \times \mathscr{V}$ (w factors) is said to be a *determinant function of order w* if it vanishes when any two of its arguments $\alpha_1, \cdots, \alpha_w$ are equal. For $w = 1$, the determinant functions are just the linear scalar functions on $\mathscr{V}$. Our major interest is in the case $w = v$ which leads to ordinary determinants.

LEMMA 6.8A.   *If D is a determinant function, then D is a skew function; i.e., D changes sign when any pair of its arguments are interchanged.*

This lemma follows from the identity

$$0 = (\cdots, \alpha + \beta, \cdots, \alpha + \beta, \cdots)D$$
$$= (\cdots, \alpha, \cdots, \alpha + \beta, \cdots)D + (\cdots, \beta, \cdots, \alpha + \beta, \cdots)D$$
$$= (\cdots, \alpha, \cdots, \alpha, \cdots)D + (\cdots, \alpha, \cdots, \beta, \cdots)D$$
$$+ (\cdots, \beta, \cdots, \alpha, \cdots)D + (\cdots, \beta, \cdots, \beta, \cdots)D$$
$$= 0 + (\cdots, \alpha, \cdots, \beta, \cdots)D + (\cdots, \beta, \cdots, \alpha, \cdots)D + 0.$$

Hence
$$(\cdots, \alpha, \cdots, \beta, \cdots)D = -(\cdots, \beta, \cdots, \alpha, \cdots)D.$$

The converse of this lemma is also true provided $\mathscr{F}$ does not have characteristic two.

LEMMA 6.8B.   *If D is a determinant function and c is a scalar, then*

$$(\alpha_1, \cdots, c\alpha_h, \cdots, \alpha_w)D = c(\alpha_1, \cdots, \alpha_h, \cdots, \alpha_w)D.$$

This is merely a restatement of one of the conditions for multilinearity.

LEMMA 6.8C.   *If the set $\{\alpha_1, \cdots, \alpha_w\}$ is dependent, then $(\alpha_1, \cdots, \alpha_w)D = 0$.* Suppose that $\alpha_w = c_1\alpha_1 + \cdots + c_{w-1}\alpha_{w-1}$. Then by the linearity of D

$$(\alpha_1, \cdots, \alpha_{w-1}, \alpha_w)D = c_1(\alpha_1, \cdots, \alpha_{w-1}, \alpha_1)D$$
$$+ \cdots + c_{w-1}(\alpha_1, \cdots, \alpha_{w-1}, \alpha_{w-1})D.$$

Each summand on the right-hand side is zero since it has two equal arguments, and therefore the entire sum is zero. A similar discussion applies if α_j ($j < w$) is dependent on the remaining α_h.

COROLLARY 6.8D.   *If $w > v$, then zero is the only determinant function.*

LEMMA 6.8E.   *If D is a determinant function, if c is a scalar, and if $i \neq h$, then*

$$(\alpha_1, \cdots, \alpha_i + c\alpha_h, \cdots, \alpha_w)D = (\alpha_1, \cdots, \alpha_i, \cdots, \alpha_w)D.$$

By the linearity of D we have

$$(\alpha_1, \cdots, \alpha_i + c\alpha_h, \cdots, \alpha_w)D = (\alpha_1, \cdots, \alpha_i, \cdots, \alpha_w)D$$
$$+ c(\alpha_1, \cdots, \alpha_h, \cdots, \alpha_w)D,$$

where the second term on the right has α_h in both the hth and ith positions and therefore vanishes.

If D_1 and D_2 are determinant functions of order w, and if c_1, c_2 are scalars, then $D = c_1 D_1 + c_2 D_2$ is clearly also a determinant function of order w. Hence *the set of all determinant functions of order w is a vector space.* We denote this space by $\mathscr{D}(v, w)$. According to Corollary 6.8D, $\mathscr{D}(v, w)$ has dimension zero if $w > v$. Our goal is to show that $\mathscr{D}(v, v)$ has dimension one.

Let $\mathscr{S} = \{\alpha_1, \cdots, \alpha_v\}$ and $\mathscr{S}' = \{\beta_1, \cdots, \beta_v\}$ be two bases for $\mathscr{V}$, let T be the unique linear transformation on $\mathscr{V}$ for which $\alpha_i T = \beta_i \, (i = 1, \cdots, v)$, and let A be the matrix of T relative to the basis $\mathscr{S}$. We can write A as a product of elementary matrices, say $A = F_1 \cdot F_2 \cdot \cdots \cdot F_k$. Then $T = T_1 \cdot T_2 \cdot \cdots \cdot T_k$ where T_j has matrix F_j relative to the basis $\{\alpha_1{}^{j-1}, \cdots, \alpha_v{}^{j-1}\} = \{\alpha_1 T_1 \cdots T_{j-1}, \cdots, \alpha_v T_1 \cdots T_{j-1}\}$ $(j = 2, \cdots, k)$ and T_1 has matrix F_1 relative to $\mathscr{S}$.

Now set $g(T_j) = -1, c, 1$ according as F_j is of the form F_{ih}, $F_i(c)$, or $F_i(c, h)$. Then for any determinant function D it follows from Lemmas 6.8A, 6.8B, and 6.8E that

$$(8.2) \qquad (\alpha_1 T_j, \cdots, \alpha_v T_j)D = (\alpha_1, \cdots, \alpha_v)D \, g(T_j).$$

Hence, in particular, for the sets $\mathscr{S}$ and $\mathscr{S}'$ described above we have

$$(8.3) \qquad (\beta_1, \cdots, \beta_v)D = (\alpha_1, \cdots, \alpha_v)D \, g(T_1) \cdots g(T_k).$$

LEMMA 6.8F. *Let D be a determinant function of order v. Then either $D = 0$, or $(\beta_1, \cdots, \beta_v)D \neq 0$ for every basis $\{\beta_1, \cdots, \beta_v\}$ of $\mathscr{V}$.*

If D is not the zero function, let $\alpha_1, \cdots, \alpha_v$ be vectors for which $(\alpha_1, \cdots, \alpha_v)D \neq 0$. Then, by Lemma 6.8C, $\{\alpha_1, \cdots, \alpha_v\}$ is independent, and now we conclude from (8.3) that $(\beta_1, \cdots, \beta_v)D \neq 0$.

LEMMA 6.8G. *Suppose that D_0 is a nonzero determinant function of order v; then any determinant function D of order v is dependent on D_0.*

Let $\mathscr{S} = \{\alpha_1, \cdots, \alpha_v\}$ be any basis for $\mathscr{V}$. Then by hypothesis $(\alpha_1, \cdots, \alpha_v)D_0 = c_0 \neq 0$. Let $(\alpha_1, \cdots, \alpha_v)D = c$. Next let $\mathscr{S}' = \{\beta_1, \cdots, \beta_v\}$ be any ordered set of v vectors. Then either $\mathscr{S}'$ is dependent, and hence $(\beta_1, \cdots, \beta_v)D_0 = (\beta_1, \cdots, \beta_v)D = 0$, or $\mathscr{S}'$ is independent, and by (8.3)

$$(\beta_1, \cdots, \beta_v) D = (\alpha_1, \cdots, \alpha_v)D g(T_1) \cdots g(T_k)$$

$$= \frac{c}{c_0} (\alpha_1, \cdots, \alpha_v)D_0 g(T_1) \cdots g(T_k)$$

$$= \frac{c}{c_0} (\beta_1, \cdots, \beta_v)D_0;$$

that is,

$$(8.4) \qquad\qquad \mathsf{D} = \frac{c}{c_0}\, \mathsf{D}_0.$$

Theorem 6.8H. *Let $\mathscr{V}$ be a vector space of dimension v. Then the set of all determinant functions of order v on $\mathscr{V}$ is of dimension one.*

We have proved that the dimension is at most one. To show that it is at least one (and therefore equal to one) we need only exhibit one nonzero determinant function on $\mathscr{V}$. To do this we choose any basis $\mathscr{S} = \{\alpha_1, \cdots, \alpha_v\}$ for $\mathscr{V}$. If $\mathscr{S}' = \{\beta_1, \cdots, \beta_v\}$, we define $(\beta_1, \cdots, \beta_v)\mathsf{D}$ to be the ordinary determinant of the matrix $B = \| b_{ij} \|$ whose rows are the coordinates of the β_h relative to $\mathscr{S}$. For this purpose we use the classical definition of determinant (Theorem 4.4A). It is obvious that this gives a multilinear function which is not identically zero since $(\alpha_1, \cdots, \alpha_v)\mathsf{D} = \det I_v = 1$.

The only nontrivial step in proving that D is a determinant function is to show that its value is zero whenever two arguments are equal. To see this suppose that $\beta_i = \beta_h, i < h$. Now let $(\lambda_1, \cdots, \lambda_v)$ be any permutation of $(1, \cdots, v)$, and associate with it the permutation $(\mu_1, \cdots, \mu_v)$ having $\mu_j = \lambda_j$ ($j \neq i$ or h) and $\mu_i = \lambda_h, \mu_h = \lambda_i$. Then the products $b_{\lambda_1 1} \cdots b_{\lambda_v v}$ and $b_{\mu_1 1} \cdots b_{\mu_v v}$ are equal since $b_{hj} = b_{ij}$. Now cf. (4.4.2′)

$$\det B = \Sigma \pi(\lambda_1, \cdots, \lambda_v) b_{\lambda_1 1} \cdots b_{\lambda_v v},$$

and by pairing terms this can be written

$$\det B = \sum_{\lambda_i < \lambda_h} [\pi(\lambda_1, \cdots, \lambda_v) + \pi(\mu_1, \cdots, \mu_v)] b_{\lambda_1 1} \cdots b_{\lambda_v v}.$$

But, since the permutations λ_j and μ_j differ by a transposition, each term in this sum vanishes, and so $\det B = 0$.

Lemma 6.8I. *If D is a determinant function and T is a linear transformation, then the function D' defined by*

$$(\alpha_1, \cdots, \alpha_w)\mathsf{D}' = (\alpha_1 \mathsf{T}, \cdots, \alpha_w \mathsf{T})\mathsf{D}$$

is a determinant function.

If, in particular, $w = v$ and $\alpha_i \mathsf{T} = \beta_i$ ($i = 1, \cdots, v$), we know from Lemma 6.8G that

$$(8.5) \qquad \begin{aligned} (\alpha_1, \cdots, \alpha_v)\mathsf{D}' &= (\beta_1, \cdots, \beta_v)\mathsf{D} \\ &= (\alpha_1, \cdots, \alpha_v)\mathsf{D}\, g(\mathsf{T}_1) \cdots g(\mathsf{T}_k). \end{aligned}$$

If D is not zero, this equation shows that the product $g(T_1) \cdots g(T_k)$ is independent of the particular factorization of T, and hence we may write

$$(8.6) \qquad\qquad\qquad D' = D \, g(T),$$

where

$$(8.7) \qquad g(T) = g(T_1) \cdots g(T_k) = \frac{(\alpha_1 T, \cdots, \alpha_v T)D}{(\alpha_1, \cdots, \alpha_v)D}.$$

We call the scalar $g(T)$ the *determinant* of T. It follows from (8.3) and (8.7) that $g(T_1 T_2) = g(T_1) \cdot g(T_2)$ and that $g(T) \neq 0$ if and only if T is nonsingular. Moreover, $g(I) = 1$.

Next, let B be the matrix of T relative to the basis $\{\alpha_1, \cdots, \alpha_v\}$. We wish to show that $g(T)$ is the ordinary determinant of B.

We may suppose D and $\{\alpha_1, \cdots, \alpha_v\}$ chosen so that $(\alpha_1, \cdots, \alpha_v)D = 1$. Then, by Lemma 6.8A for any permutation $\lambda_1, \cdots, \lambda_v$, $(\alpha_{\lambda_1}, \cdots, \alpha_{\lambda_v})D = \pi(\lambda_1, \cdots, \lambda_v)$. Hence

$$g(T) = (\beta_1, \cdots, \beta_v)D$$

$$= (\cdots, \Sigma b_{i\lambda_i}\alpha_{\lambda_i}, \cdots)D$$

$$= \sum_{\lambda_i=1}^{v} b_{1\lambda_i} \cdots b_{v\lambda_v} (\alpha_{\lambda_1}, \cdots, \alpha_{\lambda_v})D$$

$$= \Sigma\pi(\lambda_1, \cdots, \lambda_v)b_{1\lambda_1} \cdots b_{v\lambda_v}$$

$$= \det B.$$

Exercises 6.8

1. State and prove the converse of Lemma 6.8A when $\mathscr{F}$ does not have characteristic 2.

2. Show that the converse of Lemma 6.8A is false if $\mathscr{F}$ has characteristic 2.

3. Prove that $\mathscr{D}(v, w)$ has dimension $v!/(v - w)!w!$ if $w < v$. (Hint: Let $\{\alpha_1, \cdots, \alpha_v\}$ be a basis of $\mathscr{V}$. Show that any D in $\mathscr{D}(v, w)$ is determined by the values of $(\alpha_{\lambda_1}, \cdots, \alpha_{\lambda_w})D$ where $(\lambda_1, \cdots, \lambda_w)$ is an ordered combination of w of the numbers $\{1, \cdots, v\}$ by obtaining an expression similar to the last equation of this section. Next show that these values depend only on those for ordered combinations with $\lambda_1 < \cdots < \lambda_w$. Finally show that these values can be assigned independently.)

Chapter **7**	# Orthogonal and Unitary Equivalence

In this chapter we introduce the concept of length of a vector and the related concepts of distance and angle. We first treat the case of real scalars and Euclidean spaces and study orthogonality of vectors and of subspaces. Then we consider orthogonal (i.e., distance-preserving) linear transformations and matrices and show that every symmetric matrix is orthogonally similar to a diagonal matrix. We then generalize these results for complex scalars and unitary spaces.

7.1. Euclidean space and inner products. We now introduce a vector space $\mathscr{E}_n$, called *Euclidean n-space*, whose elements are row vectors $A = \| a_1 \cdots a_n \|$ with real components, and in which each vector A has a *length* $| A |$ given by

$$(1.1) \qquad | A | = (A A^{\mathsf{T}})^{1/2} = (a_1{}^2 + \cdots + a_n{}^2)^{1/2}.$$

Note that $\mathscr{E}_n$ is just $\mathscr{V}_n{}^r(\mathfrak{R})$ with the addition of a concept of length.

The reader has encountered $\mathscr{E}_1$, $\mathscr{E}_2$, and $\mathscr{E}_3$ in analytic geometry, where the length $| A |$ defined above gives the distance from the origin to the point $(a_1, \cdots, a_n)$.

Before studying properties of this length we extend these ideas. Let $\mathscr{V}$ be any (finite-dimensional) vector space over the real field $\mathfrak{R}$, and let $\mathbf{Q}$ be a positive definite quadratic function on $\mathscr{V}$ (see Section 6.6). We recall that this means $\alpha \mathbf{Q} > 0$ for every nonzero vector α in $\mathscr{V}$, and that for a given basis $\mathscr{S} = \{\alpha_1, \cdots, \alpha_n\}$ there is a positive definite matrix C such that

$$(1.2) \qquad \alpha \mathbf{Q} = \| \alpha \|_{\mathscr{S}} C \| \alpha \|_{\mathscr{S}}{}^{\mathsf{T}}$$

[cf. equation (6.6.4)]. If we define the *length* $| \alpha |$ of α to be $(\alpha \mathbf{Q})^{1/2}$, then $\mathscr{V}$ is called a *Euclidean space*.

By polarization of Q we obtain a symmetric bilinear function M; viz.,

(1.3) $(\alpha, \beta)M = \frac{1}{2}[(\alpha + \beta)Q - \alpha Q - \beta Q].$

We abbreviate $(\alpha, \beta)M$ to (α, β). It follows from (1.2) and (1.3) that

(1.4) $(\alpha, \beta) = \| \alpha \|_{\mathscr{S}} C \| \beta \|_{\mathscr{S}}^{\mathsf{T}}.$

The function (α, β) has the following properties:

    (i)   Scalar: (α, β) is a function on $\mathscr{V} \times \mathscr{V}$ into $\mathfrak{R}$.

    (ii) Bilinear: $(c\alpha, \beta)$ $= c(\alpha, \beta) = (\alpha, c\beta),$

                    $(\alpha + \alpha', \beta) = (\alpha, \beta) + (\alpha', \beta),$

(1.5) $(\alpha, \beta + \beta') = (\alpha, \beta) + (\alpha, \beta')$

              for all $\alpha, \alpha', \beta, \beta'$ in $\mathscr{V}$ and c in $\mathfrak{R}$.

    (iii) Symmetric: $(\alpha, \beta) = (\beta, \alpha).$

    (iv) Positive definite: $(\alpha, \alpha) > 0$ for all $\alpha \neq 0$.

Let $\mathscr{V}$ be any real vector space. Then a function (α, β) on $\mathscr{V} \times \mathscr{V}$ is said to be an *inner product on* $\mathscr{V}$ if it satisfies the four conditions of (1.5). For example, the product AB^{T} of two vectors A, B in $\mathscr{V}_n{}^r(\mathfrak{R})$ is an inner product [cf. formula (6.4.7)].

THEOREM 7.1A. *Let $\mathscr{V}$ be a vector space over $\mathfrak{R}$, and let (α, β) be an inner product on $\mathscr{V}$. Then the definition of length $| \alpha | = (\alpha, \alpha)^{1/2}$ makes $\mathscr{V}$ into a Euclidean space relative to the positive definite quadratic function Q:$\alpha Q = (\alpha, \alpha)$. Conversely, if $\mathscr{V}$ is a Euclidean space defined by a positive definite quadratic function Q, then (1.3) defines an inner product on $\mathscr{V}$.*

The first part of the theorem follows at once from (1.5) and the definition of positive definite quadratic function (cf. Section 6.6). We have already proved the second part.

COROLLARY 7.1B. *Euclidean n-space is a Euclidean space.*

An isomorphism $\alpha \to \alpha'$ between two Euclidean spaces $\mathscr{V}$ and $\mathscr{V}'$ is said to be an *isometry* if it preserves distances; i.e., if

(1.6) $| \alpha | = | \alpha' |$

for all α in $\mathscr{V}$.

THEOREM 7.1C. *Let $\mathscr{V}$ be a Euclidean space of dimension n. Then $\mathscr{V}$ is isometric to $\mathscr{E}_n$. Moreover, there exists a basis $\mathscr{T}$ for $\mathscr{V}$ such that*

(1.7) $(\alpha, \beta) = \| \alpha \|_{\mathscr{T}} \| \beta \|_{\mathscr{T}}^{\mathsf{T}}.$

The inner product (α, β) is defined by a positive definite quadratic function Q. According to Theorem 6.6C there exists a basis $\mathscr{T}$ for $\mathscr{V}$

such that $\alpha Q = \| \alpha \|_{\mathcal{F}} \| \alpha \|_{\mathcal{F}}{}^{\mathsf{T}}$; for this basis (1.4) becomes (1.7). Now the mapping $\alpha \to \| \alpha \|_{\mathcal{F}}$ is clearly an isometry of $\mathcal{V}$ onto $\mathcal{E}_n$.

COROLLARY 7.1D. *Two (finite-dimensional) Euclidean spaces are isometric if and only if they have the same dimension.*

Exercises 7.1

1. Let $\mathcal{V}$ be the plane in Euclidean three-space generated by $(1, 2, 2)$ and $(3, 0, -4)$. Find a basis $\mathcal{F}$ for $\mathcal{V}$ which satisfies condition (1.7).
2. Do the same for the plane $\langle (2, -3, 3), (2, 2, -1) \rangle$.
3. Do likewise for the plane $x + 2y - z = 0$.
4. Let the quadratic function Q on $\mathcal{V}_3$ have matrix

$$\left\| \begin{array}{ccc} 1 & 0 & 0 \\ 0 & 2 & 0 \\ 0 & 0 & 3 \end{array} \right\|$$

and define an inner product on $\mathcal{V}_3$. Find an isometry of $\mathcal{V}_3$ onto $\mathcal{E}_3$.

5. Do the same if Q has matrix $\left\| \begin{array}{ccc} 14 & 2 & -10 \\ 2 & 41 & -25 \\ -10 & -25 & 35 \end{array} \right\|$.

7.2. Schwartz's inequality, distance, and angle.

THEOREM 7.2A. SCHWARTZ'S INEQUALITY. *Let $\mathcal{E}$ be a Euclidean space with inner product (α, β). Then for all vectors α, β in $\mathcal{E}$ we have*

$$(2.1) \qquad (\alpha, \beta)^2 \leq (\alpha, \alpha)(\beta, \beta).$$

The equality occurs if and only if α, β are dependent.

The theorem is trivial if $\alpha = 0$. Hence suppose $\alpha \neq 0$.

Let x be a scalar variable, and let

$$(2.2) \qquad f(x) = (x\alpha + \beta, x\alpha + \beta) = x^2(\alpha, \alpha) + 2x(\alpha, \beta) + (\beta, \beta).$$

This is a quadratic function of x and will be negative for certain values of x if the discriminant $d = 4[(\alpha, \beta)^2 - (\alpha, \alpha)(\beta, \beta)]$ is positive. But according to (1.5iv), $f(x)$ is never negative; hence $d \leq 0$; i.e., $(\alpha, \beta)^2 \leq (\alpha, \alpha)(\beta, \beta)$. If equality holds, i.e., if $d = 0$, then $f(x) = 0$ has a real root c, and then we conclude from the equation $(c\alpha + \beta, c\alpha + \beta) = f(c) = 0$ that $c\alpha + \beta = 0$; i.e., β is dependent on α.

COROLLARY 7.2B. *For all α and β in $\mathcal{E}$*

$$(2.3) \qquad |(\alpha, \beta)| \leq |\alpha| \cdot |\beta|.$$

The *distance* $d(\alpha, \beta)$ between two vectors α, β is defined to be the length of the vector $\beta - \alpha$ joining α to β; i.e.,

$$(2.4) \qquad d(\alpha, \beta) = |\beta - \alpha|.$$

THEOREM 7.2C.   *The distance function* $d(\alpha, \beta)$ *has the following properties:*

(2.5) *Definite:* $\begin{cases} d(\alpha, \beta) > 0 & if \quad \alpha \neq \beta. \\ d(\alpha, \alpha) = 0. \end{cases}$

(2.6) *Symmetric:* $d(\alpha, \beta) = d(\beta, \alpha)$.

(2.7) *Invariant under translation:* $d(\alpha + \gamma, \beta + \gamma) = d(\alpha, \beta)$.

(2.8) *Triangle inequality:* $d(\alpha, \gamma) \leq d(\alpha, \beta) + d(\beta, \gamma)$.

The first two properties (2.5) and (2.6) follow at once from corresponding properties of the inner product [cf. (1.5)]; (2.7) follows from (2.4).

The triangle inequality is just the statement in vector language that in $\mathscr{E}$ the sum of the lengths of two sides of a triangle is at least as large as the length of the third side.   An important consequence is that among all polygonal paths joining two points the line segment joining them is the shortest.

The triangle inequality is a consequence of Schwarz's inequality.   First we take the case $\beta = 0$.   Then

$$\begin{aligned} d(\alpha, \gamma)^2 &= (\alpha - \gamma, \alpha - \gamma) \\ &= (\alpha, \alpha) - 2(\alpha, \gamma) + (\gamma, \gamma) & \text{[by (1.5)]} \\ &\leq [|\alpha| + |\gamma|]^2 \end{aligned}$$

by (2.3).   Thus

$$d(\alpha, \gamma) \leq d(\alpha, 0) + d(0, \gamma).$$

If in this expression α is replaced by $\alpha - \beta$ and γ by $\gamma - \beta$, formula (2.8) is an immediate consequence of (2.7).

We are now in a position to introduce angles in $\mathscr{E}$.   Any three vectors α, β, γ in $\mathscr{E}$ determine a triangle whose sides have lengths $|\alpha - \beta|$, $|\beta - \gamma|$, $|\gamma - \alpha|$.   We define the *angle* θ between two nonzero vectors α and β to be the angle between the sides of length $|\alpha|$ and $|\beta|$ in the triangle determined by the vectors α, β, 0.   Then by the law of cosines

$$(2.9) \qquad |\alpha - \beta|^2 = |\alpha|^2 + |\beta|^2 - 2|\alpha| \cdot |\beta| \cos \theta.$$

Now

$$\begin{aligned} |\alpha - \beta|^2 &= (\alpha - \beta, \alpha - \beta) \\ &= (\alpha, \alpha) - (\beta, \alpha) - (\alpha, \beta) + (\beta, \beta) \\ &= |\alpha|^2 + |\beta|^2 - 2(\alpha, \beta). \end{aligned}$$

Hence we have

(2.10) $$\cos \theta = \frac{(\alpha, \beta)}{|\alpha| \cdot |\beta|}.$$

Exercises 7.2

1. Find the cosines of the angles between each pair of rows of the matrix

$$A = \begin{Vmatrix} 3 & -1 & 1 & 0 \\ 2 & 1 & -1 & 1 \\ 0 & 1 & 2 & -2 \end{Vmatrix}.$$

2. Find the cosines of the angles of the triangle determined by the rows of the matrix A of Exercise 1.

3. Give a direct proof of Schwartz's inequality in $\mathcal{E}_n$; i.e., show that $(AB^\mathsf{T})^2 \leq (AA^\mathsf{T})(BB^\mathsf{T})$ for any two row vectors A and B.

4. State Schwartz's inequality in component form.

7.3. Orthogonality. From (2.10) we see that two vectors are perpendicular or, as we shall say, *orthogonal*, if $\theta = 90°$; i.e., if

(3.1) $$(\alpha, \beta) = 0.$$

This expression is a generalization of the familiar criterion from analytic geometry for two sets of direction numbers to represent perpendicular directions. Hereafter, our main interest in angles will be the case $\theta = 90°$.

In $\mathcal{E}_n$ the unit vectors $\delta_i = \| \, 0 \cdots 0 \, 1 \, 0 \cdots 0 \, \| \, (i = 1, \cdots, n)$ are a set of mutually orthogonal vectors. Furthermore, each has length 1. In any Euclidean space $\mathcal{E}$ a system of mutually orthogonal vectors, each of length 1, is called an *orthonormal system*. From a set $\mathcal{S}$ of mutually orthogonal vectors an orthonormal system $\mathcal{T}$, which spans the same subspace as $\mathcal{S}$, can be obtained by discarding all zero vectors and dividing each remaining vector by its length.

LEMMA 7.3A. *An orthonormal set* $\mathcal{S} = \{\alpha_1, \cdots, \alpha_r\}$ *is independent.* For, if $a_1\alpha_1 + \cdots + a_r\alpha_r = 0$, then

$$0 = (\alpha_i, 0) = (\alpha_i, a_1\alpha_1 + \cdots + a_r\alpha_r)$$
$$= a_1(\alpha_i, \alpha_1) + \cdots + a_r(\alpha_i, \alpha_r) \qquad \text{[by (1.5ii)]}$$
$$= a_i \qquad\qquad\qquad (i = 1, \cdots, r)$$

since $\mathcal{S}$ is orthonormal. Hence each a_i is 0, and $\mathcal{S}$ is independent.

An orthonormal set $\mathcal{S}$ spanning $\mathcal{V}$ is said to be *complete*.

LEMMA 7.3B. *A maximal orthonormal set* $\mathscr{S} = \{\alpha_1, \cdots, \alpha_r\}$ *is complete.*
Suppose $\alpha \neq 0$ and is not in $\langle \mathscr{S} \rangle$. Let $a_i = (\alpha, \alpha_i)$, and let

$$\beta = \alpha - a_1\alpha_1 - \cdots - a_r\alpha_r.$$

Then

$$
\begin{aligned}
(\beta, \alpha_i) &= (\alpha - a_1\alpha_1 - \cdots - a_r\alpha_r, \alpha_i) \\
&= (\alpha, \alpha_i) - a_1(\alpha_1, \alpha_i) - \cdots - a_r(\alpha_r, \alpha_i) \\
&= a_i - a_i \cdot 1 \qquad\qquad \text{(since } \mathscr{S} \text{ is orthonormal)} \\
&= 0.
\end{aligned}
$$

Also β is not in $\langle \mathscr{S} \rangle$ because α is not in $\langle \mathscr{S} \rangle$; in particular $\beta \neq 0$. Then $\{\alpha_1, \cdots, \alpha_r, \beta/|\beta|\}$ is an orthonormal system. Hence, if $\{\alpha_1, \cdots, \alpha_r\}$ is maximal, it is complete.

THEOREM 7.3C. *Every orthonormal set can be extended to be complete.*

This is an immediate consequence of Lemmas 7.3A and 7.3B.

THEOREM 7.3D. *Every Euclidean space has a complete orthonormal set.*
This important result is simply a corollary of Theorem 7.3C. It is also a consequence of Theorem 7.1C on the existence of a basis in terms of which an inner product can be expressed as a scalar product.

If the method of Lemma 7.3B is applied to a basis $\{\beta_1, \cdots, \beta_n\}$ to obtain an orthonormal set by starting with the null set and introducing the vectors $\beta_1, \cdots, \beta_n$ in turn to obtain larger and larger orthonormal sets, this entire construction is called the Gram-Schmidt orthogonalization process.

Usually when we require a basis in a Euclidean space it will be convenient to take an orthonormal basis.

LEMMA 7.3E. *Let* $\{\alpha_1, \cdots, \alpha_n\}$ *be an orthonormal basis, and let* $\alpha = c_1\alpha_1 + \cdots + c_n\alpha_n$. *Then* $|\alpha| = (c_1{}^2 + \cdots + c_n{}^2)^{1/2}$.
The proof is left as an exercise.

Exercises 7.3

1. Prove Lemma 7.3E.
2. Apply the Gram-Schmidt orthogonalization process to the vectors $(-2, 1, 7)$, $(4, 0, 3)$, of $\mathscr{E}_3$ to obtain an orthonormal basis for the subspace which they span.
3. Do the same for the vectors $(3, 1, -2, 3)$, $(6, 0, 1, 0)$, $(1, -1, 0, 2)$.
4. Find an orthonormal basis for the row space of

$$
\begin{Vmatrix}
2 & 0 & 3 & -3 \\
-2 & 1 & 7 & 4 \\
0 & 3 & 0 & -2
\end{Vmatrix}.
$$

5. Find an orthonormal basis for the plane $7x - 2y + z = 0$.

6. Find an orthonormal basis for the hyperplane $3x - y - z + 2w = 0$ in $\mathscr{E}_4$.

7.4. Orthogonal subspaces. Let $\mathscr{S}$ be a set of vectors in a Euclidean space $\mathscr{V}$. It is easy to see [using (1.5)] that the set $\mathcal{O}(\mathscr{S})$ of all vectors orthogonal to each vector in $\mathscr{S}$ is a subspace. If $\mathscr{W}$ is a subspace, we call $\mathcal{O}(\mathscr{W})$ the *orthogonal complement* of $\mathscr{W}$. The significance of this term is given by the next theorem.

THEOREM 7.4A. *If $\mathscr{W}$ is a subspace of a Euclidean space $\mathscr{V}$, then $\mathscr{V}$ is the direct sum of $\mathscr{W}$ and its orthogonal complement $\mathcal{O}(\mathscr{W})$.*

To prove this we take an orthonormal basis $\{\alpha_1, \cdots, \alpha_s\}$ of $\mathscr{W}$ and an orthonormal basis $\{\beta_1, \cdots, \beta_t\}$ of $\mathcal{O}(\mathscr{W})$. Then $\{\alpha_1, \cdots, \alpha_s, \beta_1, \cdots, \beta_t\}$ is itself orthonormal. It must be maximal because any vector orthogonal to this set must be in particular in $\mathcal{O}(\mathscr{W})$ (see Exercise 1 below). Hence, this set is complete (by Lemma 7.3B), and $\mathscr{V} = \mathscr{W} + \mathcal{O}(\mathscr{W})$ (direct).

COROLLARY 7.4B. *If $\mathscr{W}$ is a subspace of a Euclidean space $\mathscr{V}$, then $\mathcal{O}(\mathcal{O}(\mathscr{W})) = \mathscr{W}$.*

The proof is left as an exercise.

Exercises 7.4

1. If $\mathscr{S} = \{\alpha_1, \cdots, \alpha_s\}$ and $\mathscr{U} = \langle \mathscr{S} \rangle$, then $\mathcal{O}(\mathscr{U}) = \mathcal{O}(\mathscr{S})$.
2. Prove Corollary 7.4B.
3. Find a set of generators of $\mathcal{O}(\mathscr{S})$ where $\mathscr{S} = \langle (3, -2, 1) \rangle$.
4. Do likewise if $\mathscr{S} = \langle (3, -2, 1), (2, 0, -3) \rangle$.
5. Do likewise if $\mathscr{S} = \langle (3, -2, 1, 0), (2, 0, -3, 3) \rangle$.
6. Let $\mathscr{S}$ be a subset of a Euclidean space. Show that $\mathcal{O}(\mathcal{O}(\mathscr{S})) = \langle \mathscr{S} \rangle$.

7.5. Orthogonal transformations. We next investigate those linear transformations T, called *orthogonal* transformations, on a Euclidean space which preserve the inner product; i.e., for which

$$(5.1) \qquad\qquad (\alpha\mathsf{T}, \beta\mathsf{T}) = (\alpha, \beta)$$

for every pair of vectors α, β in $\mathscr{V}$. Clearly distance is invariant since, in particular,

$$(5.2) \qquad\qquad (\alpha\mathsf{T}, \alpha\mathsf{T}) = (\alpha, \alpha).$$

For example, in three-space rotations about an axis through the origin and reflections in a plane through the origin are orthogonal transformations.

Conversely, if distance is preserved, so is the inner product, and hence also angle; i.e., (5.2) implies (5.1). For

$$(\alpha + \beta, \alpha + \beta) = (\alpha, \alpha) + 2(\alpha, \beta) + (\beta, \beta)$$

and

$$((\alpha + \beta)\mathsf{T}, (\alpha + \beta)\mathsf{T}) = (\alpha\mathsf{T}, \alpha\mathsf{T}) + 2(\alpha\mathsf{T}, \beta\mathsf{T}) + (\beta\mathsf{T}, \beta\mathsf{T}).$$

From these equalities and with the help of (5.2) we immediately deduce (5.1).

We now obtain a necessary and sufficient condition on the matrix relative to an orthonormal basis $\{\alpha_1, \cdots, \alpha_v\}$ of $\mathscr{V}$ of an orthogonal linear transformation T. It follows from (5.1) that the set of images $\{\alpha_1\mathsf{T}, \cdots, \alpha_v\mathsf{T}\}$ is also an orthonormal basis. In terms of the matrix A this means that the v rows $A_1, \cdots, A_v$ satisfy the condition

$$(5.3) \qquad\qquad A_i A_j{}^\mathsf{T} = \delta_{ij} \qquad\qquad (i, j = 1, \cdots, v).$$

Conversely, if (5.3) is satisfied by A, then the set of images $\{\alpha_1\mathsf{T}, \cdots, \alpha_v\mathsf{T}\}$ is also an orthonormal basis. Finally, if $\alpha = \Sigma c_\lambda \alpha_\lambda$, then $\alpha\mathsf{T} = \Sigma c_\lambda(\alpha_\lambda\mathsf{T})$; hence, by Lemma 7.3E, $|\alpha|^2 = \Sigma c_\lambda{}^2 = |\alpha\mathsf{T}|^2$. Since distance is preserved, so is the inner product, and hence T is an orthogonal transformation.

A matrix A is called *orthogonal* if

$$(5.4) \qquad\qquad A A^\mathsf{T} = I,$$

i.e., if (5.3) is satisfied. We summarize these results.

THEOREM 7.5A. *A transformation is orthogonal if and only if its matrix with respect to an orthonormal basis is orthogonal.*

If A is orthogonal, then $\det A = \pm 1$ from (5.4). All the matrices of a given orthogonal transformation T with respect to different orthonormal bases have the same determinant. In case this common value is $+1$, T is called *properly* orthogonal or a *rotation*; when it is -1, T is called *improperly* orthogonal. For a space of dimension 2 the improper orthogonal transformations are all reflections.

Exercises 7.5

1. Prove that the product of two orthogonal transformations is orthogonal.
2. Prove that the inverse of an orthogonal transformation is orthogonal.
3. Prove that, if dim $\mathscr{V} = 2$, every orthogonal matrix has the form

$$A = \left\| \begin{matrix} \cos\theta & \sin\theta \\ -\sin\theta & \cos\theta \end{matrix} \right\| \quad \text{or } JA \quad \text{where} \quad J = \left\| \begin{matrix} 1 & 0 \\ 0 & -1 \end{matrix} \right\|.$$

4. Prove that the set of orthogonal transformations on a Euclidean space $\mathscr{V}$ forms a group and that this group is commutative if and only if dim $\mathscr{V} = 1$.

5. Prove that the restriction of an orthogonal transformation to an invariant subspace is also an orthogonal transformation. (A subspace $\mathscr{W}$ is said to be *invariant* under a linear transformation T on a space $\mathscr{V}$ if $\mathscr{W}\mathsf{T} \subseteq \mathscr{W}$.)

6. Let A be the matrix of a linear transformation T on a Euclidean space. Show that T is an isometry if and only if A is orthogonal.

7. Let S be any matrix for which $I + S$ is nonsingular. Show that S commutes with $(I + S)^{-1}$.

8. If S is skew-symmetric and if k is an eigenvalue of S, show that $-k$ is also an eigenvalue of S.

9. Let S be a skew-symmetric matrix such that $I + S$ is nonsingular. Show that $A = (I - S)(I + S)^{-1}$ is orthogonal. (Hint: see Ex. 7, 8.) Show also that $(I - A)^{-1}$ exists and $S = (I - A)(I + A)^{-1}$.

10. Using Exercise 9, show the existence of rational points on the sphere $x^2 + y^2 + z^2 = 1$.

11. Let A be a real m-by-n matrix, and let $\mathscr{W}$ be a subspace of $\mathscr{V}_m^{\,r}$ invariant under the linear transformation $X \to Y = XA$. Show that $\mathcal{O}\,(\mathscr{W})$ is invariant under the linear transformation $X \to Y = XA^{\mathsf{T}}$.

7.6. Diagonalization of symmetric matrices.

Let H be a real symmetric matrix. By Theorem 6.2C we know that H is congruent to a diagonal matrix $D = PHP^{\mathsf{T}}$. In this section we prove that this diagonalization can be achieved with an orthogonal matrix P. Since then $P^{\mathsf{T}} = P^{-1}$, H is also similar to D.

THEOREM 7.6A. *If H is a real symmetric matrix, then its eigenvalues are all real.*

We operate temporarily in the field $\mathfrak{C}$ of complex numbers. Since every nonconstant polynomial has a root, in particular the characteristic function does. Hence, there exists an eigenvalue λ in $\mathfrak{C}$; let α in $\mathscr{V}_n^{\,r}(\mathfrak{C})$ be an associated eigenvector; $\alpha H = \lambda\alpha$. Thus $\alpha H\bar{\alpha}^{\mathsf{T}} = \lambda\alpha\bar{\alpha}^{\mathsf{T}}$. Now $\alpha H\bar{\alpha}^{\mathsf{T}}$ is real since

$$\alpha H\bar{\alpha}^{\mathsf{T}} = (\alpha H\bar{\alpha}^{\mathsf{T}})^{\mathsf{T}} = \bar{\alpha}H\alpha^{\mathsf{T}} = \overline{\alpha H\bar{\alpha}^{\mathsf{T}}}.$$

Also $\alpha\bar{\alpha}^{\mathsf{T}}$ is real and not 0. Hence $\lambda = \alpha H\bar{\alpha}^{\mathsf{T}}/\alpha\bar{\alpha}^{\mathsf{T}}$ and is real.

In the proof of this theorem it was convenient to work over $\mathfrak{C}$; we now return to $\mathfrak{R}$. Since the eigenvalues and coefficients all lie in $\mathfrak{R}$, we may also find corresponding eigenvectors in $\mathscr{V}_n^{\,r}(\mathfrak{R})$; indeed, any eigenvector in $\mathscr{V}_n^{\,r}(\mathfrak{C})$ is a linear combination of eigenvectors in $\mathscr{V}_n^{\,r}(\mathfrak{R})$.

THEOREM 7.6B. *If H is a positive definite matrix, then the eigenvalues of H are all positive.*

If α is a real eigenvector belonging to the eigenvalue λ we have from the calculations given above that

$$\lambda = \alpha H\alpha^{\mathsf{T}}/\alpha\alpha^{\mathsf{T}}.$$

Now, since H is positive definite, we conclude that λ is positive.

THEOREM 7.6C. *If H is a real symmetric matrix with eigenvalues $\lambda_1, \cdots, \lambda_n$, then there exists an orthogonal matrix P such that $PHP^{-1} = D$, where*

$$D = \left\| \begin{array}{cccc} \lambda_1 & & & \\ & \cdot & & \\ & & \cdot & \\ & & & \cdot \\ & & & \lambda_n \end{array} \right\|.$$

Let α_1 be an eigenvector in $\mathscr{V}_n{}^r(\Re)$ belonging to the eigenvalue λ_1. Since $\alpha_1 \neq 0$ we may, by simply dividing α_1 by $|\alpha_1|$, assume that $|\alpha_1| = 1$. We wish to obtain a complete orthonormal system composed of eigenvectors. We proceed by induction.

Supplement α_1 to a complete orthonormal system $\mathscr{S} = \{\alpha_1, \beta_2, \cdots, \beta_n\}$. Let T be the linear transformation $\alpha \to \alpha H$. Let K be the matrix of T with respect to $\mathscr{S}$. Then $K = QHQ^{-1}$ where $Q = \| \alpha_1{}^\mathsf{T} \beta_2{}^\mathsf{T} \cdots \beta_n{}^\mathsf{T} \|$ and $Q^{-1} = Q^\mathsf{T}$. Since $\alpha_1 \mathsf{T} = \lambda_1 \alpha_1$, $K = \left\| \begin{array}{cc} \lambda_1 & 0 \\ L & H_1 \end{array} \right\|$ and $L = 0$ because K is symmetric. By induction there exists an orthogonal matrix P_1 such that

$$P_1 H_1 P_1{}^{-1} = \left\| \begin{array}{cccc} \lambda_2 & & & \\ & \cdot & & \\ & & \cdot & \\ & & & \cdot \\ & & & \lambda_n \end{array} \right\|.$$

Then $R = \left\| \begin{array}{cc} 1 & 0 \\ 0 & P_1 \end{array} \right\|$ is orthogonal, and so is $P = RQ$. Finally $PHP^{-1} = D$.

This theorem is a special case of Theorem 7.8E, and the proof given there does not use matrices.

COROLLARY 7.6D. *Let A, B be real symmetric matrices of degree n, and let A be positive definite. Then there exists a nonsingular matrix P such that $PAP^\mathsf{T} = I$ and $PBP^\mathsf{T} = D$, where D is diagonal.*

From Theorems 6.6C and 6.6D there exists a nonsingular matrix Q such that $QAQ^\mathsf{T} = I$. By Theorem 7.6C there exists an orthogonal matrix Q_1 such that $Q_1(QBQ^\mathsf{T})Q_1{}^{-1} = D$, a diagonal matrix. Then $P = Q_1 Q$ satisfies the requirements of the corollary. For $PAP^\mathsf{T} = Q_1(QAQ^\mathsf{T})Q_1{}^\mathsf{T} = Q_1 Q_1{}^\mathsf{T} = I$, since Q is orthogonal.

The next theorem is a generalization of Theorem 7.6C.

THEOREM 7.6E.   *Let $A_1, \cdots, A_t$ be a set of real symmetric matrices such that every pair commute.   Then there exists an orthogonal matrix P such that $PA_iP^{-1} = D_i$, where each D_i is diagonal $(i = 1, \cdots, t)$.*

From the preceding theorem we know that there exists an orthogonal matrix P_0 such that $P_0A_1P_0^{-1} = D_1$, where D_1 is diagonal.   If $\lambda_1, \cdots, \lambda_r$ are the *distinct* eigenvalues of A_1, then it can be assumed that D_1 has the form

$$D_1 = \left\|\begin{array}{ccc} \lambda_1 I_{n_1} & & \\ & \cdot & \\ & & \cdot \\ & & \quad \lambda_r I_{n_r} \end{array}\right\|,$$

where n_i is the multiplicity of λ_i.

The matrices $P_0A_1P_0^{-1}, \cdots, P_0A_tP_0^{-1}$ all commute with each other since $A_1, \cdots, A_t$ do.   This can be verified by direct computation or by realizing that their corresponding transformations $\mathsf{T}_1, \cdots, \mathsf{T}_t$ commute, and hence so will the matrices of the transformations with respect to any given basis.   Furthermore, the transformed matrices are symmetric since $P_0^{-1} = P_0^{\mathsf{T}}$.

Let B be a matrix commuting with D_1.   If B is partitioned just as D_1,

$$B = \left\|\begin{array}{ccc} B_{11} & \cdots & B_{1r} \\ \cdot & \cdots & \cdot \\ B_{r1} & \cdots & B_{rr} \end{array}\right\|,$$

then

$$D_1B = \left\|\begin{array}{ccc} \lambda_1 B_{11} & \cdots & \lambda_1 B_{1r} \\ \cdot & \cdots & \cdot \\ \lambda_r B_{r1} & \cdots & \lambda_r B_{rr} \end{array}\right\|, \qquad BD_1 = \left\|\begin{array}{ccc} \lambda_1 B_{11} & \cdots & \lambda_r B_{1r} \\ \cdot & \cdots & \cdot \\ \lambda_1 B_{r1} & \cdots & \lambda_r B_{rr} \end{array}\right\|.$$

Since $D_1B = BD_1$ and $\lambda_i \neq \lambda_j$ $(i \neq j)$, we conclude that $B_{ij} = 0$ $(i \neq j)$. Hence

$$B = \left\|\begin{array}{ccc} B_1 & & 0 \\ & \cdot & \\ & & \cdot \\ & & \cdot \\ 0 & & B_r \end{array}\right\|.$$

If C has the same form,

$$C = \left\| \begin{matrix} C_1 & & & 0 \\ & \cdot & & \\ & & \cdot & \\ & & & \cdot \\ 0 & & & C_r \end{matrix} \right\|,$$

and, if B and C commute, then a direct computation shows that B_i and C_i commute $(i = 1, \cdots, r)$. When these results are applied to the matrices $P_0 A_1 P_0^{-1}, \cdots, P_0 A_h P_0^{-1}$, we conclude that

$$P_0 A_i P_0^{-1} = \left\| \begin{matrix} A_{i1} & & & 0 \\ & \cdot & & \\ & & \cdot & \\ & & & \cdot \\ 0 & & & A_{ir} \end{matrix} \right\| \qquad (i = 1, \cdots, t),$$

where A_{ij} is symmetric and commutes with A_{ik} $(i = 1, \cdots, t;$ $j, k = 1, \cdots, r)$.

To complete the proof we use induction. We assume the theorem is true for a set of $t - 1$ commuting matrices. Thus, for each j from 1 to r, there exists an orthogonal matrix P_j such that $P_j A_{ij} P_j^{-1} = D_{ij}$ $(i = 2, \cdots, t)$, where D_{ij} is diagonal. But also, when $i = 1$, we have $A_{1j} = \lambda_j I_{n_j}$, and hence $P_j A_{1j} P_j^{-1} = \lambda_j I_{n_j}$, which is diagonal. Then $P = P' P_0$, where

$$P' = \left\| \begin{matrix} P_1 & & & 0 \\ & \cdot & & \\ & & \cdot & \\ & & & \cdot \\ 0 & & & P_r \end{matrix} \right\|$$

satisfies the conditions of the theorem. This completes the induction and the proof of the theorem.

Exercises 7.6

1. Let $A_1, \cdots, A_t$ be a set of matrices such that every pair commute and each is similar to a diagonal matrix. Show that there exists a nonsingular matrix P such that $P A_1 P^{-1}, \cdots, P A_t P^{-1}$ are all diagonal.

2. Under the hypothesis of Exercise 1, prove that $A_1, \cdots, A_t$ are all polynomials in a single matrix A.

3. Let $B = \begin{Vmatrix} 0 & -1 & -2 \\ -1 & \frac{4}{3} & 1 \\ -2 & 1 & \frac{15}{4} \end{Vmatrix}$. Find a diagonal matrix D orthogonally

equivalent to B. Find an orthogonal matrix P such that $PBP^{-1} = D$.

4. Let $A = \begin{Vmatrix} 14 & 2 & -10 \\ 2 & 41 & -25 \\ -10 & -25 & 35 \end{Vmatrix}$ and B be as defined in Exercise 3.

Find a nonsingular matrix P such that $PAP^\mathsf{T} = I$ and $PBP^\mathsf{T} = D$, where D is diagonal.

5. Let A be a real diagonal matrix without equal eigenvalues. Show that every matrix that commutes with A is a polynomial in A. Show that the conclusion holds even when A is not diagonal.

6. Let $A_1 = \begin{Vmatrix} 1 & 2 & 0 & 0 \\ 2 & 1 & 0 & 0 \\ 0 & 0 & 1 & 0 \\ 0 & 0 & 0 & 1 \end{Vmatrix}$, $A_2 = \begin{Vmatrix} 1 & 0 & 0 & 0 \\ 0 & 1 & 0 & 0 \\ 0 & 0 & 2 & 1 \\ 0 & 0 & 1 & 2 \end{Vmatrix}$.

Find an orthogonal matrix P such that PA_iP^{-1} is diagonal ($i = 1, 2$).

7. Do the same if

$$A_1 = \begin{Vmatrix} 10 & 0 & -5 \\ 0 & -1 & -2 \\ -5 & -2 & 1 \end{Vmatrix}, \qquad A_2 = \begin{Vmatrix} 3 & 2 & -1 \\ 2 & 1 & 4 \\ -1 & 4 & 2 \end{Vmatrix}.$$

7.7. Unitary transformations. For vector spaces over the complex field $\mathfrak{C}$ there are results analogous to those already obtained in this chapter for the real field $\mathfrak{R}$. In the remainder of this chapter we assume that $\mathscr{F} = \mathfrak{C}$. For the most part in this section we shall state definitions and results, leaving the proofs to the reader.

In the vector space $\mathscr{V}_n{}^r(\mathfrak{C})$ the *scalar product* of two vectors $\alpha = \| a_1 \cdots a_n \|$, $\beta = \| b_1 \cdots b_n \|$ is defined as $\alpha\bar\beta^\mathsf{T}$, where $\bar\beta = \| \bar{b}_1 \cdots \bar{b}_n \|$ is the (complex) conjugate of β. In a vector space $\mathscr{V}$ over $\mathfrak{C}$ an *inner product* is a positive definite Hermitian function (α, β) (see Section 6.7). A complex vector space with an inner product is called a *unitary space*.

LEMMA 7.7A. *In a finite-dimensional unitary space there exists a basis* $\mathscr{S}$ *such that* $(\alpha, \beta) = \| \alpha \|_{\mathscr{S}} \overline{\| \beta \|}_{\mathscr{S}}^{\mathsf{T}}$.

The *length* $| \alpha |$ of a vector α is defined as $| \alpha | = (\alpha,\alpha)^{1/2}$ and is therefore a non-negative real number, being 0 if and only if $\alpha = 0$. A vector α is said to be *normal* if $| \alpha | = 1$. Two vectors α, β are called *orthogonal* if $(\alpha, \beta) = 0$. An *orthonormal* set is a set in which every vector is normal and every two distinct vectors are orthogonal. Every maximal orthonormal set is a basis.

Schwarz's inequality holds for a unitary space in the generalized form

$$(\alpha, \beta)(\beta, \alpha) \leqq (\alpha, \alpha)(\beta, \beta).$$

The triangle inequality

$$| \alpha - \gamma | \leqq | \alpha - \beta | + | \beta - \gamma |$$

also holds.

The *orthogonal complement* $\mathcal{O}(\mathscr{W})$ of a subspace $\mathscr{W}$ in a unitary space $\mathscr{V}$ is defined just as in the Euclidean case. Again $\mathscr{V} = \mathscr{W} + \mathcal{O}(\mathscr{W})$ and $\mathscr{W} \cap \mathcal{O}(\mathscr{W}) = \{0\}$.

A transformation T is called *unitary* if it preserves the inner product

$$(\alpha\mathsf{T}, \beta\mathsf{T}) = (\alpha, \beta)$$

for every pair of vectors α, β in $\mathscr{V}$. For this to be true it is necessary and sufficient that distance be preserved: $| \alpha\mathsf{T} | = | \alpha |$.

A complex matrix A is called *unitary* if

$$A\bar{A}^{\mathsf{T}} = I.$$

THEOREM 7.7B. *A transformation is unitary if and only if its matrix with respect to an orthonormal basis is unitary.*

A matrix A is said to be *unitary-equivalent* to a matrix B if there exists a unitary matrix P such that $B = PAP^{-1}$.

THEOREM 7.7C. *Every Hermitian matrix H is unitary-equivalent to a diagonal matrix whose diagonal elements are the eigenvalues of H.*

COROLLARY 7.7D. *The eigenvalues of a Hermitian matrix are real.*

Let A be a unitary matrix; let λ be an eigenvalue, and α an associated eigenvector in $\mathscr{V}_n{}^r(\mathbb{C})$. Since $0 \neq (\alpha, \alpha) = (\lambda\alpha, \lambda\alpha) = \lambda\bar{\lambda}(\alpha, \alpha)$, we conclude that $\lambda\bar{\lambda} = 1$. We state this result.

THEOREM 7.7E. *The eigenvalues of a unitary matrix are all of absolute value 1.*

COROLLARY 7.7F.   *The eigenvalues of a real orthogonal matrix are all of absolute value* 1.

This is a consequence of the theorem since a real orthogonal matrix A, when considered as a complex matrix, is unitary in view of the fact that $\bar{A} = A$.   Likewise a real symmetric matrix is also Hermitian.   But it is not true that the theory of Euclidean spaces is a part of that for unitary spaces.   For in the former case all operations must be restricted to involve only real scalars.   For example, every unitary matrix is similar to a diagonal matrix; but this is not true for real orthogonal matrices when only real transforming matrices are used since the eigenvalues are imaginary unless they are ± 1.

Exercises 7.7

1. Supply proofs where needed for the statements of this section.
2. Prove that every rotation in a real space of odd dimension has an axis of rotation.
3. A matrix A is called *skew-Hermitian* if $A = -\bar{A}^{\mathsf{T}}$.   Prove that the eigenvalues of a skew-Hermitian matrix are pure imaginary.
4. Prove that, if A is Hermitian, then iA is skew-Hermitian.
5. Let A be a skew-Hermitian matrix.   Show that $U = (A - I)^{-1}(A + I)$ exists and is unitary and does not have 1 as an eigenvalue.   (Hint: see Ex. 7.5.9.)
6. Let $U = \begin{Vmatrix} 2 & 1+i \\ 1-i & 6 \end{Vmatrix}$.   Find a diagonal matrix unitary equivalent to U.

7.8. Adjoint of a linear transformation.

THEOREM 7.8A.   *Let $\mathscr{V}$ be a unitary space with inner product (α, β), and let T be a linear transformation on $\mathscr{V}$.   Then there exists a unique linear transformation T^* on $\mathscr{V}$ such that for all α, β in $\mathscr{V}$ we have*

$$(8.1) \qquad\qquad (\alpha\mathsf{T}, \beta) = (\alpha, \beta\mathsf{T}^*).$$

We call T^* the *adjoint* of T.

For fixed β the mapping $\alpha \to (\alpha\mathsf{T}, \beta)$ is a linear scalar function on $\mathscr{V}$. Since the inner product (α, β) is nonsingular, it follows (cf. Section 6.4) that there exists a unique vector γ in $\mathscr{V}$ such that $(\alpha\mathsf{T}, \beta) = (\alpha, \gamma)$ for all α in $\mathscr{V}$.   We then define $\beta\mathsf{T}^* = \gamma$ and have a mapping T^* on $\mathscr{V}$ into $\mathscr{V}$ for which (8.1) holds.   The uniqueness of T^* follows from that of γ. Let $\beta_1\mathsf{T}^* = \gamma_1$ and $\beta_2\mathsf{T}^* = \gamma_2$.   Then the equation

$$(8.2) \qquad \begin{aligned} (\alpha\mathsf{T}, c_1\beta_1 + c_2\beta_2) &= \bar{c}_1(\alpha\mathsf{T}, \beta_1) + \bar{c}_2(\alpha\mathsf{T}, \beta_2) \\ &= \bar{c}_1(\alpha, \gamma_1) + \bar{c}_2(\alpha, \gamma_2) = (\alpha, c_1\gamma_1) + (\alpha, c_2\gamma_2) \\ &= (\alpha, c_1\gamma_1 + c_2\gamma_2) \end{aligned}$$

shows that $(c_1\beta_1 + c_2\beta_2)\mathsf{T}^* = c_1\gamma_1 + c_2\gamma_2$, and hence that T^* is a linear transformation.

Let $\mathscr{S} = \{\alpha_1, \cdots, \alpha_n\}$ be a basis of $\mathscr{V}$ for which

(8.3) $$(\alpha, \beta) = \|\, \alpha \,\|_{\mathscr{S}} \overline{\|\, \beta \,\|}_{\mathscr{S}}{}^{\mathsf{T}},$$

and suppose that $A = \|\, \mathsf{T} \,\|_{\mathscr{S}\mathscr{S}}$. Then

(8.4) $$\|\, \mathsf{T}^* \,\|_{\mathscr{S}\mathscr{S}} = \bar{A}^{\mathsf{T}},$$

i.e., *the conjugate transpose of the matrix of a linear transformation is the matrix of its adjoint.*

Let $\alpha = a_1\alpha_1 + \cdots + a_n\alpha_n$, $\beta = b_1\alpha_1 + \cdots + b_n\alpha_n$. Then

(8.5) $$(\alpha\mathsf{T}, \beta) = (\Sigma a_\mu a_{\mu\lambda}\alpha_\lambda, \beta) = \Sigma a_\mu a_{\mu\lambda}\bar{b}_\lambda = \Sigma a_\mu \bar{c}_\mu$$

where

$$c_i = \Sigma \bar{a}_{i\lambda}b_\lambda \qquad\qquad (i = 1, \cdots, n).$$

It follows that $(\alpha\mathsf{T}, \beta) = (\alpha, \gamma)$ where $\gamma = c_1\alpha_1 + \cdots + c_n\alpha_n$, and hence that the mapping $\beta \to \gamma$ has matrix $\bar{A}^{\mathsf{T}}$; i.e., $\bar{A}^{\mathsf{T}}$ is the matrix of T^*.

Note that there is an unfortunate confusion of terminology here. Had we not already defined the "adjoint" of a matrix in Chapter 4, we might wish to call $\bar{A}^{\mathsf{T}}$ the adjoint of A so that the term "adjoint" for matrices would have a meaning analogous to that for linear transformations. However, the terminology is so widespread and traditional that no alternative words will be introduced here. But we do write A^* for $\bar{A}^{\mathsf{T}}$.

From the Hermitian symmetry of the inner product it can be shown that $(\mathsf{T}^*)^* = \mathsf{T}$.

A linear transformation T is called *normal* if it commutes with its adjoint; i.e., $\mathsf{TT}^* = \mathsf{T}^*\mathsf{T}$. If an orthonormal basis is used, then the matrix A of T commutes with its conjugate transpose; $AA^* = A^*A$. Such a matrix is called *normal*. In particular a Hermitian matrix $A = A^*$ is normal. So also is a unitary transformation T since then $(\alpha, \beta) = (\alpha\mathsf{T}, \beta\mathsf{T}) = (\alpha\mathsf{I}, \beta\mathsf{TT}^*)$. By the uniqueness of the adjoint $\mathsf{I}^* = \mathsf{TT}^* = \mathsf{I}$. Hence $\mathsf{T}^* = \mathsf{T}^{-1}$ and commutes with T.

LEMMA 7.8B. *A transformation* T *is normal if and only if* $(\alpha\mathsf{T}, \beta\mathsf{T}) = (\alpha\mathsf{T}^*, \beta\mathsf{T}^*)$ *for every pair of vectors* α, β.

If T is normal, then $(\alpha\mathsf{T}, \beta\mathsf{T}) = (\alpha, \beta\mathsf{TT}^*) = (\alpha, \beta\mathsf{T}^*\mathsf{T}) = (\alpha\mathsf{T}^*, \beta\mathsf{T}^*)$. Conversely, $(\alpha\mathsf{T}, \beta\mathsf{T}) = (\alpha, \beta\mathsf{TT}^*)$ and $(\alpha\mathsf{T}^*, \beta\mathsf{T}^*) = (\alpha, \beta\mathsf{T}^*\mathsf{T})$; consequently, if $(\alpha\mathsf{T}, \beta\mathsf{T}) - (\alpha\mathsf{T}^*, \beta\mathsf{T}^*) = 0$, then $0 = (\alpha, \beta\mathsf{TT}^*) - (\alpha, \beta\mathsf{T}^*\mathsf{T}) = (\alpha, \beta\mathsf{TT}^* - \beta\mathsf{T}^*\mathsf{T})$. On setting $\alpha = \beta\mathsf{TT}^* - \beta\mathsf{T}^*\mathsf{T}$, we see that $\alpha = 0$. Hence $\beta\mathsf{TT}^* = \beta\mathsf{T}^*\mathsf{T}$ for every β so that $\mathsf{TT}^* = \mathsf{T}^*\mathsf{T}$.

COROLLARY 7.8C. *If* T *is normal then* $\mathscr{K}(\mathsf{T}) = \mathscr{K}(\mathsf{T}^*)$.

In Lemma 7.8B simply take $\alpha = \beta$.

LEMMA 7.8D.   *If* T *is normal, then every eigenvector of* T *is also an eigenvector of* T* *and corresponds to the conjugate eigenvalue.*

For, if T is normal, so is $T_\lambda = T - \lambda I$ and $T_\lambda^* = T^* - \bar{\lambda}I$.   Then the set of all eigenvectors of T having eigenvalue λ is $\mathcal{K}(T_\lambda)$.   The present lemma follows from Corollary 7.8C.

THEOREM 7.8E.   *Let* T *be a normal transformation on a unitary space* $\mathcal{V}$.   *Then there exists a set of eigenvectors* $\{\alpha_1, \cdots, \alpha_v\}$ *which is an orthonormal basis of* $\mathcal{V}$.

Let α be an eigenvector for T; $\alpha T = \lambda \alpha$.   Let $\mathcal{W}$ be the subspace orthogonal to α.   Then $\mathcal{W}$ is invariant under T (cf. Ex. 7.5.5) for, if β is in $\mathcal{W}$, i.e., $(\alpha, \beta) = 0$, then $(\alpha, \beta T) = (\alpha T^*, \beta) = \bar{\lambda}(\alpha, \beta) = 0$, since α is also an eigenvector for T*.

We employ induction and assume that $\mathcal{S}_i = \{\alpha_1, \cdots, \alpha_i\}$ is an orthonormal set of eigenvectors for T.   Let $\mathcal{O}(\mathcal{S}_i) = \mathcal{W}_i$; then as above, $\mathcal{W}_i$ is invariant under T.   Let α_{i+1} be a normed eigenvector of T restricted to $\mathcal{W}_i$. Such an α_{i+1} exists since $\mathfrak{C}$ is algebraically closed.   Then $\{\alpha_1, \cdots, \alpha_{i+1}\}$ is an orthonormal set, and the induction is complete.

COROLLARY 7.8F.   *If* N *is a normal matrix, then there exists a unitary matrix* P *such that* PNP^{-1} *is diagonal.*

This is an immediate consequence of the theorem.   Theorem 7.6C is a special case of this corollary.

Exercises 7.8

1. Prove that the adjoint of a linear transformation is linear.
2. Prove that, if T* is the adjoint of T, then $(T^*)^{-1} = (T^{-1})^*$ (if T is nonsingular), $(T_1 T_2)^* = T_2^* T_1^*$, $(cT)^* = \bar{c}T^*$, $0^* = 0$, $I^* = I$.
3. Prove that, if T is normal, so is T^n for all integral n.
4. Prove that $(T^*)^* = T$.
5. Prove that the adjoint of the restriction of T to an invariant subspace $\mathcal{W}$ is the restriction to $\mathcal{W}$ of the adjoint T*.
6. Prove the following converse of Lemma 7.8C.   If T has the same eigenvectors as T* and the conjugate eigenvalues and if the eigenvectors span $\mathcal{V}$, then T is normal.
7. Let N be a real normal matrix.   Show that there exists an orthogonal matrix P such that PNP^{-1} is diagonal.
8. (Converse of Corollary 7.8F).   Show that a matrix N is normal if there exists a unitary matrix P such that PNP^{-1} is diagonal.

Chapter 8

Structure of Polynomial Rings

The central topic of this chapter is the study of rings obtained by adjunction of a single element to a field. The transcendental case (polynomial domain) is treated first, beginning with proofs of existence and uniqueness, and then continuing with development of the usual theory of factorization of polynomials.

Next, the full theory of simple algebraic extensions of a field is given. An important tool in this study is the concept of direct sum of vector spaces which is introduced and treated in Sections 8.7 and 8.8.

8.1. Rings and subrings. Let $\mathscr{T}$ be a ring (see Section 2.7 for definition). A subset $\mathscr{S}$ of $\mathscr{T}$ which is itself a ring is said to be a *subring* of $\mathscr{T}$. The sets $\{0\}$ and $\mathscr{T}$ itself are examples of subrings. The even integers are a subring of the ring of all integers. The set of upper-triangular matrices is a subring of the ring of all matrices of any given degree.

LEMMA 8.1A.   *Let $\mathscr{S}$ be a nonempty subset of a ring $\mathscr{T}$. Then $\mathscr{S}$ is a subring if it is closed under subtraction and multiplication.*

We have only to check the existential axioms A1, A3, A4, and M1 since the combinatorial ring axioms automatically hold in any subset of a ring. We have M1 by hypothesis. Now, if a is in $\mathscr{S}$, we have $a - a = 0$ also in $\mathscr{S}$; this checks A3. Next, if a is in $\mathscr{S}$, we have $0 - a = -a$ in $\mathscr{S}$; thus A4 holds. Finally, if a and b are in $\mathscr{S}$ then $-b$ is in $\mathscr{S}$ and also $a - (-b) = a + b$ is in $\mathscr{S}$; this verifies A1 and completes the proof of the lemma.

LEMMA 8.1B.   *The intersection $\mathscr{S}$ of any nonempty collection of subrings of a ring $\mathscr{T}$ is a subring of $\mathscr{T}$.*

Suppose that a and b are elements of $\mathscr{S}$, and let $\mathscr{P}$ be any of the subrings in the given collection. Then, since $\mathscr{S} \subseteq \mathscr{P}$, a and b are in $\mathscr{P}$. Hence, $a - b$ and ab are in every one of the subrings $\mathscr{P}$ and therefore in

196

the intersection $\mathscr{S}$. Next, since 0 is an element of each subring $\mathscr{P}$, the intersection $\mathscr{S}$ is not empty. The lemma now follows at once from Lemma 8.1A.

Let $\mathscr{M}$ be any nonempty subset of a ring $\mathscr{T}$. A *monomial* in $\mathscr{M}$ is a product $m_1 \cdots m_s$ or $-m_1 \cdots m_s$ where $m_1, \cdots, m_s$ are elements of $\mathscr{M}$ not necessarily distinct. Thus a monomial in $\mathscr{M}$ is an element of $\mathscr{T}$. Any (finite) sum of monomials is said to be a *polynomial* in $\mathscr{M}$. (In forming a polynomial we allow a given monomial to appear any number of times.)

THEOREM 8.1C. *Let $\mathscr{M}$ be a nonempty subset of a ring $\mathscr{T}$. Then the set $\mathscr{S}$ of all polynomials in $\mathscr{M}$ is a subring. Moreover, $\mathscr{S}$ is the intersection of all subrings of $\mathscr{T}$ which contain $\mathscr{M}$.*

Since $\mathscr{S} \supseteq \mathscr{M}$, $\mathscr{S}$ is not empty. Clearly the difference of two polynomials is a polynomial, and it follows from the distributive laws that a product of two polynomials is a polynomial. Hence $\mathscr{S}$ is a subring of $\mathscr{T}$.

Suppose that $\mathscr{P}$ is any subring which contains $\mathscr{M}$. Since $\mathscr{P}$ is closed under multiplication and subtraction, it must contain all monomials in $\mathscr{M}$; and, since $\mathscr{P}$ is closed under addition, it must contain all polynomials in $\mathscr{M}$; hence $\mathscr{P}$ contains $\mathscr{S}$. Let $\mathscr{S}'$ be the intersection of all subrings $\mathscr{P}$ of $\mathscr{T}$ which contain $\mathscr{M}$. Since each $\mathscr{P}$ contains $\mathscr{S}$, we have $\mathscr{S}' \supseteq \mathscr{S}$. On the other hand, $\mathscr{S}$ is a subring which contains $\mathscr{M}$, so that $\mathscr{S}' \subseteq \mathscr{S}$ by the definition of intersection. Hence $\mathscr{S} = \mathscr{S}'$.

Notice that $\mathscr{S}$ is thus the smallest subring of $\mathscr{T}$ which contains the given subset $\mathscr{M}$. This uniqueness of $\mathscr{S}$ justifies the following definition. We say that $\mathscr{S}$ is the subring of $\mathscr{T}$ *generated* by $\mathscr{M}$ and write $\mathscr{S} = [\mathscr{M}]$.

The *center* of a ring $\mathscr{T}$ consists of those elements c for which $cx = xc$ for all x in $\mathscr{T}$.

THEOREM 8.1D. *The center of a ring is a subring.*

If c_1 and c_2 are center elements of a ring $\mathscr{T}$, then $(c_1-c_2)x = c_1x-c_2x = xc_1-xc_2 = x(c_1-c_2)$ and $(c_1c_2)x = c_1(c_2x) = c_1(xc_2) = (c_1x)c_2 = (xc_1)c_2 = x(c_1c_2)$; thus $c_1 - c_2$ and c_1c_2 are also center elements. The zero element of $\mathscr{T}$ is always in the center, so that the center is not empty. We can now apply Lemma 8.1A.

In the ensuing development we shall be concerned primarily with rings of the following type: $\mathscr{T}$ has a unit element 1 which is also the unit element of a field $\mathscr{F}$ which is contained in the center of $\mathscr{T}$. Thus $\mathscr{T}$ is in particular an $\mathscr{F}$ algebra. Our interest will be focused on subrings (actually subalgebras) generated by $\mathscr{F}$ and a single additional element x of $\mathscr{T}$. We introduce the notation $\mathscr{F}[x]$ for the subring $[\mathscr{F}, x]$. We call $\mathscr{F}[x]$ a *simple extension* of $\mathscr{F}$. We might, for example, take $\mathscr{T}$ as the total matrix algebra of degree n, $\mathscr{F}$ as the subset of scalar matrices, and x as a matrix in $\mathscr{T}$, or x might be a linear transformation on a vector space over a field and $\mathscr{F}$ the scalar transformations on that vector space.

LEMMA 8.1E. *Let $\mathscr{T}$ be a ring with a unit element 1 which is also the unit element of a field $\mathscr{F}$ contained in the center of $\mathscr{T}$. Then the subring $\mathscr{F}[x]$ is a commutative $\mathscr{F}$ algebra.*

By virtue of the distributive laws it is sufficient to check commutativity for monomials. Since -1 is an element of $\mathscr{F}$, every monomial is now actually a product $m_1 \cdots m_s$. Any factor m_i which lies in $\mathscr{F}$ can be moved to the left past all factors x, giving a monomial $n_1 \cdots n_s$ whose last t factors ($t > 0$) are all x and whose first $s - t$ factors lie in $\mathscr{F}$. As usual we write x^t for the product of t factors x, and we let $n_1 \cdots n_{s-t} = a$, which is, of course, an element of $\mathscr{F}$. Thus we arrive at the standard form ax^t for monomials. Finally, we have $(ax^t)(bx^s) = a(x^tb)x^s = (ab)(x^tx^s) = (ba)(x^sx^t) = \cdots = (bx^s)(ax^t)$; this establishes the commutativity of multiplication for monomials.

The following lemma is an immediate consequence of the standard form for monomials.

LEMMA 8.1F. *Any element of $\mathscr{F}[x]$ can be written in the form*

$$(1.1) \qquad\qquad a_0 + a_1x + \cdots + a_rx^r$$

where $a_0, \cdots, a_r$ are elements of $\mathscr{F}$.

We sometimes use the abbreviated notation $f(x)$ for an element (1.1) and thus write $f(x) = a_0 + a_1x + \cdots + a_rx^r$. [This does not mean that we are regarding x as a variable and $f(x)$ as a function. However, the case of ordinary polynomial functions over a field is included as a particular instance.]

It may happen that 0 can be written in the form

$$(1.2) \qquad\qquad 0 = a_0 + a_1x + \cdots + a_rx^r, \quad a_r \neq 0.$$

If so, we say that x is *algebraic* over $\mathscr{F}$. If no equation of the form (1.2) holds we say that x is *transcendental* over $\mathscr{F}$. In the first case we say that $\mathscr{F}[x]$ is a *simple algebraic extension* of $\mathscr{F}$ and in the second case that $\mathscr{F}[x]$ is a *simple transcendental extension* of $\mathscr{F}$. Both cases are important for our subsequent theory; we treat the transcendental case first.

The fact that an element x is transcendental over a field $\mathscr{F}$ depends intimately on the properties of x and $\mathscr{F}$. It can easily be shown by the use of infinite cardinals that there are real numbers which are transcendental over the rational field $\mathfrak{Q}$; but to prove that any particular real number such as π or e is transcendental is more difficult.

Exercises 8.1

1. Prove that the product of two polynomials in $\mathcal{M}$ is a polynomial in $\mathcal{M}$.
2. Prove that, if the monomials in $\mathcal{M}$ commute, then so do the polynomials in $\mathcal{M}$.
3. Prove Lemma 8.1F.
4. Prove that $\sqrt{2}$ is algebraic over the rational field $\mathfrak{Q}$.
5. Prove that every element in $\mathcal{F}$ is algebraic over $\mathcal{F}$.
6. Prove that, if x^2 is algebraic over $\mathcal{F}$, then so is x.
7. Let $\mathcal{F}$ be the field of all real scalar matrices of degree 2, and let $x = \begin{pmatrix} 1 & 0 \\ 0 & 2 \end{pmatrix}$. (a) Prove that x is algebraic over $\mathcal{F}$. (b) Prove that $\mathcal{F}[x]$ consists of all real diagonal matrices of degree 2.
8. Let $\mathcal{F}$ be the field of all real scalar matrices of degree 2, and let $x = \begin{pmatrix} 0 & 1 \\ -1 & 0 \end{pmatrix}$. (a) Prove that x is algebraic over $\mathcal{F}$. (b) Prove that $\mathcal{F}[x]$ is isomorphic to the complex number field $\mathfrak{C}$ under a correspondence which maps x into i.
9. Prove that the set of upper-triangular matrices of degree n forms a ring. Find the center of this ring.
10. Determine all subrings of the set of diagonal matrices of degree 2.

8.2. Existence and uniqueness of transcendental extensions.

Let $\mathcal{F}$ be any field. We shall construct a commutative algebra $\mathcal{P}$ which contains a subfield isomorphic to $\mathcal{F}$ and an element x which is transcendental over this subfield. (A mapping of one ring into another is said to be an *isomorphism* if it is one-to-one and if under it the image of a sum or product is the sum or product, respectively, of the images of the summands or factors.)

Our construction uses as a pattern the expansion

$$f(x) = a_0 + a_1 x + \cdots + a_r x^r$$

for a polynomial. This can be replaced by the ordered set of coefficients

$$(a_0, a_1, \cdots, a_r).$$

Because the value of r is not the same for all polynomials, it is notationally simpler to adjoin 0's and use the infinite sequence

$$(a_0, a_1, \cdots, a_r, 0, 0, \cdots)$$

or

(2.1) $$(a_0, a_1, \cdots, a_r, a_{r+1}, \cdots)$$

where only a finite number of the entries are not zero. There is a one-to-one correspondence between polynomials $f(x)$ and the sequences (2.1) having a finite number of nonzero terms. The operations of addition and multiplication which we shall define for these sequences will be precisely those that one has if one operates with the corresponding polynomials.

In fact we could have used the polynomials themselves except that we do not have an element x! It is the existence of such an element that we are trying to prove, and it will of course be given by the sequence

$$(0, 1, 0, 0, \cdots)$$

which corresponds to the polynomial $f(x) = x$. The sequences exist since they are merely functions from the non-negative integers to the given field $\mathscr{F}$.

Let $\mathscr{S}$ be the set of all sequences $\alpha = (a_0, a_1, \cdots, a_n, \cdots)$ in $\mathscr{F}$. Two sequences α and $\beta = (b_0, b_1, \cdots, b_n, \cdots)$ are said to be equal if and only if all corresponding terms are equal; i.e., $a_0 = b_0, a_1 = b_1, \cdots, a_n = b_n, \cdots$. If α and β are sequences and c is a scalar, then we define

$$(2.2) \qquad \alpha + \beta = (a_0 + b_0, a_1 + b_1, \cdots, a_n + b_n, \cdots)$$

and

$$(2.3) \qquad c\alpha = (ca_0, ca_1, \cdots, ca_n, \cdots).$$

LEMMA 8.2A. *The system $\mathscr{S}$ is a vector space over $\mathscr{F}$.*

The space $\mathscr{S}$ is an infinite-dimensional generalization of the space $\mathscr{V}_n(\mathscr{F})$ of n-tuples introduced in Section 1.3, and the proof that $\mathscr{V}_n(\mathscr{F})$ is a vector space can be easily modified to apply also to $\mathscr{S}$. We omit the details.

Let $\mathscr{P}$ be the subset of $\mathscr{S}$ consisting of all sequences α in each of which all but a finite number of the terms a_i are zero. If α has k nonzero terms and β has l nonzero terms then $\alpha + \beta$ has at most $k + l$ nonzero terms. Also $c\alpha$ has at most k nonzero terms. Hence $\mathscr{P}$ is closed under addition and multiplication by scalars; i.e., *$\mathscr{P}$ is a subspace of $\mathscr{S}$.*

We next wish to define a multiplication in $\mathscr{P}$ in such a way as to make $\mathscr{P}$ into an algebra over the field $\mathscr{F}$. We set

$$(2.4) \qquad \alpha\beta = \gamma = (c_0, c_1, \cdots, c_n, \cdots),$$

where

$$c_0 = a_0 b_0,$$

$$c_1 = a_0 b_1 + a_1 b_0,$$

$$(2.5) \qquad \cdots ,$$

$$c_n = a_0 b_n + a_1 b_{n-1} + \cdots + a_n b_0 = \sum_{\nu=0}^{n} a_\nu b_{n-\nu},$$

$$\cdots .$$

To show that $\alpha\beta$ belongs to $\mathscr{P}$ we must show that all but a finite number of the c_i are zero. As an aid in doing this we introduce the concept of degree. If $\alpha \neq 0$, we say that α has *degree* n ($n \geq 0$) provided that $a_n \neq 0$ but $a_i = 0$ for all $i > n$, and we call a_n the *leading coefficient* of α. We assign no degree to the zero sequence. If α has degree n, we write $\deg \alpha = n$. If for a sequence α we know only that $0 = a_{n+1} = a_{n+2} = \cdots$, we say that α has *formal degree* n. In particular 0 has formal degree n for any $n \geq 0$.

LEMMA 8.2B. *If α and β are nonzero elements of $\mathscr{P}$ then $\alpha\beta \neq 0$, and*

$$\deg \alpha\beta = \deg \alpha + \deg \beta.$$

Let $n = \deg \alpha$, $m = \deg \beta$. Then by (2.4)

$$c_{n+m} = \sum_{\nu=0}^{m+n} a_{n+m-\nu} b_\nu.$$

Now, if $\nu > m$, then $b_\nu = 0$, if and, $\nu < m$, then $a_{n+m-\nu} = 0$; hence the sum for c_{n+m} reduces to the single term $a_n b_m$ which is not zero since by hypothesis $a_n \neq 0$, $b_m \neq 0$. On the other hand, if $i > n + m$, each term $a_{i-\nu} b_\nu$ in the sum for c_i has either $\nu > m$ and hence $b_\nu = 0$, or $\nu \leq m$ so that $i - \nu > n$ and hence $a_{i-\nu} = 0$. Therefore $c_i = 0$ if $i > n + m$. Thus $\gamma = \alpha\beta$ has degree $n + m$ as claimed.

This lemma checks closure of $\mathscr{P}$ under multiplication provided neither factor is zero. But $\alpha 0 = 0\alpha = 0$ for any α in $\mathscr{P}$. Thus $\mathscr{P}$ is closed under multiplication.

THEOREM 8.2C. *Let $\mathscr{P}$ be the set of all $\mathscr{F}$ sequences $\alpha = (a_0, a_1, a_2, \cdots)$, each of which has only a finite number of nonzero terms. Then, under the operations defined by (2.2), (2.3), (2.4), (2.5), $\mathscr{P}$ is a commutative algebra over $\mathscr{F}$ and has unity element $(1, 0, 0, \cdots)$.*

We have already checked all of the axioms except M2 (associativity), M5 (commutativity), and D1, D2 (distributivity). Each of these axioms follows by direct computation from the corresponding axioms for scalars; we omit the details.

It follows from formula (2.4) that the sequence $1' = (1, 0, \cdots, 0, \cdots)$ is the unity element for $\mathscr{P}$. For each c in $\mathscr{F}$ let $c' = c \cdot 1' = (c, 0, \cdots, 0, \cdots)$, and let $\mathscr{F}'$ be the set of all elements $c' = c \cdot 1'$ for c in $\mathscr{F}$. The mapping $c \to c'$ is one-to-one, and it preserves addition and multiplication [i.e., $(c_1 + c_2)' = c'_1 + c'_2$ and $(c_1 c_2)' = c'_1 c'_2$]. Thus $\mathscr{F}'$ is a field which is an "isomorphic" copy of $\mathscr{F}$. Moreover, for all α in $\mathscr{P}$ we have

$$c\alpha = c'\alpha;$$

i.e., $\mathscr{P}$ is also an algebra over $\mathscr{F}'$.

If we identify c with c' for each c in $\mathscr{F}$, then we have $\mathscr{F}$ as a subfield of $\mathscr{P}$ and have achieved the situation described in the preceding section of an algebra $\mathscr{P}$ and subfield $\mathscr{F}$ both having the same unity element 1. We now search for an element x in $\mathscr{P}$ which is transcendental over $\mathscr{F}$. There are actually many such elements, but the one we shall select has the additional advantage that for it $\mathscr{P} = \mathscr{F}[x]$.

Let $x = (0, 1, 0, \cdots, 0, \cdots)$, i.e., the second term is 1, and all others are 0. Then according to (2.4) we have $x^2 = (0, 0, 1, 0, \cdots, 0, \cdots)$, and by an induction argument we get

$$(2.6) \qquad x^n = (0, \cdots, 0, 1, 0, \cdots);$$

i.e., the first n terms of x^n are 0, the next is 1, and all later ones are 0.

Now consider any element $\alpha = (a_0, a_1, \cdots, a_n, 0, \cdots)$ of degree n in $\mathscr{P}$. Then $\alpha = a_0(1, 0, \cdots) + a_1(0, 1, 0, \cdots) + \cdots$; i.e.,

$$(2.7) \qquad \alpha = a_0 + a_1 x + \cdots + a_n x^n;$$

this shows that $\mathscr{P} = \mathscr{F}[x]$. Moreover, if $a_0, \cdots, a_n$ are any elements of $\mathscr{F}$, the element α defined by the right-hand side of (2.7) is 0 if and only if each a_i is zero; hence x is transcendental over $\mathscr{F}$. We can thus regard the set $\{1, x, x^2, \cdots, x^n, \cdots\}$ as the "natural" basis of $\mathscr{F}[x]$. We have established the following theorem.

Theorem 8.2D. *If $\mathscr{F}$ is any field, there exists a commutative ring $\mathscr{P}$ with the same unity element as $\mathscr{F}$ and which contains an element which is transcendental over $\mathscr{F}$.*

Theorem 8.2E. *Let $\mathscr{S}$ and $\mathscr{S}'$ be rings both containing $\mathscr{F}$ and containing elements x and y, respectively, which are transcendental over $\mathscr{F}$. Then the mapping*

$$(2.8) \qquad a_0 + a_1 x + \cdots + a_n x^n \to a_0 + a_1 + \cdots + a_n y^n$$

is an isomorphism of $\mathscr{F}[x]$ onto $\mathscr{F}[y]$.

The mapping is one-to-one since both x and y are transcendental over $\mathscr{F}$. On the other hand, the coefficients in a sum (or product) in $\mathscr{F}[x]$ depend only on the coefficients of the summands (or factors). Hence the image of a sum (or product) is the sum (or product) of the images of the summands (or factors). This proves that $\mathscr{F}[x]$ and $\mathscr{F}[y]$ are isomorphic.

The importance of this uniqueness theorem is that we need study only the properties of one simple transcendental extension to know about all such extensions. We sometimes call $\mathscr{F}[x]$ *the polynomial domain over $\mathscr{F}$* and call the element x an *indeterminate*. Elements of $\mathscr{F}[x]$ are called *polynomials*.

Exercises 8.2

1. Prove Lemma 8.2A.

2. Complete the proof of Lemma 8.2C.

3. Let $\mathscr{F}' = \{a', b', c', \cdots\}$ be a system in which two operations $+$ and $\cdot$ are defined; let $\mathscr{F} = \{a, b, c, \cdots\}$ be a field, and let $\mathsf{T} : a \to a' = a\mathsf{T}$ be a one-to-one mapping of $\mathscr{F}$ onto $\mathscr{F}'$ with the following properties: $(a + b)\mathsf{T} = a\mathsf{T} + b\mathsf{T}$ and $(ab)\mathsf{T} = (a\mathsf{T})(b\mathsf{T})$. Show that $\mathscr{F}'$ is a field; i.e., the isomorphic image of a field is a field.

4. Let x be an element of $\mathfrak{R}$ which is transcendental over $\mathfrak{Q}$. Show that $\mathscr{S}_1 = \mathfrak{Q}[x]$ is isomorphic to $\mathscr{S}_2 = \mathfrak{Q}[x^2]$ even though $\mathscr{S}_2$ is a proper subset of $\mathscr{S}_1$.

5. Show that $\mathfrak{Q}[e]$ is isomorphic to $\mathfrak{Q}(\pi)$ where e and π have their usual meanings.

6. Let $\mathscr{F}$ be any field, and let x be transcendental over $\mathscr{F}$. Let $\mathscr{K}$ be the set of ordered pairs (f, g) where f, g lie in $\mathscr{F}[x]$ and $g \neq 0$, and define addition and multiplication in $\mathscr{K}$ by

$$(f, g) + (f', g') = (fg' + f'g, gg'),$$

$$(f, g') \cdot (f', g) = (ff', gg').$$

We define a relation on $\mathscr{K}$ by

$$(f, g) \sim (f', g') \quad \text{if and only if} \quad fg' = f'g.$$

Show that addition and multiplication have the substitution property relative to $\sim$. (Note the resemblance of $\sim$ to equality of fractions.)

7. Let $\mathscr{F}$ and $\mathscr{K}$ be as in Exercise 6, and denote by $\mathscr{M}$ the set of equivalence classes in $\mathscr{K}$ relative to $\sim$. Show that $\mathscr{M}$ is a field under the operations induced in it from those in $\mathscr{K}$. (Cf. Section 5.1.)

8. Let $\mathscr{F}$, $\mathscr{K}$, and $\mathscr{M}$ be as in Exercise 7. It is customary to denote the equivalence class of (f, g) by the symbol f/g. Show that the mapping $f \to f/1$ is an isomorphism of $\mathscr{F}[x]$ into $\mathscr{M}$.

9. Let $\mathscr{F}$, $\mathscr{K}$, and $\mathscr{M}$ be as in Exercise 8. If we identify $\mathscr{F}[x]$ with its image in $\mathscr{M}$, i.e. if we identify f with $f/1$, then we can consider $\mathscr{F}[x]$ as a subring of $\mathscr{M}$. Show that then f/g is actually the quotient of f by g, and hence that $\mathscr{M}$ consists of all quotients f/g, $g \neq 0$, with f and g in $\mathscr{F}[x]$. $\mathscr{M}$ is called the *field of rational functions over* $\mathscr{F}$ and is frequently denoted by $\mathscr{F}(x)$.

8.3. Division algorithm; greatest common divisor.

Our treatment of polynomials will be limited to developing certain basic properties which will be used in our treatment of linear transformations and matrices.

Two polynomials $f(x)$ and $g(x)$ are said to be *associates* if $g(x) = c\, f(x)$ where c is a nonzero scalar. The polynomial $f(x) = a_0 + a_1 x + \cdots + a_n x^n$ is said to be *monic* if its leading coefficient a_n is equal to 1. Clearly, each nonzero polynomial has exactly one associate which is monic. If $f(x) = g(x)\, h(x)$ we say that $g(x)$ and $h(x)$ are *factors* of $f(x)$ and that $f(x)$ is *divisible* by $g(x)$ [and by $h(x)$]. A nonconstant polynomial $f(x)$ is said to be *irreducible* or *prime* if in every factorization of it one of the factors is an associate of $f(x)$.

The property of being prime depends on the field $\mathscr{F}$. Thus $x^2 - 2$ is prime if $\mathscr{F} = \mathfrak{Q}$ (rationals) but not if $\mathscr{F}$ is $\mathfrak{R}$ or $\mathfrak{C}$; also $x^2 + 1$ is prime as an element in $\mathfrak{Q}[x]$ or $\mathfrak{R}[x]$ but not in $\mathfrak{C}[x]$. In $\mathfrak{C}[x]$ every prime has degree 1, a consequence of the fundamental theorem of algebra, and in $\mathfrak{R}[x]$ the primes are of degree 1 or 2.

A polynomial $f(x)$ is said to be *primary* if it is an associate of a power of a prime polynomial $p(x)$; i.e., if $f(x) = c\,[p(x)]^e$.

LEMMA 8.3A. THE DIVISION ALGORITHM. *Let $f(x)$ and $g(x)$ be two polynomials, $f(x) \neq 0$. Then there exist unique polynomials $q(x)$ and $r(x)$, where either $r(x) = 0$ or $\deg r(x) < \deg f(x)$, such that*

(3.1) $$g(x) = f(x)\,q(x) + r(x).$$

(Dividend equals divisor times quotient plus remainder.)

We first establish the existence of $q(x)$ and $r(x)$. If $g(x) = 0$, take $q(x) = 0 = r(x)$. Otherwise let $\deg f(x) = n$ and $\deg g(x) = m$, and let a_n and b_m be the corresponding leading coefficients. If $m < n$, we take $q(x) = 0$ and $r(x) = g(x)$. Next we suppose $m \geqq n$ and an induction hypothesis that the existence of $q(x)$ and $r(x)$ is known for all polynomials $g(x)$ of degree $t < m$. To reduce to the case where the degree is less than m, we carry out essentially the first step in dividing $g(x)$ by $f(x)$. Let

(3.2) $$g_1(x) = g(x) - \frac{b_m}{a_n}\, x^{m-n} f(x)\,.$$

If $g_1(x) = 0$, then we take $q(x) = (b_m/a_n)x^{m-n}$ and $r(x) = 0$. Otherwise $\deg g_1(x) = t < m$, and hence we have $q_1(x)$ and $r(x)$ such that

(3.3) $$g_1(x) = f(x)\,q_1(x) + r(x),$$

where either $r(x) = 0$ or $\deg r(x) < n$. Now we substitute (3.2) in (3.3) solve for $g(x)$, and get (3.1) with $q(x) = q_1(x) + (b_m/a_n)\,x^{m-n}$. This completes the induction and thus establishes the existence part of the lemma.

Now to establish uniqueness of $q(x)$ and $r(x)$ we suppose that in addition to (3.1) we also have

(3.4) $$g(x) = f(x)\,q'(x) + r'(x).$$

We subtract (3.4) from (3.1) and get

(3.5) $$f(x)\,(q(x) - q'(x)) = r'(x) - r(x).$$

Suppose that $q(x) \neq q'(x)$. Then by Lemma 8.2B the left-hand side has degree at least n, whereas the right-hand side is either zero or has degree less than n. This is impossible (since x is transcendental over $\mathscr{F}$); hence we must have $q'(x) = q(x)$, and therefore also $r'(x) = r(x)$. This establishes the uniqueness of quotient and remainder.

A subring $\mathscr{S}$ of a commutative ring $\mathscr{T}$ with unity element is said to be an *ideal* in $\mathscr{T}$ if a product of elements of $\mathscr{T}$ belongs to $\mathscr{S}$ whenever any factor belongs to $\mathscr{S}$. For example the even integers are an ideal in the ring of integers, and the set of all polynomials divisible by x is an ideal in $\mathscr{F}[x]$. If b is an element of $\mathscr{T}$, we denote by (b) the set of all multiples ab of b for a in $\mathscr{T}$. Clearly (b) is an ideal; ideals of this type are called *principal*; b is said to be a generator of (b).

LEMMA 8.3B. *The principal ideals (f) and (g) are equal if and only if f and g are associates.*

If f and g are associates, then $g = cf$, and so g is contained in (f). Consequently $(g) \subseteq (f)$. Similarly, from $f = c^{-1}g$ we see that $(f) \subseteq (g)$; and hence $(f) = (g)$. Conversely, if $(f) = (g)$ then g is contained in (f), and so $g = hf$; similarly $f = kg$. Then $g = hkg$ or $1 = hk$. Hence h and k have degree 0 and must be scalars; we conclude that f and g are associates.

THEOREM 8.3C. *Let $\mathscr{F}$ be a field, and let x be an element transcendental over $\mathscr{F}$. Then any ideal $\mathscr{S}$ in the ring $\mathscr{F}[x]$ is principal. Moreover, if $\mathscr{S} \neq \{0\}$, there exists a unique monic polynomial $f(x)$ for which $\mathscr{S} = (f(x))$.*

The zero ideal $\{0\}$ is clearly (0) and therefore principal. Let $\mathscr{S}$ be a nonzero ideal in $\mathscr{F}[x]$. Then $\mathscr{S}$ contains a polynomial $f(x)$ of minimal degree n. Now suppose that $g(x)$ is any element of $\mathscr{S}$, and apply Lemma 8.3A. If we solve formula (3.1) for the remainder term $r(x)$, we get

$$(3.6) \qquad r(x) = g(x) - f(x)\, q(x).$$

Since $f(x)$ and $g(x)$ belong to $\mathscr{S}$, so does $f(x)\, q(x)$, and therefore also $r(x)$. Now, if $r(x)$ were not zero, it would have degree less than n, contrary to our hypothesis on $f(x)$. Therefore $r(x)$ is 0; i.e., $g(x)$ is a multiple of $f(x)$. This shows that $\mathscr{S} = (f(x))$, and proves the first statement of the theorem.

Let $f(x)$ and $g(x)$ be nonzero polynomials. If $(f(x)) = (g(x))$, then it follows from Lemma 8.3B that $f(x)$ and $g(x)$ are associates. Conversely, if $f(x)$ and $g(x)$ are associates, then $(f(x)) = (g(x))$. Now each polynomial has a unique monic associate, and hence each ideal has a unique monic generator.

If two polynomials $f(x)$ and $g(x)$ are each divisible by a third polynomial $h(x)$, we say that $h(x)$ is a *common divisor* of $f(x)$ and $g(x)$. A *greatest common divisor* (g.c.d.) of $f(x)$ and $g(x)$, not both 0, is defined to be a monic common divisor $d(x)$ of highest degree. Clearly, no common divisor can have degree higher than that of $d(x)$.

THEOREM 8.3D. *Let $f(x)$ and $g(x)$ be polynomials not both 0. Then the set $\mathscr{S}$ of all polynomials of the form $s(x) f(x) + t(x) g(x)$ where $s(x)$, $t(x)$ are* *arbitrary elements of $\mathscr{F}[x]$ is the ideal $(d(x))$, where $d(x)$ is a greatest common divisor of $f(x)$ and $g(x)$. In particular, there exist polynomials $f_1(x)$ and $g_1(x)$ such that*

$$(3.7) \qquad d(x) = f_1(x) f(x) + g_1(x) g(x).$$

Clearly $\mathscr{S}$ is an ideal and not (0); according to Theorem 8.3C there exists a polynomial $d_1(x)$ in $\mathscr{S}$ such that $\mathscr{S} = (d_1(x))$. Now, if $h(x)$ is any common divisor of $f(x)$ and $g(x)$, it must be a divisor of every element $s(x) f(x) + t(x) g(x)$ in $\mathscr{S}$. In particular, $d(x)$ is a divisor of $d_1(x)$; say

$$(3.8) \qquad d_1(x) = q(x) d(x).$$

On the other hand, since $\mathscr{S} = (d_1(x))$, we must have $d_1(x)$ a common divisor of $f(x)$ and $g(x)$, and therefore $\deg d_1(x) \leq \deg d(x)$. It now follows from Lemma 8.2B that $q(x)$ has degree ≤ 0; i.e., $q(x)$ is a scalar so that $d_1(x)$ is an associate of $d(x)$. But then $\mathscr{S} = (d_1(x)) = (d(x))$ as claimed. Formula (3.7) follows from the fact that $d(x)$ is an element of $\mathscr{S}$. We also have the following result.

COROLLARY 8.3E. *The greatest common divisor of two polynomials is unique.*

If the greatest common divisor of the two polynomials $f(x)$ and $g(x)$ has degree zero, i.e., if $\mathscr{S} = (1)$, then we say that $f(x)$ and $g(x)$ are *relatively prime*. The first part of the following lemma is the corresponding special case of formula (3.7).

LEMMA 8.3F. *If $f(x)$ and $g(x)$ are relatively prime, then there exist polynomials $f_1(x)$, $g_1(x)$ such that*

$$(3.9) \qquad 1 = f_1(x) f(x) + g_1(x) g(x).$$

If neither $f(x)$ nor $g(x)$ is of degree zero we may even require that $\deg g_1(x) < \deg f(x)$ and $\deg f_1(x) < \deg g(x)$.

We suppose that neither $f(x)$ nor $g(x)$ is of degree zero. It follows from (3.9) that $f(x)$ is not a factor of $g_1(x)$. Hence we may divide $g_1(x)$ by $f(x)$ giving $g_1(x) = f(x) q(x) + g'_1(x)$, where $\deg g'_1(x) < \deg f(x)$. Then substitute in (3.9); giving

$$(3.10) \qquad 1 = f'_1(x) f(x) + g'_1(x) g(x),$$

where $f'_1(x) = f_1(x) + g(x) q(x)$. Since the left-hand side has degree zero we must have $\deg f'_1(x) f(x) = \deg g'_1(x) g(x)$, and hence

$$\deg f'_1(x) = \deg g(x) + \deg g'_1(x) - \deg f(x),$$

and so $\deg f'_1(x) < \deg g(x)$.

Exercises 8.3

1. Let x be transcendental over a field $\mathscr{F}$, and let y be transcendental over $\mathscr{F}[x]$. Prove that, in the ring of all polynomials in x and y with coefficients in $\mathscr{F}$, all those with 0 constant term form an ideal and this ideal is not principal. Show that the g.c.d. of x and y is 1 although $(x, y) \neq (1)$.

2. Prove that the set $\mathscr{S}$ of Theorem 8.3D is an ideal.

3. Prove that any polynomial of degree 1 is prime.

4. Suppose that $f(x)$ and $g(x)$ are two polynomials with $f(x) \neq 0$, and let $q(x)$ and $r(x)$ satisfy (3.1). Show that the greatest common divisor of $g(x)$ and $f(x)$ is the same as that of $f(x)$ and $r(x)$.

5. Let $f(x)$ and $g(x)$ be as in Exercise 4, and set $f(x) = r_0(x)$, $q(x) = q_1(x)$, $r(x) = r_1(x)$. Now, if $r_i(x) \neq 0$, define $q_{i+1}(x)$ and $r_{i+1}(x)$ inductively as the quotient and remainder obtained on application of the division algorithm to $r_{i-1}(x)$ and $r_i(x)$; e.g.

$$r_{i-1}(x) = q_{i+1}(x)r_i(x) + r_{i+1}(x).$$

Since $t_i = \deg r_i(x)$, we have $t_0 > t_1 > \cdots > t_i$, and hence after a finite number of steps we find a k for which $r_{k+1}(x) = 0$. Show then that the monic polynomial related to $r_k(x)$ is the greatest common divisor of $f(x)$ and $g(x)$. This process is known as the *Euclidean algorithm*.

6. Use the Euclidean algorithm to find the g.c.d. of

$$f(x) = x^5 - x^4 - 2x^3 + 2x^2 + x - 1,$$

$$g(x) = x^6 - x^5 - 4x^4 + 2x^3 + 5x^2 - x - 2.$$

7. Do the same for

$$f(x) = x^4 + 2x^3 - x^2 + x + 3$$

and

$$g(x) = x^6 - x^5 - 2x^4 + 3x^3 + 2x^2 + x + 2.$$

[Hint: one can avoid the use of fractions by replacing $r_{i-1}(x)$ by $cr_{i-1}(x)$ where c is a suitable power of the leading coefficient of $r_i(x)$.]

8.4. Factorization of polynomials.

LEMMA 8.4A. *If $p(x)$ is a prime divisor of a product $f(x) g(x)$, then $p(x)$ must be a divisor either of $f(x)$ or of $g(x)$.*

Suppose that $p(x)$ is not a factor of $f(x)$. No common divisor of $p(x)$ and $f(x)$ can have degree greater than zero, and hence $p(x)$ and $f(x)$ are relatively prime. Then by Lemma 8.3E there exist polynomials $p_1(x)$ and $f_1(x)$ such that

(4.1) $$1 = p_1(x)\, p(x) + f_1(x)\, f(x).$$

By hypothesis we have $h(x)$ such that

(4.2) $$f(x)\, g(x) = p(x)\, h(x).$$

We multiply both sides by $f_1(x)$ and use (4.1) to eliminate $f(x)$ giving

$$[1 - p_1(x)\, p(x)]\, g(x) = p(x)\, h(x)$$

or

$$g(x) = p(x)\, [h(x) + p_1(x)\, g(x)].$$

This shows that $g(x)$ is divisible by $p(x)$ and establishes the lemma.

Next, by an induction argument we get the following lemma.

LEMMA 8.4B.   *If a prime polynomial $p(x)$ divides a product $f(x) = p_1(x) \cdots p_r(x)$ then $p(x)$ divides at least one of the factors $p_i(x)$.*

THEOREM 8.4C.   *Any nonzero polynomial $f(x)$ can be written in the form*

$$(4.3) \qquad\qquad f(x) = c\, p_1(x) \cdots p_r(x),$$

where the $p_i(x)$ are monic, prime polynomials.   Moreover, any second such factorization for $f(x)$ can differ from this only in the arrangement of the factors $p_i(x)$.

We call a factorization (4.3) with the properties stated in the theorem a *complete factorization*.

If $f(x)$ has degree zero, then $f(x) = c$ is a complete factorization with $r = 0$.   If $f(x)$ has degree one, say $f(x) = a_0 + a_1 x$, then $f(x) = c\, p_1(x)$ where $c = a_1$ and $p_1(x) = (x + a_0/a_1)$ has degree one, and hence (by Lemma 8.2B) is prime.   Clearly $p_1(x)$ is uniquely determined by $f(x)$.

Now take as introduction hypothesis that the theorem is true for all polynomials of degree less than n and suppose that $f(x) = a_0 + a_1 x + \cdots + a_n x^n$, $a_n \neq 0$.   If $f(x)$ is prime, then $f(x) = c\, p_1(x)$ where $c = a_n$ and $p_1(x)$ is monic and prime.   Clearly c and $p_1(x)$ are uniquely determined by $f(x)$.   Next, suppose that $f(x) = g(x)\, h(x)$ where both $g(x)$ and $h(x)$ have degree greater than zero.   Then by our induction hypothesis both $g(x)$ and $h(x)$ have complete factorizations.   The combination of these gives a complete factorization for $f(x)$.   Suppose the notation chosen so that this factorization is given by (4.3).   Here the scalar c must, of course, be a_n. Also suppose that

$$(4.4) \qquad\qquad f(x) = c'\, p'_1(x) \cdots p'_s(x)$$

is any second complete factorization of $f(x)$.   We observe first that $c' = c = a_n$.   Now we write $f(x) = g(x)\, h(x)$ where $g(x) = c'\, p'_1(x)$ and $h(x) = p'_2(x) \cdots p'_s(x)$.   Since $f(x)$ is divisible by $p_1(x)$, we have either $p_1(x) = p'_1(x)$ or $p_1(x)$ is a factor of $h(x)$.   Since $h(x)$ has degree less than n, it follows from the uniqueness part of our induction hypothesis that, if $p_1(x)$ divides $h(x)$, then $p_1(x)$ coincides with one of the factors $p'_2(x), \cdots, p'_s(x)$.   Hence, in every case $p_1(x)$ appears as one factor of $f(x)$ in every complete factorization. We may then suppose the notation so chosen in (4.4) that $p'_1(x) = p_1(x)$. Then $h(x) = p'_2(x) \cdots p'_s(x) = p_2(x) \cdots p_r(x)$ has degree less than n, and so the factors $p'_2(x), \cdots, p'_s(x)$ must be just a permutation of $p_2(x), \cdots, p_r(x)$. This completes the induction argument.

In the complete factorization of a polynomial $f(x)$ it may happen that certain factors are equal. We suppose that $p_1(x), \cdots, p_s(x)$ are the distinct prime factors of $f(x)$ and that the factor $p_i(x)$ has multiplicity l_i $(i = 1, \cdots, s)$; i.e.,

$$(4.5) \qquad f(x) = c\, p_1(x)^{l_1} \cdots p_s(x)^{l_s}.$$

Next we set $q_i(x) = p_i(x)^{l_i}$ $(i = 1, \cdots, s)$ and have

$$(4.6) \qquad f(x) = c\, q_1(x) \cdots q_s(x),$$

which is called the *primary decomposition* of $f(x)$. The uniqueness of the primary decomposition (except for the order of the factors) follows at once from the previous theorem.

Lemma 8.4A could have been proved from the following result.

LEMMA 8.4D. *If $q(x)$ divides a product $f(x)\, g(x)$ and is relatively prime to $f(x)$, then $q(x)$ divides $g(x)$.*

There is a polynomial $h(x)$ such that $f(x)\, g(x) = h(x)\, q(x)$. Also there exist polynomials $q_1(x)$ and $p_1(x)$ such that

$$1 = q_1(x)\, q(x) + f_1(x)\, f(x).$$

Hence after multiplying both sides by $g(x)$ we get

$$\begin{aligned}
g(x) &= g(x)\, q_1(x)\, q(x) + g(x)\, f_1(x)\, f(x) \\
&= g(x)\, q_1(x)\, q(x) + f_1(x)\, h(x)\, q(x) \\
&= [g(x)\, q_1(x) + f_1(x)\, h(x)]\, q(x),
\end{aligned}$$

so that evidently $q(x)$ divides $g(x)$.

LEMMA 8.4E. *If $q_1(x)$, $q_2(x)$ are relatively prime and each divides $f(x)$, then the product $q_1(x)\, q_2(x)$ divides $f(x)$.*

Since $f(x)$ is divisible by $q(x)$, we have $f(x) = q_1(x)\, g(x)$. But this product is divisible by $q_2(x)$, and, since $q_2(x)$ is relatively prime to $q_1(x)$, $q_2(x)$ divides $g(x)$; i.e., $g(x) = q_2(x)\, h(x)$. Hence $f(x) = q_1(x)\, q_2(x)\, h(x)$ which is evidently divisible by $q_1(x)\, q_2(x)$.

COROLLARY 8.4F. *If $q_1(x)$, $q_2(x), \cdots, q_s(x)$ are pairwise relatively prime and if each $q_i(x)$ divides $f(x)$, then the product $q_1(x)\, q_2(x) \cdots q_s(x)$ divides $f(x)$.*

The proof is left as an exercise.

Exercises 8.4

1. Prove Lemma 8.4B.

2. Give a proof for Corollary 8.4F.

3. Find the primary decompositions of $x^4 - 4$ over $\mathfrak{Q}$, $\mathfrak{R}$, and $\mathfrak{C}$, respectively.

4. The fundamental theorem of algebra states that every nonconstant polynomial $f(x)$ in $\mathfrak{C}[x]$ has a linear factor in $\mathfrak{C}[x]$. Show that the irreducible factors of $f(x)$ are all of degree one.

5. Let $f(x)$ be an irreducible polynomial of degree n in $\mathfrak{Q}[x]$. Show that $f(x)$ has n distinct monic linear factors in $\mathfrak{C}[x]$. [Hint: show that the g.c.d. of $f(x)$ and its derivative both lie in $\mathfrak{Q}[x]$.]

6. Find an irreducible factor of $f(x) = x^6 - x^5 + 5x^4 - 4x^3 + 8x^2 - 4x + 4$ in $\mathfrak{Q}[x]$. (Hint: test for repeated factors.)

8.5. Algebraic extensions of a field.

Let $\mathscr{F}$ be a field, let y be algebraic over $\mathscr{F}$, and let x be transcendental over $\mathscr{F}$. The basic tool in our study of the ring $\mathscr{F}[y]$ is a comparison with the ring $\mathscr{F}[x]$. We shall show that there is a correspondence between nonzero ideals in $\mathscr{F}[x]$ and the set of simple algebraic extensions of $\mathscr{F}$.

Let $f(x) = a_0 + a_1 x + \cdots + a_n x^n$. We define a mapping

$$(5.1) \qquad \mathsf{T}: \quad f(x) \to f(x)\mathsf{T} = a_0 + a_1 y + \cdots + a_n y^n$$

of $\mathscr{F}[x]$ onto $\mathscr{F}[y]$. We denote $f(x)\mathsf{T}$ by $f(y)$. This is simply an algebraic formulation of substituting a quantity y for the "variable" x. It follows from the various ring postulates that

$$(5.2) \qquad [f(x) + g(x)]\mathsf{T} = f(x)\mathsf{T} + g(x)\mathsf{T},$$

$$(5.3) \qquad [c\,f(x)]\mathsf{T} = c\,[f(x)\mathsf{T}],$$

$$(5.4) \qquad [f(x) \cdot g(x)]\mathsf{T} = [f(x)\mathsf{T}]\,[g(x)\mathsf{T}].$$

Formulas (5.2) and (5.3) show that T is a linear transformation.

LEMMA 8.5A. *The kernel $\mathscr{S}$ of T is a nonzero ideal in $\mathscr{F}[x]$.*

If $f(x)$ is in $\mathscr{S}$ and $g(x)$ is any polynomial, it follows from (5.4) that the product $f(x)\,g(x)$ is again in $\mathscr{S}$. This, together with the fact that $\mathscr{S}$ is a subspace, shows that $\mathscr{S}$ is an ideal.

Now $\mathscr{S} \neq (0)$ since y is algebraic over $\mathscr{F}$. Thus according to Theorem 8.3C there exists a unique monic polynomial $m(x) = m_0 + m_1 x + \cdots + x^r$ which generates $\mathscr{S}$. We call $m(x)$ *the minimum function* for y, and call the degree r of $m(x)$ *the degree of y over $\mathscr{F}$*. We can characterize $m(x)$ as the monic polynomial of lowest degree which is annihilated by the mapping T. We sometimes say that $m(x) = 0$ is the *minimum equation* for y.

Let $f(x)$ be any element in $\mathscr{F}[x]$, and divide $f(x)$ by $m(x)$ to obtain

$$(5.5) \qquad f(x) = m(x)\,g(x) + f'(x),$$

where either $f'(x) = 0$ or $\deg f'(x) < r$. Next apply T to both sides of (5.5) and get

$$f(y) = m(y) \cdot g(y) + f'(y) = 0 \cdot g(y) + f'(y) = f'(y).$$

This shows that, if α is any element of $\mathscr{F}[y]$, then there exist scalars $a_0, \cdots, a_{r-1}$ such that

$$(5.6) \qquad \alpha = a_0 + a_1 y + \cdots + a_{r-1} y^{r-1}.$$

THEOREM 8.5B. *If y is algebraic of degree r over a field $\mathscr{F}$, then $\mathscr{F}[y]$ has dimension r over $\mathscr{F}$. Moreover, each element α in $\mathscr{F}[y]$ has a unique representation in the form (5.6).*

We have just proved that $\mathscr{S} = \{1, y, \cdots, y^{r-1}\}$ is a spanning set for $\mathscr{F}[y]$, and hence that $\dim \mathscr{F}[y] \leq r$. Now suppose that $c_0, c_1, \cdots, c_{r-1}$ are scalars such that

$$(5.7) \qquad 0 = c_0 + c_1 y + \cdots + c_{r-1} y^{r-1}.$$

Then $n(x) = c_0 + c_1 x + \cdots + c_{r-1} x^{r-1}$ belongs to the ideal $(m(x))$, and hence there exists a polynomial $h(x)$ for which $n(x) = h(x) \, m(x)$. This contradicts Lemma 8.2B unless $n(x) = 0$, i.e., unless $c_0 = c_1 = \cdots = c_{r-1} = 0$; this shows that $\mathscr{S}$ is an independent set, and hence $\dim \mathscr{F}[y] = r$ as claimed.

This theorem completely determines the additive structure of $\mathscr{F}[y]$. We next study multiplication in $\mathscr{F}[y]$. Suppose that α is given by (5.6), let $\beta = b_0 + b_1 y + \cdots + b_{r-1} y^{r-1}$, and suppose that $\alpha\beta = \gamma = c_0 + c_1 y + \cdots + c_{r-1} y^{r-1}$. Set $a(x) = a_0 + a_1 x + \cdots + a_{r-1} x^{r-1}$, $b(x) = b_0 + b_1 x + \cdots + b_{r-1} x^{r-1}$, and suppose that

$$a(x) \, b(x) = m(x) \, g(x) + c(x),$$

where $c(x) = 0$ or $\deg c(x) < r$. Then we have $\alpha = a(y)$, $\beta = b(y)$, and hence $c(y) = a(y) \, b(y) = \alpha\beta = \gamma$. We state this result as a lemma.

LEMMA 8.5C. *If $a(x)$, $b(x)$ are polynomials of formal degree $r - 1$, then $a(y) \, b(y) = c(y)$ where $c(x)$ is the remainder obtained on division of the product $a(x) \, b(x)$ by the minimum function $m(x)$.*

This shows exactly how multiplication in $\mathscr{F}[y]$ is related to multiplication in $\mathscr{F}[x]$ and actually proves that all of the operations in $\mathscr{F}[y]$ are determined by the minimum function $m(x)$. In greater detail it becomes the following theorem.

THEOREM 8.5D. *Let y_1 and y_2 be algebraic elements over a field $\mathscr{F}$. Then there exists an isomorphism T of $\mathscr{F}[y_1]$ onto $\mathscr{F}[y_2]$ with $c\mathsf{T} = c$ for every scalar c and with $y_1\mathsf{T} = y_2$ if and only if the minimum function for y_1 is the same as that for y_2.*

If y_1 and y_2 have the same minimum function $m(x)$, then by Theorem 8.5B the mapping $(a_0 + a_1 y_1 + \cdots + a_{r-1} y_1^{r-1})\mathsf{T} = a_0 + a_1 y_2 + \cdots + a_{r-1} y_2^{r-1}$ is one-to-one from $\mathscr{F}[y_1]$ onto $\mathscr{F}[y_2]$. Moreover $c\mathsf{T} = c$ and $y_1 \mathsf{T} = y_2$. If α_1 and β_1 are elements of $\mathscr{F}[y_1]$, then clearly $(\alpha_1 + \beta_1)\mathsf{T} = \alpha_1 \mathsf{T} + \beta_1 \mathsf{T}$, and it follows from Lemma 8.5C that $(\alpha_1 \beta_1)\mathsf{T} = (\alpha_1 \mathsf{T})(\beta_1 \mathsf{T})$. Hence T is an isomorphism.

Conversely, suppose that T is an isomorphism of $\mathscr{F}[y_1]$ onto $\mathscr{F}[y_2]$ and that $m_1(x)$, $m_2(x)$, respectively, are the minimum functions for y_1 and y_2. Let $a(x) = a_0 + \cdots + a_n x^n$ be any polynomial in $\mathscr{F}[x]$; then, since T is an isomorphism, we have

$$a(y_1)\mathsf{T} = (a_0 + a_1 y_1 + \cdots + a_n y_1^n)\mathsf{T}$$

$$= a_0 \mathsf{T} + (a_1 \mathsf{T})(y_1 \mathsf{T}) + \cdots + (a_n \mathsf{T})(y_1^n)\mathsf{T}$$

$$= a_0 + a_1 y_2 + \cdots + a_n y_2^n$$

$$= a(y_2).$$

In particular, $0 = m_1(y_1) = m_1(y_2)$. Hence $m_1(x)$ is divisible by $m_2(x)$. Reversing the roles of y_1 and y_2 (and using T^{-1}), we see that $m_2(x)$ is divisible by $m_1(x)$; hence $m_1(x) = m_2(x)$ as claimed.

Exercises 8.5

1. Let $\mathscr{F} = \mathfrak{R}$. Show that $\mathfrak{R}[i]$ and $\mathfrak{R}[2i]$ are isomorphic (in fact identical) and i and $2i$ have different minimum functions.

2. Find all automorphisms (isomorphisms onto itself) of $\mathfrak{C}$ which leave each element of $\mathfrak{R}$ fixed. [Hint: $\mathfrak{C} = \mathfrak{R}[i]$ where $i^2 + 1 = 0$.]

3. Find the minimum function relative to $\mathfrak{Q}$ for each of the following elements of $\mathfrak{C}$: (a) $\sqrt[3]{2}$, (b) $\sqrt{2} - \sqrt{3}$, (c) $\sqrt{2} + i$, (d) $i\sqrt[3]{2}$.

4. Let $\mathscr{F}$ be a field, and let n be a positive integer. Show that the set of scalar matrices of degree n over $\mathscr{F}$ forms a field $\mathscr{F}'$ isomorphic to $\mathscr{F}$.

5. Let $n = 2$, and let $\mathscr{F}'$ be as in Exercise 4. Show that the matrix

$$A = \left\| \begin{array}{cc} 2 & 0 \\ 0 & -1 \end{array} \right\| \text{ is algebraic over } \mathscr{F}', \text{ and find its minimum function.}$$

6. Do the same for the matrix $B = \left\| \begin{array}{cc} 0 & 0 \\ 1 & 0 \end{array} \right\|$.

7. Do the same for the matrix $C = \left\| \begin{array}{cc} c_1 & 0 \\ 0 & c_2 \end{array} \right\|$.

8. Do the same for the matrix $D = \left\| \begin{array}{cc} 1 & -1 \\ 3 & 2 \end{array} \right\|$.

8.6. Congruence of polynomials. We have now seen how each simple algebraic extension $\mathscr{F}[y]$ is completely determined by the simple transcendental extension $\mathscr{F}[x]$ and the minimum function of y. We round out the picture by showing that each monic polynomial $m(x)$ of degree greater than zero determines an algebraic extension $\mathscr{F}[y]$ having $m(x)$ as minimum function. Our main tool in this development will be the concept of *congruence* in the polynomial ring $\mathscr{F}[x]$.

If $g(x)$ and $h(x)$ are polynomials whose difference is divisible by a third polynomial $f(x)$, we say that $g(x)$ and $h(x)$ are *congruent modulo* $f(x)$ and write

$$(6.1) \qquad\qquad g(x) \equiv h(x) \ (\operatorname{mod} f(x)),$$

read "$g(x)$ is congruent to $h(x)$ modulo $f(x)$."

LEMMA 8.6A. *Congruence of polynomials modulo a fixed polynomial $f(x)$ is an equivalence relation with the substitution property relative to addition and multiplication.*

We recall (cf. Theorem 5.1D) that to say that congruence has the substitution property relative to addition and multiplication means that, if $g_1(x) \equiv h_1(x) \ (\operatorname{mod} f(x))$ and $g_2(x) \equiv h_2(x) \ (\operatorname{mod} f(x))$, then $g_1(x)+g_2(x) \equiv h_1(x) + h_2(x) \ (\operatorname{mod} f(x))$ and $g_1(x)\, g_2(x) \equiv h_1(x)\, h_2(x) \ (\operatorname{mod} f(x))$. We leave the proof of the lemma to the exercises.

We designate by $[g(x)]$ the equivalence class consisting of all polynomials congruent to $g(x)$ modulo $f(x)$. We call $[g(x)]$ a *congruence class* modulo $f(x)$ and denote by $\mathscr{A}$ the set of all congruence classes $[g(x)]$. We introduce addition and multiplication into $\mathscr{A}$ by the definitions

$$(6.2) \qquad\qquad [g_1(x)] + [g_2(x)] = [g_1(x) + g_2(x)],$$

$$(6.3) \qquad\qquad [g_1(x)]\, [g_2(x)] = [g_1(x)\, g_2(x)].$$

It follows from Theorem 5.1D and Lemma 8.6A that these operations are well defined (i.e. independent of the choice of representatives for congruence classes).

LEMMA 8.6B. *The set $\mathscr{A}$ of congruence classes is a commutative algebra over $\mathscr{F}$.*

We have already checked the two closure axioms. The associative, distributive, and commutative laws in $\mathscr{A}$ follow from those in $\mathscr{F}[x]$. Finally the zero in $\mathscr{A}$ is the class $[0]$, and the class $[-g(x)]$ is the negative of the class $[g(x)]$. We observe that the class $[0]$ can also be characterized as the ideal $(f(x))$ of all multiples of $f(x)$.

Next we notice that the subset of classes $[c]$ for c in $\mathscr{F}$ forms a subring of $\mathscr{A}$ isomorphic to $\mathscr{F}$ under the natural mapping $c \to [c]$. We identify

[c] with c and then $\mathscr{A}$ becomes an algebra over $\mathscr{F}$ with the unity element of $\mathscr{F}$ serving also as unity element for $\mathscr{A}$.

It is clear from the definition of congruence that, if $f(x)$ and $m(x)$ are associates, then congruence modulo $f(x)$ is equivalent to congruence modulo $m(x)$; hence two associates will define the same ring $\mathscr{A}$ of congruence classes. In particular, we may use the unique monic associate $m(x)$ of $f(x)$ as modulus without changing the ring $\mathscr{A}$.

Now denote by y the congruence class $[x]$. If $g(x)=c_0+c_1x + \cdots + c_nx^n$, then $[g(x)] = c_0 + c_1y + \cdots + c_ny^n = g(y)$. Hence $\mathscr{A} = \mathscr{F}[y]$. Since $0 = [m(x)]$, we have $m(y) = 0$; hence y is algebraic over $\mathscr{F}$.

THEOREM 8.6C. *Let* $m(x) = m_0 + m_1x + \cdots + m_{r-1}x^{r-1} + x^r$ $(r > 0)$ *be a polynomial in* $\mathscr{F}[x]$ *where* x *is transcendental over* $\mathscr{F}$. *Then the ring* $\mathscr{A}$ *of congruence classes modulo* $m(x)$ *is a simple algebraic extension* $\mathscr{F}[y]$ *of* $\mathscr{F}$, *where* $y = [x]$ *has minimum function* $m(x)$.

All that remains to be proved is that y satisfies no equation of degree less than r. But, if $g(y) = 0$, we must have $g(x) \equiv 0 \pmod{m(x)}$; hence $g(x)$ as a multiple of $m(x)$ has degree at least r.

This theorem is the fundamental existence theorem for simple algebraic extensions.

Exercises 8.6

1. Prove that congruence of polynomials modulo a fixed polynomial $f(x)$ is an equivalence relation.

2. Show that congruence has the substitution property relative to addition.

3. Show that congruence has the substitution property relative to multiplication.

4. Give the details in the proof of Lemma 8.6B. Show in particular that the mapping $c \to [c]$ is an isomorphism.

5. Let $\mathfrak{C}'$ be the ring of congruence classes of $\mathfrak{R}[x]$ modulo $x^2 + 1$. Show that $\mathfrak{C}'$ is isomorphic to $\mathfrak{C}$ and exhibit such an isomorphism.

6. Let y be the congruence class $[x]$ in the ring $\mathscr{A}$ of congruences classes of $\mathfrak{Q}[x]$ modulo $x^2 - 2$. Show that $y + 1$ has an inverse in $\mathscr{A}$.

8.7. Direct sums of vector spaces.

We turn now to a discussion of some concepts which are needed for our theory of algebraic extensions of a field, as well as being important parts of the general theory of vector spaces. We will see, in particular, that these considerations will provide a geometric interpretation for the concept of partitioned matrix introduced in Section 2.8.

Suppose that $\mathscr{V}$ is a vector space over a field $\mathscr{F}$, and suppose that $\mathscr{V}_1, \cdots, \mathscr{V}_r$ are subspaces of $\mathscr{V}$ whose sum is $\mathscr{W}$. We say that their sum is *direct*, written

$$(7.1) \qquad \mathscr{W} = \mathscr{V}_1 + \cdots + \mathscr{V}_r \quad (direct)$$

if each vector β in $\mathscr{W}$ has a unique expression in the form

(7.2) $\beta = \alpha_1 + \cdots + \alpha_r, \quad \alpha_i \text{ in } \mathscr{V}_i \qquad (i = 1, \cdots, r).$

We say that α_i is the $\mathscr{V}_i$ *component* of β and call the expression (7.2) the *decomposition* of β relative to the direct sum (7.1).

For example $\mathscr{V}_6{}^r$ is the direct sum of its subspaces $\mathscr{V}_1$, $\mathscr{V}_2$, $\mathscr{V}_3$ consisting, respectively, of all vectors of the forms $\| x_1, x_2, 0, 0, 0, 0 \|$, $\| 0, 0, x_3, x_4, 0, 0 \|$, $\| 0, 0, 0, 0, x_5, x_6 \|$.

The concept of direct sum is in a sense a generalization of the concept of independent set of vectors. For let $\varepsilon_1, \cdots, \varepsilon_r$ be an independent set of vectors, and set $\mathscr{V}_i = \langle \varepsilon_i \rangle$ $(i = 1, \cdots, r)$. The sum $\mathscr{W}$ of the $\mathscr{V}_i$ is of course the space spanned by the ε_i, and, if β is a vector in $\mathscr{W}$, we have unique scalars (cf. Section 1.5) $c_1, \cdots, c_r$ such that $\beta = c_1\varepsilon_1 + \cdots + c_r\varepsilon_r$. Then $c_i\varepsilon_i$ is the (unique) $\mathscr{V}_i$ component of β.

We now obtain some criteria for directness.

THEOREM 8.7A. *Let $\mathscr{V}$ be an $\mathscr{F}$ space; let $\mathscr{V}_1, \cdots, \mathscr{V}_r$ be subspaces of $\mathscr{V}$. Then the sum $\mathscr{W} = \mathscr{V}_1 + \cdots + \mathscr{V}_r$ is direct if and only if the equation*

$$0 = \alpha_1 + \cdots + \alpha_r, \quad \alpha_i \text{ in } \mathscr{V}_i \qquad (i = 1, \cdots, r)$$

has only the trivial solution $\alpha_1 = \cdots = \alpha_r = 0$.

We always have the trivial decomposition $\alpha_1 = \cdots = \alpha_r = 0$; hence, if the sum is direct, this is the only decomposition.

Conversely suppose that 0 has a unique decomposition, and suppose that the vector β in $\mathscr{W}$ has the two decompositions

$$\beta = \alpha_1 + \cdots + \alpha_r \quad \text{and} \quad \beta = \alpha'_1 + \cdots + \alpha'_r.$$

Then form the difference $\beta - \beta$ and have

$$0 = \beta - \beta = (\alpha_1 - \alpha'_1) + \cdots + (\alpha_r - \alpha'_r)$$

as a decomposition for 0. Since 0 has a unique decomposition, $\alpha_h - \alpha'_h = 0$ $(h = 1, \cdots, r)$, and so the two decompositions for β are the same. Hence, the hypothesis that the zero vector has a unique decomposition requires that the sum shall be direct.

THEOREM 8.7B. *A sum $\mathscr{W} = \mathscr{V}_1 + \mathscr{V}_2$ of two subspaces is direct if and only if $\mathscr{V}_1 \cap \mathscr{V}_2 = 0$.*

We use the preceding theorem. If the sum is not direct, then there is a decomposition $0 = \alpha_1 + \alpha_2$ with α_1 in $\mathscr{V}_1$, α_2 in $\mathscr{V}_2$, and neither term 0. Then $\alpha_1 = -\alpha_2$ is in the intersection $\mathscr{V}_1 \cap \mathscr{V}_2$, and hence $\mathscr{V}_1 \cap \mathscr{V}_2 \neq \{0\}$. Conversely, if the intersection $\mathscr{V}_1 \cap \mathscr{V}_2$ contains a nonzero vector β, then 0 has the nontrivial decomposition $0 = \beta + (-\beta)$.

There are several generalizations of this criterion for the case of more than two summands (but none that can be expressed entirely in terms of intersections). The following lemmas prepare the way for these generalizations.

LEMMA 8.7C. *Suppose that* $\mathscr{U} = \mathscr{V}_1 + \cdots + \mathscr{V}_r$ (direct) *and that* $\mathscr{U}' = \mathscr{V}'_1 + \cdots + \mathscr{V}'_s$ (direct). *Then the sum* $\mathscr{W} = \mathscr{V}_1 + \cdots + \mathscr{V}_r + \mathscr{V}'_1 + \cdots + \mathscr{V}'_s$ *is direct if and only if* $\mathscr{U} \cap \mathscr{U}' = 0$.

Proof of "only if." Suppose that β is a nonzero vector in the intersection $\mathscr{U} \cap \mathscr{U}'$. Then we have the decompositions $\beta = \alpha_1 + \cdots + \alpha_r$ and $-\beta = \alpha'_1 + \cdots + \alpha'_s$ relative to the given direct sums for $\mathscr{U}$ and $\mathscr{U}'$, respectively. Since $\beta \neq 0$, there is at least one h for which $\alpha_h \neq 0$. Then

$$0 = \beta + (-\beta) = \alpha_1 + \cdots + \alpha_r + \alpha'_1 + \cdots + \alpha'_s$$

is a nontrivial decomposition for 0 relative to the sum $\mathscr{V}_1 + \cdots + \mathscr{V}_r + \mathscr{V}'_1 + \cdots + \mathscr{V}'_s$, and so this sum cannot be direct. Hence, the sum can be direct only if $\mathscr{U} \cap \mathscr{U}' = 0$.

Proof of "if." If $\mathscr{U} \cap \mathscr{U}' = 0$ then by the preceding theorem the sum $\mathscr{U} + \mathscr{U}'$ is direct. Clearly $\mathscr{W} = \mathscr{U} + \mathscr{U}'$. Suppose that 0 has a decomposition

$$0 = \alpha_1 + \cdots + \alpha_r + \alpha'_1 + \cdots + \alpha'_s,$$

and let $\beta = \alpha_1 + \cdots + \alpha_r$. $\beta' = \alpha'_1 + \cdots + \alpha'_s$. Then β is in $\mathscr{U}$, and β' is in $\mathscr{U}'$, so that the equation $0 = \beta + \beta'$ requires $\beta = \beta' = 0$. But then, since the sums for $\mathscr{U}$ and $\mathscr{U}'$ are direct, we must have $\alpha_1 = \cdots = \alpha_r = 0$ and $\alpha'_1 = \cdots = \alpha'_s = 0$; i.e., 0 has only the trivial decomposition. The lemma now follows from Theorem 8.7A.

LEMMA 8.7D. *Suppose that the sum* $\mathscr{W} = \mathscr{V}_1 + \cdots + \mathscr{V}_r$ *is direct, and let* $i_1, \cdots, i_s$, $s \leq r$, *be any set of s distinct integers selected from the set* $1, \cdots, r$. *Then the sum* $\mathscr{U} = \mathscr{V}_{i_1} + \cdots + \mathscr{V}_{i_s}$ *is direct.*

Any decomposition $0 = \alpha_{i_1} + \cdots + \alpha_{i_s}$ relative to the sum for $\mathscr{U}$ implies a decomposition $0 = \alpha_1 + \cdots + \alpha_r$ relative to the sum for $\mathscr{W}$ if we take $\alpha_k = 0$ for all k not in the given subset $i_1, \cdots, i_s$. Hence, if the sum for $\mathscr{W}$ is direct, so is the sum for $\mathscr{U}$.

An important consequence of this lemma is that any rearrangement of the summands in a direct sum again gives a direct sum. Another important consequence of this lemma is that a sum is direct if it can be obtained by deleting summands from a direct sum.

THEOREM 8.7E. *Let* $\mathscr{V}_1, \cdots, \mathscr{V}_r$ *be subspaces of an $\mathscr{F}$ space $\mathscr{V}$. Then the sum* $\mathscr{W} = \mathscr{V}_1 + \cdots + \mathscr{V}_r$ *is direct if and only if* $\mathscr{V}_1 \cap \mathscr{V}_2 = 0$, $(\mathscr{V}_1 + \mathscr{V}_2) \cap \mathscr{V}_3 = 0, \cdots, (\mathscr{V}_1 + \cdots + \mathscr{V}_{h-1}) \cap \mathscr{V}_h = 0, \cdots,$ *and* $(\mathscr{V}_1 + \cdots + \mathscr{V}_{r-1}) \cap \mathscr{V}_r = 0$.

The "only if" follows at once from Lemma 8.7D and the "only if" part of Lemma 8.7C.

Next consider the "if" part. Set $\mathscr{W}_h = \mathscr{V}_1 + \cdots + \mathscr{V}_h$ $(h = 1, \cdots, r)$. By Theorem 8.7B, $\mathscr{W}_2 = \mathscr{V}_1 + \mathscr{V}_2$ (direct). Take as an induction hypothesis that for some $h \leq r$ we have $\mathscr{W}_{h-1} = \mathscr{V}_1 + \cdots + \mathscr{V}_{h-1}$ (direct). By hypothesis $\mathscr{W}_{h-1} \cap \mathscr{V}_h = 0$, and so by Lemma 8.7C the sum $\mathscr{W}_h = \mathscr{V}_1 + \cdots + \mathscr{V}_h$ is direct. This completes the induction and gives, in particular, $\mathscr{W} = \mathscr{W}_r = \mathscr{V}_1 + \cdots + \mathscr{V}_r$ (direct).

THEOREM 8.7F. *Let $\mathscr{V}_1, \cdots, \mathscr{V}_r$ be subspaces of an $\mathscr{F}$ space $\mathscr{V}$. Let*
$$\mathscr{U}_h = \mathscr{V}_1 + \cdots + \mathscr{V}_{h-1} + \mathscr{V}_{h+1} + \cdots + \mathscr{V}_r \quad (h = 1, \cdots, r).$$ *Then the sum $\mathscr{W} = \mathscr{V}_1 + \cdots + \mathscr{V}_r$ is direct if and only if $\mathscr{V}_h \cap \mathscr{U}_h = 0$ $(h = 1, \cdots, r)$.*

The "only if" follows at once from Lemmas 8.7C and 8.7D. Conversely, suppose that we have a nontrivial decomposition $0 = \alpha_1 + \cdots + \alpha_r$ where, say $\alpha_h \neq 0$. Then $-\alpha_h = \alpha_1 + \cdots + \alpha_{h-1} + \alpha_{h+1} + \cdots + \alpha_r$ belongs to both $\mathscr{V}_h$ and to $\mathscr{U}_h$. Hence, if the intersections $\mathscr{V}_h \cap \mathscr{U}_h$ are all 0, the sum for $\mathscr{W}$ must be direct.

Exercises 8.7

1. Let $\mathscr{V}_1$ and $\mathscr{V}_2$ be any two $\mathscr{F}$ spaces. We introduce a new system $\mathscr{V}$ called the *Cartesian sum* of $\mathscr{V}_1$ and $\mathscr{V}_2$ and denoted by $\mathscr{V} = \mathscr{V}_1 \oplus \mathscr{V}_2$. The elements of $\mathscr{V}$ are the ordered pairs $\alpha = (\alpha_1, \alpha_2)$ with α_1 in $\mathscr{V}_1$ and α_2 in $\mathscr{V}_2$; addition and multiplication by a scalar are defined component-wise; i.e.,

$$(\alpha_1, \alpha_2) + (\beta_1, \beta_2) = (\alpha_1 + \beta_1, \alpha_2 + \beta_2),$$

$$c(\alpha_1, \alpha_2) = (c\alpha_1, c\alpha_2).$$

Show that $\mathscr{V}$ is a vector space and that dim $\mathscr{V}$ = dim $\mathscr{V}_1$ + dim $\mathscr{V}_2$.

2. Give a generalization of the concept to the case of Cartesian sum of any finite collection of vector spaces.

3. Show that the mappings $\alpha_1 \to (\alpha_1, 0)$, $\alpha_2 \to (0, \alpha_2)$ are isomorphisms of $\mathscr{V}_1$ and $\mathscr{V}_2$, respectively, into $\mathscr{V}$, and show that $\mathscr{V}$ is the direct sum of the images of $\mathscr{V}_1$ and $\mathscr{V}_2$.

4. Give a generalization of Exercise 3 to the case of $\mathscr{V} = \mathscr{V}_1 \oplus \cdots \oplus \mathscr{V}_n$.

5. Let $\mathscr{V} = \mathscr{V}_1 + \cdots + \mathscr{V}_n$ (direct). Show that $\mathscr{V}$ is isomorphic to $\mathscr{V}_1 \oplus \cdots \oplus \mathscr{V}_n$.

6. Show that $\mathscr{V}_n(\mathscr{F}) \cong \mathscr{V}_1(\mathscr{F}) \oplus \cdots \oplus \mathscr{V}_1(\mathscr{F})$ (n summands).

7. Find three distinct one-dimensional subspaces of three space whose sum is not direct.

8. Let

$$\mathscr{V}_1 = \langle \| \; 2 \quad 1 \quad 3 \quad 2 \; \|, \; \| \; 1 \quad -1 \quad 1 \quad 1 \; \| \rangle$$

and

$$\mathscr{V}_2 = \langle \| \; 3 \quad -1 \quad 2 \quad -2 \; \|, \; \| \; 6 \quad -1 \quad 6 \quad 1 \; \| \rangle.$$

Show that the sum $\mathscr{V}_1 + \mathscr{V}_2$ is not direct.

8.8. Idempotents and direct sums. In the preceding section we have obtained various criteria for direct sums. In the present section we shall give some reasons for the importance of the concept of direct sum. The most important property of a direct sum of subspaces is that all operations in such a sum can be reduced to operations in the summands. More precisely, let $\mathscr{V} = \mathscr{V}_1 + \cdots + \mathscr{V}_r$ (direct), let c be a scalar, and let α, α' be vectors in $\mathscr{V}$ whose decompositions are

$$\alpha = \alpha_1 + \cdots + \alpha_r, \qquad \alpha' = \alpha'_1 + \cdots + \alpha'_r.$$

Then the decompositions for $\alpha + \alpha'$ and for $c\alpha$ are readily seen to be

(8.1) $$\alpha + \alpha' = (\alpha_1 + \alpha'_1) + \cdots + (\alpha_r + \alpha'_r),$$

(8.2) $$c\alpha = (c\alpha_1) + \cdots + (c\alpha_r).$$

Thus we see that in a direct sum the operations of vector addition and of multiplication of a vector by a scalar can be carried out component-wise.

Since the sum $\mathscr{V} = \mathscr{V}_1 + \cdots + \mathscr{V}_r$ is direct the $\mathscr{V}_i$ component α_i of any vector α in $\mathscr{V}$ is unique. Therefore the mapping which sends α into its $\mathscr{V}_i$ component α_i is well defined. We call this mapping the *projection* of $\mathscr{V}$ onto $\mathscr{V}_i$ related to the given expression of $\mathscr{V}$ as a direct sum, and denote it by P_i $(i = 1, \cdots, r)$, written P_i: $\alpha \to \alpha\mathsf{P}_i = \alpha_i$. Equations (8.1) and (8.2) show that projections *are linear transformations*.

To illustrate the idea of projection we consider $\mathscr{V} = \mathscr{V}_2(\mathscr{F})$ which is the direct sum of $\mathscr{V}_1 = \langle \varepsilon_1 \rangle$ and $\mathscr{V}_2 = \langle \varepsilon_2 \rangle$. (Here the ε_i are the natural basis elements of $\mathscr{V}$ introduced in Section 2.3.) We may regard $\mathscr{V}_1$ as the x-axis and $\mathscr{V}_2$ as the y axis in ordinary two-space. Then the projection P_1 sends each vector (x_1, x_2) into its perpendicular projection $(x_1, 0)$ on the x axis.

A nonzero linear transformation T on a vector space $\mathscr{V}$ is said to be *idempotent* if $\mathsf{T}^2 = \mathsf{T}$. Two idempotents T and S are said to be *orthogonal* if $\mathsf{TS} = \mathsf{ST} = 0$. A set of idempotents $\mathsf{T}_1, \cdots, \mathsf{T}_r$ are said to be *pairwise orthogonal* if $\mathsf{T}_i\mathsf{T}_j = \delta_{ij}\mathsf{T}_i$ $(i, j = 1, \cdots, r)$.

LEMMA 8.8A. *Let* $\mathsf{T}_1, \cdots, \mathsf{T}_r$ *be pairwise orthogonal idempotents, and set* $\mathsf{T} = \mathsf{T}_1 + \cdots + \mathsf{T}_{h-1}$, $\mathsf{S} = \mathsf{T}_h + \cdots + \mathsf{T}_r$ *where* $1 < h < r$. *Then* T *and* S *are orthogonal idempotents. The sum* $\mathsf{T}_1 + \cdots + \mathsf{T}_r$ *is also an idempotent.*

We leave the proof as an exercise.

THEOREM 8.8B. *Let* $\mathscr{V} = \mathscr{V}_1 + \cdots + \mathscr{V}_r$ *(direct). Then the* r *projections* $\mathsf{P}_1, \cdots, \mathsf{P}_r$ *of* $\mathscr{V}$ *onto its summands are pairwise orthogonal idempotents whose sum is the identity transformation on* $\mathscr{V}$; *i.e.,*

(8.3) $$\mathsf{I}_{\mathscr{V}} = \mathsf{P}_1 + \cdots + \mathsf{P}_r$$

and

(8.4) $$\mathsf{P}_i\mathsf{P}_j = \delta_{ij}\mathsf{P}_i \qquad\qquad (i, j = 1, \cdots, r).$$

Conversely, let $P_1, \cdots, P_r$ *be pairwise orthogonal idempotents whose sum is* $I_{\mathscr{V}}$, *and let* $\mathscr{V}_i$ *be the range of* P_i $(i=1, \cdots, r)$. *Then* $\mathscr{V} = \mathscr{V}_1 + \cdots + \mathscr{V}_r$ *(direct), and* P_i *is the related projection of* $\mathscr{V}$ *onto* $\mathscr{V}_i$ $(i = 1, \cdots, r)$.

To establish formula (8.3) we observe that

$$\alpha(P_1 + \cdots + P_r) = \alpha P_1 + \cdots + \alpha P_r = \alpha_1 + \cdots + \alpha_r = \alpha$$

for all α in $\mathscr{V}$; hence $P_1 + \cdots + P_r = I_{\mathscr{V}}$.

Next, for any α in $\mathscr{V}$ we have $\alpha(P_i P_j) = (\alpha P_i)P_j = \alpha_i P_j$. Since α_i is in $\mathscr{V}_i$, all of its components are zero except for its $\mathscr{V}_i$ component which is α_i itself. Hence, $\alpha_i P_i = \alpha_i$ and $\alpha_i P_j = 0$ for $j \neq i$. Therefore $\alpha(P_i P_j) = \delta_{ij}\alpha_i = \delta_{ij}\alpha P_i$; or $P_i P_j = \delta_{ij} P_i$, which is formula (8.4).

The proof of the converse is divided into two parts. We first prove that the subspaces $\mathscr{V}_1, \cdots, \mathscr{V}_r$ span $\mathscr{V}$, i.e., that $\mathscr{V} = \mathscr{V}_1 + \cdots + \mathscr{V}_r$, and second show that this sum is direct. For the first part it is sufficient to show that any vector α in $\mathscr{V}$ can be written as a sum $\alpha = \alpha_1 + \cdots + \alpha_r$ with α_i in $\mathscr{V}_i$ $(i = 1, \cdots, r)$. To see this let $\alpha_i = \alpha P_i$. Clearly α_i is an element of the range $\mathscr{V}_i$ of P_i, and it follows from (8.3) that $\alpha = \alpha I_{\mathscr{V}} = \alpha(P_1 + \cdots + P_r) = \alpha P_1 + \cdots + \alpha P_r = \alpha_1 + \cdots + \alpha_r$.

Next, to see that the sum is direct suppose that $0 = \alpha_1 + \cdots + \alpha_r$ where α_i lies in $\mathscr{V}_i$ $(i = 1, \cdots, r)$. Since α_i lies in $\mathscr{V}_i$, there exists a vector β in $\mathscr{V}$ such that $\alpha_i = \beta P_i$. Then, since $P_i^2 = P_i$, we have $\alpha_i P_i = (\beta P_i)P_i = \beta P_i^2 = \beta P_i = \alpha_i$. Hence we could take $\beta = \alpha_i$. Suppose $j \neq i$; then $\alpha_j P_i = (\alpha_j P_j)P_i = \alpha_j(P_j P_i) = \alpha_j 0 = 0$ by (8.4). Now, from the equation $0 = \alpha_1 + \cdots + \alpha_r$ we get $0 = 0P_i = \alpha_1 P_i + \cdots + \alpha_r P_i = \alpha_i P_i = \alpha_i$. This shows that 0 has only the trivial decomposition, and hence that the sum is direct. Finally, to see that P_i is indeed the related projection of $\mathscr{V}$ onto $\mathscr{V}_i$ we observe that, if α has the decomposition $\alpha = \alpha_1 + \cdots + \alpha_r$, then $\alpha P_i = \alpha_i$.

We are now ready to establish a connection between direct sums and partitioned matrices. For simplicity we shall consider only a special case; the general case is similar but more complicated notationally.

Let T be a linear transformation on a vector space $\mathscr{V}$ which is the direct sum of two of its subspaces $\mathscr{V}_1$ and $\mathscr{V}_2$, and let P_1 and P_2 be the related projections. We wish to use these projections to break T up into a sum of linear transformations each somewhat simpler than T. We set $T_{ij} = P_i T P_j$ $(i, j = 1, 2)$. Then we have

$$T = I\,T\,I = (P_1 + P_2)T(P_1 + P_2)$$

(8.5)
$$= P_1 T P_1 + P_1 T P_2 + P_2 T P_1 + P_2 T P_2$$

$$= T_{11} + T_{12} + T_{21} + T_{22}.$$

For any vector α in $\mathscr{V}$ the image $\alpha T_{ij} = (\alpha_1 + \alpha_2)T_{ij} = \alpha_i T_{ij}$ of α under T_{ij} lies in $\mathscr{V}_j$. Hence the range of T_{ij} is $\mathscr{V}_j$. Let T'_{ij} denote the mapping of $\mathscr{V}_i$ into $\mathscr{V}_j$ obtained by restricting the domain of T_{ij} to $\mathscr{V}_i$. Clearly T'_{ij} is a linear transformation.

Now select bases $\beta_1, \cdots, \beta_{v_1}$ and $\gamma_1, \cdots, \gamma_{v_2}$ for $\mathscr{V}_1$ and $\mathscr{V}_2$, and let A_{ij} be the matrix for T'_{ij} relative to these bases $(i, j = 1, 2)$. Then we claim the matrix A of T relative to the basis $\beta_1, \cdots, \beta_{v_1}, \gamma_1, \cdots, \gamma_{v_2}$ is the partitioned matrix

$$(8.6) \qquad A = \left\| \begin{matrix} A_{11} & A_{12} \\ A_{21} & A_{22} \end{matrix} \right\|.$$

To prove this we first recall that the ith row of A is given by the coordinates of the image under T of the ith basis vector. There are two cases to consider: (1) $1 \leq i \leq v_1$, and (2) $1 \leq i - v_1 \leq v_2$.

In case 1 the ith basis vector β_i lies in $\mathscr{V}_1$, and so

$$\beta_i \mathsf{T} = \beta_i (\mathsf{T}_{11} + \mathsf{T}_{12} + \mathsf{T}_{21} + \mathsf{T}_{22})$$
$$= \beta_i \mathsf{T}_{11} + \beta_i \mathsf{T}_{12} + 0 + 0 = \beta_i \mathsf{T}'_{11} + \beta_i \mathsf{T}'_{12}.$$

Now the ith row of A_{11} is given by the coordinates of $\beta_i \mathsf{T}'_{11}$, and the ith row of A_{12} is given by the coordinates of $\beta_i \mathsf{T}'_{12}$. This shows that the ith row of A is as indicated in formula (8.6).

In case 2 set $i' = i - v_1$. Then the argument is similar and leads to the result that the ith row of A is the i'th row of A_{21} followed (horizontally) by the i'th row of A_{22}. Here the ith basis vector is $\gamma_{i'}$. This completes the proof of formula (8.6).

The operations on partitioned matrices could have been determined by considering the related linear transformations. We illustrate this with an example of multiplication.

Suppose that S is a second linear transformation on $\mathscr{V}$, let $\mathsf{R} = \mathsf{TS}$, and define the transformations S_{ij}, S'_{ij} and R_{ij}, R'_{ij} from S and R in the same fashion as the T_{ij}, T'_{ij} were determined from T. Then we have

$$(8.7) \quad \begin{aligned} \mathsf{R}_{ij} &= \mathsf{P}_i \mathsf{TS} \mathsf{P}_j = \mathsf{P}_i \mathsf{T}(\mathsf{P}_1 + \mathsf{P}_2)\mathsf{S}\mathsf{P}_j = \mathsf{P}_i \mathsf{T}\mathsf{P}_1 \mathsf{S}\mathsf{P}_j + \mathsf{P}_i \mathsf{T}\mathsf{P}_2 \mathsf{S}\mathsf{P}_j \\ &= (\mathsf{P}_i \mathsf{T}\mathsf{P}_1)(\mathsf{P}_1 \mathsf{S}\mathsf{P}_j) + (\mathsf{P}_1 \mathsf{T}\mathsf{P}_2)(\mathsf{P}_2 \mathsf{T}\mathsf{P}_j) = \mathsf{T}_{i1}\mathsf{S}_{1j} + \mathsf{T}_{i2}\mathsf{S}_{2j}. \end{aligned}$$

If B and C are the matrices of S and R and are partitioned in the same manner as A, then we have

$$(8.8) \qquad C_{ij} = A_{i1}B_{1j} + A_{i2}B_{2j},$$

which is the counterpart for multiplication of partitioned matrices of formula (8.7).

To extend these results to the general case of rectangular partitioned matrices we begin with two spaces $\mathscr{V}$ and $\mathscr{W}$, each of which is a direct sum of subspaces. We must then use the related projections P_i in $\mathscr{V}$ and Q_j

in $\mathscr{W}$ so as to split a linear transformation T of $\mathscr{V}$ into $\mathscr{W}$ into a sum of linear transformations $\mathsf{T}_{ij} = \mathsf{P}_i\mathsf{T}\mathsf{Q}_j$. It is recommended that the student work out the details of this extension.

Exercises 8.8

1. Prove Lemma 8.8A.
2. Find two different idempotents E_1, E'_1 which map $\mathscr{V}_2$ onto its subspace $\mathscr{W} = \langle \| 1 \ 0 \| \rangle$. Find idempotents E_2, E'_2 orthogonal to E_1, E'_1, respectively, and find the images of $\mathscr{V}_2$ under E_2 and E'_2.

8.9. Decomposition of algebras. Let $\mathscr{A}$ be an algebra over a field $\mathscr{F}$, and let $\mathscr{A}_1, \cdots, \mathscr{A}_s$ be subalgebras of $\mathscr{A}$. We say that $\mathscr{A}$ is the *direct sum* of $\mathscr{A}_1, \cdots, \mathscr{A}_s$ if, first, $\mathscr{A}$ considered as a vector space is the direct sum of the $\mathscr{A}_i$ (also considered as vector spaces) and, second, the product $\alpha\beta$ vanishes whenever α and β belong to distinct subalgebras in the given set.

Let α and β be elements of $\mathscr{A}$, and suppose that $\mathscr{A}$ is the direct sum of $\mathscr{A}_1, \cdots, \mathscr{A}_s$. Then we can write

$$(9.1) \qquad \alpha = \alpha_1 + \cdots + \alpha_s \quad (\alpha_i \text{ in } \mathscr{A}_i),$$

and

$$(9.2) \qquad \beta = \beta_1 + \cdots + \beta_s \quad (\beta_i \text{ in } \mathscr{A}_i),$$

where the components α_i and β_i are uniquely determined by α and β, respectively. Moreover, it follows from the vector space theory that the ith component of the sum $\alpha + \beta$ is the sum $\alpha_i + \beta_i$ of the ith components of α and β; i.e.,

$$(9.3) \qquad \alpha + \beta = (\alpha_1 + \beta_1) + \cdots + (\alpha_s + \beta_s).$$

Next, consider the product $\alpha\beta$. Since by our hypothesis $\alpha_i\beta_j = 0$ if $i \neq j$, we have

$$(9.4) \qquad \alpha\beta = \alpha_1\beta_1 + \cdots + \alpha_s\beta_s.$$

We also have for each scalar c

$$(9.5) \qquad c\alpha = c\alpha_1 + \cdots + c\alpha_n.$$

From (9.3), (9.4), (9.5) we see that all operations in $\mathscr{A}$ can be carried out component-wise, or in other words $\mathscr{A}$ is entirely determined by its subalgebras $\mathscr{A}_i$. The next theorem shows that direct sum decompositions of algebras are determined by decompositions of the unity element.

THEOREM 8.9A. *Let $\mathscr{A}$ be an algebra with unity element 1. If*

$$(9.6) \qquad 1 = e_1 + \cdots + e_s$$

is a decomposition of 1 *into a sum of orthogonal idempotents* $e_1, \cdots, e_s$ *which lie in the center of* $\mathscr{A}$, *then* $\mathscr{A}$ *is the direct sum of the subalgebras* $\mathscr{A}_1, \cdots, \mathscr{A}_s$ *where* $\mathscr{A}_i$ *has unity element* e_i *and consists of all elements* αe_i *with* α *in* $\mathscr{A}$ $(i = 1, \cdots, s)$.

Conversely, if $\mathscr{A}$ *is the direct sum of subalgebras* $\mathscr{A}_1, \cdots, \mathscr{A}_s$, *then* $\mathscr{A}_i$ *has a unity element* e_i $(i = 1, \cdots, s)$, *and these* e_i *are orthogonal idempotents which have sum* 1 *and which lie in the center of* $\mathscr{A}$.

We begin the proof of the direct part by showing that $\mathscr{A}_i$ is a subalgebra with unity element e_i. If c is a scalar and α, β lie in $\mathscr{A}$, we have $c(\alpha e_i) = (c\alpha)e_i$, $\alpha e_i + \beta e_i = (\alpha + \beta)e_i$, and $(\alpha e_i)(\beta e_i) = (\alpha e_i \beta)e_i$; hence $\mathscr{A}_i$ is a subalgebra of $\mathscr{A}$. Finally, since e_i is an idempotent and lies in the center of $\mathscr{A}$, we have $e_i(\alpha e_i) = (\alpha e_i)e_i = \alpha(e_i e_i) = \alpha e_i$, which shows that e_i is unity element for $\mathscr{A}_i$.

Next, since the idempotents $e_1, \cdots, e_s$ are orthogonal, we have $(\alpha e_i)(\beta e_j) = (\alpha \beta)(e_i e_j) = 0$ if $i \neq j$. This shows that a product vanishes if its factors lie in two different subalgebras $\mathscr{A}_i$ and $\mathscr{A}_j$.

All that remains now is to prove that, considered as a vector space, $\mathscr{A}$ is the direct sum of its subspaces $\mathscr{A}_1, \cdots, \mathscr{A}_s$. The equation

$$\alpha = \alpha 1 = \alpha(e_1 + \cdots + e_s) = \alpha e_1 + \cdots + \alpha e_s$$

shows that $\mathscr{A} = \mathscr{A}_1 + \cdots + \mathscr{A}_s$. Next, consider any decomposition

$$0 = \alpha_1 + \cdots + \alpha_s$$

where α_i lies in $\mathscr{A}_i$ $(i = 1, \cdots, s)$. Then, since $\alpha_j e_i = 0$ if $j \neq i$ and $\alpha_i e_i = \alpha_i$, we have

$$0 = 0e_i = \alpha_i \qquad\qquad (i = 1, \cdots, s).$$

This shows that the sum is direct (see Theorem 8.7A) and completes the proof of the direct part of the theorem.

Next, we establish the converse part. Since $\mathscr{A}$ is the sum of the $\mathscr{A}_i$, we can write

$$1 = \alpha_1 + \cdots + \alpha_s$$

with α_i in $\mathscr{A}_i$ $(i = 1, \cdots, s)$. Since the sum for $\mathscr{A}$ is direct, we have $\alpha_i \alpha_j = 0$ if $i \neq j$. But then

$$\alpha_i = \alpha_i 1 = \alpha_i \alpha_1 + \cdots + \alpha_i \alpha_s = \alpha_i \alpha_i.$$

This shows that $\alpha_1, \cdots, \alpha_s$ are orthogonal idempotents.

Next, if β_i is any element of $\mathscr{A}_i$, we have $\alpha_j \beta_i = 0$ if $j \neq i$, and so

$$\beta_i = 1\beta_i = (\alpha_1 + \cdots + \alpha_s)\beta_i = \alpha_i \beta_i.$$

Similarly, $\beta_i = \beta_i \alpha_i$. Hence α_i is unity element for $\mathscr{A}_i$. Finally to see that α_i lies in the center of $\mathscr{A}$ we consider any element β in $\mathscr{A}$. Since $\mathscr{A}$

is the sum of the $\mathscr{A}_i$, there exists a decomposition $\beta = \beta_1 + \cdots + \beta_s$ with β_i in $\mathscr{A}_i$ $(i = 1, \cdots, s)$. Now,

$$\beta\alpha_i = \beta_1\alpha_i + \cdots + \beta_s\alpha_i = \beta_i\alpha_i = \beta_i,$$

and similarly $\alpha_i\beta = \beta_i$, whence $\alpha_i\beta = \beta\alpha_i$. This shows that α_i lies in the center of $\mathscr{A}$ and completes the proof of the theorem.

We next study one of the $\mathscr{A}_i$. Consider the mapping $\mathsf{T}_i\colon\ c \to ce_i$ of $\mathscr{F}$ into $\mathscr{A}_i$, and set $\mathscr{F}_i = \mathscr{F}\mathsf{T}_i$. This is a one-to-one mapping since, if $ce_i = 0$, then $c = 0$. For, otherwise, if $c \neq 0$ then $\dfrac{1}{c}\,(ce_i) = \dfrac{1}{c} \cdot 0 = 0$ whereas $\left(\dfrac{1}{c}\,c\right)e_i = e_i \neq 0$, a contradiction. Also, $\mathscr{F}_i$ has a unity element $1e_i = e_i$. Next $\mathscr{F}_i$ is a field since, if c is any nonzero scalar and c' is its reciprocal, then $(ce_i)(c'e_i) = cc'e_i = 1 \cdot e_i = e_i$. Finally the equations

$$c_1e_i + c_2e_i = (c_1 + c_2)e_i, \qquad (c_1e_i)(c_2e_i) = (c_1c_2)e_i$$

show that T_i is an isomorphism of the field $\mathscr{F}$ onto the field $\mathscr{F}_i$.

Thus there are s isomorphic images of $\mathscr{F}$. These images are all distinct since $\mathscr{F}_i \subseteq \mathscr{A}_i$ and $\mathscr{A}_i$ has only 0 in common with $\mathscr{A}_j$ $(j \neq i)$. Each $\mathscr{A}_i$ is an algebra over $\mathscr{F}$ and can also be taken as an algebra over $\mathscr{F}_i$. But one should not identify $\mathscr{F}$ with any $\mathscr{F}_i$ since (unless $s = 1$) they are distinct subfields of $\mathscr{A}$.

An idempotent e is said to be *primitive* in a ring $\mathscr{A}$ if the equations $e = e_1 + e_2$, $e_1{}^2 = e_1$, $e_2{}^2 = e_2$, $e_1e_2 = e_2e_1 = 0$ require either $e_1 = 0$ or $e_2 = 0$.

LEMMA 8.9B. *Let $\mathscr{A}$ be a commutative ring with unity element 1, and suppose that $\mathscr{A}$ contains primitive idempotents $e_1, \cdots, e_s$ which are pairwise orthogonal and whose sum is 1. Then $e_1, \cdots, e_s$ are the only primitive idempotents in $\mathscr{A}$. Moreover, if f is any idempotent in $\mathscr{A}$, then f is a sum of certain of the e_i.*

Let f and e be any two idempotents in $\mathscr{A}$. Then $e = e_1 + e_2$, where $e_1 = fe$ and $e_2 = e - fe$. Now, $e_1{}^2 = fefe = ffee = fe = e_1$, $e_2{}^2 = (e - fe)(e - fe) = e^2 - fee - efe + fefe = e - fe = e_2$, and similarly $e_1e_2 = e_2e_1 = 0$. In particular, if e is primitive we must have either $fe = 0$ or $fe = e$.

Next, we have

$$(9.7) \qquad\qquad f = f1 = fe_1 + \cdots + fe_s.$$

Since each e_i is primitive, we have either $fe_i = 0$ or $fe_i = e_i$, and so f is a sum of certain of the e_i. In particular, if f is primitive, then the sum (9.7) for f must reduce to a single term.

An algebra is said to be *indecomposable* if it cannot be written as the direct sum of two nonzero subalgebras. The lemma just proved and Theorem 8.9A yield the next result.

THEOREM 8.9C. *If a commutative algebra $\mathscr{A}$ with unity element is a direct sum of indecomposable subalgebras $\mathscr{A}_1, \cdots, \mathscr{A}_s$, then this decomposition is unique in the sense that the terms in any other such decomposition of $\mathscr{A}$ must just be a permutation of $\mathscr{A}_1, \cdots, \mathscr{A}_s$.*

Exercise 8.9

1. Find the primitive idempotents and the corresponding direct sum decomposition if $\mathscr{A}$ is (a) the set of 2-rowed diagonal matrices over $\mathscr{F}$, (b) the set of n-rowed diagonal matrices over $\mathscr{F}$, (c) the set of all matrices over $\mathscr{F}$ of degree n.

8.10. Decomposition of simple algebraic extensions. We now restrict ourselves to simple algebraic extensions of a field. Suppose that y is algebraic over a field $\mathscr{F}$ with minimum function $m(x) = m_0 + m_1 x + \cdots + m_{r-1} x^{r-1} + x^r$, and consider the algebra $\mathscr{F}[y]$. In this section we shall show that $\mathscr{F}[y]$ decomposes into a direct sum of subalgebras, each of which corresponds to a primary factor of $m(x)$. Since this decomposition is reflected in the idempotents, we first turn our attention to an idempotent $e_1 \neq 1$ in $\mathscr{F}[y]$. Then $e_2 = 1 - e_1$ is also an idempotent, and the pair e_1, e_2 satisfy the hypothesis of Theorem 8.9A, and so define a decomposition of $\mathscr{F}[y]$. According to Theorem 8.5B there exists polynomials $e_1(x), e_2(x)$, each of degree less than r, such that $e_1 = e_1(y)$ and $e_2 = e_2(y)$. Then the equations $e_1 + e_2 = 1$ and $e_1 e_2 = 0$ imply the congruences

(10.1) $$e_1(x) + e_2(x) \equiv 1 \ (\mathrm{mod} \ m(x))$$

and

(10.2) $$e_1(x) \, e_2(x) \equiv 0 \ (\mathrm{mod} \ m(x)).$$

Since the degrees of $e_1(x)$ and $e_2(x)$ are both less than that of $m(x)$, the first congruence must actually be an equality; i.e.,

(10.3) $$e_1(x) + e_2(x) = 1.$$

Suppose that $p_1, \cdots, p_s$ are the distinct prime factors of $m(x)$ and that

(10.4) $$m(x) = q_1(x) \cdots q_s(x) \quad \text{where} \quad q_i(x) = p_i(x)^{l_i} \quad (i=1, \cdots, s).$$

It follows from (10.3) that $e_1(x)$ and $e_2(x)$ are relatively prime. Now, if a product $e_1(x) \, e_2(x)$ of two relatively prime factors is divisible by $m(x)$, then each primary factor $q_i(x)$ of $m(x)$ must be a factor of exactly one of $e_1(x)$, $e_2(x)$.

We say that a simple algebraic extension $\mathscr{F}[y]$ is *primary* if the minimum function for y is a primary polynomial.

THEOREM 8.10A. *Every primary simple algebraic extension $\mathscr{F}[y]$ is an indecomposable algebra whose only idempotent is its unity element.*

Suppose that $e \neq 1$ is an idempotent in $\mathscr{F}[y]$. Then we have seen that there exists a polynomial $e(x)$ of degree less than r such that each primary factor of $m(x)$ is a factor either of $e(x)$ or of $1 - e(x)$. But, if $m(x) = q(x)$ is primary, this is clearly impossible. Hence 1 is the only idempotent in $\mathscr{F}[y]$, and so, by Theorem 8.9A, $\mathscr{F}[y]$ is indecomposable.

Our next lemma gives a construction for idempotents in a simple algebraic extension. This will lead to a decomposition of the algebra $F[y]$ (see Theorem 8.10C below).

LEMMA 8.10B. *Let $\mathscr{F}[y]$ be a simple algebraic extension of $\mathscr{F}$, and let the minimum function $m(x)$ of y have the primary decomposition $m(x) = q_1(x) \cdots q_s(x)$. Then there exists a decomposition of 1 into a sum of s orthogonal idempotents $e_1(y), \cdots, e_s(y)$.*

For $s = 1$ there is nothing to be proved. Suppose $s \geq 2$. Let $q^*_i(x) = m(x)/q_i(x)$ $(i = 1, \cdots, s)$. Then $q_i(x)$ and $q^*_i(x)$ are relatively prime since $q^*_i(x) = \prod_{j \neq i} q_j(x)$, and the $q_i(x)$ are relatively prime. By Lemma 8.3F there exist polynomials $h_i(x)$ and $h^*_i(x)$ such that

$$(10.5) \qquad 1 = h_i(x)q_i(x) + h^*_i(x)q^*_i(x),$$

Let $e_i(x) = h^*_i(x)q^*_i(x)$; then

$$(10.6) \qquad e_i(x) \equiv 0 \ (\mathrm{mod}\ q_j(x)) \qquad\qquad (j \neq i).$$

Also, by (10.5),

$$(10.7) \qquad e_i(x) \equiv 1 \ (\mathrm{mod}\ q_i(x)).$$

In the remainder of the proof we shall use the fact that, if $f(x) \equiv 0$ $(\mathrm{mod}\ q_k(x))$ for $k = 1, \cdots, s$, then $f(y) = 0$. For, $f(x) \equiv 0$ $(\mathrm{mod}\ q_1(x) \cdots q_s(x))$ by Lemma 8.4E since the $q_k(x)$ are relatively prime; thus $f(x) \equiv 0$ $(\mathrm{mod}\ m(x))$ or $f(y) = 0$.

From (10.6) and (10.7),

$$1 \equiv e_1(x) + \cdots + e_s(x) \ (\mathrm{mod}\ q_k(x))$$

for $k = 1, \cdots, s$. Hence by the remark above

$$1 = e_1(y) + \cdots + e_s(y).$$

Next, also by (10.6) and (10.7), $e_i^2(x) \equiv e_i(x) \ (\mathrm{mod}\ q_k(x))$ for $k = 1, \cdots, s$. Hence $e_i^2(y) = e_i(y)$; i.e., the $e_k(y)$ are idempotent. Finally, again by

(10.6) and (10.7), $e_i(x) e_j(x) \equiv 0 \pmod{q_k(x)}$ for $k = 1, \cdots, s$. Hence $e_i(y) e_j(y) = 0$; i.e., the $e_k(y)$ are orthogonal. This completes the proof.

THEOREM 8.10C. *Let $\mathscr{F}[y]$ be a simple algebraic extension of $\mathscr{F}$, and suppose that the minimum function $m(x)$ has s distinct primary factors $q_1(x), \cdots, q_s(x)$. Then there exist elements $y_1, \cdots, y_s$ in $\mathscr{F}[y]$ such that $\mathscr{F}[y]$ is the direct sum of primary subalgebras $\mathscr{F}_1[y_1], \cdots, \mathscr{F}_s[y_s]$ where $\mathscr{F}_i$ is isomorphic to $\mathscr{F}$ and the minimum function for y_i in $\mathscr{F}_i[y_i]$ is the image of $q_i(x)$ over $\mathscr{F}_i$ (i.e., replace the coefficients by their images in $\mathscr{F}_i$). This decomposition is unique.*

This is the fundamental decomposition theorem for simple algebraic extensions.

Let $e_i = e_i(y)$ be the orthogonal idempotents described in the preceding lemma. Since $\mathscr{F}[y]$ is commutative (i.e., $\mathscr{F}[y]$ is its own center), we may now apply Theorem 8.9A to obtain the direct decomposition

$$\mathscr{F}[y] = \mathscr{A}_1 + \cdots + \mathscr{A}_s \quad \text{(direct sum)}$$

where $\mathscr{A}_i$ is the set of all multiples αe_i of e_i in $\mathscr{F}[y]$ $(i = 1, \cdots, s)$.

Let T_i and $\mathscr{F}_i$ $(i = 1, \cdots, s)$ be the mappings and fields introduced in the discussion preceding Lemma 8.9B. Now we observe that, if α is any element in $\mathscr{F}[y]$ and c is any scalar, then $c(\alpha e_i) = c(\alpha e_i e_i) = (ce_i)(\alpha e_i)$. Hence, for each element α_i in $\mathscr{A}_i$ we have $c\alpha_i = (ce_i)\alpha_i$. Therefore, $\mathscr{A}_i$ is a vector space over $\mathscr{F}_i$, and the dimension of $\mathscr{A}_i$ over $\mathscr{F}_i$ is the same as the dimension of $\mathscr{A}_i$ over $\mathscr{F}$.

Let x_i be a transcendental element over $\mathscr{F}_i$. We extend T_i into an isomorphism of $\mathscr{F}[x]$ onto $\mathscr{F}_i[x_i]$ by the definition

$$[a_0 + a_1 x + \cdots + a_n x^n]\mathsf{T}_i = a_0\mathsf{T}_i + (a_1\mathsf{T}_i)x_i + \cdots + (a_n\mathsf{T}_i)x_i^n.$$

We denote the image of a polynomial $f(x)$ under T_i by $f^{(i)}(x_i)$.

Now let $\alpha = f(y) = a_0 + a_1 y + \cdots + a_n y^n$. Then

$$\alpha e_i = a_0 e_i + (a_1 y)e_i + \cdots + (a_n y^n)e_i$$
$$= a_0 e_i + (a_1 e_i)(ye_i) + \cdots + (a_n e_i)(ye_i)^n$$
$$= f^{(i)}(y_i),$$

where $y_i = ye_i$. This shows that $\mathscr{A}_i = \mathscr{F}_i[y_i]$.

Finally, suppose that $q_i(x) = b_0 + b_1 x + \cdots + x^t$. Then $q_i^{(i)}(x_i) = b_0 e_i + (b_1 e_i)x_i + \cdots + e_i x_i^t$ is the image of $q_i(x)$ over $\mathscr{F}_i$, and we wish to show that $q_i^{(i)}(x_i)$ is the minimum function for y_i in $\mathscr{F}_i[y_i]$. Now consider $q_i^{(i)}(y_i)$. We have, since $y_i^h = (ye_i)^h = y^h e_i$, that

$$q_i^{(i)}(y_i) = b_0 e_i(y) + b_1 e_i(y)y_i + \cdots + e_i(y)y_i^t$$
$$= (b_0 + b_1 y + \cdots + y^t)e_i(y)$$
$$= q_i(y) \, e_i(y).$$

Now, by (10.6), $q_i(x) \cdot e_i(x)$ is divisible by $m(x)$. Hence $q_i^{(i)}(y_i) = q_i(y)e_i(y) = 0$. This shows that the minimum function for y_i in $\mathscr{F}_i[y_i]$ is a factor of $q_i^{(i)}(x_i)$, and hence that $r_i = \dim \mathscr{F}_i[y_i] \leq \deg q_i^{(i)}(x_i) = \deg q_i(x)$. Now, since $\mathscr{F}[y]$ is the direct sum of $\mathscr{F}_1[y_1], \cdots, \mathscr{F}_s[y_s]$, we have

$$r = r_1 + \cdots + r_s \leq \deg q_1(x) + \cdots + \deg q_s(x)$$

$$= \deg m(x) = r.$$

This continued equality shows that $r_i = \deg q_i(x)$ $(i = 1, \cdots, s)$, and hence shows that $q_i^{(i)}(x_i)$ is actually the minimum function for y_i in $\mathscr{F}_i[y_i]$.

Finally the uniqueness is an immediate consequence of the indecomposability of primary subalgebras (Theorem 8.10A) and the uniqueness of a decomposition into indecomposable subalgebras (Theorem 8.9C).

Exercises 8.10

1. Find the decomposition into primary subalgebras of $\mathfrak{R}[y]$ where y has the minimum function $x(x - 1)$.

2. Suppose that in Lemma 8.10B, the polynomials $e_1(x), \cdots, e_s(x)$ are taken so as to have degree less than degree $m(x)$ (cf. Theorem 8.5B). Prove that

$$1 = e_1(x) + \cdots + e_s(x).$$

3. Suppose that $f(x)$ and $g(x)$ are relatively prime polynomials in $\mathscr{F}[x]$ neither of degree zero, and set $h(x) = f(x)\, g(x)$. Show that there exist unique polynomials $f_1(x)$, $g_1(x)$ such that

$$\frac{1}{h(x)} = \frac{f_1(x)}{f(x)} + \frac{g_1(x)}{g(x)}$$

and with $\deg f_1(x) < \deg f(x)$ and $\deg g_1(x) < \deg g(x)$.

4. Let $f(x)$, $g(x)$, $h(x)$ be as in Exercise 3, and let $h_1(x)$ be any polynomial of degree less than that of $h(x)$. Show that there exist unique polynomials $f_1(x)$, $g_1(x)$ for which

$$\frac{h_1(x)}{h(x)} = \frac{f_1(x)}{f(x)} + \frac{g_1(x)}{g(x)}$$

and with (i) $\deg f_1(x) < \deg f(x)$ or $f_1(x) = 0$ and (ii) $\deg g_1(x) < \deg g(x)$ or $g_1(x) = 0$.

5. Give an example illustrating the case $f_1(x) = 0$ in Exercise 4. Give a necessary and sufficient condition for $f_1(x) = 0$.

6. State and prove generalizations of Exercises 3 and 4 to the case where $h(x)$ is a product of any number of pairwise relatively prime factors.

7. Let $m(x)$ be a monic polynomial with primary factorization $m(x) = q_1(x) \cdots q_s(x)$. Show that the decomposition

$$\frac{1}{m(x)} = \frac{f_1(x)}{q_1(x)} + \cdots + \frac{f_s(x)}{q_s(x)}$$

where $\deg f_i(x) < \deg q_i(x)$ $(i = 1, \cdots, s)$ can be used to give a new proof of Lemma 8.10B, in which we take $e_i(x) = f_i(x) \, q^*{}_i(x)$. Show, moreover, that these $e_i(x)$ satisfy the conditions of Exercise 2.

8. Show that the construction of the polynomials $f_1(x), \cdots, f_s(x)$ in Exercise 7 can be reduced to the solution of a system of r linear nonhomogeneous equations in r unknowns. [Hint: Use the method of undetermined coefficients for the $f_i(x)$. These coefficients are the unknowns.]

9. Find polynomials $e_1(x)$, $e_2(x)$, $e_3(x)$ which satisfy the conditions of Exercise 2 for the polynomial $m(x) = x^2(x - 1)(x + 1)$.

10. Let $m(x) = x^4 - 4$ be the minimum function of y. Find the decomposition of $\mathscr{F}[y]$ for each of the cases $\mathscr{F} = \mathfrak{Q}$, $\mathscr{F} = \mathfrak{R}$, $\mathscr{F} = \mathfrak{C}$.

11. Show how the results of Exercise 6 for the case $\mathscr{F} = \mathfrak{R}$ can be used in the integration of rational fractions. (See the sections on "partial fractions" in any elementary calculus textbook.)

Chapter 9 — Equivalence of Matrices over a Ring

Chapter **9**

Equivalence
of Matrices
over a Ring

9.1. Matrices over a ring. None of the basic operations with matrices make use of division by scalars (i.e., of field postulate M4), nor does commutativity of scalars under multiplication play an essential role. We may, accordingly, introduce matrices whose elements belong to a ring (rather then to a field).

Let $\mathscr{S} = \{a, b, \cdots\}$ be any ring. (We use lower-case roman letters to indicate that the ring elements are now the "scalars.") We define $\mathscr{S}$ matrices just as we earlier defined matrices over a field (see Section 2.2). The basic matrix operations, i.e., addition, multiplication, and multiplication by scalars, are defined exactly as in the field case (cf. Sections 2.5 and 2.6). Postulates A1, A2, A3, A4, A5, M1, M2, D1, D2, S1, S2, S3, S4 hold for $\mathscr{S}$ matrices in precisely the same way they do for $\mathscr{F}$ matrices. If, moreover, $\mathscr{S}$ has a unity element 1, then M3 and S5 also hold.

Unless the ring $\mathscr{S}$ is further restricted, concepts such as rank and determinant do not carry over naturally for $\mathscr{S}$ matrices. However, if we assume that $\mathscr{S}$ is a commutative ring, then our definition of determinant applies to $\mathscr{S}$ matrices, and det A is an element of $\mathscr{S}$. We may also use any of the theorems on determinants which do not depend on nonzero scalars having inverses. In particular, if $\mathscr{S}$ is commutative, we use the determinantal definition of rank for $\mathscr{S}$ matrices. It follows from Theorem 4.6A that the determinant of a product is the product of the determinants of the factors and that the rank of a product cannot exceed the rank of any of its factors.

The fact that elements of $\mathscr{S}$ need not have inverses is reflected in the fact that a square $\mathscr{S}$ matrix need not have an inverse, even if its rank is equal to its degree. Indeed, no $\mathscr{S}$ matrix can have an inverse unless the ring $\mathscr{S}$ has a unity element. An $\mathscr{S}$ matrix that has an inverse is said to be *unimodular*; an element of $\mathscr{S}$ that has an inverse is said to be *regular* or a *unit*.

LEMMA 9.1A. *Let $\mathscr{S}$ be a commutative ring with unity element. Then a square $\mathscr{S}$ matrix is unimodular if and only if its determinant is regular.*

Suppose first that $AB = BA = I$. Then $1 = \det I = \det AB = \det A \cdot \det B$. Hence, if A is unimodular then $\det A$ is regular in $\mathscr{S}$.

Next, suppose that $\det A = a$ is regular in $\mathscr{S}$, say $ab = 1$. Then let $B = b \operatorname{adj} A$. It follows from Theorem 4.7B that $AB = BA = I$; i.e., A is unimodular.

We denote by $\mathscr{M}_{vw}(\mathscr{S})$ the set of all v-by-w $\mathscr{S}$ matrices.

LEMMA 9.1B. *Let $\mathscr{S}$ be any ring with unity element. Then the set of unimodular matrices in $\mathscr{M}_{vv}(\mathscr{S})$ is a group under matrix multiplication, which we denote by $\mathscr{U}_v(\mathscr{S})$ and which we call the unimodular group of degree v.*

The closure postulate M1 follows from the equation $(AB)^{-1} = B^{-1}A^{-1}$; M2 holds in $\mathscr{M}_{vv}(\mathscr{S})$ and therefore also in $\mathscr{U}_v(\mathscr{S})$; M3 holds since I_v is its own inverse; and M4 holds by the definition of $\mathscr{U}_v(\mathscr{S})$.

Two $\mathscr{S}$ matrices A and B are said to be *equivalent*, written $A \overset{\mathrm{E}}{=} B$, if there exist unimodular matrices P and Q such that $PAQ = B$.

LEMMA 9.1C. *Let $\mathscr{S}$ be any ring with unity element. Then equivalence of $\mathscr{S}$ matrices is an equivalence relation.*

The proof is left as an exercise.

The determination of a full set of invariants for equivalence for an arbitrary ring $\mathscr{S}$ with unity element is an unsolved problem. We treat this problem in the two special cases: the ring $\mathscr{F}[x]$ where x is transcendental over a field $\mathscr{F}$, and the ring of integers.

Exercises 9.1

1. Prove Lemma 9.1C.
2. Prove that $\mathscr{M}_{23}(\mathscr{M}_{22}(\mathscr{F}))$ is isomorphic to $\mathscr{M}_{46}(\mathscr{F})$.
3. Let $\mathscr{S}$ be the ring of all complex numbers $a + bi$ where a, b are integers. Determine the regular elements of $\mathscr{S}$.

In the following exercises we consider matrices over the ring of integers:

4. Which of the following matrices are nonsingular? Which are unimodular?

$$A_1 = \left\| \begin{array}{cc} 2 & 3 \\ 1 & 2 \end{array} \right\|, \qquad A_2 = \left\| \begin{array}{ccc} 3 & 2 & 1 \\ 1 & 0 & 2 \\ 1 & 2 & 3 \end{array} \right\|, \qquad A_3 = \left\| \begin{array}{ccc} 2 & 1 & 1 \\ 3 & -2 & 1 \\ 5 & -1 & 2 \end{array} \right\|.$$

5. Let $B = \left\| \begin{array}{cc} a & 2 \\ 2 & a + 2 \end{array} \right\|$. For what values of a is B unimodular?

6. When is a triangular matrix unimodular?

9.2. Equivalence of matrices with polynomial elements. Let $\mathscr{F}$ be a field, let x be transcendental over $\mathscr{F}$, and let $A = \| a_{ij} \|$ be a v-by-w matrix over $\mathscr{F}[x]$. Consider the ideal $\mathscr{J}_s = \mathscr{J}_s(A)$ generated by the determinants of all of the s-rowed square submatrices of A. By Theorem 8.3C $\mathscr{J}_s$ is a principal ideal, say $\mathscr{J}_s = (d_s)$, where $d_s = d_s(x)$ is either zero or is the monic generator of $\mathscr{J}_s$. We call d_s the sth *determinantal divisor* of the matrix A, $(s = 1, \cdots, \min{(v, w)})$, and set $d_0 = 1$. Of course, $d_s = 0$ if $s > r = \operatorname{rank} A$. Let $C = \| c_{ij} \|$ be an s-rowed square submatrix of A. The expansion formula $\det C = \sum_{\nu=1}^{s} {}^{\cdot} (-1)^{1+\nu} c_{1\nu} \det C[1 \mid \nu]$ shows that $\mathscr{J}_s$ is contained in $\mathscr{J}_{s-1}$ and hence that $d_{s-1}(x)$ is a divisor of $d_s(x)$ $(s = 1, \cdots, r)$. The quotient $m_s(x) = d_s(x)/d_{s-1}(x)$ is called the sth *invariant factor* of A $(s = 1, \cdots, r)$. We define $m_s(x)$ to be 0 if $s > r$. To indicate the dependence on A we sometimes use the notations $d_s(A, x)$, $m_s(A, x)$. The primary factors of the invariant factors of A are called its *elementary divisors*.

LEMMA 9.2A. *The determinantal divisors and the invariant factors are invariants under equivalence.*

It follows from Theorem 4.6A that, if A, P, and Q are any matrices and if $B = PAQ$, then $\mathscr{J}_s(B)$ is contained in $\mathscr{J}_s(A)$. If P and Q are unimodular we have also $P^{-1}BQ^{-1} = A$, and so $\mathscr{J}_s(A)$ is contained in $\mathscr{J}_s(B)$. Hence, if A is equivalent to B, $\mathscr{J}_s(A) = \mathscr{J}_s(B)$ $(s = 1, 2, \cdots)$. This shows that equivalent matrices have the same set of determinantal divisors and, therefore, also the same set of invariant factors.

Our next task is to show that these invariants form a complete set for equivalence. This is accomplished by obtaining a canonical form. We make use of elementary transformations on rows and columns. Of course, we are restricted to those elementary transformations whose matrices are unimodular. These are R_{ih}, $R_i(c, h)$ where c is in $\mathscr{F}[x]$, and $R_i(c)$ where c is in $\mathscr{F}$ and the column analogs C_{ih}, $C_i(c, h)$, $C_i(c)$. Since the unimodular matrices form a group, any matrix B obtained from a given matrix A by a sequence of these row and column elementary transformations will be equivalent to A.

THEOREM 9.2B. *Let $\mathscr{F}$ be a field, let $\mathscr{F}[x]$ be a transcendental extension of $\mathscr{F}$, and let $A = \| a_{ij} \|$ be a matrix in $\mathscr{M}_{vw}(\mathscr{F}[x])$ whose rank is r. Then A is equivalent to the matrix*

$$(2.1) \quad B = \left\| \begin{matrix} B' & 0 \\ 0 & 0 \end{matrix} \right\| \quad \text{where} \quad B' = \left\| \begin{matrix} m_1 & & & & \\ & m_2 & & & \\ & & \cdot & & \\ & & & \cdot & \\ & & & & \cdot \\ & & & & & m_r \end{matrix} \right\|$$

is the diagonal matrix with $m_s = m_s(x)$ *the sth invariant factor of A. More-over,* m_s *is a factor of* m_{s+1} $(s = 1, \cdots, r - 1)$.

To avoid complex notation we shall designate each matrix by $\| a_{ij} \|$, even though the elements change under successive elementary transformations.   We first show that A is equivalent to a matrix of the form (2.1), where each m_s is monic and where m_s is a factor of m_{s+1} $(s = 1, \cdots, r - 1)$.

If all the elements are 0, we already have the form desired.   Otherwise there is a nonzero element, which may be taken as a_{11} after interchanging certain rows and also certain columns if necessary.   We shall try to get a_{11} to have the lowest possible degree; i.e., the degree of a_{11} cannot be decreased by applying further elementary transformations.

Suppose there is an element a_{i1} in the first column not divisible exactly by a_{11}.   (This will be the case, in particular, if a_{i1} has lower degree.)   By the division algorithm for polynomials, $a_{i1} = qa_{11} + r$ where $r \neq 0$ and has smaller degree than a_{11}.   The transformation $R_i(-q, 1)$ replaces a_{i1} by r, and then R_{i1} replaces a_{11} by the polynomial r of smaller degree.   Thus the degree of a_{11} can be lowered until all elements in the first column, and also in the first row, are divisible by a_{11}.   Of course one has to come to such a situation finally since the degree of a_{11} can be lowered only a finite number of times.

Now $a_{i1} = qa_{11}$, and the transformation $R_i(-q, 1)$, replaces a_{i1} by 0. In this way every element except a_{11} in the first column and next also every one in the first row are made equal to zero.

It may happen among the other elements there is one, a_{ij}, which is not divisible by a_{11}.   Then $R_i(1, i)$ replaces a_{1j}, which was 0, by a_{ij}.   Since this new a_{1j} is not divisible by a_{11}, further reduction of the degree of a_{11} is possible, according to the method described above.

Again after a finite number of steps we have the situation where a_{11} divides every a_{ij}, and all elements in either the first row or first column except a_{11} are 0.   Using an operation $R_1(c)$, we may suppose also that a_{11} is monic.

We now operate on the last $v - 1$ rows and last $w - 1$ columns with elementary transformations to obtain for a_{22} a monic element which divides all other elements in these rows and columns and having all elements in the second row or second column equal to 0 except a_{22}.   These transformations do not affect the values already obtained for the elements in the first row or first column because, except for a_{11}, they are all 0; moreover a_{11} divides a_{22}.

Repetition of this process yields a matrix B which has the form (2.1) with m_s a factor of m_{s+1} $(s = 1, \cdots, r - 1)$ and which is equivalent to A. All that remains to be proved is that the nonzero elements of B are the invariant factors of A.   But, since B is equivalent to A, it follows from

Lemma 9.2A that we need only show that the m_s are the invariant factors of B. To do this we compute the determinantal divisors of B. For each $s \leq r$ the only nonzero s-rowed minors of B have the form $m_{i_1} m_{i_2} \cdots m_{i_s}$ where $1 \leq i_1 < \cdots < i_s \leq r$. Clearly, $k \leq i_k$ $(k = 1, \cdots, s)$, and therefore m_k divides m_{i_k}. Hence $m_1 \cdots m_s$ divides $m_{i_1} \cdots m_{i_s}$, and $m_1 \cdots m_s$ is a common divisor of every s-rowed minor of B. Therefore, since each m_i is monic, we have $d_s = m_1 \cdots m_s$ as the sth determinantal divisor of B $(s = 1, \cdots, r)$ (and, of course, $d_s = 0$ when $s > r$). Then we have $d_s/d_{s-1} = m_s$. This shows that m_s is the sth invariant factor of B and hence also of A as claimed.

A matrix over $\mathscr{F}[x]$ is said to be in *Smith canonical form* if it has the form (2.1). The use of the term "canonical" is justified since each equivalence class contains exactly one member in this form. Moreover, a matrix B in this form has the advantage of being explicitly determined by the invariant factors of any matrix A to which it is equivalent. Thus, if we can compute the determinantal divisors d_s of a matrix A, we can write down the equivalent matrix B in Smith canonical form without going through any reduction process.

THEOREM 9.2C. *Any unimodular matrix in $\mathscr{M}_{vv}(\mathscr{F}[x])$ is a product of unimodular elementary matrices.*

Let A be unimodular. Then by Lemma 9.1A the vth determinantal divisor d_v of A is 1. Since $d_v = m_1 \cdots m_v$, we have $m_s = 1$ $(s = 1, \cdots, v)$, and hence the Smith canonical form of A is I_v. But in the proof of Theorem 9.2B we saw that there exist matrices P and Q, each a product of unimodular elementary matrices such that $PAQ = I_v$. Hence, $A = P^{-1}Q^{-1}$ is a product of unimodular elementary matrices.

The following three lemmas provide a means for computing determinantal divisors and invariant factors in certain important cases (cf. Theorem 10.4E).

LEMMA 9.2D. *Let* $g_{11}(x), \cdots, g_{1t_1}(x)$; $g_{21}(x), \cdots, g_{2t_2}(x)$; $\cdots$; $g_{r1}(x), \cdots, g_{rt_r}(x)$ *be polynomials, and let* $g_i(x)$ *be the greatest common divisor of* $g_{i1}(x), \cdots, g_{it_i}(x)$ $(i = 1, \cdots, r)$. *Then* $g(x) = g_1(x) \cdots g_r(x)$ *is the greatest common divisor of the set of the* $t_1 t_2 \cdots t_r$ *products* $g_{1j_1}(x) g_{2j_2}(x) \cdots g_{rj_r}(x)$.

Suppose that $g_i(x) = s_{i1}(x) g_{i1}(x) + \cdots + s_{it_i}(x) g_{it_i}(x)$ $(i = 1, \cdots, r)$. Then

$$g(x) = g_1(x) \cdots g_r(x) = \Sigma s_{1j_1}(x) s_{2j_2}(x) \cdots s_{rj_r} g_{1j_1}(x) g_{2j_2}(x) \cdots g_{rj_r}(x),$$

where the sum is over the $t_1 t_2 \cdots t_r$ choices for $j_1, j_2, \cdots, j_r$ with $1 \leq j_i \leq t_i$ $(i = 1, \cdots, r)$. Hence any common divisor of the given set of products is a divisor of $g(x)$. On the other hand, since $g_i(x)$ divides $g_{ij}(x)$, $g(x)$ divides each of the products. Finally $g(x)$ is monic since it is a product of monic polynomials. Hence $g(x)$ is the greatest common divisor.

LEMMA 9.2E.   Let $A = \begin{Vmatrix} A_1 & & 0 \\ & \cdot & \\ & & \cdot \\ 0 & & A_r \end{Vmatrix}$ where A_j is a square submatrix

of degree w_j $(j = 1, \cdots, r)$.   Then $d_i(A, x)$ is the greatest common divisor of all products of the form $d_{i_1}(A_1, x) \cdots d_{i_r}(A_r, x)$, where $i_1 + \cdots + i_r = i$ and $0 \leq i_j \leq w_j$ $(j = 1, \cdots, r)$.

Let B be any square submatrix of A.   Then B has the form

$$B = \begin{Vmatrix} B_1 & & & 0 \\ & B_2 & & \\ & & \cdot & \\ & & & \cdot \\ 0 & & & B_r \end{Vmatrix},$$

where B_j is a submatrix of A_j $(j = 1, \cdots, r)$.   Since B is square, either every B_j is square or there exists at least one B_j with more columns than rows.   In the latter case every square submatrix of B which has the same column indices as B_j must have at least one zero row, and hence det $B = 0$ (cf. Theorem 4.4B).   Hence, the only square submatrices B that need be considered in computing the determinantal divisors are those in which each B_j is square.   Let B_j have degree f_j.   Then det B is a product of the form $g_1(x) \cdots g_r(x)$ where $g_j(x) = \det B_j$.   It now follows from the preceding lemma that $d_{i_1}(A_1, x) \cdots d_{i_r}(A_r, x)$ is the greatest common divisor of all square i-rowed submatrices B having f_1 rows of A_1, f_2 rows of $A_2, \cdots, f_r$ rows of A_s.   The lemma is an immediate consequence.

We now restrict the matrices B_i to be of a certain type which occurs in the theory of similarity of matrices.   These matrices are square and have the property that all determinantal divisors equal 1 except possibly the last, which equals det B_i.

LEMMA 9.2F.

$$\text{Let } A = \begin{Vmatrix} A_1 & & \\ & \cdot & \\ & & \cdot \\ & & A_r \end{Vmatrix} \text{ be a square matrix of degree } v$$

where A_j is a square matrix of degree w_j of the type described in the preceding paragraph and such that $\det A_j$ *divides* $\det A_{j-1}$ $(j = 1, \cdots, r)$. *Then* $d_i(A, x) = 1$ $(i = 1, \cdots, v - r)$ *and* $d_{v-j+1}(A, x) = \det A_j \cdots \det A_r$ $(j = 1, \cdots, r)$. *Moreover, for the invariant factors of A we have* $m_i(A, x) = 1$ $(i = 1, \cdots, v - r)$ *and* $m_{v-j+1}(A, x) = \det A_j$ $(j = 1, \cdots, r)$.

This lemma is an immediate corollary to the preceding one. For consider any product $d_{i_1}(A_1, x) \cdots d_{i_r}(A_r, x)$. If $i_j < w_j$ the jth factor is 1, and if $i_j = w_j$ the jth factor is $\det A_j$. Now, if $i \leq v - r$, we can write $i = i_1 + \cdots + i_r$, where $0 \leq i_j \leq w_j - 1$ $(j = 1, \cdots, r)$, and hence $d_i(A, x) = 1$. On the other hand, if $i = v - j + 1$, where $1 \leq j \leq r$ and $i = i_1 + \cdots + i_r$, at least $r - j + 1$ of the summands $i_1, \cdots, i_r$ must satisfy the equality $i_j = w_j$. Then $d_i(A, x)$ must be divisible by some product $\det A_{h_1} \cdots \det A_{h_{r-j+1}}$ where $h_1 < h_2 < \cdots < h_{r-j+1}$, and hence must be divisible by the product $\det A_j \cdots \det A_r$. But, if $i_1 = w_1 - 1, \cdots$, $i_{j-1} = w_{j-1} - 1$, $i_j = w_j, \cdots, i_r = v_r$, then $\det B = \det A_j \cdots \det A_r$. Hence $d_i(A, x) = \det A_j \cdots \det A_r$ where $j = v - i + 1$.

The statement about the invariant factors now follows immediately from the definition $m_s(x) = d_s(x)/d_{s-1}(x)$.

Exercises 9.2

For the following matrices A: (a) Find the determinantal divisors. (b) Find the invariant factors. (c) Find a matrix B in Smith canonical form equivalent to A. (d) Find unimodular matrices P, Q such that $B = PAQ$.

1.
$$A = \left\| \begin{array}{ccc} x(x-1) & x-1 & x^2-1 \\ x(x-2) & 1 & x \end{array} \right\|.$$

2.
$$A = \left\| \begin{array}{ccc} x(x-1) & 0 & 0 \\ 0 & x^2(x^2-1) & 0 \\ 0 & 0 & x(x+1) \end{array} \right\|.$$

3.
$$A = \left\| \begin{array}{ccccc} x-2 & 1 & 0 & 0 & 0 \\ 0 & x-2 & 1 & 0 & 0 \\ 0 & 0 & x-2 & 0 & 0 \\ 0 & 0 & 0 & x-2 & 0 \\ 0 & 0 & 0 & 0 & x-2 \end{array} \right\|.$$

4.
$$A_1 = \left\| \begin{array}{cccc} x-2 & 1 & 0 & 0 \\ 0 & x-2 & 1 & 0 \\ 0 & 0 & x-2 & 1 \\ 0 & 0 & 0 & x-2 \end{array} \right\|.$$

5.
$$A_2 = \begin{Vmatrix} x & -1 & 0 & 0 \\ 0 & x & -1 & 0 \\ 0 & 0 & x & -1 \\ 16 & -32 & 24 & x-8 \end{Vmatrix}.$$

6.
$$A_3 = \begin{Vmatrix} x-a & 1 & 0 & 0 \\ 0 & x-a & 1 & 0 \\ 0 & 0 & x-a & 1 \\ 0 & 0 & 0 & x-a \end{Vmatrix}.$$

7.
$$A_4 = \begin{Vmatrix} x & -1 & 0 & 0 \\ 0 & x & -1 & 0 \\ 0 & 0 & x & -1 \\ a_4 & a_3 & a_2 & x+a_1 \end{Vmatrix}.$$

8. Show that the matrices in Exercises 4 through 7 are of the type described in the paragraph preceding Lemma 9.2F. Find the invariant factors of

$$\begin{Vmatrix} A_1 & & & \\ & A_2 & & \\ & & A_3 & \\ & & & A_4 \end{Vmatrix}, \text{ if } a = 3, a_1 = -10, a_2 = 37, a_3 = -60, a_4 = 36.$$

9.3. Matrices with integer elements.

We next consider equivalence of matrices over the ring $\mathfrak{J}$ of integers. The only units in $\mathfrak{J}$ are 1 and -1; hence a square matrix A in $\mathcal{M}_{vv}(\mathfrak{J})$ is unimodular if and only if det $A = \pm 1$. In particular, the only unimodular elementary matrices are F_{ij}, $F_i(\pm 1)$, and $F_i(c, h)$ where c is any integer.

LEMMA 9.3A. DIVISION ALGORITHM FOR INTEGERS. *Let a and b be integers, with $b > 0$. Then there exist unique integers q and r such that*

(3.1) $a = qb + r$ *where* $0 \leq r < b.$

Consider the set $\mathcal{S}$ of all nonnegative integers of the form $y = a - bx$ where x is in $\mathfrak{J}$. Clearly $\mathcal{S}$ is not empty since at least one of $a - b \cdot 0$ and $a - b(a)$ lies in $\mathcal{S}$. Hence (cf. Appendix I) $\mathcal{S}$ has a least member which we denote by r. Choose q so that $r = a - bq$. Now, suppose $r \geq b$. Then $0 \leq r - b = a - b(q+1) < r$; this contradicts the definition of r. Hence $0 \leq r < b$ as required. If also $a = q'b + r'$ where $1 \leq r' < b$, then $0 = a - a = (q' - q)b + (r' - r)$, and so $r' - r$ is divisible by b. Since r was the smallest number in $\mathcal{S}$, we have $0 \leq r' - r \leq r' < b$.

Since no positive integer less than b is divisible by b, this requires $r'-r=0$. Thus $r' = r$ and $q' = q$.

THEOREM 9.3B. *Every ideal in $\mathfrak{J}$ is principal.*

A proof can be based on the preceding lemma. We leave the details to the reader.

An ideal $(f(x))$ in $\mathscr{F}[x]$ can also be generated by any associate $cf(x)$ of $\mathscr{F}[x]$ where c is in $\mathscr{F}$. An ideal (a) in $\mathfrak{J}$ can also be generated by $-a$, and this is the only other generator. If b and c are integers not both zero, we denote by d the positive integer such that (d) is the smallest ideal that contains b and c and call d the *greatest common divisor* of b and c. The definitions given in the preceding section for determinantal divisors and invariant factors can now be applied to $\mathfrak{J}$ matrices. The proof given there for Lemma 9.2A carries over without change for equivalence of $\mathfrak{J}$ matrices.

Moreover, Theorem 9.2B holds for $\mathfrak{J}$ matrices if we replace the first sentence by *"Let $A = \| a_{ij} \|$ be a matrix in $\mathscr{M}_{vw}(\mathfrak{J})$ whose rank is r."* The proof requires certain minor modifications which we leave as an exercise for the reader. The definition of Smith canonical form goes over unchanged, and Theorem 9.2C holds when $\mathscr{F}[x]$ is replaced by $\mathfrak{J}$.

Exercises 9.3

1. Find the Smith canonical form for each of the following matrices:

(a)
$$A_1 = \left\| \begin{array}{ccc} 2 & 3 & 1 \\ -1 & 2 & 5 \end{array} \right\|,$$

(b)
$$A_2 = \left\| \begin{array}{cc} 2 & 4 \\ -6 & -10 \end{array} \right\|,$$

(c)
$$A_3 = \left\| \begin{array}{cccc} 3 & 6 & 0 & 2 \\ 1 & 4 & 3 & 1 \\ 0 & 2 & -3 & -1 \end{array} \right\|.$$

2. Write each of the following matrices as a product of elementary matrices:

(a)
$$A_4 = \left\| \begin{array}{cc} 2 & 1 \\ 1 & 0 \end{array} \right\|,$$

(b)
$$A_5 = \left\| \begin{array}{ccc} 3 & 1 & 0 \\ 1 & 2 & -1 \\ 3 & 3 & -1 \end{array} \right\|,$$

(c)
$$A_6 = \left\| \begin{array}{cc} 4 & 5 \\ 5 & 6 \end{array} \right\|.$$

3. Prove Lemma 9.3A by an induction on a.

4. Prove Theorem 9.3B.

5. Show that the Euclidean algorithm applies for integers as a consequence of the division algorithm.

6. Use the Euclidean algorithm to find the greatest common divisor of each of the following pairs of integers: (i) 72, 28; (ii) 108, 420; (iii) 2717, 6409.

9.4. Vector spaces over the integers.

Any set $\mathscr{V}$ which satisfies the vector space axioms (see Section 1.4) with the scalars restricted to $\mathfrak{J}$ rather than to a field $\mathscr{F}$ is called a *vector space over* $\mathfrak{J}$. The fact that the scalars now need not have inverses makes the theory more complicated, although parts of it are unchanged.

The set $\mathscr{V}_n(\mathfrak{J})$ of all integral n-tuples is a vector space over $\mathfrak{J}$, and it has many properties in common with ordinary vector spaces. In particular $\mathscr{V}_n(\mathfrak{J})$ satisfies the condition

(S6) $$c\alpha \neq 0 \quad \text{unless} \quad c = 0 \quad \text{or} \quad \alpha = 0.$$

A vector space over $\mathfrak{J}$ which satisfies S6 is said to be *free*. A vector space $\mathscr{V}$ over $\mathfrak{J}$ is said to be *finitely generated* if it is spanned by a finite set of vectors (called *generators*). In the present section we shall study finitely generated free vector spaces over $\mathfrak{J}$, and in the next section we shall classify all finitely generated vector spaces over $\mathfrak{J}$.

We recall (cf. Section 2.7) that a system $\mathscr{G}$ which satisfies axioms A1, A2, A3, A4, A5 is an abelian group. Thus, in particular, every vector space is an abelian group. We now observe that, conversely, every abelian group can be regarded as a vector space over $\mathfrak{J}$. To see this we assume that the operation is designated by $+$; then for each group element α and each integer c we define $c\alpha$ to be

$$\alpha + \cdots + \alpha \quad (c \text{ summands}) \qquad \text{if } c \text{ is positive,}$$

$$0 \qquad \qquad \text{if } c \text{ is } 0,$$

$$(-\alpha) + \cdots + (-\alpha) \quad (-c \text{ summands}) \quad \text{if } c \text{ is negative.}$$

Then axioms S2, S3, S4, S5 are readily verified. Thus the study of vector spaces over $\mathfrak{J}$ is the same as the study of abelian groups.

Let $\mathscr{V}$ be a free vector space over $\mathfrak{J}$. We carry over the usual definitions of dependence, independence, and related concepts (see Section 1.5). Lemmas 1.5A and 1.5B are valid in $\mathscr{V}$ since their proofs do not require division by scalars. The proof of Lemma 1.5C involved division, and so we should not expect it to hold; indeed, this lemma is false for $\mathscr{V}$. To see this we observe that α is not dependent on the set $\mathscr{S} = \{\beta\}$ where $\beta = 2\alpha$; but the set $\{\alpha, \beta\}$ is dependent since $\beta - 2\alpha = 0$.

Theorem 1.5D is true for $\mathscr{V}$ but the proof needs modification. We retain the first two paragraphs of the old proof and continue as follows. If not every one of $c_{1t}, \cdots, c_{st}$ is zero, then they generate an ideal in $\mathfrak{J}$. Since every ideal in $\mathfrak{J}$ is principal, this ideal has a generator d (the greatest common divisor of $c_{1t}, \cdots, c_{st}$) which can be written as

$$d = b_1 c_{1t} + \cdots + b_s c_{st}.$$

We can number the α_j so that $b_s \neq 0$. Now let

(4.1) $$\alpha = b_1 \alpha_1 + \cdots + b_s \alpha_s;$$

then the coefficient of β_t in α is d. Next, set

(4.2) $$\gamma_i = \alpha_i - \frac{c_{it}}{d}\alpha \qquad (i = 1, \cdots, s-1),$$

and let $\mathscr{S}'' = \{\gamma_1, \cdots, \gamma_{s-1}\}$. Note that $\mathscr{S}''$ is dependent on $\mathscr{T}'$ since the coefficient of β_t in γ_i is $c_{it} - \frac{c_{it}}{d}d = 0$. Next, we see that $\mathscr{S}''$ is independent. For suppose that

(4.3) $$d_1 \gamma_1 + \cdots + d_{s-1} \gamma_{s-1} = 0.$$

Then, letting $c = -\frac{1}{d}\sum_{\lambda=1}^{s-1} c_{\lambda t}$, and substituting (4.2) in (4.3), we get

$$d_1 \alpha_1 + \cdots + d_{s-1} \alpha_{s-1} + c\alpha = 0.$$

Next, substituting for α from (4.1), we have

(4.4) $$(d_1 + cb_1)\alpha_1 + \cdots + (d_{s-1} + cb_{s-1})\alpha_{s-1} + cb_s \alpha_s = 0.$$

Now, since $\mathscr{S}$ is independent, we have $cb_s = 0$, and, since $b_s \neq 0$, we must have $c = 0$. It follows that $d_1 = \cdots = d_{s-1} = 0$, and hence that $\mathscr{S}''$ is independent. The remainder of the original proof can now be applied in the present case.

We can next define dimension and basis as in Section 1.6, but Theorem 1.6A is no longer true. Consider the space $\mathscr{V}$ consisting of all rational numbers. It is free and has dimension one, but has no basis at all. On the other hand $\mathscr{V}_1(\mathfrak{J})$ has $\{1\}$ as a basis. Equality of dimension is thus seen to be a necessary but not a sufficient condition for isomorphism of $\mathfrak{J}$ spaces. Moreover, it follows from Theorem 1.5D that, if $\{\alpha_1, \cdots, \alpha_r\}$ is a basis for a free $\mathfrak{J}$ space $\mathscr{V}$, then dim $\mathscr{V} = r$.

In the next section we shall show that every finitely generated free space has a basis; we now establish this for subspaces of $\mathscr{V}_n(\mathfrak{J})$.

THEOREM 9.4A.   *Let $\mathscr{W}$ be a subspace of $\mathscr{V}_n(\mathfrak{J})$. Then $\mathscr{W}$ has a basis.*
Consider the subset $\mathscr{S}_1$ of $\mathfrak{J}$ made up of all first components e_1 for vectors $(e_1, \cdots, e_n)$ in $\mathscr{W}$.   This set $\mathscr{S}_1$ is an ideal because $\mathscr{W}$ is closed under subtraction and multiplication by scalars.   This ideal, being principal, has a generator m_1 which is the first component of some vector $\alpha_1 = (m_1, \cdots)$.

Similarly in the set $\mathscr{W}_i$ of all vectors in $\mathscr{W}$ of the form $(0, \cdots, 0, e_i, e_{i+1}, \cdots, e_n)$ there is one $\alpha_i = (0, \cdots, 0, m_i, \cdots)$ such that the ith component e_i of every vector in $\mathscr{W}_i$ is a multiple of m_i.

In this way we obtain n vectors $\alpha_1, \cdots, \alpha_n$, some of which may be 0. We next show that $\mathscr{W} = \langle \alpha_1, \cdots, \alpha_n \rangle$.   We start first with those vectors in $\mathscr{W}_n$; they have the form $\alpha = (0, \cdots, 0, e_n)$.   Since e_n is a multiple of m_n, α is the same multiple of α_n.   This is the start of an induction on the decreasing set $n, \cdots, 2, 1$.   We assume then as induction hypothesis that all vectors in $\mathscr{W}_i$ are dependent on $\{\alpha_i, \alpha_{i+1}, \cdots, \alpha_n\}$ and will show that $\mathscr{W}_{i-1}$ is dependent on $\{\alpha_{i-1}, \cdots, \alpha_n\}$.   Let $\alpha = (0, \cdots, 0, e_{i-1}, \cdots, e_n)$ be in $\mathscr{W}_{i-1}$.   Since e_{i-1} is a multiple of m_{i-1}, $e_{i-1} = cm_{i-1}$ for some integer c.   Then $c\alpha_{i-1} = (0, \cdots, 0, cm_{i-1}, \cdots) = (0, \cdots, 0, e_{i-1}, \cdots)$.   Hence $\alpha - c\alpha_{i-1}$ is in $\mathscr{W}_i$, and therefore by the induction hypothesis has the form $c_i\alpha_i + \cdots + c_n\alpha_n$.   Thus $\alpha = c\alpha_{i-1} + c_i\alpha_i + \cdots + c_n\alpha_n$; this completes the induction.

The set $\mathscr{S} = \{\alpha_1, \cdots, \alpha_n\}$ is triangular; hence the nonzero vectors in $\mathscr{S}$ will be an independent set which is a basis for $\mathscr{W}$.

Exercises 9.4

1. Find a basis for the subspace of $\mathscr{V}_4(\mathfrak{J})$ spanned by $\| \ 3 \quad 1 \quad 2 \quad 4 \ \|$, $\| \ 6 \quad 2 \quad 3 \quad 6 \ \|$, $\| \ 2 \quad 4 \quad -3 \quad 8 \ \|$, $\| \ 2 \quad 1 \quad 2 \quad 10 \ \|$, $\| \ 3 \quad 2 \quad -4 \quad -4 \ \|$.

2. Find a basis for the subspace of $\mathscr{V}_3(\mathfrak{J})$ spanned by the rows of the matrix

$$A = \begin{Vmatrix} 2 & 6 & 3 \\ -4 & 12 & 9 \\ 4 & 9 & 12 \\ 2 & -6 & -6 \end{Vmatrix}.$$

9.5. Finitely generated vector spaces over the integers.

An $\mathfrak{J}$ space $\mathscr{W}$ is said to be *cyclic* if it has a single generator.   If $\mathscr{W}$ is cyclic and free, then it is isomorphic to $\mathscr{V}_1(\mathfrak{J})$.   If $\mathscr{W}$ is cyclic, say $\mathscr{W} = \langle \alpha \rangle$, and is not free, then some multiple of α is zero.   Let m be the smallest integer for which $m\alpha = 0$.   We then say that $\mathscr{W}$ is cyclic of *order* m; in this case $\mathscr{W}$ consists of the m distinct vectors, $0, \alpha, \cdots, (m-1)\alpha$ and is isomorphic to the set of integers modulo m.   Such a space exists for each integer m. A vector α is said to have (*finite*) *order* m if $\langle \alpha \rangle$ has order m.

Our definition of direct sum of subspaces (Section 8.7) can be applied without change to $\mathfrak{I}$ spaces. We now state a main theorem; its proof is broken down into a series of lemmas some of which have independent interest.

THEOREM 9.5A. (FUNDAMENTAL THEOREM ON $\mathfrak{I}$ SPACES.) *Let $\mathscr{V}$ be a finitely generated $\mathfrak{I}$ space. Then $\mathscr{V}$ is a direct sum*

$$\mathscr{V} = \mathscr{W}_1 + \cdots + \mathscr{W}_{r+s}$$

of cyclic subspaces with the following properties: (i) *The first s ($s \geq 0$) are finite, and the last r ($r \geq 0$) are free.* (ii) *Let m_i be the order of $\mathscr{W}_i$ ($i = 1, \cdots, s$). Then $m_1 > 1$, and m_i is a divisor of m_{i+1} ($i = 1, \cdots, s-1$). Moreover, the integers $m_1, \cdots, m_s$, and r are uniquely determined by $\mathscr{V}$.*

In more detail, the uniqueness stated in the theorem means that any second decomposition $\mathscr{V} = \mathscr{W}'_1 + \cdots + \mathscr{W}'_{k'}$ satisfying conditions (i) and (ii) will have $s' = s$, $r' = r$, and $m'_i = m_i$ ($i = 1, \cdots, s$).

LEMMA 9.5B. *Every finitely generated $\mathfrak{I}$ space $\mathscr{V}$ has a decomposition with the properties described in the fundamental theorem.*

Let $\mathscr{S} = \{\beta_1, \cdots, \beta_k\}$ be a set of generators for $\mathscr{V}$. An element $\alpha = e_1\beta_1 + \cdots + e_k\beta_k$ of $\mathscr{V}$ is determined by the row matrix

(5.1) $$\| e_1 \cdots e_k \|.$$

Different matrices may give the same α. For example, if $n_1\beta_1 = 0$, then

$$\| n_1\, 0 \cdots 0 \| \quad \text{and} \quad \| 0\ 0\ \cdots\ 0 \|$$

both determine the zero vector.

Consider all expressions of 0:

(5.2) $$b_1\beta_1 + \cdots + b_k\beta_k = 0.$$

The corresponding matrices $\| b_1 \cdots b_k \|$ form a subspace $\mathscr{W}$ of $\mathscr{V}_k^r(\mathfrak{I})$. For, if $b_1\beta_1 + \cdots + b_k\beta_k = b'_1\beta_1 + \cdots + b'_k\beta_k = 0$, then the sum $0 = 0 + 0 = (b_1\beta_1 + \cdots + b_k\beta_k) + (b'_1\beta_1 + \cdots + b'_k\beta_k) = (b_1 + b'_1)\beta_1 + \cdots + (b_k + b'_k)\beta_k = 0$. Also

$$0 = c0 = c(b_1\beta_1 + \cdots + b_k\beta_k) = (cb_1)\beta_1 + \cdots + (cb_k)\beta_k.$$

According to Theorem 9.4A the subspace $\mathscr{W}$ has a finite basis $\{B_1, \cdots, B_v\}$. If we form a matrix B with these vectors as rows, then $\mathscr{R}(B) = \mathscr{W}$, and by Theorem 9.2B as modified for integer scalars there exist unimodular matrices P, Q such that $C = PBQ$ is in Smith canonical form. To interpret C we consider the effect of P and Q.

First, since P has an inverse, PB has the same row space as B (cf. Theorem 3.7G); thus $\mathscr{R}(PB) = \mathscr{R}(B) = \mathscr{W}$.

Next, the role of Q is simply to supply a different set of generators $\{\gamma_1, \cdots, \gamma_k\}$ for $\mathscr{V}$ in place of $\{\beta_1, \cdots, \beta_k\}$, where

$$\gamma_i = \Sigma q'_{i\lambda}\beta_\lambda$$

and $\| q'_{ij} \|$ is the inverse of Q (cf. Section 5.4).

Hence, $C = PBQ$ is the matrix whose row space is the set of all row matrices $\| c_1 \cdots c_k \|$ for which $c_1\gamma_1 + \cdots + c_k\gamma_k = 0$.

We now use the fact that C is in Smith canonical form. The nonzero rows of C have the form

(5.3) $$\| 0 \cdots 0 \; c_i \; 0 \cdots 0 \| \qquad\qquad (i = 1, \cdots, t)$$

where t is the rank of C. Hence in the space $\mathscr{V}$

(5.4) $$c_i\gamma_i = 0 \qquad\qquad (i = 1, \cdots, t).$$

The form of the matrix C makes it easy to tell when two vectors in $\mathscr{V}$ are equal. For suppose that

$$a_1\gamma_1 + \cdots + a_k\gamma_k = a'_1\gamma_1 + \cdots + a'_k\gamma_k.$$

Then

$$(a_1 - a'_1)\gamma_1 + \cdots + (a_k - a'_k)\gamma_k = 0;$$

hence the row matrix

$$\| (a_1 - a'_1) \cdots (a_k - a'_k) \|$$

is in $\mathscr{R}(C)$. But this will be true if and only if

(5.5) $$\begin{aligned} a_i - a'_i \text{ is divisible by } c_i \qquad & (i = 1, \cdots, t) \\ a_i - a'_i = 0 \qquad & (i = t + 1, \cdots, k). \end{aligned}$$

In other words, a_i and a'_i must have the same remainder on division by c_i $(i = 1, \cdots, t)$, and a_i must equal a'_i $(i = t + 1, \cdots, k)$. It follows that we will obtain each vector α in $\mathscr{V}$ exactly once if for $i = 1, \cdots, t$ we let $f_i = 0, 1, \cdots, c_i - 1$, and for $i = t + 1, \cdots, k$ we let f_i range through all integers.

One of the properties of the Smith canonical form is that c_i is a divisor of c_{i+1} $(i = 1, \cdots, t - 1)$. It may happen that some of the $c_i = 1$, say $c_1 = \cdots = c_q = 1$, $c_{q+1} > 1$. Then, since $1\alpha = \alpha$ for all α in $\mathscr{V}$, the equation $c_i\gamma_i = 0$ requires $\gamma_i = 0$ $(i = 1, \cdots, q)$, and hence $\mathscr{V}$ is generated by $\{\gamma_{q+1}, \cdots, \gamma_t, \cdots, \gamma_k\}$. With this in view we now set $r = k - t$, $s = t - q$, and then set $m_i = c_{q+i}$ $(i = 1, \cdots, s)$, and $\alpha_i = \gamma_{q+i}$ $(i = 1, \cdots, r + s)$. Then we have

(5.6) $$\mathscr{V} = \mathscr{W}_1 + \cdots + \mathscr{W}_{r+s} \quad \text{(direct)},$$

where $\mathscr{W}_i = \langle \alpha_i \rangle$. This sum is direct by virtue of (5.5), and satisfies conditions (i) and (ii) of the fundamental theorem. This completes the proof of Lemma 9.5B.

LEMMA 9.5C.   *The integers r and m_s in the fundamental theorem are invariants of $\mathscr{V}$.*

We observe that $m_s\mathscr{V}$ is a free space of dimension r, since $m_s\mathscr{W}_i = 0$ $(i = 1, \cdots, s)$. Moreover, if m is any integer for which $m\mathscr{V}$ is a free space, then $m\mathscr{W}_i = 0$ $(i = 1, \cdots, s)$, and hence m is divisible by m_s. Thus m_s *is the smallest positive integer m for which $m\mathscr{V}$ is free.* This shows that m_s is an invariant for $\mathscr{V}$ (i.e., must be the same in all decompositions of $\mathscr{V}$).

Next we observe that $m_s\mathscr{V}$ has the basis $\{m_s\alpha_{s+1}, \cdots, m_s\alpha_{s+r}\}$ and hence has dimension r. This shows that r is an invariant of $\mathscr{V}$. In fact, r is also the dimension of $\mathscr{V}$, since a vector of finite order is always dependent.

LEMMA 9.5D.   *The integers $m_1, \cdots, m_s$ are invariants of $\mathscr{V}$.*

A vector α in $\mathscr{V}$ has finite order if and only if it lies in the subspace $\mathscr{W} = \mathscr{W}_1 + \cdots + \mathscr{W}_s$. This shows that $\mathscr{W}$ is uniquely defined as the subspace consisting of all elements of finite order in $\mathscr{V}$. It follows that for each positive integer h the order $n(h)$ of the subspace $h\mathscr{W}$ is an invariant of $\mathscr{V}$. We will establish the lemma by showing that each of the integers m_i $(i = s - 1, \cdots, 1)$ can be expressed in terms of m_s and certain of the $n(h)$.

It follows from (5.6) that for each h the subspace $h\mathscr{W}$ is the direct sum of $h\mathscr{W}_1, \cdots, h\mathscr{W}_s$. Moreover, if h is a divisor of m_i, it follows from (5.5) that $h\mathscr{W}_i$ has order m_i/h, and, if h is a multiple of m_i, then $h\mathscr{W}_i$ has order 1 (i.e., $h\mathscr{W}_i$ is the zero vector alone). In particular, for $h = m_i$ we have

$$(5.7) \qquad n(m_i) = \frac{m_{i+1}}{m_i} \cdots \frac{m_s}{m_i} = (m_{i+1} \cdots m_s)/m_i^{s-i}$$
$$(i = s - 1, \cdots, 1).$$

For $i = s - 1$, this gives $m_{s-1} = m_s/n(m_{s-1})$; proceeding inductively (for decreasing i), we have

$$(5.8) \qquad m_i^{s-i} = m_{i+1} \cdots m_s/n(m_i),$$

which determines m_i in terms of $n(m_i)$ and the m_j with $j > i$. The lemma follows from (5.8).

Theorem 9.5A now follows from Lemmas 9.5B, C, and D.

COROLLARY 9.5E.   *Every finitely generated free space over $\mathfrak{J}$ is the direct sum of a space of finite order and a free space; the summand of finite order is unique.*

We have $\mathscr{V} = \mathscr{W} + \mathscr{U}$ where $\mathscr{W} = \mathscr{W}_1 + \cdots + \mathscr{W}_s$ and $\mathscr{U} = \mathscr{W}_{s+1} + \cdots + \mathscr{W}_{s+r}$. The uniqueness of $\mathscr{W}$ was established in the process of proving Lemma 9.5D.

COROLLARY 9.5F. *Every finitely generated free space over $\mathfrak{J}$ has a basis.*
We established this for subspaces of $\mathscr{V}_n(\mathfrak{J})$ in Section 9.4. The general
case follows from Theorem 9.5A since a space $\mathscr{V}$ is free if and only if $s = 0$;
and then the vectors $\alpha_1, \cdots, \alpha_r$ form a basis for $\mathscr{V}$.

Exercises 9.5

1. Show that in any $\mathfrak{J}$ space the elements of finite order form a subspace.
This is called the *torsion space* of $\mathscr{V}$.

2. Give an example of an infinite $\mathfrak{J}$ space which is its own torsion space.

3. Let $\mathscr{V}$ be the $\mathfrak{J}$ space consisting of the real numbers reduced modulo 1
(the elements of $\mathscr{V}$ can be represented as real numbers in the interval
$0 \leq x < 1$, and the sum of α and β is that member of the pair $\{\alpha+\beta, \alpha+\beta-1\}$
which lies in the given interval). Find the torsion subspace of $\mathscr{V}$.

4. An $\mathfrak{J}$ space $\mathscr{V}$ is generated by $\alpha_1, \alpha_2, \alpha_3, \alpha_4$. All expressions of 0 are
generated by $2\alpha_1 - \alpha_3 + 2\alpha_4 = 0, \alpha_1 + \alpha_4 = 0, 3\alpha_1 + \alpha_3 + 3\alpha_4 = 0$. Express
$\mathscr{V}$ as a direct sum of cyclic subspaces.

5. The set of remainders on division by 24 is an $\mathfrak{J}$ space. Express it as a
sum of cyclic subspaces.

9.6. Systems of linear differential equations with constant coefficients.
As an application of the Smith canonical form we discuss differential
equations with constant coefficients. A linear homogeneous differential
equation with constant coefficients may be written in the form

$$(6.1) \qquad y^{(s)} + c_{s-1}y^{(s-1)} + \cdots + c_2y'' + c_1y' + c_0y = 0.$$

Here we assume that the scalar field $\mathscr{F}$ is either $\mathfrak{R}$ or $\mathfrak{C}$, and the dependent
variable $y = y(x)$ is to be a function on $\mathscr{F}$ to $\mathscr{F}$. Let t be transcendental
over $\mathscr{F}$. We call

$$(6.2) \qquad f(t) = t^s + c_{s-1}t^{s-1} + \cdots + c_1t + c_0$$

the *characteristic polynomial* of the differential equation (6.1). We assume
that the reader is familiar with the connection between the complete
factorization of $f(t)$ in $\mathscr{F}[t]$ and the solutions of (6.1).

Let D denote the differential operator d/dx. Then $\mathsf{D}\colon y \to \mathsf{D}y = y'$ is a
linear transformation on the vector space $\mathscr{V}$ of all infinitely-often-
differentiable functions y of $\mathscr{F}$ into $\mathscr{F}$. In particular all polynomials
with coefficients in $\mathscr{F}$ belong to $\mathscr{V}$. The set of all scalar mappings
$\mathsf{T}_c\colon y \to cy$ with c in $\mathscr{F}$ is isomorphic with $\mathscr{F}$, and we identify T_c with c.

Now D is transcendental over $\mathscr{F}$. For, if $f(\mathsf{D}) = a_n\mathsf{D}^n + a_{n-1}\mathsf{D}^{n-1}$
$+ \cdots + a_0$, with $a_n \neq 0$, then $f(\mathsf{D})x^n \neq 0$.

Note that $\mathsf{D}^ny = y^{(n)}$, the nth derivative.

We may now write the equation (6.1) in the more compact form

$$(6.3) \qquad f(\mathsf{D})y = 0.$$

Similarly, a system of m linear homogeneous differentiable equations in n dependent variables $y_1, \cdots, y_n$ and the independent variable x has the form

$$a_{11}(\mathsf{D})y_1 + \cdots + a_{1n}(\mathsf{D})y_n = 0,$$
$$(6.4) \qquad \cdots$$
$$a_{m1}(\mathsf{D})y_1 + \cdots + a_{mn}(\mathsf{D})y_n = 0,$$

where the $a_{ij}(\mathsf{D})$ are polynomials in D.

We can write (6.4) in matrix form if we again generalize our concept of matrix. One can consider matrices whose entries are elements of very general type, provided only that sums $a_{ij} + b_{ij}$, and sums of products $\Sigma a_{i\lambda} b_{\lambda j}$ are defined when they arise. For example, we can consider a partitioned matrix as being a matrix whose elements are smaller matrices. Then $A + B$ is defined if and only if corresponding submatrices have the same degrees. In our present case $a_{ij}(\mathsf{D})y_j$ is a function of the same class as y_j, and so we can write (6.4) in the form

$$(6.5) \qquad AY = 0$$

where $A = \| a_{ij}(\mathsf{D}) \|$ and $Y = \| y_i \|$ is a column vector whose elements are functions on $\mathscr{F}$ to $\mathscr{F}$.

According to our definition in Section 9.1 a matrix $M = \| m_{ij}(\mathsf{D}) \|$ is said to be unimodular if it has an inverse; in this case $\det M$ is a nonzero element in the field $\mathscr{F}$.

If $P = \| p_{ij}(\mathsf{D}) \|$ is a unimodular matrix of degree m, then $A' = PA$ is the matrix of a system that is equivalent to (6.5) (i.e., one having the same solutions).

If $Q = \| q_{ij}(\mathsf{D}) \|$ is a unimodular matrix of degree n, then $Z = QY = \| z_i \|$ is a column vector whose elements are new dependent variables. If we can determine Z, then the equation $Y = Q^{-1}Z$ will determine Y. Under this change of variable (6.1) becomes $AQ^{-1}Z = 0$.

If we first pass to an equivalent system $A' = PA$ and then change variables by $Y = Q^{-1}Z$, we get a new system

$$(6.6) \qquad BZ = 0, \qquad \text{where} \qquad B = PAQ^{-1}.$$

The mapping $Y = Q^{-1}Z$ sets up an isomorphism between the space of solutions of (6.6) and the space of solutions of (6.5).

Now choose P and Q^{-1} so that B is in Smith canonical form

$$(6.7) \qquad B = \left\|\begin{matrix} B_1 & 0 \\ 0 & 0 \end{matrix}\right\| \qquad \text{where} \qquad B_1 = \left\|\begin{matrix} m_1(\mathsf{D}) & & & \\ & \cdot & & \\ & & \cdot & \\ & & & \cdot \\ & & & m_r(\mathsf{D}) \end{matrix}\right\|$$

This has the effect of separating the dependent variables; i.e., (6.5) reduces to the r equations

$$(6.8) \qquad\qquad m_i(\mathsf{D})z_i = 0 \qquad\qquad (i = 1, \cdots, r)$$

each of type (6.1). The $n - r$ variables $z_{r+1}, \cdots, z_n$ are unrestricted. Since the set of all functions on $\mathscr{F}$ to $\mathscr{F}$ has infinite dimension over $\mathscr{F}$, the space of all solutions has infinite dimension if $n > r$.

If, however, $r = n$, the dimension of the space of solutions is the sum of the degrees of $m_1(\mathsf{D}), \cdots, m_r(\mathsf{D})$; i.e., is the degree of the rth determinantal divisor $d_r(\mathsf{D})$ of A. Note that, if A is unimodular, i.e., if $d_r(\mathsf{D}) = 1$, then this dimension is zero, in which case the system (6.5) has only the trivial solution $Y = 0$.

Next consider the nonhomogeneous system

$$(6.9) \qquad\qquad AY = K,$$

where $K = \| k_i(x) \|$ is a column matrix whose elements are given functions in $\mathscr{F}$. We do not insist that each $k_i(x)$ shall have all of $\mathscr{F}$ as its domain, but we do ordinarily require that they all be defined on some common interval. By change of variable and premultiplication by a unimodular matrix we change to the new system

$$(6.10) \qquad\qquad BZ = L \qquad \text{where} \qquad L = PK,$$

and where B is in Smith canonical form.

We see that there is no solution at all unless $l_i(x)$ is the zero function for $i > r$. This can be stated in the following form. The nonhomogeneous system (6.9) will have a solution only if *the rank of the augmented matrix* $\| A \ K \|$ *is equal to the rank of the matrix A of coefficients.*

If this necessary condition is satisfied, then the system reduces to the r separate equations

$$(6.11) \qquad\qquad m_i(\mathsf{D})z_i = l_i(x) \qquad\qquad (i = 1, \cdots, r)$$

which can be treated by elementary methods.

Exercise 9.6

1. Solve the system of equations, using the method described in this section:
$$(\mathsf{D}^2 - 1)y_1 + (\mathsf{D}^2 - 3\mathsf{D} + 2)y_2 + (2\mathsf{D} - 2)y_3 = 0,$$
$$(\mathsf{D}^2 - 1)y_1 + (-\mathsf{D}^3 + \mathsf{D}^2 + \mathsf{D} - 1)y_2 + (\mathsf{D}^3 - \mathsf{D})y_3 = 0,$$
$$(\mathsf{D}^2 - 1)y_1 + (-\mathsf{D}^3 + \mathsf{D}^2 - 4\mathsf{D} + 2)y_2 + (\mathsf{D}^3 + \mathsf{D} - 2)y_3 = 0.$$

Chapter 10

Similarity
of Matrices

Similarity of matrices was defined in Section 5.5, and part of the theory was presented there. In particular, a canonical form was obtained for matrices with distinct eigenvalues. In this chapter two canonical forms for the general case will be found, one of which reduces to the form derived earlier for that special case. These results permit a simple treatment of the topic of the equivalence of pairs of matrices.

10.1. Minimum function. Let $\mathcal{V}$ be a vector space of dimension v over a field $\mathcal{F}$, and let T be a linear transformation on $\mathcal{V}$. We have seen (cf. Section 2.7) that the set of all linear transformations on $\mathcal{V}$ is an algebra of dimension v^2 over $\mathcal{F}$. The mapping $c \to c|_{\mathcal{V}}$ is an isomorphism of $\mathcal{F}$ into this algebra, and we identify $\mathcal{F}$ with its image under this isomorphism. We next consider the subalgebra $\mathcal{F}[\mathsf{T}]$ obtained by adjoining T to $\mathcal{F}$; we call $\mathcal{F}[\mathsf{T}]$ the *algebra generated by the linear transformation* T. Since $\mathcal{F}[\mathsf{T}]$ is contained in an algebra of dimension v^2 over $\mathcal{F}$, T must be algebraic over $\mathcal{F}$. Let $m(x) = m_0 + m_1 x + \cdots + m_{r-1}x^{r-1} + x^r$ be the minimum function of T. Clearly, $r \leq v^2$.

Let α be any vector in $\mathcal{V}$. We say that a polynomial $g(x)$ is a T *annihilator* of α if $\alpha g(\mathsf{T}) = 0$. In particular, $m(x)$ is a T annihilator since $m(\mathsf{T}) = 0$; i.e., $m(\mathsf{T})$ annihilates every vector.

LEMMA 10.1A. *The set of all* T *annihilators of* α *is an ideal in* $\mathcal{F}[x]$.

Suppose that $g(x)$, $g_1(x)$, $g_2(x)$ are T annihilators of α and that $h(x)$ is any polynomial. Then the equations

$$\alpha[g_1(\mathsf{T}) + g_2(\mathsf{T})] = \alpha\, g_1(\mathsf{T}) + \alpha\, g_2(\mathsf{T})$$
$$= 0 + 0$$
$$= 0,$$
$$\alpha[g(\mathsf{T})\, h(\mathsf{T})] = [\alpha\, g(\mathsf{T})]\, h(\mathsf{T})$$
$$= 0\, h(\mathsf{T})$$
$$= 0$$

show that the set of T annihilators is an ideal in $\mathcal{F}[x]$.

This ideal has a unique monic generator $m(\alpha; x)$ (Theorem 8.3C) which can be described as the monic polynomial of smallest degree that annihilates α. This polynomial is called the *minimum function of* T *relative to* α.

A major goal of this section is a proof of the statement that, if $m(x)$ is the minimum function of T, then there is a vector α for which $m(\alpha; x) = m(x)$.

LEMMA 10.1B.   *For every* α *in* $\mathscr{V}$ *the relative minimum function* $m(\alpha; x)$ *of* T *is a divisor of the minimum function* $m(x)$ *of* T. *Moreover,* $m(x)$ *is the least common multiple of the set of all relative minimum functions* $m(\alpha; x)$ *of* T.

For any α we have $\alpha\, m(\mathsf{T}) = \alpha 0 = 0$; thus, $m(x)$ is a T annihilator of α, and hence $m(x)$ is a multiple of $m(\alpha; x)$. Suppose, next, that $g(x)$ is a multiple of $m(\alpha; x)$ for every α in $\mathscr{V}$. It follows that $\alpha\, g(\mathsf{T}) = 0$ for all α in $\mathscr{V}$, and hence that $g(\mathsf{T}) = 0$. But then by definition of the minimum function of T we must have $g(x)$ a multiple of $m(x)$. Hence $m(x)$ is the least common multiple of the set of all $m(\alpha; x)$.

This characterization of $m(x)$ requires consideration of an infinite number of polynomials $m(\alpha; x)$. The following lemma gives a finite characterization.

LEMMA 10.1C.   *Let* $\{\alpha_1, \cdots, \alpha_s\}$ *be a spanning set for* $\mathscr{V}$. *Then the minimum function* $m(x)$ *for* T *is the least common multiple of the relative minimum functions* $m(\alpha_1; x), \cdots, m(\alpha_s; x)$.

Suppose that $g(x)$ is the least common multiple of $m(\alpha_1; x), \cdots, m(\alpha_s; x)$; thus, in particular, $\alpha_i g(\mathsf{T}) = 0$ $(i = 1, \cdots, s)$. Now for any α in $\mathscr{V}$ we have scalars $c_1, \cdots, c_s$ such that $\alpha = c_1\alpha_1 + \cdots + c_s\alpha_s$. Hence,

$$\alpha\, g(\mathsf{T}) = c_1(\alpha_1 g(\mathsf{T})) + \cdots + c_s(\alpha_s g(\mathsf{T})) = 0 + \cdots + 0 = 0.$$

Therefore $g(\mathsf{T}) = 0$, and so $g(x)$ is a multiple of $m(x)$. But $m(x)$ is a multiple of $m(\alpha_1; x), \cdots, m(\alpha_s; x)$, and hence is a multiple of their least common multiple $g(x)$. Since $g(x)$ and $m(x)$ are multiples of each other and are monic, they are equal.

COROLLARY 10.1D.   *Let* $q(x)$ *be a primary factor of the minimum function* $m(x)$ *of* T. *Then there is a vector* α *whose minimum function* $m(\alpha; x)$ *has* $q(x)$ *as a primary factor.*

For $q(x)$ is a power $p(x)^e$ of a prime polynomial $p(x)$. Let $\alpha_1, \cdots, \alpha_s$ be as in the lemma above, and let $p(x)^{e_i}$ be a primary factor of $m(\alpha_i; x)$. Necessarily $e = \max(e_1, \cdots, e_s)$. Hence, for some k, $e = e_k$. Then $\alpha = \alpha_k$ satisfies the conclusion of the corollary.

LEMMA 10.1E.   *Let* α *be any vector in* $\mathscr{V}$ *and* $g(x)$ *be any monic divisor of* $m(\alpha; x)$. *Then there is a vector* β *in* $\mathscr{V}$ *for which* $m(\beta; x) = g(x)$.

Let $h(x) = m(\alpha; x)/g(x)$. Then $\beta = \alpha h(\mathsf{T})$ is effective in the lemma. For $\beta g(\mathsf{T}) = \alpha h(\mathsf{T})\, g(\mathsf{T}) = \alpha m(\alpha; \mathsf{T}) = 0$; hence $m(\beta; x)$ divides $g(x)$. On the other hand, $0 = \beta m(\beta, \mathsf{T}) = \alpha h(\mathsf{T}) m(\beta; \mathsf{T})$. Thus $m(\alpha; x)$ divides $h(x) m(\beta; x) = [m(\alpha; x)/g(x)] m(\beta; x) = m(\alpha; x)[m(\beta; x)/g(x)]$; consequently $g(x)$ divides $m(\beta; x)$. Finally, since $g(x)$ and $m(\beta; x)$ are monic and divide each other, they are equal.

LEMMA 10.1F. *Suppose that* α_1 *and* α_2 *are vectors whose relative minimum functions* $m(\alpha_1; x)$ *and* $m(\alpha_2; x)$ *for* T *are relatively prime. Then* $m(\alpha_1 + \alpha_2; x) = m(\alpha_1; x) \cdot m(\alpha_2; x)$.

Let $\alpha = \alpha_1 + \alpha_2$. First

$$\alpha[m(\alpha_1; \mathsf{T}) \, m(\alpha_2; \mathsf{T})] = \alpha_1[m(\alpha_1; \mathsf{T}) \, m(\alpha_2; \mathsf{T})] + \alpha_2[m(\alpha_2; \mathsf{T}) m(\alpha_1; \mathsf{T})]$$
$$= 0 m(\alpha_2; \mathsf{T}) + 0 m(\alpha_1; \mathsf{T})$$
$$= 0;$$

hence $m(\alpha; x)$ divides $m(\alpha_1; x) \, m(\alpha_2; x)$. Also $\alpha_1 = \alpha - \alpha_2$ and

$$\alpha_1[m(\alpha; \mathsf{T}) \, m(\alpha_2; \mathsf{T})] = \alpha[m(\alpha; \mathsf{T}) \, m(\alpha_2; \mathsf{T})] - \alpha_2[m(\alpha_2; \mathsf{T}) \, m(\alpha; \mathsf{T})]$$
$$= 0;$$

hence $m(\alpha_1; x)$ divides $m(\alpha; x) \, m(\alpha_2; x)$; consequently $m(\alpha_1; x)$, being prime to $m(\alpha_2; x)$, divides $m(\alpha; x)$. Similarly $m(\alpha_2; x)$ divides $m(\alpha; x)$. Thus $m(\alpha; x)$ is a multiple of the relatively prime polynomials $m(\alpha_1; x)$ and $m(\alpha_2; x)$ and hence of their product.

Finally, $m(\alpha; x) = m(\alpha_1; x) \, m(\alpha_2; x)$ since each side is monic and divides the other side.

COROLLARY 10.1G. *Suppose that* $\alpha_1, \cdots, \alpha_s$ *are vectors whose relative minimum functions* $m(\alpha_1; x), \cdots, m(\alpha_s; x)$ *are relatively prime in pairs. Then* $m(\alpha_1 + \cdots + \alpha_s; x) = m(\alpha_1; x) \cdots m(\alpha_s; x)$.

This can be proved by induction. The details are left as an exercise.

THEOREM 10.1H. *Let* $\mathscr{V}$ *be a vector space of dimension* v *over a field* $\mathscr{F}$ *and let* T *be a linear transformation on* $\mathscr{V}$. *Then there exists a vector* α *in* $\mathscr{V}$ *whose relative minimum function* $m(\alpha; x)$ *for* T *is the minimum function* $m(x)$ *of* T.

Let $m(x) = q_1(x) \cdots q_s(x)$ be the primary decomposition of $m(x)$. By Corollary 10.1D there is a vector α_j which has $q_j(x)$ $(j = 1, \cdots, s)$ as a primary factor of $m(\alpha_j; x)$, and then by Lemma 10.1E there exists a vector β_j such that $m(\beta_j; x) = q_j(x)$. Then $\alpha = \beta_1 + \cdots + \beta_s$ has $m(\alpha; x) = m(x)$ by Corollary 10.1G.

Exercises 10.1

1. Prove Corollary 10.1G.

2. Let T be a linear transformation on $\mathscr{V}_3{}^r$ whose matrix is $A_1 = \begin{Vmatrix} 3 & 0 & 0 \\ 0 & 3 & 0 \\ 0 & 0 & 3 \end{Vmatrix}$.

Find the minimum function for T.

In Exercises 3 through 5, find the minimum function of T relative to each of the basis vectors and the minimum function $m(x)$ for T. Find a vector α for which $m(\alpha; x) = m(x)$. Verify in each case that $m(x)$ is a factor of the characteristic function.

3. T has matrix
$$\left\| \begin{array}{ccc} 3 & 0 & 0 \\ 0 & 3 & 0 \\ 0 & 0 & 3 \end{array} \right\| .$$

4. T has matrix
$$\left\| \begin{array}{ccc} 3 & 0 & 0 \\ 0 & 4 & 0 \\ 0 & 0 & 5 \end{array} \right\| .$$

5. T has matrix
$$\left\| \begin{array}{ccc} 3 & 0 & 0 \\ 0 & 3 & 1 \\ 0 & 0 & 3 \end{array} \right\| .$$

10.2. Invariant subspaces. We now return to the problem of obtaining additional invariants for similarity. It is not always possible to obtain a set of eigenvectors which generate $\mathscr{V}$; an example illustrating this was given at the end of Section 5.5. We introduce the concept of invariant subspace as a generalization of that of eigenvector. This new concept leads to a general solution of the similarity problem.

Let $\mathscr{V}$ be a vector space of finite dimension v over a field $\mathscr{F}$, and let T be a linear transformation on $\mathscr{V}$. We say that a subspace $\mathscr{W}$ of $\mathscr{V}$ is *invariant under* T (Ex. 7.5.5) if

(2.1) $$\mathscr{W}\mathsf{T} \subseteq \mathscr{W},$$

i.e., if for each vector β in $\mathscr{W}$ the image vector $\beta\mathsf{T}$ also lies in $\mathscr{W}$. In particular, if β is an eigenvector for T, then $\mathscr{W} = \langle \beta \rangle$ is an invariant subspace of dimension one; conversely every invariant subspace of dimension one is spanned by an eigenvector. The zero space and the entire space $\mathscr{V}$ are always invariant.

LEMMA 10.2A. *Let $\mathscr{W}$ be a subspace of $\mathscr{V}$ invariant under* T. *Then the set of polynomials $g(x)$ such that $\mathscr{W}g(\mathsf{T}) = 0$ is an ideal in $\mathscr{F}[x]$.*

We leave the proof as an exercise (cf. Lemma 10.1A). We denote by $m(\mathscr{W}; x)$ the unique monic polynomial which generates this ideal and call it the *minimum function of* T *relative to* $\mathscr{W}$. If $\mathscr{W} = \mathscr{V}$, then $m(\mathscr{V}; x) = m(x)$, the minimum function of T. Clearly $m(\mathscr{W}; x)$ is always a factor of $m(x)$. We observe, more generally, that, if $\mathscr{W}_1 \subseteq \mathscr{W}_2$, then $m(\mathscr{W}_1; x)$ is a factor of $m(\mathscr{W}_2; x)$.

LEMMA 10.2B. *Let $\mathscr{W}_1$ and $\mathscr{W}_2$ be subspaces of $\mathscr{V}$ invariant under* T. *Then $\mathscr{W}_1 + \mathscr{W}_2$ and $\mathscr{W}_1 \cap \mathscr{W}_2$ are invariant under* T. *Moreover, $m(\mathscr{W}_1 + \mathscr{W}_2; x)$ is the least common multiple of $m(\mathscr{W}_1; x)$ and $m(\mathscr{W}_2; x)$, and $m(\mathscr{W}_1 \cap \mathscr{W}_2; x)$ is a factor of the greatest common divisor of $m(\mathscr{W}_1; x)$ and $m(\mathscr{W}_2; x)$.*

Let $\alpha = \alpha_1 + \alpha_2$ where α_i is in $\mathscr{W}_i$. Then the equation $\alpha\mathsf{T} = \alpha_1\mathsf{T} + \alpha_2\mathsf{T}$ shows that $(\mathscr{W}_1 + \mathscr{W}_2)\mathsf{T} = \mathscr{W}_1\mathsf{T} + \mathscr{W}_2\mathsf{T} \subseteq \mathscr{W}_1 + \mathscr{W}_2$. Next, if α is in $\mathscr{W}_1 \cap \mathscr{W}_2$, then $\alpha\mathsf{T}$ is in $\mathscr{W}_1\mathsf{T} \cap \mathscr{W}_2\mathsf{T}$, which is contained in $\mathscr{W}_1 \cap \mathscr{W}_2$.

Next, let $g(x)$ be the least common multiple of $m(\mathscr{W}_1; x)$ and $m(\mathscr{W}_2; x)$, and let $d(x)$ be their greatest common divisor. Clearly, $(\alpha_1 + \alpha_2) g(\mathsf{T}) = 0$ if α_1 is in $\mathscr{W}_1$ and α_2 is in $\mathscr{W}_2$. Hence $g(x)$ is a multiple of $m(\mathscr{W}_1 + \mathscr{W}_2; x)$. On the other hand, both $\mathscr{W}_1$ and $\mathscr{W}_2$ are contained in $\mathscr{W}_1 + \mathscr{W}_2$; hence $m(\mathscr{W}_1 + \mathscr{W}_2; x)$ is divisible by both $m(\mathscr{W}_1; x)$ and $m(\mathscr{W}_2; x)$ and therefore also by $g(x)$. This shows that $g(x) = m(\mathscr{W}_1 + \mathscr{W}_2; x)$. Finally, $m(\mathscr{W}_1 \cap \mathscr{W}_2; x)$ must divide both $m(\mathscr{W}_1; x)$ and $m(\mathscr{W}_2; x)$ and therefore divide $d(x)$.

COROLLARY 10.2C. *Let $\mathscr{W}_1$ and $\mathscr{W}_2$ be invariant subspaces under* T, *and suppose that $m(\mathscr{W}_1; x)$ and $m(\mathscr{W}_2; x)$ are relatively prime. Then the sum $\mathscr{W}_1 + \mathscr{W}_2$ is direct.*

Let $\mathscr{W} = \mathscr{W}_1 \cap \mathscr{W}_2$. By the lemma just proved, $m(\mathscr{W}; x)$ is a divisor of the greatest common divisor $d(x)$ of $m(\mathscr{W}_1; x)$ and $m(\mathscr{W}_2; x)$; by the hypotheses of the corollary $d(x) = 1$; hence $m(\mathscr{W}; x) = 1$. Now, a space $\mathscr{W}$ is annihilated by the identity transformation if and only if it is the zero space. Hence $\mathscr{W} = \mathscr{W}_1 \cap \mathscr{W}_2 = 0$, and consequently the sum $\mathscr{W}_1 + \mathscr{W}_2$ is direct.

We now introduce an important type of invariant subspace.

THEOREM 10.2D. *Let* T *be a linear transformation on a vector space $\mathscr{V}$, and let α be a vector in $\mathscr{V}$. Denote by $\mathscr{V}(\alpha, \mathsf{T})$ the subspace of $\mathscr{V}$ spanned by $\{\alpha, \alpha\mathsf{T}, \alpha\mathsf{T}^2, \cdots, \alpha\mathsf{T}^n, \cdots\}$. Then $\mathscr{V}(\alpha, \mathsf{T})$ is invariant under* T, $m(\mathscr{V}(\alpha, \mathsf{T}); x) = m(\alpha; x)$, *and* $\dim \mathscr{V}(\alpha, \mathsf{T}) = \deg m(\alpha; x)$. *Moreover, $\mathscr{V}(\alpha, \mathsf{T})$ is contained in any invariant subspace $\mathscr{W}$ which contains α.*

We call $\mathscr{V}(\alpha, \mathsf{T})$ the cyclic space generated by α under T.

Let $\beta = a_0\alpha + a_1\alpha\mathsf{T} + \cdots + a_n\alpha\mathsf{T}^n$ be any element in $\mathscr{V}(\alpha, \mathsf{T})$. Then $\beta = \alpha h(\mathsf{T})$ where $h(x) = a_0 + a_1x + \cdots + a_nx^n$, and $\beta\mathsf{T} = \alpha h(\mathsf{T})\mathsf{T}$ is clearly again in $\mathscr{V}(\alpha, \mathsf{T})$. Hence $\mathscr{V}(\alpha, \mathsf{T})$ is an invariant space under T.

Any invariant subspace $\mathscr{W}$ which contains α must also contain $\alpha\mathsf{T}, \alpha\mathsf{T}^2, \cdots$ and hence $\mathscr{W} \supseteq \mathscr{V}(\alpha, \mathsf{T})$.

Let $h(x)$ be any polynomial, and let $h'(x)$ be the remainder obtained upon division of $h(x)$ by $m(\alpha; x)$; say $h(x) = m(\alpha; x) g(x) + h'(x)$. By the division algorithm $h'(x)$ has formal degree less than $s = \deg m(\alpha; x)$; say

$h'(x) = b_0 + b_1 x + \cdots + b_{s-1} x^{s-1}$.   Now $\beta = \alpha h(\mathsf{T}) = \alpha[m(\alpha; \mathsf{T})\, g(\mathsf{T}) + h'(\mathsf{T})] = 0 + \alpha h'(\mathsf{T}) = b_0 \alpha + b_1 \alpha \mathsf{T} + \cdots + b_{s-1}\alpha \mathsf{T}^{s-1}$.   This equation shows that $\mathscr{S} = \{\alpha, \alpha \mathsf{T}, \cdots, \alpha \mathsf{T}^{s-1}\}$ spans $\mathscr{V}(\alpha, \mathsf{T})$. Also $\mathscr{S}$ must be independent, since any dependence relation on $\mathscr{S}$ would give a polynomial of degree less than s in the ideal of T annihilators of α.   Hence $\mathscr{S}$ is a basis for $\mathscr{V}(\alpha, \mathsf{T})$.

Finally, we observe that for any $\beta = \alpha g(\mathsf{T})$ we have $\beta m(\alpha; \mathsf{T}) = \alpha g(\mathsf{T})\, m(\alpha; \mathsf{T}) = \alpha m(\alpha; \mathsf{T})\, g(\mathsf{T}) = 0 g(\mathsf{T}) = 0$; hence $m(\mathscr{V}(\alpha, \mathsf{T}); x)$ is a factor of $m(\alpha; x)$.   On the other hand, if $\mathscr{V}(\alpha, \mathsf{T})\, h(\mathsf{T}) = 0$, then $\beta h(\mathsf{T}) = 0$ for each β in $\mathscr{V}(\alpha, \mathsf{T})$; in particular, for $\beta = \alpha$; hence $h(x)$ must be a multiple of $m(\alpha; x)$. We conclude that $m(\mathscr{V}(\alpha, \mathsf{T}); x) = m(\alpha; x)$ as claimed.

Our solution of the similarity problem will be based on the concept of cyclic space. We say that a linear transformation T on a space $\mathscr{V}$ is *cyclic* if there exists a vector α in $\mathscr{V}$ such that $\mathscr{V} = \mathscr{V}(\alpha, \mathsf{T})$, and will say that a matrix A is *cyclic* if it corresponds to a cyclic linear transformation. Not every linear transformation T is cyclic, but the restriction of T to a cyclic subspace is cyclic.   For example, the identity transformation is not cyclic if dim $\mathscr{V} > 1$. We will show later that any vector space $\mathscr{V}$ is a direct sum of cyclic subspaces for a given T.   For the present we develop the similarity theory when T is cyclic.

THEOREM 10.2E.   *Let* T *be a cyclic linear transformation on a vector space* $\mathscr{V}$, *and let* $m(x) = m_0 + m_1 x + \cdots + x^r$ *be the minimum function of* T. *Then* $m(x)$ *is the characteristic function of* T, *and there exists a basis for* $\mathscr{V}$ *relative to which*

$$(2.2) \qquad C = \begin{Vmatrix} 0 & 1 & 0 & \cdots & 0 \\ 0 & 0 & 1 & \cdots & 0 \\ \cdot & \cdot & \cdot & \cdots & \cdot \\ 0 & 0 & 0 & \cdots & 1 \\ -m_0 & -m_1 & -m_2 & \cdots & -m_{r-1} \end{Vmatrix}$$

is the matrix for T.

We call C the *companion matrix of the monic polynomial* $m(x)$.   Because of the importance of companion matrices, we give a verbal description of C. Let $g(x) = a_0 + a_1 x + \cdots + x^r$ be a monic polynomial of degree r. The companion matrix $C = \| c_{ij} \|$ of $g(x)$ is a square matrix of degree r

having 0's everywhere except for a stripe of 1's just above the diagonal and a last row $-a_0, -a_1, \cdots, -a_{r-1}$ formed from the negatives of the coefficients of $g(x)$ disregarding the leading coefficient 1 and in the order of the degrees of the terms. In symbols $c_{ij} = \delta_{i+1,j}$ $(i = 1, \cdots, r-1;$ $j = 1, \cdots, r)$ and $c_{rj} = -a_{j-1}$ $(j = 1, \cdots, r)$, where a_j is the coefficient of x^j in $g(x)$. We sometimes use the notation $C(g(x))$ for the companion matrix of $g(x)$.

For example, $C(x^2 + 2x - 3) = \left\| \begin{matrix} 0 & 1 \\ 3 & -2 \end{matrix} \right\|$, $C(x-a) = \| \, a \, \|$, and $C(1)$ is a null matrix.

By hypothesis there exists a vector α such that $\mathscr{V} = \mathscr{V}(\alpha, \mathsf{T})$. Then $\{\alpha, \alpha\mathsf{T}, \cdots, \alpha\mathsf{T}^{r-1}\}$ is a basis for $\mathscr{V}$; let $C = \| \, c_{ij} \, \|$ be the corresponding matrix for T. Denote $\alpha\mathsf{T}^{j-1}$ by α_j $(j = 1, \cdots, r)$. Then the ith row of C is determined by the equation

$$\alpha_i\mathsf{T} = c_{i1}\alpha_1 + \cdots + c_{ir}\alpha_r.$$

Now, if $i < r$, $\alpha_i\mathsf{T} = \alpha_{i+1}$, and hence $c_{ij} = \delta_{i+1,j}$. For $i = r$, $\alpha_r\mathsf{T} = \alpha\mathsf{T}^r = -m_0\alpha - m_1\alpha\mathsf{T} - \cdots - m_{r-1}\alpha\mathsf{T}^{r-1} = -m_0\alpha_1 - m_1\alpha_2 - \cdots - m_{r-1}\alpha_r$ and so the last row of C has the form given by (2.2).

The characteristic function of T (and of C) is

$$(2.3) \quad f(x) = \det(xI - C) = \left| \begin{matrix} x & -1 & & & & \\ & x & -1 & & & \\ & & & \cdot & \cdot & \\ & & & & \cdot & \cdot \\ & & & & x & -1 \\ m_0 & m_1 & & & m_{r-2} & x+m_{r-1} \end{matrix} \right|.$$

We evaluate $f(x)$ by expanding the determinant according to the last row of $xI - C$. For $0 \leq j \leq r-1$ the coefficient of m_j in this expansion is

$$(2.4) \qquad (-1)^{r+j+1} \left| \begin{matrix} A_j & 0 \\ 0 & B_j \end{matrix} \right|$$

where

$$
(2.5) \qquad A_j =
\begin{Vmatrix}
x & -1 & & & & \\
& x & -1 & & & \\
& & \cdot & \cdot & & \\
& & & \cdot & \cdot & \\
& & & & \cdot & \cdot \\
& & & & x & -1 \\
& & & & & x
\end{Vmatrix}
\qquad (j \text{ rows})
$$

and

$$
B_j =
\begin{Vmatrix}
-1 & & & & \\
x & -1 & & & \\
& x & -1 & & \\
& & \cdot & \cdot & \\
& & & \cdot & \cdot \\
& & & & \cdot & \cdot \\
& & & & x & -1
\end{Vmatrix}
\qquad (r - j - 1 \text{ rows}).
$$

Now, since A_j and B_j are triangular, we have $\det A_j = x^j$ and $\det B_j = (-1)^{r-j-1}$. Hence (see Theorem 4.4B) the coefficient of m_j is

$$
(2.6) \qquad (-1)^{r+j+1} \det A_j \det B_j = (-1)^{r+j+1} x^j \cdot (-1)^{r-j-1} = x^j.
$$

Adding the term x^r which comes from the diagonal, we see that $f(x) = m(x)$. This completes the proof of the theorem.

THEOREM 10.2F. *A linear transformation (or matrix) is cyclic if and only if its minimum function is equal to its characteristic function.*

The "only if" part follows from the preceding theorem, and the "if" part is a consequence of Theorem 10.1H which assures the existence of an element α having $m(\alpha, x)$ equal to the minimum function of the linear transformation.

THEOREM 10.2G. *Two cyclic matrices A and B are similar if and only if they have the same characteristic function.*

The "only if" is part of Lemma 5.5E.

If A is cyclic and has characteristic function $m(x)$, then it follows from Theorem 10.2E that the linear transformation T defined by A also corresponds to the companion matrix C of $m(x)$. Hence A is similar to C. Since $m(x)$ is also the characteristic function of B, B is likewise similar to C and hence also to A.

In the discussion above we have shown that $\mathscr{V}(\alpha, \mathsf{T})$ has a basis

$$(2.7) \qquad\qquad \alpha, \quad \alpha\mathsf{T}, \quad \cdots, \quad \alpha\mathsf{T}^{r-1}$$

where $r = \deg m(\alpha; x) = \dim \mathscr{V}(\alpha, \mathsf{T})$. This basis leads to the companion matrix which is a canonical form. If $m(\alpha; x))$ is primary, i.e., $m(\alpha; x) = p(x)^e$ where $p(x)$ is irreducible, then there is another basis which is convenient and leads to another canonical form. Suppose $\deg p(x) = f$. Then we assert that

$$
(2.8) \qquad
\begin{array}{llcl}
\alpha, & \alpha\mathsf{T}, & \cdots, & \alpha\mathsf{T}^{f-1}, \\[4pt]
\alpha p(\mathsf{T}), & \alpha\mathsf{T}p(\mathsf{T}), & \cdots, & \alpha\mathsf{T}^{f-1}p(\mathsf{T}), \\[4pt]
& \cdots, & & \\[4pt]
\alpha p(\mathsf{T})^{e-1}, & \alpha\mathsf{T}p(\mathsf{T})^{e-1}, & \cdots, & \alpha\mathsf{T}^{f-1}p(\mathsf{T})^{e-1}
\end{array}
$$

is a basis. This is true because, if $\alpha\mathsf{T}^s p(\mathsf{T})^t$ is a vector in (2.8), i.e., $0 \leq s < f$, $0 \leq t < e$, then in its expansion in terms of the basis (2.7), $\alpha\mathsf{T}^{s+ft}$ appears with coefficient 1 and no higher power of T is present. Thus, if we use as an induction assumption that the first $s + ft$ vectors of (2.7) and the first $s + ft$ vectors of (2.8) span the same subspace, we can conclude that the first $s + ft + 1$ vectors of each of the two sets (2.7) and (2.8) also span the same subspaces. Finally, (2.8) is a basis for $\mathscr{V}$ since (2.7) is.

If we use the basis (2.8), we obtain the following matrix for T:

$$
\left\|\begin{array}{cccccc}
P & Q & & & & \\
 & P & Q & & & \\
 & & \cdot & \cdot & & \\
 & & & \cdot & \cdot & \\
 & & & & P & Q \\
 & & & & & P
\end{array}\right\|
\qquad \text{where} \qquad
Q = \left\|\begin{array}{cccc}
0 & 0 & \cdots & 0 \\
\cdot & \cdot & \cdots & \cdot \\
0 & 0 & \cdots & 0 \\
1 & 0 & \cdots & 0
\end{array}\right\|
$$

and P is the companion matrix of $p(x)$.

We have now completed the theory of similarity for the cyclic case. An invariant criterion for the cyclic property has been found. Also two canonical forms have been provided, both being special cases of the canonical forms to be found for the general case.

Exercises 10.2

1. Let $\mathscr{V} = \mathscr{V}_2{}^r$ and $\mathsf{T} = \mathsf{I}$. Let $\mathscr{W}_1$ be the set of vectors of the form $(a, 0)$ and $\mathscr{W}_2$ those of the form $(0, b)$. Show that $m(\mathscr{W}_1; x) = x - 1 = m(\mathscr{W}_2; x) = m(\mathscr{W}_1 + \mathscr{W}_2; x)$, and that $m(\mathscr{W}_1 \cap \mathscr{W}_2; x) = 1$.

2. Prove that, if $m(x) = (x - 1)^2$, then C is not similar to a diagonal matrix.

3. Let $\mathscr{V}(\alpha, \mathsf{T})$ be a cyclic space, and let S be any linear transformation which commutes with T. Prove that S is a polynomial in T.

4. Prove that every invariant subspace of dimension 1 is spanned by an eigenvector.

5. Prove that $\mathscr{V}$ is cyclic if T has distinct eigenvalues.

6. Prove Lemma 10.2A.

7. Let $A = \begin{Vmatrix} 3 & 0 & 0 \\ 0 & 2 & 0 \\ 0 & 0 & -2 \end{Vmatrix}$. Find the minimum function $m(x)$ for A, and

find the companion matrix for $m(x)$.

10.3. Cayley-Hamilton Theorem.

The main theorem of this section states that the minimum function of T divides the characteristic function.

Lemma 10.3A. *Let T be a linear transformation on a vector space $\mathscr{V}$, and let $\mathscr{W}$ be a subspace of $\mathscr{V}$ invariant under T. Let $\{\alpha_1, \cdots, \alpha_v\}$ be a basis for $\mathscr{V}$ whose first w vectors form a basis for $\mathscr{W}$, and let A be the matrix of T relative to this basis for $\mathscr{V}$. Then*

$$(3.1) \qquad A = \begin{Vmatrix} A_1 & 0 \\ A_3 & A_4 \end{Vmatrix},$$

where A_1 is the matrix of the transformation T_1 obtained by restricting the domain of T from $\mathscr{V}$ to $\mathscr{W}$, relative to the basis $\{\alpha_1, \cdots, \alpha_w\}$.

If $i \leq w$, we have $\alpha_i\mathsf{T}$ expressible in terms of $\alpha_1, \cdots, \alpha_w$, and hence each of the first w rows of A will have zeros in the last $v - w$ entries. By the definition of restriction of a function we have $\alpha\mathsf{T} = \alpha\mathsf{T}_1$ for all vectors α in $\mathscr{W}$. Hence $\alpha_i\mathsf{T} = \alpha_i\mathsf{T}_1$ $(i = 1, \cdots, w)$, or in other words A_1 is the matrix for T_1.

Corollary 10.3B. *Let T_1 be the restriction of a linear transformation T*

to an invariant subspace. Then the characteristic function $f_1(x)$ of T_1 is a factor of the characteristic function $f(x)$ of T.

We have from (3.1) that

$$f(x) = \det (xI_v - A) = \begin{Vmatrix} xI_w - A_1 & 0 \\ -A_3 & xI_{v-w} - A_4 \end{Vmatrix},$$

and hence (cf. Theorem 4.4B) that

$$f(x) = \det (xI_w - A_1) \cdot \det (xI_{v-w} - A_4) = f_1(x) \cdot f_4(x),$$

since $f_1(x) = \det (xI_w - A_1)$.

THEOREM 10.3C. CAYLEY-HAMILTON THEOREM. *Let T be a linear transformation on a vector space $\mathscr{V}$. Then the minimum function of T is a factor of the characteristic function of T.*

Of course, this result holds also for any square matrix A. The usual formulation of this theorem, namely, that a matrix satisfies its characteristic equation, is an immediate consequence of this theorem. For, if $f(x) = m(x) \cdot g(x)$, then $f(A) = m(A) \cdot g(A) = 0 \cdot g(A) = 0$.

To prove this theorem we first select α such that $m(\alpha; x) = m(x)$ (cf. Theorem 10.1H), and take $\mathscr{W} = \mathscr{V}(\alpha, \mathsf{T})$. Let T_1 be the restriction of T to $\mathscr{W}$. Then, by Theorem 10.2E, $m(x)$ is the characteristic function of T_1. But by Corollary 10.3B the characteristic function of T_1 is a factor of the characteristic function $f(x)$ of T; i.e., $m(x)$ is a factor of $f(x)$.

We give an alternative proof which does not depend on the existence of an α with $m(\alpha; x) = m(x)$. Let α be any vector in $\mathscr{V}$. Let $\mathscr{W} = \mathscr{V}(\alpha, \mathsf{T})$, and, as above, prove that $m(\alpha; x)$ divides $f(x)$. Hence $\alpha f(\mathsf{T}) = 0$. Since this is true for every α in $\mathscr{V}$, $f(\mathsf{T}) = 0$. Thus $f(x)$ is a multiple of $m(x)$.

LEMMA 10.3D. *Let T be a linear transformation on a vector space $\mathscr{V}$, and suppose that $\mathscr{V}$ is the direct sum of the invariant subspaces $\mathscr{W}_1, \cdots, \mathscr{W}_r$. Let $\mathscr{S} = \{\alpha_1, \cdots, \alpha_v\}$ be a basis for $\mathscr{V}$ in which the first w_1 vectors form a basis for $\mathscr{W}_1$, the next w_2 a basis for $\mathscr{W}_2 \cdots$, and the last w_r a basis for $\mathscr{W}_r$. Then relative to this basis T has the matrix*

$$(3.2) \qquad A = \begin{Vmatrix} A_1 & & & 0 \\ & A_2 & & \\ & & \ddots & \\ 0 & & & A_r \end{Vmatrix}$$

where A_h is the matrix for the restriction of T to $\mathscr{W}_h$ relative to the given basis for $\mathscr{W}_h$ $(h = 1, \cdots, r)$.

Let $A = \| a_{ij} \|$ be the matrix of T relative to the basis $\mathscr{S}$. We have $\alpha_i \mathsf{T} = a_{i1}\alpha_1 + \cdots + a_{iv}\alpha_v$. Suppose that α_i is in $\mathscr{W}_h$. Then, since $\mathscr{W}_h$ is invariant, we must have $a_{ij} = 0$ unless α_j is in $\mathscr{W}_h$. Hence the ith row of A will be zero except for the block of columns corresponding to the basis vectors for $\mathscr{W}_h$, and the places in this block of columns will be occupied by the elements of the i'th row of A_h where $i' = i - w_1 - w_2 - \cdots - w_{h-1}$.

Ultimately we shall show that $\mathscr{V}$ is a direct sum of cyclic subspaces (Theorem 10.5B). This lemma thus reduces the problem of similarity to that for cyclic subspaces and these we treated in Section 10.2.

Exercises 10.3

Check the Cayley-Hamilton Theorem for the matrices in Exercises 1 through 4.

1.
$$A = \begin{Vmatrix} 1 & 2 \\ -3 & 4 \end{Vmatrix}.$$

2.
$$A = \begin{Vmatrix} 1 & 0 & 2 \\ -3 & 1 & 4 \\ -1 & 2 & 2 \end{Vmatrix}.$$

3.
$$A = \begin{Vmatrix} a & b \\ c & d \end{Vmatrix}.$$

4.
$$A = \| a \|.$$

5. (a) What is the characteristic function of $A = \begin{Vmatrix} 2 & -1 & 1 \\ 1 & 3 & -2 \\ 5 & 1 & 0 \end{Vmatrix}$?

(b) Check your result by a method other than recomputation.

6. Prove that every eigenvalue of a matrix A occurs as a root of the minimum function of A.

7. Let A be a matrix with a minimum function $m(x)$ and characteristic function $f(x)$. Suppose that $m(x)$ splits into linear factors over the field of scalars. Show that $f(x)$ is a factor of some power of $m(x)$. (Hint: use Ex. 6.)

10.4. Primary linear transformations.

Let $\mathscr{V}$ be a vector space of finite dimension v over a field $\mathscr{F}$. A linear transformation T on $\mathscr{V}$ is said to be *primary* if its minimum function is primary, say $m(x) = p(x)^e$ where $p(x) = p_0 + p_1 x + \cdots + x^f$ is a prime polynomial. This definition applies also to matrices. In the present section we shall settle the similarity problem for primary transformations and then in the next section treat the general case by means of a reduction to the primary case.

Let $\mathscr{W} = \mathscr{V}(\alpha_1, \mathsf{T}) + \cdots + \mathscr{V}(\alpha_r, \mathsf{T})$ be a direct sum of cyclic subspaces of $\mathscr{V}$. Since T is primary we have $m(\alpha_i; x) = p(x)^{e_i}$. We suppose the α_i so ordered that $e_1 \geq e_2 \geq \cdots \geq e_r > 0$ and set $e_{r+1} = e_{r+2} = \cdots = 0$. We call the sequence $e_1, e_2; \cdots$ the *exponents* of $\mathscr{W}$. Let $\mathscr{W}'$ be a second such direct sum with exponent sequence $e'_1, e'_2, \cdots$. We say that $\mathscr{W}'$ is *higher* than $\mathscr{W}$ if the first nonvanishing term of the difference sequence $e'_1 - e_1, e'_2 - e_2, \cdots$ is positive. For example, a space with exponents $5, 4. 1, 1, 0, 0, \cdots$ is higher than a space with exponents $5, 3, 3, 3, 2, 0, 0, \cdots$.

LEMMA 10.4A. *If $\mathscr{W}''$ is higher than $\mathscr{W}'$ and if $\mathscr{W}'$ is higher than $\mathscr{W}$, then $\mathscr{W}''$ is higher than $\mathscr{W}$.*

Suppose that $e''_1 = e'_1, \cdots, e''_{i-1} = e'_{i-1}, \ e''_i > e'_i$ and that $e'_1 = e_1, \cdots, e'_{j-1} = e_{j-1}, e'_j > e_j$. If $i \leq j$, we have $e''_1 = e_1, \cdots, e''_{i-1} = e_{i-1}, {}''e_i > e_i$; if $i > j$, we have $e''_1 = e_1, \cdots, e''_{j-1} = e_{j-1}, e''_j > e_j$. Thus in all cases $\mathscr{W}''$ is higher than $\mathscr{W}$.

LEMMA 10.4B. *Let $\mathscr{W}_0 = 0, \mathscr{W}_1, \mathscr{W}_2, \cdots, \mathscr{W}_s$ be a set of direct sums of cyclic subspaces of $\mathscr{V}$ such that $\mathscr{W}_i$ is higher than $\mathscr{W}_{i-1}$ $(i = 1, \cdots, s)$. Then $s \leq (v + 1)^v$.*

This bound for s is by no means the best possible, but all we need to know for our application of this lemma is that s is bounded by some integer which depends only on the dimension v of $\mathscr{V}$.

We first observe that, if $\mathscr{W}$ has exponent sequence $e_1, e_2, \cdots, e_r, 0, 0, \cdots$, then dim $\mathscr{W} = f(e_1 + e_2 + \cdots + e_r)$, and hence $e_1 + e_2 + \cdots + e_r \leq v$. In particular, $r \leq v$. It follows that the number of different exponent sequences is at most equal to the number of solutions of the equation

$$x_1 + \cdots + x_v \leq v$$

where $0 \leq x_i \leq v$ $(i = 1, \cdots, v)$. This number of solutions is, in turn, bounded by the number $(v + 1)^v$ of "vectors" $(x_1, \cdots, x_v)$ having $0 \leq x_1 \leq v, \cdots, 0 \leq x_v \leq v$.

Finally, it follows from Lemma 10.4A that no two of $\mathscr{W}_1, \cdots, \mathscr{W}_s$ can have the same exponent sequence, and hence $s \leq (v + 1)^v$.

LEMMA 10.4C. *Let $\mathscr{W} = \mathscr{V}(\alpha_1, \mathsf{T}) + \cdots + \mathscr{V}(\alpha_r, \mathsf{T})$ (direct) be a proper subspace of $\mathscr{V}$. Then there exists a direct sum $\mathscr{W}' = \mathscr{V}(\alpha'_1, \mathsf{T}) + \cdots + \mathscr{V}(\alpha'_{r'}, \mathsf{T})$ in $\mathscr{V}$ which is higher than $\mathscr{W}$.*

Let β be a vector in $\mathscr{V}$ which does not lie in $\mathscr{W}$. We employ it to obtain $\mathscr{W}'$. The set of polynomials $g(x)$ for which $\beta g(\mathsf{T})$ lies in $\mathscr{W}$ is clearly an ideal which contains $m(x)$. Hence there exists an integer

$t \geq 1$ such that this ideal is $(p(x)^t)$. Also there exist polynomials $g_1(x), \cdots, g_r(x)$ such that

$$(4.1) \qquad \beta p(\mathsf{T})^t = \gamma = \alpha_1 g_1(\mathsf{T}) + \cdots + \alpha_r g_r(\mathsf{T}).$$

First suppose that each $g_i(x)$ is divisible by $p(x)^t$; i.e., there exist polynomials $g'_i(x)$ such that $g_i(x) = p(x)^t g'_i(x)$ $(i = 1, \cdots, r)$; let $\gamma' = \alpha_1 g'_1(\mathsf{T}) + \cdots + \alpha_r g'_r(\mathsf{T})$, and let $\beta' = \beta - \gamma'$. Then $\beta' p(\mathsf{T})^t = 0$, and the equation $\beta = \beta' + \gamma'$ shows that $\beta' p(\mathsf{T})^{t'}$ does not lie in $\mathscr{W}$ for any $t' < t$. Hence $m(\beta'; x) = p(x)^t$, and also $\mathscr{V}(\beta', \mathsf{T}) \cap \mathscr{W} = 0$. Thus

$$\mathscr{W}' = \mathscr{V}(\alpha_1, \mathsf{T}) + \cdots + \mathscr{V}(\alpha_r, \mathsf{T}) + \mathscr{V}(\beta', \mathsf{T})$$

is a direct sum; it is higher than $\mathscr{W}$ since its exponents are just those of $\mathscr{W}$ except for the additional nonzero term t.

Next, if not every $g_i(x)$ is divisible by $p(x)^t$, let $g_{h+1}(x)$ be the one having the smallest subscript; then $0 \leq h < r$. Also $g_i(x) = p(x)^t g'_i(x)$ $(i = 1, \cdots, h)$; let $\gamma'' = \alpha_1 g'_1(\mathsf{T}) + \cdots + \alpha_h g'_h(\mathsf{T})$, and set $\beta'' = \beta - \gamma''$. Now $\beta'' p(\mathsf{T})^t$ lies in $\mathscr{W}_{h+1} + \cdots + \mathscr{W}_r$, so that $\mathscr{V}(\beta'', \mathsf{T}) \cap (\mathscr{W}_1 + \cdots + \mathscr{W}_h) = 0$. Hence $\mathscr{W}'' = \mathscr{W}_1 + \cdots + \mathscr{W}_h + \mathscr{V}(\beta'', \mathsf{T})$ is a direct sum. We shall show that $\mathscr{W}''$ is higher than $\mathscr{W}$ by showing that $e_{h+1} < e$, where e is given by $m(\beta'', x) = p(x)^e$.

Let $p(x)^{f_{h+1}}$ be the highest power of $p(x)$ dividing $g_{h+1}(x)$; then $f_{h+1} < t$ by the definition of h. Also $t \leq e$. Furthermore, since

$$0 = \beta'' p(\mathsf{T})^e = \beta'' p(\mathsf{T})^t p(\mathsf{T})^{e-t}$$
$$= \alpha_{h+1} g_{h+1}(\mathsf{T}) p(\mathsf{T})^{e-t} + \cdots + \alpha_s g_s(\mathsf{T}) p(\mathsf{T})^{e-t},$$

and, since the sum for $\mathscr{W}$ is direct, $\alpha_{h+1} g_{h+1}(\mathsf{T}) p(\mathsf{T})^{e-t} = 0$; hence $g_{h+1}(x) p(x)^{e-t}$ is divisible by $p(x)^{e_{h+1}}$. Thus $e_{h+1} \leq f_{h+1} + e - t$. Finally, $e \geq e_{h+1} + (t - f_{h+1}) > e_{h+1}$.

THEOREM 10.4D. *Let $\mathscr{V}$ be a vector space of finite dimension v over a field $\mathscr{F}$, and let T be a primary linear transformation on $\mathscr{V}$. Then there exist vectors $\alpha_1, \cdots, \alpha_r$ in $\mathscr{V}$ such that $\mathscr{V} = \mathscr{V}(\alpha_1, \mathsf{T}) + \cdots + \mathscr{V}(\alpha_r, \mathsf{T})$ (direct sum); i.e., $\mathscr{V}$ is a direct sum of cyclic subspaces.*

We have merely to apply the preceding lemmas. Start with any cyclic space $\mathscr{W}_1$, and proceeding in this fashion, construct a sequence $0 = \mathscr{W}_0, \mathscr{W}_1, \mathscr{W}_2, \cdots, \mathscr{W}_s$, where each $\mathscr{W}_i$ is a direct sum of cyclic subspaces and $\mathscr{W}_i$ is higher than $\mathscr{W}_{i-1}$. By Lemma 10.4B, this process must terminate after at most $(v + 1)^v$ steps, and, by Lemma 10.4C, the final member $\mathscr{W}_s$ must be $\mathscr{V}$.

We next find a matrix corresponding to T. Consider the set $\mathscr{S}_i = \{\alpha_i, \alpha_i \mathsf{T}, \cdots, \alpha_i \mathsf{T}^{w_i-1}\}$, where $w_i = e_i f$ is the dimension of $\mathscr{V}(\alpha_i, \mathsf{T})$

$(i = 1, \cdots, r)$. Relative to the basis $\mathscr{S}_i$ for $\mathscr{V}(\alpha_i, \mathsf{T})$, the restriction of T to $\mathscr{V}(\alpha_i, \mathsf{T})$ has matrix $A_i = C(p(x)^{e_i})$. Hence, by Lemma 10.3D, T has matrix

$$
(4.2) \qquad A = \left\|
\begin{array}{ccccc}
C(p(x)^{e_1}) & & & & \\
& C(p(x)^{e_2}) & & & \\
& & \cdot & & \\
& & & \cdot & \\
& & & & \cdot \\
& & & & C(p(x)^{e_r})
\end{array}
\right\|
$$

relative to the basis $\mathscr{S} = \{\mathscr{S}_1, \mathscr{S}_2, \cdots, \mathscr{S}_r\}$ of $\mathscr{V}$.

THEOREM 10.4E. *Let* T *be a primary linear transformation on* $\mathscr{V}$, *and suppose that* $\mathscr{V}$ *is the direct sum of the cyclic subspaces* $\mathscr{V}(\alpha_1, \mathsf{T}), \cdots, \mathscr{V}(\alpha_r, \mathsf{T})$, *where* $m(\alpha_i, x) = p(x)^{e_i}$ *and* $e_1 \geq e_2 \geq \cdots \geq e_r > 0 = e_{r+1} = \cdots = e_v$. *Then* $p(x)^{e_i}$ *is the* $(v + 1 - i)$*th invariant factor of* T $(i = 1, \cdots, v)$.

We consider the matrix $M = xI - A$ where A is the matrix for T given by (4.2). This matrix satisfies the hypotheses of Lemma 9.2F, and the results of that lemma give the conclusion here since by Theorem 10.2E det $(xI - C(p(x)^{e_i})) = p(x)^{e_i}$.

THEOREM 10.4F. *Let* B *be a primary matrix of degree* v *with invariant factors* $m_{v+1-i}(A, x) = p(x)^{e_i}$ *where* $e_1 \geq e_2 \geq \cdots \geq e_r > 0 = e_{r+1} = \cdots = e_v$. *Then* B *is similar to the matrix* A *given by* (4.2).

Let T be the linear transformation on $\mathscr{V} = \mathscr{V}_v{}^r$ whose matrix relative to the natural basis of $\mathscr{V}$ is B. Then, since B is primary, so is T, and hence by a new choice of basis we get A as the matrix for T since A is uniquely determined by its invariant factors. Hence B is similar to A.

THEOREM 10.4G. *Let* B_1 *and* B_2 *be two primary matrices of degree* v. *Then* B_1 *and* B_2 *are similar if and only if* $m_i(B_1, x) = m_i(B_2, x)$ $(i=1, \cdots, v)$; *i.e., two primary matrices are similar if and only if they have the same invariant factors.*

If B_1 and B_2 have the same invariant factors, say $m_i(B_1, x) = m_i(B_2, x) = p(x)^{e_i}$, then both are similar to A and hence to each other. Conversely, if $PB_1P^{-1} = B_2$, then $P(xI - B_1)P^{-1} = xI - B_2$, and so the invariant factors of B_2 must be the same as those of B_1.

Putting these two theorems together, we see that (4.2) is a canonical form for similarity in the case of primary matrices.

If $r = 1$, then T is cyclic, and A becomes $C(p(x)^{e_1})$, which was proved earlier to be canonical.   Another canonical form for this case is given by the matrix $C^*(p(x)^e)$ described below in (4.3).

LEMMA 10.4H.   *Let $p(x)$ be a monic prime polynomial of degree f, and let $P = C(p(x))$, and let Q be the square matrix of degree f whose only nonzero entry is a one in the lower left-hand corner.   Then*

$$(4.3) \qquad C(p(x)^e) \sim C^*(p(x)^e) = \begin{Vmatrix} P & Q & & & & 0 \\ & P & Q & & & \\ & & & \cdot & \cdot & \\ & & & & \cdot & \cdot \\ & & & & P & Q \\ 0 & & & & & P \end{Vmatrix}.$$

For example, if the scalar field is $\mathfrak{Q}$ and $p(x) = x^2 - 3x + 4$, then

$$C^*((x^2 - 3x + 4)^3) = \begin{Vmatrix} 0 & 1 & 0 & 0 & & \\ -4 & 3 & 1 & 0 & & \\ & & 0 & 1 & 0 & 0 \\ & & -4 & 3 & 1 & 0 \\ & & & & 0 & 1 \\ & & & & -4 & 3 \end{Vmatrix}.$$

In $C^*(p(x))^e$, as in $C(p(x)^e)$, there is a stripe of 1's just above the diagonal.

Let $\mathscr{V}$ be a primary cyclic space relative to a linear transformation T, say $\mathscr{V} = \mathscr{V}(\alpha, \mathsf{T})$ where $m(\alpha; x) = p(x)^e$.   Then

$$(4.4) \quad \mathscr{S} = \{\alpha, \alpha\mathsf{T}, \cdots, \alpha\mathsf{T}^{f-1}, \alpha p(\mathsf{T}), \alpha\mathsf{T}p(\mathsf{T}), \cdots, \alpha\mathsf{T}^{f-1}p(\mathsf{T}), \alpha p(\mathsf{T})^2, \cdots,$$
$$\alpha\mathsf{T}^{f-1}p(\mathsf{T})^{e-1}\}$$

is readily seen to be a basis for $\mathscr{V}$.   The matrix for T relative to $\mathscr{S}$ is $C^*(p(x)^e)$.   To see that $C^*(p(x)^e)$ is the matrix for T is trivial for all rows except those whose indices are divisible by f.   Now, if $i = hf$, then $\alpha_i = \alpha\mathsf{T}^{f-1}p(\mathsf{T})^{h-1}$ and

$$\alpha_i\mathsf{T} = \alpha\mathsf{T}^f p(\mathsf{T})^{h-1}$$
$$(4.5) \quad = \alpha(p(\mathsf{T}) - p_0 - p_1\mathsf{T} - \cdots - p_{f-1}\mathsf{T}^{f-1})p(\mathsf{T})^{h-1}$$
$$= -p_0\,\alpha p(\mathsf{T})^{h-1} - p_1\alpha\mathsf{T}\,p(\mathsf{T})^{h-1} - \cdots - p_{f-1}\alpha\mathsf{T}^{f-1}\,p(\mathsf{T})^{h-1} +$$
$$+ \alpha\,p(\mathsf{T})^h$$

where $p(x) = p_0 + p_1 x + \cdots + x^f$.   Formula (4.5) establishes (4.3).

Exercises 10.4

1. Prove that in $C^*(p(x))^e$ the elements in position $(i, i + 1)$ all equal 1.

2. Prove that the $\mathscr{S}$ described by (4.4) is a basis of $\mathscr{V}$.

3. Let the scalar field be $\mathfrak{C}$, and let $p(x) = x + 2$. Find $C(p(x)^4)$ and $C^*(p(x)^4)$.

4. Let the scalar field be $\mathfrak{Q}$, and let $p(x) = x^3 - x + 1$. Find $C(p(x)^2)$ and $C^*(p(x)^2)$.

5. Let T be a linear transformation on $\mathscr{V}_{10}(\mathfrak{Q})$ whose invariant factors are $(x^2 + 1)^3$, $(x^2 + 1)$, $(x^2 + 1)$. Find canonical forms for the matrix of T first using C and then using C^*.

6. Let $p(x) = x^2 - x + 1$, let the scalar field be $\mathfrak{Q}$, and let $P = C(p(x))$. Show that

$$\left\| \begin{matrix} P & Q \\ 0 & P \end{matrix} \right\| \sim \left\| \begin{matrix} P & I \\ 0 & P \end{matrix} \right\|.$$

7. Let $p(x)$ be a monic prime polynomial; we set

$$C^{**}(p(x)^e) = \left\| \begin{matrix} P & I & & & 0 \\ & P & I & & \\ & & \ddots & & \\ & & & P & I \\ 0 & & & & P \end{matrix} \right\|.$$

Show that $C^{**}(p(x)^e)$ is similar to $C(p(x)^e)$ (provided the scalar field has characteristic 0).

10.5. Similarity, general case. Let $\mathscr{V}$ be a vector space of finite dimension v over a field $\mathscr{F}$, and let T be a linear transformation on $\mathscr{V}$. An invariant subspace $\mathscr{W}$ of $\mathscr{V}$ is said to be *primary* if the restriction of T to $\mathscr{W}$ is primary or equivalently if the relative minimum function $m(\mathscr{W}; x)$ for T on $\mathscr{W}$ is a primary polynomial. We first show that $\mathscr{V}$ can be decomposed into a direct sum of primary subspaces; for these a canonical form was obtained in the last section.

THEOREM 10.5A. *Let T be a linear transformation on a vector space $\mathscr{V}$, and let $m(x) = q_1(x) \cdots q_s(x)$ be the primary factorization of the minimum function of T. Then $\mathscr{V}$ is the direct sum of s primary subspaces $\mathscr{W}_1, \cdots, \mathscr{W}_s$ where $m(\mathscr{W}_j; x) = q_j(x)$ $(j = 1, \cdots, s)$. Moreover, $\mathscr{W}_j$ is the kernel of $q_j(\mathsf{T})$.*

We call $\mathscr{W}_1, \cdots, \mathscr{W}_s$ the *primary components* of $\mathscr{V}$.

If we choose $e_i(y)$ as in Lemma 8.10B with $y = \mathsf{T}$ and set $\mathsf{E}_i = e_i(\mathsf{T})$

$(i = 1, \cdots, s)$, then we have $I = E_1 + \cdots + E_s$ where the E_j are ortho-gonal idempotents which commute with T. Let $\mathscr{W}_j = \mathscr{V} E_j \ (j = 1, \cdots, s)$. The equation $\alpha = \alpha_1 + \cdots + \alpha_s$ where $\alpha_j = \alpha E_j$ shows that $\mathscr{V} = \mathscr{W}_1 + \cdots + \mathscr{W}_s$. We observe that, if α_j is in $\mathscr{W}_j$, then $\alpha_j = \alpha_j E_j$. Moreover, if $i \neq j$, then $\alpha_j E_i = (\alpha_j E_j) E_i = \alpha_j (E_j E_i) = \alpha_j 0 = 0$. Hence, if $0 = \alpha_1 + \cdots + \alpha_s$ with α_j in $\mathscr{W}_j \ (j = 1, \cdots, s)$, then $0 = 0 \cdot E_i = \alpha_1 E_i + \cdots + \alpha_s E_i = \alpha_i E_i = \alpha_i$. Hence the sum $\mathscr{W}_1 + \cdots + \mathscr{W}_s$ is direct.

Since $q_i{}^*(T) q_i(T) = 0$, we have $\mathscr{W}_i q_i(T) = 0$; hence $\mathscr{W}_i$ is contained in the kernel of $q_i(T)$. So, if α_i is in $\mathscr{W}_i \ (i = 1, \cdots, s)$, then $m(\alpha_i; x)$ divides $q_i(x)$. Therefore, by Corollary 10.1G, $q_i(T)$ annihilates $\alpha = \alpha_1 + \cdots + \alpha_s$ only if all terms in α, except possibly α_i, are 0. Hence $\mathscr{W}_i$ is the kernel of $q_i(T)$. But by Lemma 10.1E there is an element β_i for which $m(\beta_i, x) = q_i(x)$. This β_i must lie in $\mathscr{W}_i$. Hence $m(\mathscr{W}_i; x) = q_i(x)$. This completes the proof of the theorem.

Incidentally $\mathscr{W}_i$ is uniquely determined as being the kernel of the $q_i(T)$.

Now choose vectors $\alpha_{i1}, \cdots, \alpha_{ir_i}$ so that $\mathscr{W}_i$ is the direct sum of its cyclic subspaces $\mathscr{V}(\alpha_{i1}, T), \cdots, \mathscr{V}(\alpha_{ir_i}, T) \ (i = 1, \cdots, s)$. We suppose the vectors so ordered that $m(\alpha_{ij}; x) = p_i(x)^{e_{ij}}$ where $e_{i1} \geq e_{i2} \geq \cdots \geq e_{ir_i} > 0 = e_{i,r_i+1} = \cdots = e_{iv}$ and $p_i(x)$ is the prime factor of $q_i(x)$. Let A_i denote the canonical matrix [i.e., in the form (4.2)] of the restriction of T to $\mathscr{W}_i \ (i = 1, \cdots, s)$. Then, putting together the basis vectors already selected in each $\mathscr{W}_i$, we get a basis for $\mathscr{V}$ relative to which T has the matrix

$$(5.1) \qquad A = \left\|\begin{array}{cccc} A_1 & & & \\ & \cdot & & \\ & & \cdot & \\ & & & \cdot \\ & & & A_s \end{array}\right\|,$$

where

$$(5.2) \qquad A_i = \left\|\begin{array}{cccc} C(p_i(x)^{e_{i1}}) & & & \\ & \cdot & & \\ & & \cdot & \\ & & & \cdot \\ & & & C(p_i(x)^{e_{ir_i}}) \end{array}\right\|.$$

We have proved the following theorem.

THEOREM 10.5B. *Let* T *be a linear transformation on a vector space* $\mathscr{V}$. *Then* $\mathscr{V}$ *is a direct sum of primary cyclic subspaces.*

THEOREM 10.5C. *Let* T *be a linear transformation on a vector space* $\mathscr{V}$, *and let* $m_1(x), \cdots, m_v(x)$ *be the invariant factors of* T *and suppose that*

$m_{v-r}(x) = 1$ but $m_{v-r+1}(x) \neq 1$.   Then there exist vectors $\alpha_1, \cdots, \alpha_r$ such that $m(\alpha_j; x) = m_{v+1-j}(x)$ $(j = 1, \cdots, r)$ and such that $\mathscr{V}$ is the direct sum of the cyclic subspaces $\mathscr{V}(\alpha_1, \mathsf{T}), \cdots, \mathscr{V}(\alpha_r, \mathsf{T})$.

We select vectors α_{ij} as above and set $\alpha_{ij} = 0$ if $j > r_i$. Let $t = \max (r_1, \cdots, r_s)$ and set $\alpha_j = \alpha_{1j} + \cdots + \alpha_{sj}$. Clearly $\alpha_j \neq 0$ $(j = 1, \cdots, t)$. Then it follows from Corollary 10.1G that $m(\alpha_j; x) = p_1(x)^{e_{1j}} \cdots p_s(x)^{e_{sj}}$, and hence that $\mathscr{V}(\alpha_j, \mathsf{T}) = \mathscr{V}(\alpha_{1j}, \mathsf{T}) + \cdots + \mathscr{V}(\alpha_{sj}, \mathsf{T})$ $(j = 1, \cdots, t)$. Since $\mathscr{V}$ is the direct sum of the nonzero $\mathscr{V}(\alpha_{ij}, \mathsf{T})$ and since none of the α_j is zero, it follows that $\mathscr{V}$ is the direct sum of $\mathscr{V}(\alpha_1, \mathsf{T}), \cdots, \mathscr{V}(\alpha_t, \mathsf{T})$.

Let e_j be the degree of $m(\alpha_j; x)$. Then the set $\mathscr{S} = \{\alpha_1, \alpha_1\mathsf{T}, \cdots, \alpha_1\mathsf{T}^{e_1-1}, \cdots, \alpha_s, \alpha_s\mathsf{T}, \cdots, \alpha_s\mathsf{T}^{e_s-1} \}$ is a basis for $\mathscr{V}$ and relative to this basis T has the matrix

$$(5.3) \qquad B = \left\|\begin{array}{ccc} B_1 & & \\ & \cdot & \\ & & \cdot \\ & & & B_t \end{array}\right\|,$$

where $B_j = C(m(\alpha_j; x))$ $(j = 1, \cdots, t)$.   Since $e_{i1} \geq e_{i2} \geq \cdots \geq e_{ir}$ $(i = 1, \cdots, s)$, we have $m(\alpha_j, x)$ a factor of $m(\alpha_{j-1}; x)$ $(j = 2, \cdots, r)$. Now, by Lemma 9.2F, $m(\alpha_j; x) = m_{v+1-j}(x)$ $(j = 1, \cdots, t)$ and $m_i(x) = 1$ for $i \leq v - t$. Hence, $t = r$, and the theorem is proved.

COROLLARY 10.5D.   *The elementary divisors of* T *are the invariant factors of the restrictions of* T *to the primary components of* $\mathscr{V}$.

By definition the elementary divisors of T are the primary factors of the invariant factors of T.   But we have just seen that $m_j(x)$ has the primary decomposition $m_{v+1-j}(x) = p_1(x)^{e_{1j}} \cdots p_s(x)^{e_{sj}}$ where $p_i(x)^{e_{ij}}$ is the $(v + 1 - j)$th invariant factor of the restriction of T to $\mathscr{W}_i$.

Translating these results into matrix language we have the following theorems.

THEOREM 10.5E.   *Let D be any square matrix.   Then D is similar to the matrix*

$$(5.4) \qquad B = \left\|\begin{array}{ccc} C(m_v(x)) & & \\ & \cdot & \\ & & \cdot \\ & & \cdot \\ & & C(m_{v-r+1}(x)) \end{array}\right\|$$

where $m_j(x)$ is the jth invariant factor of D and $m_j(x) = 1$ for $j \leq v - r$.

THEOREM 10.5F. *Two matrices D_1 and D_2 are similar if and only if they have the same invariant factors.*

Indeed (5.4) provides a canonical form for similarity. It is called the *rational canonical form*; note that the rational canonical form depends directly on the invariant factors.

Formulas (5.1) and (5.2) also provide a canonical form, and this form depends directly on the elementary divisors. To see that the elementary divisors form a complete set of invariants, we need only show that they determine the invariant factors. The following theorem does this and more.

THEOREM 10.5G. *Let $t_1(x), \cdots, t_n(x)$ be any set of monic primary polynomials all of degree at least one. Then there exists a unique matrix A whose nontrivial elementary divisors are $t_1(x), \cdots, t_n(x)$.*

Let $p_1(x), \cdots, p_s(x)$ be the monic prime polynomials occurring as divisors of the $t_j(x)$. We can arrange the $t_j(x)$ so that they are $p_1(x)^{e_{11}}$, $p_1(x)^{e_{12}}, \cdots, p_1(x)^{e_{ir_1}}, \cdots, p_s(x)^{e_{s1}}, \cdots, p_s(x)^{e_{srs}}$, where $n = r_1 + \cdots + r_s$ and $e_{ij} \geq e_{i,j+1}$ $(j = 1, \cdots, r_i - 1)$. Then by Corollary 10.5D the matrix A given by (5.1) and (5.2) has the desired elementary divisors, and its invariant factors are given by $m_{v+1-j} = p_1(x)^{e_{1j}} \cdots p_s(x)^{e_{sj}}$ where we set $e_{ij} = 0$ if $j > r_i$. This also gives the following theorem.

THEOREM 10.5H. *Two matrices D_1 and D_2 are similar if and only if they have the same elementary divisors.*

The canonical form ordinarily associated with the elementary divisors is obtained from (5.2) by replacing each $C(p_i(x)^{e_{ij}})$ by $C^*(p_i(x)^{e_{ij}})$ [cf. (4.3)]. This form is called the *classical canonical form*. In case $\mathscr{F}$ is the field of complex numbers each $p_i(x)$ becomes linear and takes the form $p_i(x) = x - \lambda_i$. Then $C(p_i(x)) = \| \lambda_i \|$, and the matrix Q of (4.3) becomes $\| 1 \|$, and so

$$(5.5) \qquad C^*(p_i(x)^{e_{ij}}) = \begin{Vmatrix} \lambda_i & 1 & & & 0 \\ & \cdot & \cdot & & \\ & & \cdot & \cdot & \\ & & & \cdot & 1 \\ 0 & & & & \lambda_i \end{Vmatrix}$$

is a square matrix of degree e_{ij} with zeros everywhere except for λ_i on the diagonal and a stripe of 1's immediately above the diagonal.

We return now to the arbitrary field $\mathscr{F}$. The integers e_{ij} are called the *Segre characteristics* of T or of any of its matrices. We see that two matrices with the same minimum functions are similar if and only if they have the same set of Segre characteristics.

The rational canonical form takes its name from the fact that, if $\mathscr{F}_1$ is a subfield of $\mathscr{F}_2$, then the rational canonical form for an $\mathscr{F}_1$ matrix is the same whether we consider $\mathscr{F}_1$ or $\mathscr{F}_2$ as the scalar domain. It corresponds to a decomposition of the underlying vector space into a direct sum of as few cyclic spaces as possible. On the other hand, the classical canonical form for a matrix definitely depends upon the field of scalars and corresponds to a decomposition of the underlying vector space into a direct sum of as many cyclic spaces as possible. The dependence of the classical canonical form on the field of scalars is of course a consequence of the fact that a polynomial which is prime in a field $\mathscr{F}_1$ need not remain prime in an extension field $\mathscr{F}_2$.

Exercises 10.5

1. Find the matrix in rational canonical form whose nontrivial invariant factors are $(x - 3)^3(x - 2)$, $(x - 3)^2(x - 2)$, and $(x - 2)$. Find a matrix in classical canonical form with these same invariant factors.

2. Let the characteristic function of a linear transformation T be $x^4 - 9$. Show that this is also the minimum function of T, and find a matrix for T in classical canonical form for each of the three fields $\mathfrak{Q}$, $\mathfrak{R}$, and $\mathfrak{C}$.

3. Find the invariant factors and elementary divisors of the following matrices.

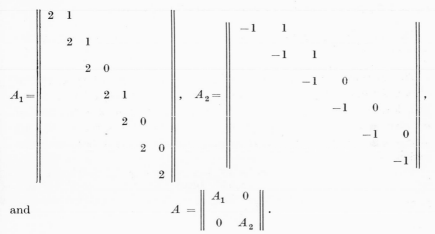

and
$$A = \left\| \begin{array}{cc} A_1 & 0 \\ 0 & A_2 \end{array} \right\|.$$

4. Find the Segre characteristics of each of the matrices in the preceding exercises.

5. Find the dimensions of the null spaces of $A_1 - 2$, $(A_1 - 2)^2$, $(A_1 - 2)^3$, $(A_1 - 2)^4$ where A_1 is the matrix given in Exercise 3.

6. Show for every linear transformation T on a vector space $\mathscr{V}$ that the characteristic function is a factor of some power of the minimum function. (Cf. Ex. 10.3.7.)

7. Let $\lambda_1, \cdots, \lambda_n$ be the eigenvalues of A. Show that $\lambda_1{}^s, \cdots, \lambda_n{}^s$ are the eigenvalues of A^s $(s = 1, 2, \cdots)$.

8. Find the monic polynomial whose roots are the squares of the roots of $f(x) = x^3 + 2x^2 - x + 1$. [Hint: apply Ex. 7 with $A = C(f(x))$.]

9. Let $\mathscr{F}$ be a subfield of $\mathscr{F}'$, and let A and B be n-by-n $\mathscr{F}$ matrices. Show that, if A and B are similar over $\mathscr{F}'$, then they are already similar over $\mathscr{F}$.

10. List all matrices in classical canonical form that have characteristic function $(x - 2)^4$.

11.
$$\text{Are the matrices} \quad A = \begin{Vmatrix} 49 & -29 \\ 78 & -46 \end{Vmatrix} \quad \text{and} \quad B = \begin{Vmatrix} 1 & -2 \\ 3 & 2 \end{Vmatrix} \quad \text{similar?}$$

12.
$$\text{Are the matrices } A = \begin{Vmatrix} -1 & 1 & 0 \\ -9 & 5 & 1 \\ 8 & -3 & -1 \end{Vmatrix} \quad \text{and} \quad B = \begin{Vmatrix} 3 & 1 & 0 \\ -4 & -1 & 0 \\ -10 & -5 & 1 \end{Vmatrix}$$
similar?

13. Under what circumstances can one conclude that two matrices are similar by looking only at their characteristic functions?

14. What conclusions may be drawn about an n-by-n matrix and its canonical forms if (a) its eigenvectors span $\mathscr{V}_n{}^r$, (b) its eigenvectors do not span $\mathscr{V}_n{}^r$, (c) it has no eigenvectors, (d) it has an infinite set of eigenvectors no two of which are dependent?

15. Find the classical canonical form for $\begin{Vmatrix} 1 & 0 & 1 \\ 2 & 0 & 3 \\ 1 & 1 & 2 \end{Vmatrix}$.

16. Let $B = \begin{Vmatrix} 2 & 7 \\ -1 & 3 \end{Vmatrix}$. Find the classical canonical form for B if $\mathscr{F} = \mathfrak{R}$ and if $\mathscr{F} = \mathfrak{C}$.

17. Let T be a linear transformation on $\mathscr{V}_4{}^r$ whose minimum function is $x^4 - 4$. Find the classical canonical form matrices for T relative to $\mathfrak{Q}$, $\mathfrak{R}$, and $\mathfrak{C}$. Find the rational canonical matrices for T relative to $\mathfrak{Q}$, $\mathfrak{R}$, and $\mathfrak{C}$.

18. Let A be an n-by-n matrix; let $\mathscr{W}$ be a subspace of $\mathscr{E}_n$ invariant under A; let C be an m-by-n matrix whose rows form a basis for $\mathscr{W}$; set $D = CAC'$ where $C' = C^T(CC^T)^{-1}$ is a right inverse for C (cf. Exercise 1 of Section 4.6); let $f(x)$ be an arbitrary polynomial; and let $r(x)$ be the minimum function for D.

Prove that (a) $Cf(A) = f(D)C$, (b) $Cf(A) = 0$ if and only if $f(D) = 0$, and (c) $r(x)$ is the minimum function of A relative to $\mathscr{W}$. (T. N. E. Greville.)

19. The characteristic matrix of A has the following nontrivial determinantal divisors $x^5(x - 2)^4$, $x^2(x - 2)^2$, x. (a) What are the invariant factors of A? (b) What are the elementary divisors of A? (c) Find canonical forms for A.

20. How many matrices of degree five over $\mathfrak{C}$ and in classical canonical form have a given quadratic minimum function?

21. Show that the only eigenvalues of an idempotent transformation are zero and one.

22. Show that two idempotent matrices (of the same degree) are similar if and only if they have the same rank.

23. Show that every idempotent matrix is similar to a diagonal matrix.

24. Let A be a square $\mathfrak{C}$ matrix. Show that some power of A is the identity matrix if and only if (1) every eigenvalue of A is a root of unity and (2) the minimum function for A has no repeated roots.

25. Show that a square $\mathfrak{C}$ matrix A is similar to a diagonal matrix if and only if its minimum function has no repeated root.

26. A transformation is said to be an *involution* if it is its own inverse. Show that the only eigenvalues of an involution are 1, -1.

27. Let T be an involution on a vector space $\mathscr{V}$. Show that $\mathscr{V} = \mathscr{V}_1 + \mathscr{V}_2$ (direct) where $\mathscr{V}_1$ and $\mathscr{V}_2$ are invariant subspaces of $\mathscr{V}$ such that the restriction of T to $\mathscr{V}_1$ is I and to $\mathscr{V}_2$ is $-\mathsf{I}$.

28. Let A be a square matrix. Show that the eigenvalues of $\left\| \begin{matrix} 0 & A \\ A & 0 \end{matrix} \right\|$ are those of A together with those of $-A$.

10.6. Segre characteristics.

Let T be a primary linear transformation on a vector space $\mathscr{V}$, and suppose that $\alpha_1, \cdots, \alpha_r$ are vectors for which Theorem 10.4E holds, and let $e = e_1 \geq e_2 \geq \cdots \geq e_r > 0$ be the Segre characteristics of T; i.e., α_i has relative minimum function $p(x)^{e_i}$ $(i = 1, \cdots, r)$ where $p(x)$ is an irreducible polynomial of degree f.

Let

$$(6.1) \qquad m = n/f = e_1 + \cdots + e_r, \qquad e_1 \geq e_2 \geq \cdots \geq e_r > 0,$$

i.e., $e_1, e_2, \cdots, e_r$ is an ordered partition of m. (A set of non-negative integers $a_1, \cdots, a_k$ is said to be a *partition* of m if $a_1 + \cdots + a_k = m$. If, moreover, $a_1 \geq a_2 \geq \cdots \geq a_h > a_{h+1} = \cdots = a_k = 0$, we say that $a_1, \cdots, a_k$ is an *ordered* partition of m into h parts.) Let $h_j =$ number of e_ν which are greater than or equal to j $(j = 1, \cdots, e(= e_1))$. Clearly $h_1 = r$; we now show that

$$(6.2) \qquad m = h_1 + \cdots + h_e.$$

To establish this consider the e-by-r matrix P whose jth column has 1 in each of its first e_j rows and zeros below $(j = 1, \cdots, r)$. For example, the matrix

$$P = \left\| \begin{matrix} 1 & 1 & 1 & 1 & 1 & 1 \\ 1 & 1 & 1 & 0 & 0 & 0 \\ 1 & 1 & 0 & 0 & 0 & 0 \\ 1 & 1 & 0 & 0 & 0 & 0 \\ 1 & 0 & 0 & 0 & 0 & 0 \end{matrix} \right\|$$ describes the partition $14 = 5 + 4 + 2 + 1 + 1 + 1$.

Then the sum of the elements of P is $m = e_1 + \cdots + e_r$. On the other hand, h_i is by definition equal to the number of nonzero entries in the ith row of P and hence is the sum of the elements in the ith row of P. It follows that $m = h_1 + \cdots + h_e$, and, moreover, that $h_1 \geq h_2 \geq \cdots \geq h_e > 0$.

Two partitions of m are said to be *conjugate* if the matrix of one is the transpose of the matrix of the other. For example, the conjugate of the partition 5, 4, 2, 1, 1, 1 is 6, 3, 2, 2, 1. Every partition has a unique conjugate and is the conjugate of its conjugate. Clearly, $e_1, \cdots, e_r$ and $h_1, \cdots, h_e$ are conjugate partitions of m. Thus the Segre characteristics and the numbers $h_1, \cdots, h_e$, called the *Weyr numbers*, determine each other uniquely. We now give two direct characterizations of the Weyr numbers.

THEOREM 10.6A. *Let* $\mathscr{W}_i = \mathscr{V} p(\mathsf{T})^i$ $(i = 0, 1, \cdots, e)$ *and let* $\mathscr{U}_i$ *be the kernel of* $p(\mathsf{T})^i$ $(i = 0, 1, \cdots, e)$. *Then* $fh_i = \dim \mathscr{W}_{i-1} - \dim \mathscr{W}_i = \dim \mathscr{U}_i - \dim \mathscr{U}_{i-1}$ $(i = 1, \cdots, e)$.

We have
$$\mathscr{V} = \mathscr{V}(\alpha_1, \mathsf{T}) + \cdots + \mathscr{V}(\alpha_r, \mathsf{T}) \qquad \text{(direct sum)};$$
then
$$\mathscr{W}_j = \mathscr{V}(\alpha_{1j}, \mathsf{T}) + \cdots + \mathscr{V}(\alpha_{rj}, \mathsf{T}) \qquad \text{(direct sum)}$$
where $\alpha_{ij} = \alpha_i p(\mathsf{T})^j$. (We agree to delete zero summands.) Now $\dim \mathscr{V}(\alpha_{ij}, \mathsf{T}) = 0$ if $e_i \leq j$ and $\dim \mathscr{V}(\alpha_{ij}, \mathsf{T}) = f(e_i - j)$ if $e_i \geq j$. The first equality follows at once.

Next observe that $\mathscr{U}_j = \mathscr{V}(\beta_{1j}, \mathsf{T}) + \cdots + \mathscr{V}(\beta_{rj}, \mathsf{T})$ (direct sum) where $\beta_{ij} = \alpha p(\mathsf{T})^{e_i - j}$. Now, a similar argument gives the remaining equality.

This theorem gives a new proof of the invariance of the Segre characteristics.

In the general case the Weyr numbers of a linear transformation T are defined to be the elements of the conjugate partitions of the Segre characteristics of the primary components of T and can be used to determine the dimensions of the kernel and range of $g(\mathsf{T})$ where $g(x)$ is any polynomial. We first write $g(x) = g^*(x) p_1(x)^{t_1} \cdots p_s(x)^{t_s}$ where $g^*(x)$ is relatively prime to all of the $p_i(x)$. Then the range of $g(\mathsf{T})$ has dimension
$$k = \Sigma f_i k_i$$
where
$$k_i = \sum_{j=1}^{r_i} \max(0, e_{ij} - t_i)$$
and the kernel of $g(\mathsf{T})$ has dimension
$$l = \Sigma f_i l_i$$

where
$$l_i = \sum_{j=1}^{r_i} \min(e_{ij}, t_i).$$

Exercises 10.6

1. Show that $k_i + l_i = n_i / f_i = e_{i1} + \cdots + e_{ir_i}$.
2. Show that $l_i = h_{i1} + \cdots + h_{it_i}$.
3. Let $\mathscr{F} = \mathfrak{Q}$, and let T be a linear transformation with elementary divisors $(x^2 + 2x + 2)^4$, $(x^2 + 2x + 2)^2$, $(x^2 + 2x + 2)$, $(x^2 + 2x + 2)$, $(x - 1)^5$, $(x - 1)^5$, $(x - 1)^3$, $(x + 2)^4$, $(x + 2)$, $(x + 2)$, $(x + 2)$, $(x + 2)$.
Find the invariant factors, the Segre characteristics, the Weyr numbers of T. Find the determinantal divisors of $Ix - A$ where A is a matrix for T.
4. Let $\mathscr{F} = \mathfrak{Q}$, and let T be a linear transformation for which the irreducible factors of the minimum function are $p_1(x) = (x^2 + 1)$, $p_2(x) = (x^3 + x - 1)$, $p_3(x) = (x - 2)$ and whose Weyr numbers are given by the matrix

$$H = \| h_{ij} \| = \begin{Vmatrix} 5 & 3 & 1 & 0 & 0 \\ 2 & 1 & 1 & 1 & 0 \\ 4 & 4 & 2 & 1 & 1 \end{Vmatrix}.$$

Find the invariant factors, the elementary divisors, and the Segre characteristics of T.
5. Let T be as in Exercise 3, and let $g(x) = (x^2 + 3x + 2)(x^2 + 2x + 2)^2 \cdot (x - 1)^2 (x + 2)$. Find the dimension of the range and kernel of $g(\mathsf{T})$.
6. Do the same for T in Exercise 4 and $g(x) = (x^2 + 1)(x - 2)^3$.

10.7. Pairs of bilinear forms; systems of linear differential equations.

Let A_1, A_2, B_1, B_2 be square matrices of degree v. We ask under what conditions the ordered pair A_1, A_2 is (simultaneously) equivalent to the ordered pair B_1, B_2; i.e., when do there exist nonsingular matrices P, Q for which

$$(7.1) \qquad PA_iQ = B_i \qquad\qquad (i = 1, 2)?$$

THEOREM 10.7A. *Let A_1, A_2, B_1, B_2 be square matrices of degree v, and suppose that A_2 and B_2 are nonsingular. Then the pair A_1, A_2 is equivalent to the pair B_1, B_2 if and only if $A_1 A_2^{-1}$ is similar to $B_1 B_2^{-1}$.*

We first establish the "if" part. Suppose that

$$(7.2) \qquad PA_1 A_2^{-1} P^{-1} = B_1 B_2^{-1}.$$

Then let $Q = A_2^{-1} P^{-1} B_2$, and we have (7.1).
Conversely, if (7.1) holds, then

$$(7.3) \qquad PA_1 A_2^{-1} P^{-1} = PA_1 QQ^{-1} A_2^{-1} P^{-1} = B_1 B_2^{-1}.$$

We leave as an exercise the proof that a similar result holds if any linear combination of B_1 and B_2 is nonsingular.

We saw in Section 9.6 that systems of linear differential equations could be treated by matrix methods. We now consider a special case in more detail. We operate over the field $\mathfrak{C}$ of complex numbers. Let $y_1, \cdots, y_v$ be dependent variables, let D be the differential operator $\mathsf{D} = d/dx$, and consider the system

$$(7.4) \qquad\qquad (A\mathsf{D} + B)Y = K,$$

where $Y = \| y_i \|$, $K = \| k_i(x) \|$, and A, B, are square $\mathfrak{C}$ matrices of degree v. If A were singular, then premultiplication of (7.4) by an appropriate nonsingular matrix would lead to an equivalent system in which one or more of the equations would involve no derivatives. These equations could then be used to express certain of the dependent variables y_i as linear functions of the remaining ones; these variables could then be eliminated, leading to a system in fewer unknowns. Hence we suppose that A is nonsingular.

We begin by considering two possible ways of simplifying the system (7.4): the first is to replace the equations by equivalent linear combinations, this amounts to left multiplication by a nonsingular matrix P whose elements are constants; the second is to change variables by a linear substitution $Y = QZ$ where Q is also a nonsingular matrix with constant entries. The effect of both changes is to replace (7.4) by

$$(7.5) \qquad\qquad (PAQ\mathsf{D} + PBQ)Z = PK.$$

Let $Q = A^{-1}P^{-1}$; then (7.5) becomes

$$(7.6) \qquad\qquad (I_v\mathsf{D} + P(BA^{-1})P^{-1})Z = PK,$$

where we can now choose P so as to put $PBA^{-1}P^{-1}$ into one of the canonical forms for similarity. In particular, we may choose P so that $PBA^{-1}P^{-1}$ is a slight modification of the classical canonical form for which (7.6) separates into a set of systems each of the form

$$(7.7) \qquad\qquad (I_s\mathsf{D} + Q_\lambda)U = L,$$

where $L = \| l_i(x) \|$ is a column of known functions and

$$(7.8) \qquad\qquad Q_\lambda = \begin{Vmatrix} \lambda & & & 0 \\ -1 & \cdot & & \\ & \cdot & \cdot & \\ & & \cdot & \cdot \\ 0 & & -1 & \lambda \end{Vmatrix}.$$

Next, let $U = e^{-\lambda x}W$, and then (7.7) becomes

(7.9) $(I_s D + Q_0)W = e^{\lambda x}L = H$,

or

(7.10)
$$w'_1 = h_1(x),$$
$$w'_2 = h_2(x) + w_1,$$
$$\cdot \quad \cdot \quad \cdot$$
$$w'_s = h_s(x) + w_{s-1}.$$

This reduces obtaining the solution of the original system to integrating known functions.

Exercises 10.7

1. Let A_1, A_2, B_1, B_2 be square matrices of degree v, and suppose that a scalar c exists such that $A_3 = A_1 + cA_2$ and $B_3 = B_1 + cB_2$ are nonsingular. Show then that the ordered pair A_1, A_2 is equivalent to the ordered pair B_1, B_2 if and only if $A_2 A_3^{-1}$ is similar to $B_2 B_3^{-1}$.

2. Solve the system (7.4) when

$$A = \left\| \begin{array}{ccc} 1 & 0 & 0 \\ -2 & 1 & 0 \\ 1 & 0 & 1 \end{array} \right\|,$$

$$B = \left\| \begin{array}{ccc} 2 & 0 & 0 \\ 1 & 2 & 0 \\ 2 & -1 & -1 \end{array} \right\|,$$

and

$$K = \left\| \begin{array}{c} 1 \\ x \\ x^2 \end{array} \right\|.$$

3. Are the bilinear forms $x_1 y_1 + x_2 y_2 + x_3 y_3$ and $2x_1 y_1 + 2x_1 y_2 + 3x_1 y_3 + 3x_2 y_2 + x_2 y_3 + x_3 y_3$ simultaneously equivalent to $x_1 y_1 + 2x_2 y_2 + x_2 y_2$ $3x_3 y_1 + 2x_3 y_2 + x_3 y_3$ and $2x_1 y_1 + 2x_1 y_2 + 3x_1 y_3 + 4x_2 y_1 + 5x_2 y_2 + 7x_2 y_3 + 6x_3 y_1 + 12x_3 y_2 + 12x_3 y_3$?

10.8. Pairs of quadratic forms.

The concept of simultaneous equivalence of ordered pairs introduced in the preceding section can be extended in a natural way to congruence and similarity and to ordered sets of any size. In the present section we study simultaneous congruence.

The following theorem provides a canonical form under simultaneous congruence for pairs of quadratic forms when the first member is positive definite.

THEOREM 10.8A. *Let A_1, A_2 be real symmetric matrices of degree v, and suppose A_1 is positive definite. Then there exists a nonsingular matrix P such that*

$$(8.1) \qquad PA_1P^\mathsf{T} = I_v, \qquad PA_2P^\mathsf{T} = D,$$

where D is a diagonal matrix whose diagonal elements are the roots of $\det (xA_1 - A_2) = 0$.

Since A_1 is positive definite, there exists a nonsingular matrix Q such that $QA_1Q^\mathsf{T} = I$ (Theorem 6.6D). Now $C = QA_2Q^\mathsf{T}$ is symmetric, and hence there is an orthogonal matrix $R = (R^{-1})^\mathsf{T}$ such that $D = RCR^\mathsf{T}$ is diagonal; also $RIR^\mathsf{T} = I$. Now set $P = RQ$, and we have (8.1). Moreover, the diagonal elements of D are the roots of $\det (xI - D)$; this equals $\det P(xA_1 - A_2)P^\mathsf{T} = (\det P)^2 \det (xA_1 - A_2)$. Thus D is uniquely determined up to a permutation of its diagonal elements.

Let A_1, A_2 be real symmetric matrices which are simultaneously equivalent to the real symmetric pair B_1, B_2, say

$$B_1 = QA_1R, \qquad B_2 = QA_2R,$$

where Q and R are nonsingular. If A_1 and B_1 are positive definite, then by Theorems 10.7A and 10.8A the pairs are also congruent; i.e., there exists a nonsingular matrix P such that

$$B_1 = PA_1P^\mathsf{T}, \qquad B_2 = PA_2P^\mathsf{T}.$$

We now consider a somewhat similar situation over the field of complex numbers.

THEOREM 10.8B. *Let $\mathscr{F} = \mathfrak{C}$, and let $\{A_1, \cdots, A_k\}$ and $\{B_1, \cdots, B_k\}$, be two ordered sets of symmetric matrices. Then, if these sets are simultaneously equivalent, they are simultaneously congruent.*

This theorem follows immediately from the next lemma.

LEMMA 10.8C. *If A, B are symmetric and $B = QAR$ where Q and R are nonsingular, then there exists a nonsingular matrix P, dependent only on Q and R, such that $B = PAP^\mathsf{T}$.*

First $QAR = B = B^\mathsf{T} = R^\mathsf{T}AQ^\mathsf{T}$; hence, if $S = (R^\mathsf{T})^{-1}Q$, we have

$$(8.2) \qquad SA = AS^\mathsf{T}.$$

From (8.2), $S^2A = SAS^\mathsf{T} = A(S^\mathsf{T})^2$, and by an induction argument

$$S^iA = A(S^\mathsf{T})^i.$$

Consequently, for any polynomial $g(x)$ in $F[x]$,

$$(8.3) \qquad\qquad g(S)A = Ag(S^\mathsf{T}).$$

Now S is nonsingular since Q and R are; thus S has a square root (cf. Theorem 10.10C) U which is a polynomial in S.   Then

$$UA = AU^\mathsf{T}$$

or $A = U^{-1}AU^\mathsf{T}$.   Hence $B = QU^{-1}AU^\mathsf{T}R$.   Since $U^2 = (R^\mathsf{T})^{-1}Q$, we get $R^\mathsf{T}U = QU^{-1}$, so that with $P^\mathsf{T} = U^\mathsf{T}R$ we have $P = QU^{-1}$.   Finally, $B = PAP^\mathsf{T}$.

We return now to consider simultaneous congruence of pairs A_1, A_2 and B_1, B_2 of symmetric matrices over the field $\mathfrak{C}$.   By Theorem 10.8B, this occurs if they are simultaneously equivalent, and from Theorem 10.7A this will happen, when A_2 and B_2 are nonsingular, if and only if $\lambda A_2 - A_1$ and $\lambda B_2 - B_1$ have the same invariant factors.   Thus the set of invariant factors (or of elementary divisors) is a complete set of invariants.   There remains the question of whether for each set of elementary divisors there is a related pair of symmetric matrices.   From the direct sum decomposition into blocks corresponding to the elementary divisors, it is sufficient to prove this only for the case of a single elementary divisor $(\lambda - a)^e$, and for it we give the example of the e-rowed square matrices

$$A_1 = \begin{Vmatrix} & & & a \\ & & a & 1 \\ & \cdot & \cdot & \\ \cdot & \cdot & & \\ a & 1 & & \end{Vmatrix}, \qquad A_2 = \begin{Vmatrix} & & & 1 \\ & & \cdot & \\ & \cdot & & \\ \cdot & & & \\ 1 & & & \end{Vmatrix}$$

Clearly, for $\lambda A_2 - A_1$, the determinantal divisors $d_n = (\lambda - a)^e$ and $d_{n-1} = 1$.

10.9. Applications to projective geometry.   A *point* P in n-dimensional *projective space* $\mathscr{P}_n(\mathscr{F})$ is by definition a one-dimensional subspace $\mathscr{L}$ (or line through O) of $\mathscr{V}_{n+1}(\mathscr{F})$.   A *representative* of P is any vector $\alpha \neq 0$ of $\mathscr{L}$; if β is another representative, then $\beta = k\alpha$ where $k \neq 0$ and is in $\mathscr{F}$. A common method of obtaining at most one representative for each point P is to take in $\mathscr{V}_{n+1}$ a hyperplane $\mathscr{H}$ not passing through the origin and intersect it with $\mathscr{L}$ (a *hyperplane* of $\mathscr{V}_{n+1}$ is the set of all vectors $\alpha + \gamma$ where γ is fixed and α ranges through all vectors in an n-dimensional subspace $\mathscr{S}$ of $\mathscr{V}_{n+1}$); no intersection occurs for the subspaces $\mathscr{L}$ in $\mathscr{S}$

since $\gamma \neq 0$, and such points of $\mathscr{P}_n$ are called *ideal points* with respect to $\mathscr{H}$. Also, subspaces of $\mathscr{V}_{n+1}$ contained in $\mathscr{S}$ are called *ideal elements* of $\mathscr{P}_n$ with respect to $\mathscr{H}$; in particular, $\mathscr{H}$ is itself called the *hyperplane at infinity* of $\mathscr{P}_n$ with respect to $\mathscr{H}$.

Since a nonsingular transformation T on $\mathscr{V}_{n+1}$ sends one-dimensional subspaces into one-dimensional subspaces, it can be considered as a transformation on $\mathscr{P}_n$; then T is called a *projective transformation*. It is easily seen that $k\mathsf{T}$, where k is a nonzero scalar, is the same projective transformation as T; the converse is also true (its proof is left as an exercise).

We first ask which points P of $\mathscr{P}_n$ are *fixed* under T; viz., are such that $P\mathsf{T} = P$. Let α in $\mathscr{V}_{n+1}$ be a representative of P. Then we must have $\alpha\mathsf{T} = \lambda\alpha$ for a suitable scalar $\lambda \neq 0$. Thus the fixed points of $\mathscr{P}_n$ under T are represented precisely by eigenvectors of $\mathscr{V}_{n+1}$. Since T is nonsingular, no eigenvalue equals 0.

Next we discuss the introduction of coordinates. Let $\{\alpha_1, \cdots, \alpha_{n+1}\}$ be a basis of $\mathscr{V}_{n+1}$, so chosen that $\mathscr{H}$ has the equation $x_{n+1} = 1$; i.e., $\mathscr{S} = \langle \alpha_1, \cdots, \alpha_n \rangle$ and $\gamma = \alpha_{n+1}$. The representatives will then be $\xi = (x_1, \cdots, x_n, 1)$ and, on $\mathscr{S}$, will be $\xi' = (x_1, \cdots, x_n)$. Also, to a two-dimensional subspace of $\mathscr{V}_{n+1}$, called a line in $\mathscr{P}_n$, determined by ξ_1 and ξ_2, will correspond on $\mathscr{S}$ the line determined by ξ'_1 and ξ'_2; and similarly in general for all subspaces of $\mathscr{V}_{n+1}$ and subsets of $\mathscr{P}_n$ of one lower dimension. The ideal points are represented by vectors $\alpha = (a_1, \cdots, a_{n+1})$ with $a_{n+1} = 0$. If $(x_1, \cdots, x_n, x_{n+1})$ is a point on $\mathscr{L}$, then its representative on $\mathscr{H}$, $x_{n+1} = 1$, is given by $(x_1/x_{n+1}, \cdots, x_n/x_{n+1}, 1)$. To see a reason why the ideal points are also called *points at infinity*, we take $\mathscr{F} = \mathfrak{R}$, and a vector $\xi = (x_1, \cdots, x_n, x_{n+1})$. Holding $x_1, \cdots, x_n$ constant and letting x_{n+1} approach 0, we see that the representative in the plane $x_{n+1} = 1$ goes to infinity in the direction on $\mathscr{H}$ whose direction numbers are $x_1, \cdots, x_n$. In this geometry of $\mathscr{P}_n$ there is exactly one point at infinity on each line except for the lines at infinity. Also every pair of lines of $\mathscr{P}_n$ lying in the same plane either coincide or intersect in exactly one point.

We next determine the relationship between different matrices giving the same transformation T in $\mathscr{P}_n$. A change of basis in $\mathscr{V}_{n+1}$ will give rise to a similar matrix QAQ^{-1}, and a change of representative of P will lead to multiplication (or division) of the matrix by a nonzero scalar. Thus, if A is one matrix for T on $\mathscr{P}_n$, then B is also a matrix for T if and only if B has the form $cQAQ^{-1}$ where $c \neq 0$ and Q is nonsingular.

We now assume that $\mathscr{F} = \mathfrak{C}$. Two matrices A and B are similar if and only if they have the same nontrivial elementary divisors

(9.1) $(x - \lambda_1)^{e_{11}}, (x - \lambda_1)^{e_{12}}, \cdots, (x - \lambda_s)^{e_{st_s}},$

and then both A and B are similar to the canonical matrix

$$C = \left\| \begin{matrix} M_{11} & & & \\ & \cdot & & \\ & & \cdot & \\ & & & \cdot \\ & & & M_{st} \end{matrix} \right\|,$$

where

$$M_{gh} = \left\| \begin{matrix} \lambda_g & 1 & & \\ & \cdot & \cdot & \\ & & \cdot & \cdot \\ & & & \cdot & \cdot \\ & & & & 1 \\ & & & & \lambda_g \end{matrix} \right\|$$

and has e_{gh} rows. Now cM_{gh} has $(x - c\lambda_g)^{e_{gh}}$ as its only nontrivial elementary divisor. Hence cC and likewise cA have as their nontrivial elementary divisors

(9.2) $$(x_1 - c\lambda_1)^{e_{11}}, \cdots, (x - c\lambda_s)^{e_{st_s}}.$$

Conversely, two matrices A and A' can represent the same linear transformation in $\mathscr{P}_n$ if their elementary divisors are related as in (9.1) and (9.2).

We next give geometrical interpretations to the various possible Segre characteristics in the two-dimensional case $\mathscr{P}_2$; the general case $\mathscr{P}_n$ is very similar:

$$\left\| \begin{matrix} 1 \\ 1 \\ 1 \end{matrix} \right\|$$ Exactly three fixed noncollinear points.

$$\left\| \begin{matrix} 1 & 1 \\ 1 & 0 \end{matrix} \right\|$$ A line pointwise fixed and another fixed point.

(9.3) $\| \, 1 \quad 1 \quad 1 \, \|$ The identity; every point fixed.

$$\left\| \begin{matrix} 2 \\ 1 \end{matrix} \right\|$$ Exactly two fixed points.

$\| \, 2 \quad 1 \, \|$ A line pointwise fixed.

$\| \, 3 \, \|$ Exactly one fixed point.

Let $q(x) = 0$ be a homogeneous quadratic equation with symmetric matrix A. Its locus is a conic. Under a change of coordinates A is replaced by a congruent matrix $B = PAP^\mathsf{T}$, and, allowing for the homogeneity, actually all matrices representing the same locus have the form $B = cPAP^\mathsf{T}$ where $c \neq 0$ and P is nonsingular.

Rank is the only invariant, and, if we take $n = 3$, then when $r = 3$ we have a nondegenerate conic, when $r = 2$ we have two distinct lines, when $r = 1$ we have a single line, and finally if $r = 0$ we have the entire plane.

We next discuss the geometrical significance of simultaneous congruence of two pairs A_1, A_2 and B_1, B_2 of symmetric matrices, where A_2 and B_2 are nonsingular. This is made easy by the use of the canonical form given at the end of the preceding section. When $n = 2$, i.e., in complex two-dimensional projective space, we have the canonical pairs of forms:

$$
\begin{aligned}
f &= \lambda_1 x_1{}^2 + \lambda_2 x_2{}^2 + \lambda_3 x_3{}^2, \\
g &= x_1{}^2 + x_2{}^2 + x_3{}^2;
\end{aligned}
\tag{9.4}
$$

$$
\begin{aligned}
f &= 2\lambda_1 x_1 x_2 + x_1{}^2 + \lambda_2 x_3{}^2, \\
g &= 2x_1 x_2 + x_3{}^2;
\end{aligned}
\tag{9.5}
$$

$$
\begin{aligned}
f &= 2\lambda_1 x_1 x_3 + \lambda_1 x_2{}^2 + 2x_1 x_2, \\
g &= 2x_1 x_3 + x_2{}^2.
\end{aligned}
\tag{9.6}
$$

Characteristic geometrical properties based on categories of intersection differentiate between these cases, in fact also when repeated eigenvalues or zero eigenvalues are considered. We list the cases; first, when g is nondegenerate:

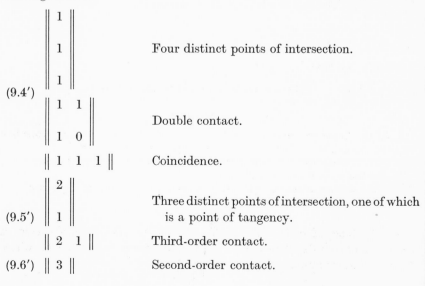

(9.4′)

$$
\begin{Vmatrix} 1 \\ & 1 \\ & & 1 \end{Vmatrix}
$$
Four distinct points of intersection.

$$
\begin{Vmatrix} 1 & 1 \\ 1 & 0 \end{Vmatrix}
$$
Double contact.

$\| \, 1 \quad 1 \quad 1 \, \|$ Coincidence.

(9.5′)

$$
\begin{Vmatrix} 2 \\ & 1 \end{Vmatrix}
$$
Three distinct points of intersection, one of which is a point of tangency.

$\| \, 2 \quad 1 \, \|$ Third-order contact.

(9.6′) $\| \, 3 \, \|$ Second-order contact.

We next consider those cases in which the second conic g is degenerate. These are characterized by the presence of 0 as an eigenvalue. In the following Segre matrices the first row corresponds to the 0 eigenvalue.

In the first five cases the degenerate conic consists of two distinct lines.

$$\begin{Vmatrix} 1 \\ 1 \\ 1 \end{Vmatrix}$$ Four distinct points of intersection.

$$\begin{Vmatrix} 1 & 0 \\ 1 & 1 \end{Vmatrix}$$ Both lines are tangent to f.

$$\begin{Vmatrix} 1 \\ 2 \end{Vmatrix}$$ One line is tangent to f, and the other intersects f in two additional points.

$$\begin{Vmatrix} 2 \\ 1 \end{Vmatrix}$$ The lines intersect on f, and each has an additional intersection with f.

$$\begin{Vmatrix} 3 \end{Vmatrix}$$ The lines intersect on f and one is tangent to f.

In the next two cases the degenerate conic consists of one (double) line.

$$\begin{Vmatrix} 1 & 1 \\ 1 & 0 \end{Vmatrix}$$ The line is not tangent to the conic.

$$\begin{Vmatrix} 2 & 1 \end{Vmatrix}$$ The line is tangent to the conic.

Finally, we have

$$\begin{Vmatrix} 1 & 1 & 1 \end{Vmatrix}$$ The second equation is identically zero.

Exercises 10.9

1. If the linear transformations T and S in $\mathscr{V}_{n+1}$ give the same projective transformation, show that $\mathsf{S} = k\mathsf{T}$ where k is a nonzero scalar.

2. Give a classification of projectivities in the one-dimensional case.

3. Do the same for dimension three.

4. Give a classification of quadratic forms in the one-dimensional case.

5. Do the same for dimension three.

10.10. Roots of matrices. In this section we take $\mathfrak{C}$ as the field of scalars, and consider the solution of the matrix equation $X^t = A$, where t is any natural number.

If A is similar to A', say $A' = PAP^{-1}$, then $X^t = A$ if and only if $X'^t = A'$ where $X' = PXP^{-1}$. Hence, we may suppose that A is in classical canonical form (see formulas 4.3 and 5.5); e.g.

$$(10.1) \qquad A = \begin{Vmatrix} A_1 & & & \\ & \cdot & & \\ & & \cdot & \\ & & & \cdot \\ & & & & A_m \end{Vmatrix},$$

where

$$(10.2) \qquad A_i = \begin{Vmatrix} a_i & 1 & & \\ & \cdot & \cdot & \\ & & \cdot & \cdot \\ & & & \cdot & 1 \\ & & & & a_i \end{Vmatrix}$$

is primary and cyclic $(i = 1, \cdots, m)$.

If $B_i^t = A_i$ $(i = 1, \cdots, m)$, then

$$(10.3) \qquad B = \begin{Vmatrix} B_1 & & & \\ & \cdot & & \\ & & \cdot & \\ & & & \cdot \\ & & & & B_m \end{Vmatrix}.$$

will be a tth root of A.

We introduce the name *stripe matrix* to mean an upper-triangular matrix $C = \| c_{ij} \|$ in which

$$(10.4) \qquad\qquad c_{1j} = c_{1,j+i-1} \qquad\qquad (i = 2, 3, \cdots).$$

For example, the matrices A_i are stripe matrices.

LEMMA 10.10A. *Let C and D be stripe matrices of degree h, and suppose that $c_{11}c_{12} \neq 0$. Then there exist scalars $a_1, \cdots, a_h$ such that*

$$(10.5) \qquad\qquad D = a_1 C + \cdots + a_h C^h.$$

Moreover, D is similar to C if and only if $d_{11} = c_{11}$ and $d_{12} \neq 0$.

Using the determinantal criterion we see that, if $d_{12} = \cdots = d_{1,s+1} = 0$, $d_{1,s+2} \neq 0$ then the minimum function for D is

$$(10.5) \qquad\qquad (x - d_{11})^{h-s}.$$

Moreover, if $s = 0$, i.e., if $d_{12} \neq 0$, the minimum function is $(x - d_{11})^h$, and D is cyclic. We conclude that D is similar to C if and only if $d_{11} = c_{11}$ and $d_{12} \neq 0$.

Next, we observe that the set of all stripe matrices of degree h is an algebra $\mathscr{A}$ of dimension h over $\mathfrak{C}$. The set $\{D, D^2, \cdots, D^{h-s}\}$ is independent if $d_{11} \neq 0$ and all higher powers of D are dependent on this set. Hence, if $d_{11} \neq 0$, D generates a subalgebra of dimension $h - s$. In particular, the subalgebra generated by C has dimension h and hence coincides with $\mathscr{A}$. It follows that D can be written in the form (10.5). This completes the proof of the lemma.

LEMMA 10.10B.   *Let C be a nonsingular cyclic stripe matrix. Then there exists a stripe matrix D for which $D^t = C$. Moreover, D is contained in the space spanned by the (positive integral) powers of C.*

Let F be a stripe matrix having $f_{11}{}^t = c_{11}, f_{12} = 1, f_{1j} = 0 \, (j = 3, \cdots, h)$. Then $C' = F^t$ has $c'_{11} = c_{11}$, $c'_{12} = t f_{11}{}^{t-1} \neq 0$. Now, since C is cyclic, $c_{12} \neq 0$. Hence, by Lemma 10.10A, C is similar to C', say $C = PC'P^{-1}$. Then $D = PFP^{-1}$ is a tth root of C. Moreover, according to Lemma 10.10A, F can be written as a polynomial in C'; hence, D belongs to the space spanned by the powers of C.

THEOREM 10.10C.   *Let A be a nonsingular $\mathfrak{C}$ matrix, and let t be any natural number. Then there exists a $\mathfrak{C}$ matrix B for which $B^t = A$. Moreover, B can be selected as a polynomial in A.*

Since A is nonsingular, each of its eigenvalues a_i is different from zero. Hence each of the matrices A_i in (10.2) satisfies the hypotheses of Lemma 10.10B and thus has a tth root B_i. We then get a B from (10.3) which has $A = B^t$.

The equation $B^2 = I$ where $B = \left\| \begin{matrix} 1 & 0 \\ 0 & -1 \end{matrix} \right\|$ shows that it is not always

possible to express every tth root as a polynomial.

To construct a tth root B which is polynomial in A we first group together any components A_i of A which have the same eigenvalue. Suppose that $a_1 = a_2$ and that deg $A_1 \geq$ deg A_2. Then, by Lemma 10.10B we can find a polynomial $c_1 x + c_2 x^2 + \cdots$ such that $B_1 = c_1 A_1 + c_2 A_1{}^2 + \cdots$ is a tth root of A_1. Now partition A_1 in the form

$$A_1 = \left\| \begin{matrix} A_2 & * \\ 0 & * \end{matrix} \right\|.$$

Using the properties of partitioned matrices, we see that

$$B_1 = \left\| \begin{array}{cc} B_2 & * \\ 0 & * \end{array} \right\|,$$

where $B_2 = c_1 A_2 + c_2 A_2{}^2 + \cdots$, and, moreover,

$$A_1 = B_1{}^t = \left\| \begin{array}{cc} B_2{}^t & * \\ 0 & * \end{array} \right\|,$$

so that B_2 is a tth root of A_2. This shows that each primary component of A has a tth root which is a polynomial in A.

Next suppose that

$$A = \left\| \begin{array}{cc} C_1 & 0 \\ 0 & C_2 \end{array} \right\|,$$

where C_1 and C_2 have relatively prime minimum functions $m_1(x)$, $m_2(x)$ and that there exist polynomials $f_1(x)$ and $f_2(x)$ for which $D_i = f_i(C_i)$ is a tth root of $C_i (i = 1, 2)$. Now set

$$D = \left\| \begin{array}{cc} D_1 & 0 \\ 0 & D_2 \end{array} \right\|.$$

We search for a polynomial $f(x)$ which is congruent to $f_i(x)$ modulo $m_i(x)$ $(i = 1, 2)$. Since $m_1(x)$ and $m_2(x)$ are relatively prime, we can write

$$1 = s_1(x) \, m_1(x) + s_2(x) \, m_2(x).$$

Now set

$$f(x) = f_1(x) + (f_2(x) - f_1(x))(1 - s_2(x) \, m_2(x)),$$

and we have $D = f(A)$. A simple induction on the primary components of A based on this result completes the proof of the theorem.

Exercises 10.10

1. Let D be a stripe matrix with $d_{11} = d_{12} = \cdots = d_{1s} = 0$, $d_{1,s+1} \neq 0$. Find the dimension of the subalgebra of $\mathscr{A}$ spanned by the powers of D.

2. Show that the matrix $A = \left\| \begin{array}{cc} 0 & 1 \\ 0 & 0 \end{array} \right\|$ has no square root, but that the matrix $\left\| \begin{array}{cc} A & 0 \\ 0 & A \end{array} \right\|$ has a square root.

3. Let A be a nilpotent matrix (i.e. one whose eigenvalues are all zero). Give a necessary and sufficient condition in terms of its Segre characteristics that A have a square root. (Hint: consider the possible Segre characteristics for squares of nilpotent matrices.)

4. Find a stripe matrix D that is a square root of the matrix

$$A = \left\| \begin{array}{cccc} a & 1 & 0 & 0 \\ 0 & a & 1 & 0 \\ 0 & 0 & a & 1 \\ 0 & 0 & 0 & a \end{array} \right\|, \qquad a \neq 0.$$

Chapter 11 | Linear Inequalities

11.1. Definitions and notation. A full treatment of systems of linear inequalities is beyond the scope of this text. However, because of the importance of the topic we include a few of the basic theorems and some of their applications to game theory and linear programming. Throughout this chapter the scalar field is the set $\Re$ of real numbers.

Let $\alpha = \| a_1 \cdots a_n \|$ and $\beta = \| b_1 \cdots b_n \|$ be vectors in $\mathscr{V}_n{}^r$. We introduce an order relation $\alpha \geq \beta$ by the definition

(1.1) $$\alpha \geq \beta \quad \text{if and only if} \quad a_i \geq b_i \qquad (i = 1, \cdots, n).$$

If $\alpha \geq \beta$, we also write $\beta \leq \alpha$. For example, $\| 2 \quad 1 \| \geq \| -1 \quad 0 \|$, $\| 1 \quad 3 \| \geq \| -1 \quad 0 \|$, $\| 2 \quad 3 \| \geq \| -1 \quad 3 \|$, but $\geq$ does not hold between any pair of the vectors $\| 2 \quad 1 \|, \| 1 \quad 3 \|, \| 3 \quad 0 \|$. This illustrates the fact that the relation $\geq$ for vectors is only a partial order on $\mathscr{V}_n{}^r$.

In general, a relation $\mathscr{R}$ on a set $\mathscr{S} = \{\alpha, \beta, \cdots\}$ is said to be a *partial order* if it is *reflexive*, *antisymmetric*, and *transitive*; i.e., if, respectively,

(1.2) $$\alpha \mathscr{R} \alpha \text{ for all } \alpha \text{ in } \mathscr{S},$$

(1.3) $$\alpha \mathscr{R} \beta \text{ and } \beta \mathscr{R} \alpha \text{ implies } \alpha = \beta,$$

and

(1.4) $$\alpha \mathscr{R} \beta \text{ and } \beta \mathscr{R} \gamma \text{ implies } \alpha \mathscr{R} \gamma.$$

A partial order is said to be a *complete* (or *total* or *linear*) *order* if also

(1.5) *For each pair* α, β *in* $\mathscr{S}$ *at least one of the relations* $\alpha \mathscr{R} \beta$, $\beta \mathscr{R} \alpha$ *holds.*

Note that the relation $\geq$ for vectors in $\mathscr{V}_n{}^r$ satisfies (1.5) if and only if $n = 1$. It clearly satisfies (1.2), (1.3), and (1.4).

We introduce two further order relations $>$ and $\geq$ in $\mathscr{V}_n{}^r$ by the definitions:

(1.6) $\qquad\qquad \alpha > \beta \quad \text{if and only if} \quad a_i > b_i \qquad\qquad (i = 1, \cdots, n)$

and

(1.7) $\qquad\qquad \alpha \geq \beta \quad \text{if and only if} \quad \alpha \geqq \beta \quad \text{but} \quad \alpha \neq \beta.$

In these cases we also write, respectively, $\beta < \alpha$ and $\beta \leq \alpha$.

A relation $\mathscr{R}$ is said to be *asymmetric* if

(1.8) $\qquad\qquad \alpha\mathscr{R}\beta \text{ and } \beta\mathscr{R}\alpha \text{ never both hold.}$

The relations $>$ and $\geq$ are both asymmetric and transitive.

A vector α is said to be *strictly positive* if $\alpha > 0$ and is said to be *positive* if $\alpha \geq 0$. A positive vector for which $a_1 + \cdots + a_n = 1$ is called a *probability vector*. If β is any positive vector and if $c = 1/(b_1 + \cdots + b_n)$, then $\alpha = c\beta$ is a probability vector. We denote by $\mathscr{P}_n{}^r$ the set of all probability vectors in $\mathscr{V}_n{}^r$.

The set of all vectors for which $\alpha \geq 0$ is called the *positive orthant* in $\mathscr{V}_n{}^r$. We denote it by $\mathscr{Q}_n{}^r$. The positive vectors are just the nonzero elements of $\mathscr{Q}_n{}^r$, and the strictly positive vectors are the interior points of $\mathscr{Q}_n{}^r$.

Analogous definitions apply to the column spaces $\mathscr{V}_m{}^c$.

Exercises 11.1

1. Find vectors α, β in $\mathscr{V}_3{}^r$ for which neither $\alpha > \beta$ nor $\beta > \alpha$.

2. Show that, if $\alpha > \beta$ and c is a positive scalar, then $c\alpha > c\beta$, $-c\beta > -c\alpha$, $\alpha - \beta > 0$. Do the same for $\geq$ and $\geqq$.

3. Show that, if $\alpha > \beta$ and $\alpha' > \beta'$, then $\alpha + \alpha' > \beta + \beta'$, and similarly for $\geq$ and $\geqq$.

4. Give geometric interpretations for the sets $\mathscr{Q}_2{}^r$, $\mathscr{P}_2{}^r$, $\mathscr{Q}_3{}^r$, $\mathscr{P}_3{}^r$.

5. Prove that an asymmetric relation is not reflexive.

6. Let E be an n-by-m matrix all of whose elements are 1 and ξ be in $\mathscr{P}_n{}^r$ and η in $\mathscr{P}_m{}^c$. Prove that $\xi E\eta = 1$.

7. Give examples of vectors in $\mathscr{V}_3{}^r$ which illustrate the differences among the relations $>$, $\geq$, $\geqq$. Do such examples exist in $\mathscr{V}_1{}^r$?

11.2. Inequalities and convex sets.

Let $x_1, \cdots, x_n$ be the components of a variable column vector ξ, and let $\alpha = \| a_1 \cdots a_n \|$ be a nonzero row vector. The set of values of ξ that satisfy the linear equation

(2.1) $\qquad\qquad \alpha\xi + k = a_1 x_1 + \cdots + a_n x_n + k = 0$

is said to be a hyperplane π in $\mathscr{V}_n{}^c$. The set of solutions of

(2.2) $\qquad\qquad\qquad \alpha\xi + k \geqq 0$

is called a *closed half space* $\mathscr{H}_c$, and the set of solutions of

(2.3) $\qquad\qquad\qquad \alpha\xi + k > 0$

is called an *open half space* $\mathscr{H}_o$. We shall use the term "half space" to mean "closed half space."   Note that π consists of precisely those vectors that lie in $\mathcal{H}_c$ but not in $\mathcal{H}_o$.

The terms "open" and "closed" are used in a sense analogous to their use in describing intervals. To see this we make use of the ideas of *length* of a vector and of *distance* between two vectors that were introduced in Sections 7.1 and 7.2. If α is any vector and b is a positive real number, the set of all vectors ξ for which

$$|\xi - \alpha| < b$$

is called a *spherical* neighborhood of α, we denote this set by $\mathcal{N}_b(\alpha)$. A set $\mathcal{S}$ of vectors is said to be *open* if for each α in $\mathcal{S}$ there exists a positive real number b such that $\mathcal{N}_b(\alpha) \subseteq \mathcal{S}$. A vector β is said to be a *limit point* of a set $\mathcal{S}$ if every spherical neighborhood of β has at least one vector distinct from β in common with $\mathcal{S}$. The set $\overline{\mathcal{S}}$ consisting of all points of $\mathcal{S}$ together with all limit points of $\mathcal{S}$ is called the *closure* of $\mathcal{S}$. A set $\mathcal{S}$ is said to be *closed* if $\mathcal{S} = \overline{\mathcal{S}}$. It is easy to show that $\mathcal{H}_o$ is open, that $\mathcal{H}_c$ is closed, and that $\mathcal{H}_c$ is the closure of $\mathcal{H}_o$.

A vector α is said to be in the *boundary* of $\mathcal{S}$ if every spherical neighborhood of α contains vectors in $\mathcal{S}$ and also vectors not in $\mathcal{S}$. Thus the boundary of both $\mathcal{H}_o$ and $\mathcal{H}_c$ is the hyperplane $\alpha\xi + k = 0$.

The system of two inequalities $\alpha\xi + k \geq 0$ and $-\alpha\xi - k \geq 0$ is equivalent to the equality (2.1). Hence, it is natural to include equalities in considering systems of inequalities.

Any system of linear inequalities in $x_1, \cdots, x_n$ can be reduced to the form

$$A_1\xi + K_1 > 0,$$
$$(2.4) \qquad A_2\xi + K_2 \geq 0,$$
$$A_3\xi + K_3 = 0,$$

where A_i and K_i are, respectively, m_i-by-n and m_i-by-1 matrices ($i=1, 2, 3$).

We might ask if the case

$$(2.5) \qquad\qquad A_4\xi + K_4 \geq 0$$

is included in (2.4). The answer is yes. For, let E be the row vector $\| 1 \cdots 1 \|$ in $\mathcal{V}_m{}^r$. Then the system $A_4\xi + K_4 \geq 0$, $E(A_4\xi + K_4) > 0$ is equivalent to (2.5).

The example $x_1 > 0$ and $-x_1 > 1$ shows that not every system has a solution. There will be solutions if and only if the hyperplanes and half spaces defined by the individual equations and inequalities have a non-empty intersection.

If $\xi^{(1)}, \cdots, \xi^{(m)}$ are any vectors in $\mathscr{V}_n{}^c$ and if $\| \, p_1 \cdots p_m \, \|$ is a probability vector, we say that

$$(2.6) \qquad\qquad \xi = p_1\xi^{(1)} + \cdots + p_m\xi^{(m)}$$

is a *convex combination* of $\xi^{(1)}, \cdots, \xi^{(m)}$.   A set of $\mathscr{S}$ vectors is said to be *convex* if every convex combination of vectors in $\mathscr{S}$ is again in $\mathscr{S}$.   It is easy to see that *a set is convex if and only if it contains all convex combinations of pairs of its vectors.*

It follows from the form of the definition of convexity that the intersection of a collection of convex sets is again convex.   Moreover, the empty set and all sets of one element are convex.

THEOREM 11.2A.   *The set of solutions of a simultaneous system of inequalities is convex.*

Let ξ be defined by (2.6); then, for all α and k,

$$\alpha\xi + k = \alpha(p_1\xi^{(1)} + \cdots + p_m\,\xi^{(m)}) + (p_1 + \cdots + p_m)k$$
$$= p_1(\alpha\xi^{(1)} + k) + \cdots + p_m(\alpha\xi^{(m)} + k).$$

From this it follows that hyperplanes and half spaces (open or closed) are convex.   Hence the set of all solutions of a system of inequalities is an intersection of convex sets and therefore is itself convex.

Exercises 11.2

1. Prove that $\mathscr{H}_o$ is open, and that $\mathscr{H}_c$ is the closure of $\mathscr{H}_o$.
2. Prove that the closure of any set is closed.
3. Prove that every set is contained in its closure.
4. Show that any intersection of closed sets is closed.
5. Show that the set of solutions of (2.4) is closed if A_1 and K_1 are missing, i.e. if there are no strict inequalities in the system.
6. Plot the region defined by the system

$$\begin{aligned} x_1 + x_2 &\leqq 1, \\ x_1 &\leqq 2, \\ 2x_1 - x_2 &\leqq 5, \\ x_2 - x_1 &\leqq 2. \end{aligned}$$

7. Find the region defined by

$$\begin{aligned} x_1 &\geqq 0, \\ x_2 &\geqq 0, \\ x_1 + 2x_2 &\leqq 5, \\ 2x_1 + x_2 &\leqq 4, \\ x_1 + x_2 &\leqq 3. \end{aligned}$$

8. Find the region defined by

$$\begin{aligned} x_1 &\geqq 0, \\ x_2 &\geqq 0, \\ x_2 - x_1 &\leqq 1, \\ 2x_2 - x_1 &\leqq 4, \\ 2x_2 - x_1 &\geqq -5. \end{aligned}$$

11.3. Convex cones. A nonempty subset $\mathscr{C}$ of $\mathscr{V}_n{}^r$ is said to be a *convex cone* if it is closed under addition and under multiplication by non-negative scalars. Let $\mathscr{S}$ be any subset of $\mathscr{V}_n{}^r$. We denote by $\mathscr{C}(\mathscr{S})$ the set of all vectors

$$(3.1) \qquad\qquad \alpha = c_1\alpha_1 + \cdots + c_m\alpha_m,$$

where $\alpha_1, \cdots, \alpha_m$ lie in $\mathscr{S}$ and where $\gamma = \| c_i \|$ lies in the positive orthant $\mathscr{Q}_m{}^c$ of $\mathscr{V}_m{}^c$ (i.e. $\gamma \geq 0$). (If $\mathscr{S}$ is the empty set, we set $\mathscr{C}(\mathscr{S}) = \{0\}$.) Clearly $\mathscr{C}(\mathscr{S})$ is a convex cone: we call it the *convex cone* generated by $\mathscr{S}$; e.g., if $\mathscr{S}_1 = \{\| 1 \ \ 0 \|, \| 0 \ \ 1 \|\}$, then $\mathscr{C}(\mathscr{S}_1) = \mathscr{Q}_2{}^r$. A cone $\mathscr{C}$ is said to be *finitely generated* if $\mathscr{C} = \mathscr{C}(\mathscr{S})$ where $\mathscr{S}$ is finite.

We know that the subspace $\langle\mathscr{S}\rangle$ of $\mathscr{V}_n{}^r$ can be described not only as the set spanned by $\mathscr{S}$ but also, dually, as the set of all solutions of a (finite) system of homogeneous linear equations. In the present section we prove the analogous duality theorem for a finitely generated convex cone $\mathscr{C}(\mathscr{S})$: namely, that $\mathscr{C}(\mathscr{S})$ is the intersection of a finite number of half spaces, each of which contains the zero vector on its boundary. Let $\varphi = \| f_i \|$ be a vector in $\mathscr{V}_n{}^c$, and let $\xi = \| x_1 \cdots x_n \|$ be in $\mathscr{V}_n{}^r$. Then all solutions $\xi = \alpha$ of the inequality $\xi\varphi \geq 0$ constitute a half space $\mathscr{H}(\varphi)$ which contains the origin. We say that $\mathscr{H}(\varphi)$ is a *support* for the set $\mathscr{S}$ if every vector α in $\mathscr{S}$ lies in $\mathscr{H}(\varphi)$. A support $\mathscr{H}(\varphi)$ is said to be an *extreme support* for $\mathscr{S}$ if the hyperplane $\xi\varphi = 0$ is spanned by vectors of $\mathscr{S}$. Since $\mathscr{S}$ is finite, it has at most a finite number of extreme supports; it may have none at all. In the example above, $x_1 + x_2 \geq 0$ defines a support of $\mathscr{S}_1$, and $x_1 \geq 0$ defines an extreme support of $\mathscr{S}_1$. The set $\mathscr{S} = \{\| 1 \ \ 0 \ \ 0 \|\}$ has no extreme support since its single vector cannot span a hyperplane (e.g. plane). The set

$$\mathscr{S}_3 = \{\| 1 \ \ 0 \|, \| -1 \ \ 0 \|, \| 0 \ \ 1 \|, \| 0 \ \ -1 \|\}$$

has no extreme support since $\mathscr{C}(\mathscr{S}_3) = \mathscr{V}_2{}^r$ and hence cannot lie in any half space. We shall see below that these simple examples illustrate the only ways in which a set $\mathscr{S}$ can fail to have an extreme support.

THEOREM 11.3A. *Let $\mathscr{S} = \{\alpha_1, \cdots, \alpha_m\}$ be a set of vectors that spans $\mathscr{V}_n{}^r$. Then either $\mathscr{C}(\mathscr{S}) = \mathscr{V}_n{}^r$ or $\mathscr{C}(\mathscr{S})$ is the intersection of the extreme supports of $\mathscr{S}$.*

Suppose* that $\mathscr{C}(\mathscr{S}) \neq \mathscr{V}_n{}^r$, and let $\beta = \| b_1 \cdots b_n \|$ be any vector that does not lie in $\mathscr{C}(\mathscr{S})$. To prove the theorem it is sufficient to show the existence of an extreme support $\mathscr{H}(\varphi)$ for $\mathscr{S}$ which does not contain β.

---

*The proof which we give here was communicated to us by David Gale and A. W. Tucker.

Since $\mathscr{S}$ spans $\mathscr{V}_n{}^r$ and $\beta \neq 0$, we can find a subset $\mathscr{T}'$ of $n-1$ vectors of $\mathscr{S}$ such that $\mathscr{T} = \{\mathscr{T}', -\beta\}$ spans $\mathscr{V}_n{}^r$. Then $\mathscr{C}(\mathscr{T})$ has dimension n. Let ε be any vector that lies in $\mathscr{C}(\mathscr{T})$, but not in any of the spaces generated by subsets of $n-1$ vectors selected from the set $\{\mathscr{S}, -\beta\}$. Such a vector exists since each of the excluded spaces has dimension less than n, and only a finite number of spaces are excluded.

Next select among all expressions (finite in number) of ε as a positive linear combination of $-\beta$ and $n-1$ vectors of $\mathscr{S}$ that one in which the coefficient of $-\beta$ is maximal. We may suppose the notation chosen so that this linear combination is

$$(3.2) \qquad \varepsilon = c(-\beta) + \sum_{\lambda=1}^{n-1} c_\lambda \alpha_\lambda,$$

where $c > 0$, $c_i > 0$ $(i = 1, \cdots, n-1)$ and c is maximal.

Then there exists a unique vector $\varphi = \| f_i \|$ in $\mathscr{V}_n{}^c$ such that

$$(3.3) \qquad \alpha_i \varphi = 0 \qquad\qquad (i = 1, \cdots, n-1)$$

and

$$(3.4) \qquad \beta \varphi = -1$$

[i.e., the components of φ are coefficients of the hyperplane spanned by $\{\alpha_1, \cdots, \alpha_{n-1}\}$, normalized so as to satisfy (3.4)].

We now claim that $\mathscr{H}(\varphi)$ is an extreme support for $\mathscr{C}(\mathscr{S})$ which separates $\mathscr{C}(\mathscr{S})$ from β. In view of (3.3) and (3.4) we need only verify that $\alpha\varphi \geq 0$ for all α in $\mathscr{S}$. Let α be any vector in $\mathscr{S}$. Then, since $\mathscr{V}_r{}^n$ is spanned by $\{-\beta, \alpha_1, \cdots, \alpha_{n-1}\}$, we have an equation

$$(3.5) \qquad \alpha = d(-\beta) + \sum_{\lambda=1}^{n-1} d_\lambda \alpha_\lambda.$$

It follows from (3.3) and (3.4) that

$$(3.6) \qquad \alpha\varphi = d.$$

Suppose now that $d < 0$. We cannot have every $d_i \leq 0$ lest β lie in $\mathscr{C}(\mathscr{S})$. Thus we can suppose the notation chosen so that d_1 is positive and so that $a = c_1/d_1$ is the smallest of the ratios c_i/d_i for d_i positive. Now from (3.5) and (3.2) we get

$$(3.7) \qquad \varepsilon - a\alpha = (c - ad)(-\beta) + \sum_{\lambda=1}^{n-1} (c_\lambda - ad_\lambda)\alpha_\lambda$$

or

$$(3.8) \qquad \varepsilon = (c - ad)(-\beta) + \sum_{\lambda=2}^{n-1} (c_\lambda - ad_\lambda)\alpha_\lambda + a\alpha.$$

Now, since $d < 0$, this is an expression of ε as a positive linear combination of $(-\beta)$ and $n-1$ vectors of $\mathscr{S}$ in which the coefficient $(c - ad)$ of $-\beta$ exceeds c. This contradicts our hypothesis that c was maximal. This in turn contradicts the possibility that d is negative. We conclude that $d \geq 0$ for all α in $\mathscr{S}$ and hence that $\mathscr{H}(\varphi)$ is an extreme support for $\mathscr{C}(\mathscr{S})$. This completes the proof of the theorem.

THEOREM 11.3B. *Let $\mathscr{S} = \{\alpha_1, \cdots, \alpha_m\}$ be a set of vectors in $\mathscr{V}_n^r$. Then $\mathscr{C}(\mathscr{S})$ is either the intersection of a finite number of half spaces, or $\mathscr{C}(\mathscr{S})$ is the entire space.*

The case when $\mathscr{S}$ spans $\mathscr{V} = \mathscr{V}_n^r$ is covered by the theorem just proved. Suppose next that $\mathscr{W} = \langle \mathscr{S} \rangle$ has dimension $k < n$. We may choose coordinates so that $\mathscr{W}$ is defined by the equations $x_{k+1} = \cdots = x_n = 0$. Now apply the theorem to $\mathscr{C}(\mathscr{S})$ considered as a subset which spans $\mathscr{W}$. If $c_1 x_1 + \cdots + c_k x_k \geq 0$ is an extreme support for $\mathscr{C}(\mathscr{S})$ in $\mathscr{W}$, then $c_1 x_1 + \cdots + c_k x_k + 0 x_{k+1} + \cdots + 0 x_n \geq 0$ is a support for $\mathscr{C}(\mathscr{S})$ in $\mathscr{V}$. The half spaces $x_h \geq 0$, $x_h \leq 0$ $(h = k+1, \cdots, n)$ are also supports of $\mathscr{C}(\mathscr{S})$ in $\mathscr{V}$, and $\mathscr{C}(\mathscr{S})$ is the intersection of these supports together with those supports that come from the extreme supports of $\mathscr{C}(\mathscr{S})$ in $\mathscr{W}$.

Exercises 11.3

1. Find the convex cone spanned by the vectors $\| 1 \quad 2 \|$, $\| -1 \quad 2 \|$, $\| 3 \quad 4 \|$, and find the extreme supports of this cone.

2. Find vectors that span the convex cone defined by the inequality system

$$x_1 + x_2 - x_3 \geq 0,$$
$$x_1 \geq 0,$$
$$x_2 \geq 0,$$
$$x_3 \geq 0,$$
$$x_1 - x_2 + 2x_3 \geq 0.$$

3. Find the extreme supports of the cone spanned by the vectors

$$\| 1 \quad 0 \quad 0 \|, \quad \| 0 \quad 1 \quad 0 \|, \quad \| 0 \quad 0 \quad 1 \|, \quad \| 1 \quad 0 \quad 2 \|, \quad \| 0 \quad 1 \quad 1 \|, \quad \| 1 \quad 1 \quad 0 \|.$$

4. Prove that, if (3.3) and (3.4) are regarded as a single system of equations in the components of φ, then the matrix of coefficients is nonsingular, and hence Cramer's Rule provides another proof of the existence and uniqueness of φ.

11.4. Polar cones and double description. We saw in Chapter 3 that for each subspace $\mathscr{W}$ of $\mathscr{V}_n$ we can find matrices A and B such that $\mathscr{W}$ is the row space of A and also the row kernel of B. We gave the name "double description" to this dual characterization of $\mathscr{W}$ and called the set A, B an apolar pair of matrices. Then in Section 6.5 we discussed the pairing of $\mathscr{W}$ with the subspace of $\mathscr{V}_n^c$ consisting of all vectors β for which

$\alpha\beta = 0$ for all α in $\mathcal{W}$. This subspace is, of course, the column space of the matrix B and is in geometry sometimes called the *polar* space of $\mathcal{W}$.

We next consider the analogous problem for convex cones. If $\mathcal{C}$ is any convex cone in $\mathcal{V}_n{}^r$, we consider the set $\mathcal{C}^*$ of all vectors φ in $\mathcal{V}_n{}^c$ such that $\alpha\varphi \geq 0$ for all α in $\mathcal{C}$. It is easy to see that $\mathcal{C}^*$ is again a convex cone; it is called the *polar cone* of $\mathcal{C}$. Similarly, each convex cone $\mathcal{D}$ in $\mathcal{V}_n{}^c$ has a polar cone $\mathcal{D}^*$ in $\mathcal{V}_n{}^r$. It follows from Theorem 11.3B that, if $\mathcal{C}$ is generated by a finite set of vectors, then there exists a finitely generated cone $\mathcal{D}$ in $\mathcal{V}_n{}^c$ which has $\mathcal{C}$ as its polar, $\mathcal{C} = \mathcal{D}^*$; e.g., $\mathcal{D}$ is the cone generated by the columns which are the coefficients of the extreme supports of $\mathcal{C}$.

It is clear from the definition of polar that, if $\mathcal{C}_1 \supseteq \mathcal{C}_2$, then $\mathcal{C}^*_1 \subseteq \mathcal{C}^*_2$, and moreover that for any $\mathcal{C}$, $\mathcal{C}^{**} \supseteq \mathcal{C}$.

THEOREM 11.4A. *Let* $\mathcal{S} = \{\alpha_1, \cdots, \alpha_m\}$ *be a set of vectors in* $\mathcal{V}_n{}^r$, *and let* $\mathcal{C} = \mathcal{C}(\mathcal{S})$ *be the convex cone generated by* $\mathcal{S}$. *Then* $\mathcal{C} = \mathcal{C}^{**}$; *i.e.,* $\mathcal{C}$ *is the polar of its polar.*

Suppose that $\mathcal{C} = \mathcal{D}^*$. Then $\mathcal{C}^* = \mathcal{D}^{**} \supseteq \mathcal{D}$. Hence $\mathcal{C} = \mathcal{D}^* \supseteq \mathcal{C}^{**}$. From this and the universal relation $\mathcal{C} \subseteq \mathcal{C}^{**}$ the theorem follows.

This is the double-description theorem for finitely generated convex cones. A reformulation in matrix language may help in visualizing the situation. Let A be an m-by-n matrix. We associate four convex cones with A (compare this with the four subspaces defined by a matrix), namely:

$\mathcal{C}^r(A)$, the convex cone in $\mathcal{V}_n{}^r$ generated by the rows of A.

$\mathcal{C}^c(A)$, the convex cone in $\mathcal{V}_m{}^c$ generated by the columns of A.

$\mathcal{D}^c(A)$, the convex cone in $\mathcal{V}_n{}^c$ defined by $A\xi \geq 0$.

$\mathcal{D}^r(A)$, the convex cone in $\mathcal{V}_m{}^r$ defined by $\eta A \geq 0$.

It follows from Theorems 11.3B and 11.4A that $(\mathcal{C}^r(A))^* = \mathcal{D}^c(A)$ and $(\mathcal{C}^c(A))^* = \mathcal{D}^r(A)$. We might call $\mathcal{D}^r(A)$ a *finite-intersection convex cone*, and $\mathcal{C}^r(A)$ a *finite-sum convex cone*. One consequence of our double-description theorem is that these concepts coincide, and hence we use the term "finitely generated" to refer to both types. The term *polyhedral cone* is also used for this concept.

COROLLARY 11.4B. *Let* $\mathcal{C}$ *be any polyhedral cone in* $\mathcal{V}_n{}^r$. *Then there exist matrices* A *and* B *such that*

$$\mathcal{C} = \mathcal{C}^r(A) = \mathcal{D}^r(B).$$

THEOREM 11.4C. FARKAS' LEMMA. *Let* A *be an* m-by-n *matrix. Then a vector* α *in* $\mathcal{V}_n{}^r$ *will satisfy the condition* $\alpha\varphi \geq 0$ *for all vectors* φ *in* $\mathcal{V}_n{}^c$

for which $A\varphi \geqq 0$ if and only if there exists a vector $\gamma \geqq 0$ in $\mathscr{V}_m{}^r$ such that
$\alpha = \gamma A$.

This theorem is merely a restatement in matrix language of Theorem
11.4A.   For this interpretation we let $\mathscr{C} = \mathscr{C}^r(A)$.   Then the hypothesis
of the theorem states that α is a vector in $\mathscr{C}^{**}$, and the conclusion states
that α is in $\mathscr{C}$.

The following theorem gives a stronger, nonhomogeneous formulation
of this result.

THEOREM 11.4D.   *Let A be an m-by-n matrix, let δ be a vector in $\mathscr{V}_m{}^c$, let
k be a scalar, and suppose that there is at least one vector φ in $\mathscr{V}_n{}^c$ such that*

$$(4.1) \qquad\qquad A\varphi \geqq \delta.$$

*Then a vector α in $\mathscr{V}_n{}^r$ will satisfy the condition $\alpha\varphi \geqq k$ for all φ that
satisfy (4.1) if and only if there exists a vector $\gamma \geqq 0$ in $\mathscr{V}_m{}^r$ such that
$\alpha = \gamma A$ and $\gamma\delta \geqq k$.*

The "if" is trivial.   To prove the "only if" we rephrase the problem in
homogeneous form; viz., we assume that the system

$$(4.2) \qquad\qquad A\xi - \delta x_0 \geqq 0, \qquad x_0 \geqq 0$$

has a solution $(\xi^{(1)}, 1)$ and assume that for every solution (ξ, x_0) of (4.2)
with $x_0 > 0$ we have

$$(4.3) \qquad\qquad \alpha\xi - kx_0 \geqq 0.$$

Then the conclusion becomes: there exists a row vector $\gamma \geqq 0$ and a
non-negative scalar c_0 such that

$$(4.4) \qquad\qquad \alpha = \gamma A \quad \text{and} \quad k = \gamma\delta - c_0.$$

If (4.3) holds also for all solutions of (4.2) with $x_0 = 0$, then Theorem
11.4C can be applied to

$$(4.5) \qquad A' = \left\| \begin{matrix} A & -\delta \\ 0 & 1 \end{matrix} \right\|, \qquad \alpha' = \| \ \alpha \quad -k \ \|$$

to obtain a vector $\gamma' \geqq 0$ for which $\alpha' = \gamma'A'$.   Then, if we set
$\gamma' = \| \ \gamma \ c_0 \ \|$, we have (4.4).

Thus, either the theorem is true or there exists a vector $\varphi^{(1)}$ for which

$$(4.6) \qquad\qquad A\varphi^{(1)} \geqq 0, \qquad \alpha\varphi^{(1)} < 0.$$

Then let $\xi = \varphi^{(1)} + x_0 \xi^{(1)}$ and have

(4.7) $$A\xi = A\varphi^{(1)} + x_0 A\xi^{(1)} \geq 0 + \delta x_0,$$

and

(4.8) $$\alpha\xi = \alpha\varphi^{(1)} + x_0 \alpha\xi^{(1)}.$$

Now from this equation for x_0 sufficiently small (and positive) we have

(4.9) $$\alpha\xi < kx_0$$

which together with (4.7) contradicts our hypothesis (4.3). Hence we cannot have (4.6), and the theorem follows.

Exercises 11.4

1. Let
$$A = \begin{Vmatrix} 3 & 2 & 1 \\ 2 & 4 & -1 \\ 1 & 1 & 0 \end{Vmatrix}, \qquad \alpha = \begin{Vmatrix} 9 & 9 & 1 \end{Vmatrix}, \qquad \beta = \begin{Vmatrix} 4 & 5 & 0 \end{Vmatrix}.$$

Show that $\alpha\varphi \geq 0$ for all φ such that $A\varphi \geq 0$. Does there exist any solution of $A\varphi \geq 0$ for which $\beta\varphi < 0$?

2. Let $A = \begin{Vmatrix} 2 & 1 \\ 1 & 3 \end{Vmatrix}$, $\alpha = \begin{Vmatrix} 4 & 7 \end{Vmatrix}$, $\delta = \begin{Vmatrix} 1 \\ 2 \end{Vmatrix}$. Then show that $\alpha\varphi \geq 5$

for all φ such that $A\varphi \geq \delta$.

11.5. Linear programming. Let $A = \begin{Vmatrix} a_{ij} \end{Vmatrix}$ be an n-by-m matrix, and let $\beta = \begin{Vmatrix} b_i \end{Vmatrix}$, $\gamma = \begin{Vmatrix} c_j \end{Vmatrix}$, be vectors in $\mathscr{V}_n^c$, $\mathscr{V}_m^r$, respectively. The problem of linear programming is to find a vector $\xi = \begin{Vmatrix} x_i \end{Vmatrix}$ in $\mathscr{V}_m^c$ that minimizes the linear form

(5.1) $$\gamma\xi$$

subject to the inequalities

(5.2) $$A\xi \geq \beta, \qquad \xi \geq 0.$$

A vector ξ is said to be *feasible* if it satisfies (5.2); a feasible vector ξ^0 is said to be *optimal feasible* if $M = \gamma\xi^0 \leq \gamma\xi$ for all feasible ξ.

A classical illustration of linear programming is given by the diet problem. Suppose that there are n nutrients to be obtained from a combination of m foods. Let a_{ij} be the amount of nutrient i contained in a unit of food j, let b_i be the amount of nutrient i needed in a satisfactory diet, and let c_j be the unit cost of food j. Then a combination made up of x_j units of food j $(j = 1, \cdots, m)$ gives a satisfactory diet if $\xi = \begin{Vmatrix} x_i \end{Vmatrix}$ is a feasible vector. An optimal feasible combination is one that meets all nutritional needs at minimum cost.

A linear programming problem may fail to have a solution either because there is no feasible vector or because there is no minimum to the values of $\gamma\xi$ for feasible vectors ξ.

Let $\eta = \| y_j \|$ be a variable vector in $\mathscr{V}_n{}^r$. The problem of maximizing the form

(5.3) $\eta\beta$

subject to the inequalities

(5.4) $\eta A \leqq \gamma, \qquad \eta \geqq 0.$

is said to be the dual to the minimum problem given by (5.1) and (5.2).

THEOREM 11.5A. *A linear programming problem has a solution if and only if the dual problem has a solution. A linear programming problem has a solution if and only if it and its dual are both feasible. If solutions exist, then the minimum M of (5.1) is equal to the maximum M' of (5.3).*

First assume that feasible solutions ξ and η of the two problems exist. Let $\bar{M}$ be the greatest lower bound of $\gamma\xi$ and $\bar{M}'$ be the least upper bound of $\eta\beta$ for feasible solutions. The inequalities

(5.5) $\gamma\xi \geqq \eta A\xi \geqq \eta\beta$

show that $\bar{M}$ and $\bar{M}'$ are both finite and moreover that

(5.6) $\bar{M} \geqq \bar{M}'.$

Now we have

(5.7) $\gamma\xi \geqq \bar{M}$

for all ξ that satisfy (5.2); hence, by Theorem 11.4D there exists a vector η^o in $\mathscr{Q}_n{}^r$ and a vector $\zeta = \| z_i \|$ in $\mathscr{Q}_m{}^r$ such that

(5.8) $\| \eta^o \; \zeta \| \; \left\| \begin{matrix} A \\ \\ I \end{matrix} \right\| = \eta^o A + \zeta = \gamma$

and

(5.9) $\eta^o\beta \geqq \bar{M}.$

Since $\zeta \geqq 0$, this shows that η^o is a feasible vector; also we conclude that $\bar{M}' \geqq \eta^o\beta \geqq \bar{M}$ which with (5.6) gives $\bar{M} = \bar{M}'$. Moreover, $\eta^o\beta = \bar{M}'$ so that $\bar{M}'$ is not only the least upper bound but also the maximum of $\eta\beta$, and so η^o is an optimal feasible vector. By a dual argument we conclude that the minimum problem has a solution and that $M = M'$.

Next suppose that ξ^o is an optimal feasible solution of the minimum problem. Then (5.7) holds for all feasible ξ and again by Theorem 11.4D we get η^o and $\zeta \geqq 0$ which satisfy (5.8). Hence, both problems are feasible, and we are back in the first case.

The remaining statements in the theorem now follow trivially. Moreover, the argument following (5.7) and leading to the conclusion that the dual problem is feasible depends only on the existence of a finite lower bound to $\gamma\xi$ for feasible vectors ξ. Thus we have established the following theorem.

THEOREM 11.5B. *A minimization linear programming problem has a solution if it is feasible and if the form to be minimized has a finite lower bound for feasible vectors.*

The dual result of course holds for maximum problems.

COROLLARY 11.5C. *The linear programming problem given by* (5.1) *and* (5.2) *has a solution if* $\beta > 0$, $\gamma > 0$, *and each row of* A *is* ≥ 0.

It is clear from the hypothesis that, if $\xi > 0$, then $A\xi > 0$, and hence, if we choose a scalar k sufficiently large, $k\xi$ will be feasible. It also follows from the hypothesis that $\gamma\xi > 0$ for all feasible vectors ξ. The existence of a solution now follows from Theorem 11.5B.

The "diet" problem satisfies the hypotheses of this corollary and hence has a solution.

Exercises 11.5

1. Show that the set of optimal feasible vectors for (5.2) is a closed convex set.
2. Find the maximum of $3x + 2y$ subject to the inequalities $x \geq 0$, $y \geq 0$, $x \leq 5$, $y \leq 4$, $x + y \leq 7$.
3. Formulate and solve the dual of the problem given in Exercise 2.

11.6. The Minimax Theorem.

THEOREM 11.6A. *Let* $A = \| a_{ij} \|$ *and* $B = \| b_{ij} \|$ *be two* n-by-m *matrices with* $a_{ij} > 0$ *for all* i, j. *Then there exist probability vectors* $\xi = \| x_i \|$ *in* $\mathscr{V}_n{}^r$ *and* $\eta = \| y_j \|$ *in* $\mathscr{V}_m{}^c$ *and a unique scalar* k *such that*

$$(6.1) \qquad\qquad (kA - B)\eta \geq 0$$

and

$$(6.2) \qquad\qquad \xi(kA - B) \leq 0.$$

First consider (6.1). Since A has positive elements and η is a probability vector, it is clear that

$$(6.3) \qquad\qquad A\eta > 0.$$

Hence, for each η the set of values of k for which (6.1) holds has a least element; we designate this least value by $k(\eta)$. Observe that $k(\eta)$ is a continuous function of η. Now, since the set of probability vectors in $\mathscr{V}_m{}^c$ is compact, the function $k(\eta)$ will have a minimum. Let the minimum value be designated by k^* and a minimizing vector by η^*.

Let $K = k^*A - B$. The result just proved implies that there exists no vector $\zeta \geq 0$ for which

$$(6.4) \qquad\qquad K\zeta > 0;$$

for otherwise k^* would not be minimal.

Now suppose that $\xi K \leq 0$ has as a solution no probability vector ξ or, equivalently, no vector $\xi \geq 0$. This can be restated in the form $\xi D \geq 0$ has no solution, where $D = \| -K \quad I \|$. Then, by Theorem 11.3B,

$\mathscr{C}^c(D) = \mathscr{V}_n{}^c$. This implies that there exists a column vector $\rho = \left\| \begin{matrix} \zeta \\ \zeta' \end{matrix} \right\| \geq 0$ such that

$$(6.5) \qquad\qquad D\rho = -K\zeta + \zeta' < 0.$$

But this contradicts (6.4). Hence, we conclude that there exists a probability vector ξ^* for which $\xi^*(k^*A - B) \leq 0$.

Suppose that ξ, η, k give another solution of (6.1) and (6.2). By the definition of k^* we know that $k \geq k^*$. Suppose that $k > k^*$. Then

$$(6.6) \qquad (kA - B)\eta^* > (k^*A - B)\eta^* \geqq 0.$$

Now from (6.2) and (6.6) we get

$$(6.7) \qquad 0 \geqq [\xi(kA - B)]\eta^* = \xi[(kA - B)\eta^*] > 0.$$

This contradiction establishes the uniqueness of k^* and completes the proof of the theorem.

COROLLARY 11.6B. *Let* k, ξ, η *be solutions of* (6.1) *and* (6.2); *let* $(kA - B)\eta = \| c_i \|$ *and* $\xi(kA - B) = \| d_j \|$. *Then* $c_i x_i = d_j y_j = 0$ $(i = 1, \cdots, m; \; j = 1, \cdots, n)$.

From (6.1) and (6.2) we get

$$\xi(kA - B)\eta = 0,$$

i.e., $\xi \| c_i \| = \| d_j \| \eta = 0$. Now, since the vectors ξ, η, $\| c_i \|$, $\| d_j \|$ are all non-negative, each summand $x_i c_i$ and $d_j y_j$ must vanish.

THEOREM 11.6C. MINIMAX THEOREM. *Let* $f(\xi, \eta) = \xi C\eta$ *be a bilinear form whose matrix is an n-by-m real matrix* C. *Then, if* ξ *and* η *are restricted to the probability spaces* $\mathscr{P}_n{}^r$ *and* $\mathscr{P}_m{}^c$, *respectively, we have*

$$(6.8) \qquad \min_{\eta} \max_{\xi} f(\xi, \eta) = \max_{\xi} \min_{\eta} f(\xi, \eta).$$

First, we observe that all of the minima and maxima cited exist since $f(\xi, \eta)$ is a continuous function with a compact domain.   We set $g(\xi) = \min_{\eta} f(\xi, \eta)$ and $h(\eta) = \max_{\xi} f(\xi, \eta)$, $M = \max_{\xi} g(\xi)$, $m = \min_{\eta} h(\eta)$.   Then the theorem states that $m = M$.

We first show that $m \geq M$.   For let ξ', η' be vectors for which $f(\xi', \eta') = m$, and let ξ'', η'' be vectors for which $f(\xi'', \eta'') = M$.

Now, by the definition of $h(\eta)$, we have for all ξ that $m = h(\eta') \geq f(\xi, \eta')$ and similarly $M = g(\xi'') \leq f(\xi'', \eta)$ for all η.   Hence, in particular,

$$(6.9) \qquad\qquad m \geq f(\xi'', \eta') \geq M.$$

Note that in proving that $m \geq M$ we used only the facts that $f(\xi, \eta)$ is a continuous function and that the domains of ξ and η are compact.   Now for the reverse inequality $M \geq m$ we make full use of the specific nature of the function $f(\xi, \eta)$.   Let E be the n-by-m matrix all of whose elements are 1.   We observe that for all probability vectors ξ and η we have $\xi E \eta = 1$.   Next we apply Theorem 11.6A with $A = E$ and $B = C$.   Let ξ^* and η^* be vectors for which

$$(6.10) \qquad\qquad kE\eta^* \geq C\eta^*; \qquad k\xi^*E \leq \xi^*C$$

where k is the unique scalar whose existence is proved in that theorem.

Now for every ξ we have

$$(6.11) \qquad\qquad f(\xi, \eta^*) = \xi C\eta^* \leq k\xi E\eta^* = k.$$

Therefore, in particular, $h(\eta^*) = k$, and now by the definition of m we have

$$(6.12) \qquad\qquad m \leq h(\eta^*) \leq k.$$

A dual argument applied to the second part of (6.10) gives

$$(6.13) \qquad\qquad M \geq g(\xi^*) \geq k.$$

The theorem now follows at once from (6.9), (6.12), and (6.13).

Exercises 11.6

1. Show that every square matrix with positive elements has a positive eigenvector belonging to a positive eigenvalue. [Hint: take $B = I$ in Theorem 11.6A; note that (6.1) and (6.2) then imply $k > 0$ and $\xi > 0$; next apply Corollary 11.6B.]

2. If $A = \begin{Vmatrix} 1 & 1 \\ 1 & 1 \end{Vmatrix}$ and $B = \begin{Vmatrix} 1 & -1 \\ -1 & 1 \end{Vmatrix}$, find vectors ξ and η whi^{ch}

satisfy the conditions of Theorem 11.6A, given that $k = 0$.

3. Find the $\min_{\eta} \max_{\xi} \xi C\eta$ for probability vectors ξ and η for each of the following matrices:

$$C_1 = \left\| \begin{array}{ccc} 1 & 0 & 2 \\ 3 & 2 & 0 \end{array} \right\|,$$

$$C_2 = \left\| \begin{array}{cc} 2 & 1 \\ 1 & 3 \end{array} \right\|,$$

$$C_3 = \left\| \begin{array}{ccc} -1 & 0 & 4 \\ 2 & 1 & 3 \\ 3 & -2 & -4 \end{array} \right\|,$$

$$C_4 = \left\| \begin{array}{ccccc} 8 & 6 & 4 & 2 & 0 \\ 0 & 3 & 4 & 5 & 7 \end{array} \right\|.$$

11.7. Matrix games. Let C be an n-by-m real matrix. The matrix game corresponding to C is played by two opponents here called players I and II. Simultaneous choices are made by I of a vector ξ in $\mathscr{P}_n{}^r$ and by II of a vector η in $\mathscr{P}_m{}^c$. Then player II pays the amount $\xi C\eta$ to player I. (If this number is negative the absolute value of the payment is of course made from player I to player II.) The vectors ξ and η are called *strategies*. If player I chooses strategy ξ, then the best that player II can do against this is

(7.1) $$g(\xi) = \min_{\eta} \xi C\eta.$$

If player I chooses ξ so as to maximize $g(\xi)$, he can assure himself of a payment of at least

(7.2) $$v = \max_{\xi} \min_{\eta} \xi C\eta.$$

Similarly, by choosing η so as to minimize

(7.3) $$h(\eta) = \max_{\xi} \xi C\eta$$

player II can assure himself of making a payment of no more than

(7.4) $$v' = \min_{\eta} \max_{\xi} \xi C\eta.$$

According to the minimax theorem $v = v'$; this number is called the *value* of the game.

We denote by E a vector all of whose components are 1, and use subscripts to indicate the number of components and superscripts to indicate whether it is a row or column vector; e.g., $E_2{}^r = \left\| \begin{array}{cc} 1 & 1 \end{array} \right\|$.

If v is the value of a game with n-by-m matrix C, then probability vectors ξ^o and η^o are called *optimal strategies* for I and II, respectively, if

(7.5) $\xi^o C \geq v E_m{}^r$ and $C\eta^o \leq vE_n{}^c$.

THEOREM 11.7A. *Let $\mathscr{S}_{\mathrm{I}}, \mathscr{S}_{\mathrm{II}}$ be the sets of optimal strategies for* I *and* II, *respectively. Then $\mathscr{S}_{\mathrm{I}}$ and $\mathscr{S}_{\mathrm{II}}$ are nonempty closed convex sets.*

The existence of at least one optimal strategy for each player is a consequence of the minimax theorem. For the jth column of $\xi^o C$ equals $\xi^o C \eta_j$, where $\eta_j = \| \ 0 \cdots 0 \ \ 1 \ \ 0 \cdots \ \|$, the 1 being in the jth column. The convexity of $\mathscr{S}_{\mathrm{I}}$ and $\mathscr{S}_{\mathrm{II}}$ follows from Theorem 11.2A.

There are a number of methods for obtaining the value v and the sets $\mathscr{S}_{\mathrm{I}}$ and $\mathscr{S}_{\mathrm{II}}$ for a given matrix. Discussion of these is beyond the scope of this text; references are given in the bibliography. We do give a few further results in the theory of matrix games.

THEOREM 11.7B. *Let v be the value of a game with matrix C. Then the value of the game with matrix $C + kE$ is $v + k$. Moreover, the optimal strategies for the two games are the same.*

THEOREM 11.7C. *Let C be a matrix with non-negative elements, and let v be the value of the game with matrix C. Then $v \geq 0$. If, moreover, no column of C is zero, then $v > 0$.*

Both of these theorems follow immediately from the minimax theorem. For, if ξ^o is an optimal strategy for the game with matrix C, we have $\xi^o(C + kE) \geq (v + k)E^r$, and similarly for the second player. Theorem 11.7B follows at once.

Theorem 11.7C is obviously true since $\xi C \eta \geq 0$ if $C \geq 0$.

THEOREM 11.7D. *Let C be a skew-symmetric matrix of degree n. Then the value of the game with matrix C is zero. Moreover, each vector in $\mathscr{S}_{\mathrm{I}}$ is the transpose of a vector in $\mathscr{S}_{\mathrm{II}}$, and conversely.*

Let v be the value of the game, and let ξ^o, η^o be optimal strategies for players I and II, respectively;

(7.6) $\xi^o C \geq vE_n{}^r$, $C\eta^o \leq vE_n{}^c$;

then

$$vE_n{}^c \leq (\xi^o C)^{\mathsf{T}} = C^{\mathsf{T}}\xi^{o\mathsf{T}} = -C\xi^{o\mathsf{T}},$$

or

(7.7) $C\xi^{o\mathsf{T}} \leq -vE_n{}^c$.

From (7.7) we conclude that $v \leq -v$. Similarly, we get

(7.8) $\eta^{o\mathsf{T}}C \geq -vE_n{}^r$,

and, hence, $-v \leq v$. From these inequalities we get $v = 0$, and now (7.7) and (7.8) show that the transpose of an optimal strategy for one player is an optimal strategy for his opponent.

We conclude this section with a treatment of the connection between linear programming and the theory of matrix games. It is easy to reduce the game problem to a problem in linear programming. For [cf. (7.5)] according to the minimax theorem v is the maximum value of the linear form $x_0 = 0x_1 + \cdots + 0x_n + 1x_0$ subject to the system of inequalities

$$\xi C - x_0 E_m^r \geq 0,$$
(7.9) $$\xi \geq 0,$$
$$\xi E_n^c = 1.$$

If $v > 0$, we can also effect the reduction in the following way. Let $v\bar{\xi} = \xi$. Then $1/v$ is the minimum of the linear form $\bar{\xi} E_n^r$ subject to the system

(7.10) $$\bar{\xi} C \geq E_m^r, \qquad \bar{\xi} \geq 0.$$

This formulation involves one less variable than the first. Moreover, we may assume $v > 0$ without loss of generality, since, if D is any matrix, we can choose k so that $C = D + kE$ has all its entries positive and therefore also has positive value. According to Theorem 11.7B knowledge of the value and optimal strategies for the game with matrix C gives those for the game with matrix D. Another advantage of this formulation is that the linear programming problem which we obtain satisfies the hypotheses of Corollary 11.5C. This leads to a new proof of the minimax theorem.

We now consider the reverse equivalence. We return to the linear programming problem given by (5.1) and (5.2), together with the dual problem given by (5.3) and (5.4). By virtue of Theorem 11.5A and formula (5.5) a pair of vectors ξ, η will be optimal feasible if it satisfies (5.2), (5.4), and also

(7.11) $$-\gamma\xi + \eta\beta \geq 0.$$

Now consider the game with matrix C defined by

(7.12) $$\left\| \begin{array}{ccc} 0 & -A & \beta \\ A^\mathsf{T} & 0 & -\gamma^\mathsf{T} \\ -\beta^\mathsf{T} & \gamma & 0 \end{array} \right\|,$$

and let ζ be an optimal strategy for the player I. If the last component z_0 of ζ is not zero, we define vectors ξ and η by the equation

(7.13) $$\zeta = z_0 \| \; \eta \quad \xi^\mathsf{T} \quad 1 \; \|.$$

Now, by Theorem 11.7D, the value of the game with matrix C is zero; i.e.,

(7.14) $\zeta C \geq 0$.

Next, dividing through by z_0, we get

(7.15) $\xi^T A^T - \beta^T \geq 0$, $\xi^T \geq 0$, $-\eta A + \gamma \geq 0$, $\eta \geq 0$, $\eta \beta - \xi^T \gamma^T \geq 0$;

these inequalities are equivalent to (5.2), (5.4), and (7.11); hence ξ and η are optimal feasible vectors.

Conversely, if ξ and η are optimal feasible vectors and if we define z_0 by the equation

(7.16) $(\eta E_m{}^c + E_n{}^r \xi + 1)z_0 = 1$,

then the vector ζ given by (7.13) will be an optimal strategy with positive last component for the game with matrix C. This establishes the following equivalence theorem.

THEOREM 11.7E. *The linear programming problem given by (5.1) and (5.2) has an optimal feasible vector if and only if the game with matrix C given by (7.12) has an optimal strategy with positive last component. Moreover, formulas (7.13) and (7.16) set up a one-to-one correspondence between the optimal strategies ζ with positive last component for the game with matrix C and pairs ξ, η of optimal feasible vectors for the linear programming problem (5.1), (5.2), and its dual (5.3), (5.4).*

Exercises 11.7

In each of the following matrix games find the value and an optimal strategy for each player.

1. $C = \left\| \begin{matrix} 1 & 2 \\ -1 & 3 \end{matrix} \right\|$.

2. $C = \left\| \begin{matrix} 2 & 3 \\ 4 & 2 \end{matrix} \right\|$.

3. $C = \left\| \begin{matrix} 3 & 2 & 1 \\ 0 & 2 & 4 \end{matrix} \right\|$.

4. $C = \left\| \begin{matrix} 0 & 1 & -1 \\ -1 & 0 & 1 \\ 1 & -1 & 0 \end{matrix} \right\|$.

5. $C = \left\| \begin{matrix} 6 & 2 & 1 & 0 \\ -1 & 3 & 5 & 4 \end{matrix} \right\|$.

Appendix I

Mathematical Induction

Mathematical induction can be considered as one of the postulates for the set $\mathfrak{J}$ of natural numbers (positive integers) $1, 2, 3, \cdots$.

First statement of mathematical induction. *Suppose that $\mathscr{K}$ is a subset of the set $\mathfrak{J}$ of natural numbers such that*

    (a) the number 1 is in $\mathscr{K}$, and

    (b) if, whenever a number k belongs to $\mathscr{K}$, the number $k+1$ also belongs to $\mathscr{K}$;

then $\mathscr{K} = \mathfrak{J}$.

In applications of this theorem the subset $\mathscr{K}$ is usually the set of positive integers for which a certain statement is true.

For example, let us use mathematical induction to prove that

$$(1) \qquad\qquad 1 + 2 + \cdots + n = \tfrac{1}{2}n(n+1)$$

for all n in $\mathfrak{J}$.

Let $\mathscr{K}$ be the set of all integers n of $\mathfrak{J}$ for which (1) is true. First, (a) 1 is in $\mathscr{K}$ since (1) holds for $n = 1$. Next, (b) if (1) is true for $n = k$, i.e., if

$$1 + 2 + \cdots + k = \tfrac{1}{2}k(k+1),$$

then by adding $k+1$ to both sides we obtain

$$1 + 2 + \cdots + k + (k+1) = \tfrac{1}{2}k(k+1) + (k+1)$$
$$= \tfrac{1}{2}(k+1)\,[(k+1)+1],$$

and this is (1) with $n = k+1$. Thus both hypotheses (a) and (b) have been satisfied, and consequently $\mathscr{K} = \mathfrak{J}$; hence (1) holds for all n in $\mathfrak{J}$, i.e., for all positive integers.

As a second example we prove by induction that

$$(2) \qquad\qquad n^2 - n \text{ is divisible by } 2$$

302

for all integers, positive or negative or zero.   Let $\mathfrak{J}_1$ be the set of all positive integers n satisfying (2).   Clearly 1 is in $\mathfrak{J}_1$.   Next, if $k^2 - k$ is divisible by 2, then, for $n = k + 1$,

$$n^2 - n = (k + 1)^2 - (k + 1)$$
$$= (k^2 - k) + 2k,$$

and this is divisible by 2 since each of the two terms in the last member is. Hence $\mathfrak{J}_1 = \mathfrak{J}$; i.e., (2) is true for all positive integers.   Next let $\mathfrak{J}_2$ be the set of all positive integers m whose negatives $n = -m$ satisfy (2).   Then 1 is in $\mathfrak{J}_2$ since $(-1)^2 - (-1) = 2$ is divisible by 2.   If k is in $\mathfrak{J}_2$, then $(-k)^2 - (-k)$ is divisible by 2, and also

$$[-(k + 1)]^2 - [-(k + 1)] = [(-k)^2 - (-k)] - 2k$$

is divisible by 2, and hence $k + 1$ is in $\mathfrak{J}_2$.   Thus $\mathfrak{J}_2 = \mathfrak{J}$ and every negative integer n satisfies (2).   Finally the only integer neither positive nor negative is 0, and (2) is satisfied for $n = 0$.   This completes the proof.

A third application of induction is in the proof of the following result.

THEOREM A.1.   *Every nonempty subset $\mathcal{M}$ of positive integers has a smallest integer.*

Let $\mathfrak{J}_1$ be the set of all integers smaller than every integer in $\mathcal{M}$.   If 1 is in $\mathcal{M}$, it is the smallest integer in $\mathcal{M}$.   Otherwise 1 is in $\mathfrak{J}_1$.   Since $\mathfrak{J}_1 \neq \mathfrak{J}$, there must be by (b) an integer k in $\mathfrak{J}_1$ for which $k + 1$ is not in $\mathfrak{J}_1$. Then $k < m$ for every m in $\mathcal{M}$.   Hence

$$(3) \qquad\qquad k + 1 \leq m$$

for every m in $\mathcal{M}$.   But, since $k + 1$ is not in $\mathfrak{J}_1$, equality must hold in (3) for one m' in $\mathcal{M}$.   Thus $k + 1 = m' \leq m$ for every m in $\mathcal{M}$.   This implies that m' is the smallest integer in $\mathcal{M}$.

Conversely, the postulate of mathematical induction can be proved from this theorem, but we shall not do this.   Induction and the theorem are thus equivalent.

Second statement of mathematical induction.   *Suppose that $\mathcal{K}$ is a subset of the set $\mathfrak{J}$ of natural numbers such that*

   (a)   *the integer 1 is in $\mathcal{K}$, and*

   (b)   *if, whenever all positive integers less than k belong to $\mathcal{K}$, the integer k also belongs to $\mathcal{K}$;*

then $\mathcal{K} = \mathfrak{J}$.

This will be proved from the first statement.   Let $\mathcal{K}'$ be the set of elements k of $\mathcal{K}$ for which all natural numbers less than k belong to $\mathcal{K}$.

By hypothesis, 1 is in $\mathscr{K}'$. Next, if k is in $\mathscr{K}'$ then all numbers less than k belong to $\mathscr{K}$, but then by assumption (b) in the second statement k belongs to $\mathscr{K}$. Hence all numbers less than $k+1$ belong to $\mathscr{K}$, and consequently $k+1$ is in $\mathscr{K}'$. By the first statement of induction $\mathscr{K}' = \mathfrak{J}$. Since $\mathfrak{J} = \mathscr{K}' \subseteq \mathscr{K} \subseteq \mathfrak{J}$, we must have $\mathscr{K} = \mathfrak{J}$. This finishes the proof.

A sequence is a function $f(n)$ defined for every positive integer n. The factorial function $n! = 1 \cdot 2 \cdots n$ is an example.

A sequence is defined *recursively* if

(a) $f(1)$ *is given;*

(b) *the value of $f(n)$ is expressed in terms of one or more $f(i)$ with $i < n$.*

For example, a recursive definition of $n!$ is given by $1! = 1$ and $n! = (n-1)!n$.

In Theorem 1.2A the left-to-right product $(\cdots (a_1 a_2)a_3 \cdots)a_n = a_1 a_2 \cdots a_n$ can be defined recursively by

$$a_1 = a_1,$$
$$a_1 a_2 \cdots a_n = (a_1 a_2 \cdots a_{n-1})a_n \qquad\qquad (n \geq 2).$$

Sometimes we use induction to prove a statement which is true for all integers greater than or equal to some given integer m. This occurs for $m = 3$ in the proof of the general associative law.

COROLLARY A.2. *Suppose that $\mathscr{M}$ is a set of integers not necessarily all positive such that*

(a) *a given integer m_1 is in $\mathscr{M}$, and*

(b) *if whenever an integer $m \geq m_1$ belongs to $\mathscr{M}$, the integer $m+1$ also belongs to $\mathscr{M}$.*

Then $\mathscr{M}$ contains all integers greater than or equal to m_1.

To prove this, let $\mathscr{K}$ be the set of positive integers having the form $k = m - m_1 + 1$, where m is in $\mathscr{M}$. It is easy to verify that conditions (a) and (b) of the first statement of induction hold. Consequently, $\mathscr{K}$ is the set of all positive integers. Hence $\mathscr{M}$ contains all integers of the form $m = m_1 + k - 1$ where $k \geq 1$. Thus $\mathscr{M}$ contains all integers $m \geq m_1$.

COROLLARY A.3. *If $\mathscr{Q}$ is a subset of the positive integers such that*

(a) *1 is in $\mathscr{Q}$, and*

(b) *if, for a given m, whenever $q < m$ and q is in $\mathscr{Q}$, then $q+1$ is in $\mathscr{Q}$;*

then $\mathscr{Q}$ contains all the positive integers less than or equal to m.

Let $\mathscr{K}$ be the set consisting of the elements of $\mathscr{Q}$ together with all integers $k > m$. Clearly 1 is in $\mathscr{K}$. Next, suppose k is in $\mathscr{K}$. Either

(i) $k < m$, and then k is in $\mathcal{Q}$, so that $k + 1$ is in $\mathcal{Q}$, and hence in $\mathcal{K}$, or (ii) $k \geq m$, and then $k + 1 > m$, and hence again $k + 1$ is in $\mathcal{K}$. Consequently $\mathcal{K}$ is the set of all integers, and thus $\mathcal{Q}$ must have contained all positive integers $q \leq m$.

Exercises

Prove using mathematical induction:

1. The number of subsets, including the null set, of a set of n objects is 2^n.

2. Every nonempty set of integers that has an upper bound has a largest integer.

3. $$1^2 + 2^2 + \cdots + n^2 = \frac{n(2n + 1)(n + 1)}{6}.$$

4. For all n, $n^3 - n$ is divisible by 3.

5. Generalize Exercise 4, and give a proof.

6. Find the fallacy in the following proof that in every set of n objects all the objects are equal. Let $\mathcal{K}$ be the values of n for which the statement is true. Obviously 1 is in $\mathcal{K}$. Suppose k is in $\mathcal{K}$ and let $a_1, \cdots, a_k, a_{k+1}$ be a set of $k + 1$ objects. Then $a_1 = \cdots = a_k$ since k is in $\mathcal{K}$. Also, if a_k is deleted from the set, there remains a set of k objects, among which is a_{k+1}. Hence $a_1 = a_{k+1}$. Consequently $a_1 = \cdots = a_k = a_{k+1}$ and $k + 1$ is in $\mathcal{K}$. By induction $\mathcal{K} = \mathfrak{J}$, and the statement is true for all n.

Appendix II | Relations and Mappings

Let $\mathscr{A}$ and $\mathscr{B}$ be two sets. We call the set of all ordered pairs (a, b), a in $\mathscr{A}$ and b in $\mathscr{B}$, the *Cartesian product* of $\mathscr{A}$ and $\mathscr{B}$ and denote it by the symbol $\mathscr{A} \times \mathscr{B}$. A subset $\mathscr{R}$ of $\mathscr{A} \times \mathscr{B}$ is called a *relation between* $\mathscr{A}$ *and* $\mathscr{B}$ or a *relation in* $\mathscr{A} \times \mathscr{B}$. If (a, b) is in $\mathscr{R}$, we sometimes write $a \mathscr{R} b$, read "a is in the relation $\mathscr{R}$ to b."

The name Cartesian product is suggested by the special case $\mathscr{A} = \mathscr{B} = \Re$ in which $\mathscr{A} \times \mathscr{B}$ is the ordinary real plane whose elements are points given by their Cartesian coordinates (x, y). The ordinary relation $<$ on the real numbers is given by the region $<$ in $\Re \times \Re$ consisting of all points above the line $y = x$. For another example of a relation in the real plane consider the points on the ellipse $x^2 + 4y^2 = 4$.

Intuitively, one might consider a relation as being a many-valued function which assigns to an element a in $\mathscr{A}$ the set of all those b in $\mathscr{B}$ for which $a \mathscr{R} b$ (this set might be empty). We call the set of all a in $\mathscr{A}$ for which there is at least one b in $\mathscr{B}$ such that $a \mathscr{R} b$ the *domain* of the relation $\mathscr{R}$; similarly the *range* of $\mathscr{R}$ is the set of all b in $\mathscr{B}$ for which there is at least one a in $\mathscr{A}$ such that $a \mathscr{R} b$. For example, in the case of the ellipse relation $x^2 + 4y^2 = 4$ the domain is the set $\{x \mid -2 \leq x \leq 2\}$, and the range is set $\{y \mid -1 \leq y \leq 1\}$.

If, in particular, for each a in the domain of a relation $\mathscr{R} \subseteq \mathscr{A} \times \mathscr{B}$ there is exactly one b in $\mathscr{B}$ such that $a \mathscr{R} b$, we call $\mathscr{R}$ a *function* in $\mathscr{A} \times \mathscr{B}$. The term "mapping" is used as a synonym for "function."

In the case of the real plane, a function is a relation that has at most one point on any line parallel to the y axis. If $\mathscr{R}$ is a function, we sometimes use one of the notations $b = \mathscr{R}(a)$ or $b = a \mathscr{R}$ to indicate that b is uniquely determined by a. If the domain of a function $\mathscr{R}$ in $\mathscr{A} \times \mathscr{B}$ is all of $\mathscr{A}$, we say that $\mathscr{R}$ is a *function on $\mathscr{A}$ into $\mathscr{B}$* (mapping of $\mathscr{A}$ into $\mathscr{B}$).

In the special case when the range of $\mathscr{R}$ is all of $\mathscr{B}$, we say that $\mathscr{R}$ is a function *on $\mathscr{A}$ onto $\mathscr{B}$* (mapping of $\mathscr{A}$ onto $\mathscr{B}$). (Note that in this terminology to say that "$\mathscr{R}$ is a function of $\mathscr{A}$ into $\mathscr{B}$" includes the possibility that the function is actually "onto $\mathscr{B}$." This possibility is important because in many instances it is not known whether a given function has all or just part of $\mathscr{B}$ as its range, and we need a terminology that is suitable for handling such instances.)

We say that two functions $\mathscr{R}_1$ and $\mathscr{R}_2$ are *equal* if (i) domain $\mathscr{R}_1 =$ domain $\mathscr{R}_2$ and (ii) $\mathscr{R}_1(a) = \mathscr{R}_2(a)$ for each a in domain $\mathscr{R}_1$. Thus to define a function $\mathscr{R}$ we must first specify its domain and then specify the *image* $b = \mathscr{R}(a)$ for each element a in this domain. Thus, if $\mathscr{A} = \mathfrak{R} = \mathscr{B}$, then the functions defined by $|a|$ and $\sqrt{a^2}$ are equal.

Let $\mathscr{R}$ be a function $b = a\mathscr{R}$ on $\mathscr{A}$ into $\mathscr{B}_1$, and let $\mathscr{A}_1$ be a subset of $\mathscr{A}$. We denote by $\mathscr{A}_1\mathscr{R}$ the set of all b in $\mathscr{B}$ such that $b = a_1\mathscr{R}$ for a_1 in $\mathscr{A}_1$. Thus $\mathscr{R}$ maps $\mathscr{A}$ onto $\mathscr{B}$ if and only if $\mathscr{B} = \mathscr{A}\mathscr{R}$.

Corresponding to each relation $\mathscr{R}$ in $\mathscr{A} \times \mathscr{B}$ we define a new relation $\mathscr{R}^*$ in $\mathscr{B} \times \mathscr{A}$ called the *transpose* of $\mathscr{R}$ by the statement

$$(b, a) \text{ is in } \mathscr{R}^* \quad \text{if and only if} \quad (a, b) \text{ is in } \mathscr{R};$$

i.e., $\mathscr{R}^*$ is essentially the same as $\mathscr{R}$ except that the roles of $\mathscr{A}$ and $\mathscr{B}$ are interchanged by reversing the order of elements in each ordered pair (a, b) in $\mathscr{R}$. For example, the transpose of the relation $<$ is the relation $>$.

If a relation $\mathscr{R}$ and its transpose $\mathscr{R}^*$ are both functions, we say that $\mathscr{R}$ is a *one-to-one function* (or mapping). In this case $\mathscr{R}^*$ is of course a function on $\mathscr{A}\mathscr{R}$ to $\mathscr{A}$ and is called the *inverse* of $\mathscr{R}$. For instance, a one-to-one function in $\mathfrak{R} \times \mathfrak{R}$ is a region in the plane which is cut in at most one point by any vertical line or by any horizontal line (say a rising curve). Hence, specifying an x determines at most one y, and specifying a y determines at most one x.

In the case of vector spaces we shall use the term "mapping" more often than "function," and certain special cases of mappings will be given names (e.g., isomorphism, linear transformation). The following statements will occur frequently in the text:

(1) Let T be a mapping of a vector space $\mathscr{V}$ *into* a vector space $\mathscr{W}$.

(2) Let T be a mapping of a vector space $\mathscr{V}$ *onto* a vector space $\mathscr{W}$.

(3) Let T be a *one-to-one* mapping of a vector space $\mathscr{V}$ *into* a vector space $\mathscr{W}$.

(4) Let T be a *one-to-one* mapping of a vector space $\mathscr{V}$ *onto* a vector space $\mathscr{W}$.

Each of these statements implies that T is a function whose domain is $\mathscr{V}$ and whose range is contained in $\mathscr{W}$, and this is all that is said in (1).

We have the additional information in (2) that the range of T is all of $\mathscr{W}$ and in (3) that T is a one-to-one mapping. In (4) we have the information of both (2) and (3).

In case (1) above we shall ordinarily write $\beta = \alpha\mathsf{T}$ to indicate that β is the image of α under T. Then, in (1) and (3) we have $\mathscr{V}\mathsf{T} \subseteq \mathscr{W}$, whereas in (2) and (4) $\mathscr{V}\mathsf{T} = \mathscr{W}$.

Appendix III | Bibliography

The present book is designed as a textbook rather than as a treatise. Almost every topic treated herein has important ramifications and generalizations which could not be included in the space allotted here. The student who wishes to go beyond what we have provided, or who wishes to see the same material from other points of view may find this bibliography useful.

The bibliography is in two parts of which the second refers only to the final chapter.

In the General Bibliography we have included (i) textbooks on matrix theory both modern and classical, (ii) treatises and books which cover special topics, and (iii) general books in algebra which go beyond the present text in level of treatment.

In the Bibliography for Linear Inequalities, Game Theory, and Linear Programming we have given a short selection of some of the leading books. Many of these books include extensive lists of research papers.

General Bibliography

(i)

Aitken, A. C.: *Determinants and matrices*, New York, Interscience Publishers, 1954.

Albert, A. A.: *Modern higher algebra*, University of Chicago Press, Chicago, 1937.

Beaumont, R. A., and R. W. Ball: *Introduction to modern algebra and matrix theory*, Rinehart & Co., New York, 1954.

Birkhoff, G., and S. MacLane: *A survey of modern algebra*, Macmillan Co., New York, 1953.

Bocher, M.: *Introduction to higher algebra*, Macmillan Co., New York, 1930.

Dickson, L. E.: *Modern algebraic theories*, Benj. H. Sanborn & Co., Chicago, 1930.

Halmos, P. R.: *Finite dimensional vector spaces*, Princeton University Press, Princeton, N. J., 1942.

MacDuffee, C. C.: *Vectors and matrices*, Mathematical Association of America, 1943.

Perlis, S.: *Theory of matrices*, Addison-Wesley Press, Cambridge, Mass., 1952.

Schreier, O., and E. Sperner: *Vorlesungen über Matrizen*, Teubner, Leipzig, 1932.

Schwerdtfeger, H.: *Introduction to linear algebra and the theory of matrices*, P. Noordhoff N. V., Groningen, 1950.

Stoll, R. R.: *Linear algebra and matrix theory*, McGraw-Hill Book, Co., New York, 1952.

Turnbull, H. W., and A. C. Aitken: *An introduction to the theory of canonical matrices*, Blackie & Son, Glasgow, 1948.

(ii)

Dwyer, P. S.: *Linear computations*, John Wiley & Sons, New York, 1951.
Frazer, R. A., W. J. Duncan, and A. R. Collar: *Elementary matrices*, University Press, Cambridge, 1938.
MacDuffee, C. C.: *The theory of matrices*, Chelsea Publishing Co., New York, 1946.
Wedderburn, J. H. M.: *Lectures on matrices*, American Mathematical Society, New York, 1934.

(iii)

Artin, E., C. J. Nesbitt, and R. M. Thrall: *Rings with minimum condition*, University of Michigan Press, Ann Arbor, 1944.
Jacobson, N.: *Lectures in abstract algebra*, D. Van Nostrand Co., New York, 1953.
Kaplansky, I.: *Infinite abelian groups*, University of Michigan Press, Ann Arbor, 1954.
van der Waerden, B. L.: *Moderne algebra*, Verlag von Julius Springer, Berlin, 1937.

Bibliography for Linear Inequalities, Game Theory, and Linear Programming

Antosiewicz, H. A. (editor): *Second symposium linear programming*, sponsored by the Office of Scientific Research of the Air Research and Development Command held jointly by the National Bureau of Standards and the Directorate of Management Analysis, DCS/Comptroller, USAF, Washington, D. C., 1955, Vols. I and II.
Blackwell, D. and M. A. Girshick: *Theory of games and statistical decisions*, John Wiley & Sons, New York, 1954.
Charnes, A., W. W. Cooper, and A. Henderson: *An introduction to linear programming*, John Wiley & Sons, New York, 1953.
Koopmans, T. C. (editor): *Activity analysis of production and allocation* (Cowles Commission Monograph 13), John Wiley & Sons, New York, 1951.
Kuhn, H. W.: *Lectures on the theory of games*, Princeton University, Department of Mathematics, 1953.
Kuhn, H. W., and A. W. Tucker (editors): *Contributions to the theory of games*, Volume I (Annals of Mathematics Study No. 24) Princeton, 1950; Volume II (Annals of Mathematics Study No. 28) Princeton, 1953.
McKinsey, J. C. C.: *Introduction to the theory of games* (RAND series), McGraw-Hill Book Co., 1952.
von Neumann, J., and O. Morgenstern.: *Theory of games and economic behavior*, Princeton University Press, 1944; 2nd ed., 1947.
Orden, A., and L. Goldstein (editors): *Symposium on linear inequalities and programming*, Project SCOOP, Comptroller, Headquarters USAF, Washington, D. C., 1952.
Williams, J. D.: *The compleat strategyst* (RAND series), McGraw-Hill Book Co., 1954.

Glossary of Special Symbols

$\|\alpha\|_{\mathscr{A}}$	row matrix of coordinates of α relative to basis $\mathscr{A}$	41
$\|T\|_{\mathscr{A}\mathscr{B}}$	matrix of T relative to bases $\mathscr{A}$ and $\mathscr{B}$	41
$+$	sum of subspaces	26
$\cap$	intersection of subspaces	27
$I_{\mathscr{V}}$	identity transformation on $\mathscr{V}$	43
I_v	identity matrix of degree v	43
$A \times B$	Kronecker product of A and B	67
$\langle \mathscr{S} \rangle$	space spanned by $\mathscr{S}$	25
$[\mathscr{M}]$	subring generated by $\mathscr{M}$	197
$\mathscr{F}[x]$	simple extension of $\mathscr{F}$	197
$\leqq$	is less than or equal to	284
$\leq$	is less than	285
$<$	is strictly less than	285
$\subseteq$	is a subset of	286, 308
$\subset$	is a proper subset of	
$\supseteq$	contains	
$\supset$	contains properly	

Index

A1, A2, A3, A4, A5, 10
Abelian group, 61, 238
Adapted basis, 26
Adjoint, of matrix, 129
  of transformation, 163, 193
Algebra, 61
Algebraically closed field, 5
Algebraic over a field, 198
Alias, 137
Alibi, 137
Angle, 182
Annihilator, 166, 247
Apolar pair of matrices, 79, 81
Associate, 203
Associativity, 4, 5, 47, 52
Asymmetry, 285
Augmented matrix, 107, 246
Axioms, 4
  for field, 4
  for vector space, 10

Basis, adapted to a subspace, 26
  change of, 139
  of vector space, 19, 239
Bilinear form, 149
Bilinear function, 68, 161, 163
Boundary, 286

$\mathscr{C}(A)$, 73
$\mathscr{C}^c(A)$, $\mathscr{C}^r(A)$, 291
$\mathscr{C}(\mathscr{S})$, 288
Canonical form, 135
Cartesian product, 132, 306

Cartesian space, 8
Cartesian sum, 217
Cayley–Hamilton theorem, 147, 257
Center, 197
Characteristic equation, 144
Characteristic function, 144, 244
Characteristic of a field, 5
Characteristic root, 142
Chio's condensation, 120
Classical canonical form, 266
Closure, 4
Column degree, 36
Column-echelon form of matrix, 102
Column kernel, 78
Column matrix, 69
Column space, 69
  of a matrix, 73
Combinatorial axiom, 25
Common divisor, 205
Commutative algebra, 224
Commutativity, 4
Companion matrix, 252
Complementary minors, 121
Complementary submatrices, 121
Complete orthonormal set, 183
Complete set of invariants, 136
Complex number, 5
Component, 3, 8, 215
Conformable partitioning, 65
Congruence, 134, 213
  class, 213
Congruent forms, 151
Congruent matrices, 151, 168

Conjugate of transformation, 163
Conjunctive matrices, 172
Consistent equations, 107
Convex combination, 287
Convex cone, 288, 291
Convex set, 287
Cramer's rule, 130
Cyclic linear transformation, 252
Cyclic matrix, 252
Cyclic space, 240, 251

D1, D2, 58, 60
$\mathscr{D}^c(A)$, $\mathscr{D}^r(A)$, 291
Decomposition, 215
  of an algebra, 221
Definite, 168
$\deg_c$, $\deg_r$, 36
Degree, 201, 210
  of matrix, 42
Dependent on a set, 15
Dependent set of vectors, 13, 17
Dependent vector, 14
Determinant, 110, 178, 229
  classical definition, 122
  of a product, 125, 127
  of linear transformation, 178
Determinantal divisor, 231
Determinant function, 175
Diagonal matrix, 42, 114, 143
Diagonal of a matrix, 42
Differential equation, 244, 272
Dimension, 19, 27, 34, 74, 239
Direct sum, 214, 221, 241
Distance, 182
Distributivity, 4, 8, 58
Divisible, 203
Division algorithm, 204, 236
Domain, 33, 306
Double description, 31, 80, 291
Dual basis, 58
Duality, 167
Dual space, 57, 160, 163

$E_i{}^c$, $E_i{}^r$, 298
$\mathscr{E}_n$, 179
eigenvalue, 142, 144, 187, 192, 195

Eigenvector, 142, 144, 195
Elementary column transformation, 101
  improper, 102
Elementary divisor, 231, 265, 266
Elementary matrix, 96, 116
  improper, 96
Elementary operation, 84, 231
  proper or improper, 84
Elementary row operation, 85, 115
  proper or improper, 85
Element of a matrix, 36
Entry, 36
Equality of linear transformations, 33
Equivalence class, 133
Equivalence relation, 132, 150
Equivalent forms, 150, 158, 168
Equivalent functions, 173
Equivalent matrices, 102, 104, 141, 150, 230
Equivalent systems of equations, 82
Equivalent transformations, 147
Euclidean algorithm, 207
Euclidean space, 179
Existential axiom, 25
Expansion of determinant, 111
Extension, 34, 210
Extreme support, 288

Factor, 203
Factorization, complete, 208
Farkas' lemma, 291
Feasible vector, 293
Field, 4
Finitely generated, 238
Free, 238
Function, 306
  equal, 307
  into, onto, 306
  one-to-one, 307
Fundamental theorem of algebra, 210

Game, 298
Generate, 25, 197, 238, 247
Greatest common divisor, 205, 237

Group, 61
  Abelian or commutative, 61, 238
  full linear, 63

$\mathscr{H}_c$, $\mathscr{H}_o$, 285
Half space, 285
  open, closed, 285
Hermite matrix, 91
Hermite set of vectors, 89
Hermitian form, 172
Hermitian function, 171
Hermitian matrix, 171, 192
Homogeneous linear equations, 11, 93, 131
Homomorphism, 32
Hyperplane, 275
  at infinity, 276
  supporting, 288

$\mathfrak{J}$, 236
Ideal, 205
  element, 276
  principal, 205, 237
Idempotent, 218
  matrix, 93
Identity matrix, 43
Identity transformation, 43
Image space, 33
Improper equivalence, 105
Indecomposable, 224
Independent set of vectors, 13
Indeterminate, 202
Indices, of Hermite matrix, 91
  of row-echelon matrix, 86
  of subspace, 90
Induced mapping, 34
Induction, 5, 302
Inner product, 161, 180, 191
Integral matrix, 236
Intersection, 27
Invariant, 135
Invariant factor, 231
Invariant subspace, 186, 250
Inverse, 48, 53, 99, 130, 229
  of a product, 49, 54
  of the transpose, 72
  right or left, 47, 53, 129

Inversion function, 111
Inversions of a sequence, 122
Involution, 70
Irreducible, 203
Isometry, 180
Isomorphism, 22, 33, 199
  into and onto, 23

$\mathscr{K}^c(A)$, $\mathscr{K}^r(A)$, 78
$\mathscr{K}(\mathsf{T})$, 33
Kernel, 33, 78
Kronecker delta function, 62
Kronecker product, 67, 106, 147

L1, L2, L3, L4, 32
$\mathscr{L}(A)$, 78
$\mathscr{L}_n(\mathscr{F})$, 11
Laplace expansion, 123
Latent root, 142
Leading coefficient, 201
Length, 179, 192
Limit, lower or upper, 37
Limit point, 286
Linear combination, 14
Linear dependence, 13
Linear equation, 11, 12, 16, 78, 106, 131
Linear function, 68, 161
Linear group, full, 63
Linear programming, 293, 300, 301
  dual problem, 294
Linear transformation, 32, 41
  addition of, 55
  extension of, 34
  induced, 34
  multiplication of, 45
  power of, 47
  restriction of, 34
Lower triangular matrix, 89

M1, M2, M3, M4, M5, 60
Matrix, 36
  degree of, 42
  games, 298, 301
  multiplication of, 51
  nilpotent, 283
  of coefficients, 78

Matrix (*continued*)
  of form, 149
  row and column of, 36
  stripe, 280
Minimax theorem, 296, 300
Minimum equation, 210
Minimum function, 210, 248
  relative, 250
Minor of determinant, 120
Modulo, 134
Monic polynomial, 203
Monic triangular set, 89
Monic vector, 86
Monomial, 197
Multilinear, 163
Multilinear scalar function, 174
Multiplication criterion, 46

$\mathcal{N}_b(\alpha)$, 286
Natural basis, 44, 57, 69
Negative definite, 168
Nilpotent matrix, 283
Nonhomogeneous linear equation, 106
Nonsingular, 48, 53, 76, 97, 161
Normal form, 135
Normal linear transformation, 194
Normal matrix, 174, 194
Normal vector, 192
n-tuple, 8
Null matrix, 66
Null space (Kernel), 33

$\mathcal{O}(\mathcal{S})$, 185
Order, 61, 110, 284
  of cyclic space, 240
  of element of group, 243
  of minor, 120
  of summation, 38
  of vector, 240
  partial, 284
Orthant, 285
Orthogonal, 183, 192
Orthogonal complement, 185, 192
Orthogonal idempotents, 218
Orthogonal matrix, 186

Orthogonal transformation, 185
Orthonormal, 183, 192, 195

$\mathcal{P}_n{}^r$, 285
Pairs of matrices, 271, 274
Partial fraction, 228
Partial order, 284
Partition, 269
  conjugate of, 270
  of set, 133
Partitioning of matrix, 64, 219
Permutation, 75
Polar cone, 291
Polar form, 159
Polarization, 180
Polar space, 291
Polynomial, 7, 197, 202
Polynomial domain, 202
Positive definite, 168, 169, 187
Positive orthant, 285
Positive semidefinite, 168, 169
Primary, 204
Primary components, 263
Primary decomposition, 209, 215
Primary extension, 225
Primary invariant subspace, 263
Primary linear transformation, 258
Prime, 203, 207
Primitive idempotent, 223
Principal ideal, 205, 237
Principal minor, 170
Principal submatrix, 170
Probability vector, 285
Product, of linear transformations, 45
  of matrices, 51
  of partitioned matrices, 65
  of scalar and linear transformation, 55
Projection, 218
Projective geometry, 275
Projective transformation, 276

$\mathcal{Q}_n{}^r$, 285
Quadratic form, 158
Quadratic function, 167
Quotient space, 134

$\mathscr{R}(A)$, 73
Range, 33, 306
Rank, 74, 76
    determinantal criterion, 126
    of adjoint, 130
    of bilinear function, 165
    of form, 158
    of product, 75
Rational canonical form, 266
Rational function, 7, 203
Rational number, 5
Real number, 5
Recursive definition, 304
Reflexivity, 132
Regular, 229
Related matrices, 91
Relation, 132, 284, 306
Relatively prime, 206
Restriction, 34
Reversible linear substitution, 150
Ring, 61, 196, 229
    commutative, 61
    with unity element, 61
Roots of matrices, 279
Rotation, 41, 186
Row-by-column rule, 52
Row degree, 36
Row-echelon matrix, 86, 91
Row equivalence, 99, 141
Row kernel, 78
Row matrix, 68
Row space, 68
    of a matrix, 73

S1, S2, S3, S4, S5, 10
Scalar, 4
Scalar function, 160, 174
Scalar matrix, 42, 114
Scalar product, 166, 191
Scalar transformation, 42
Schwartz's inequality, 181, 192
Secular value, 142
Segre characteristic, 266, 269, 277
Semilinear function, 171
Signature, 169, 173
Similar matrices, 142, 148, 263

Similar transformations, 148
Simple extension, 197, 224
    algebraic and transcendental, 198
Simultaneous equivalence, 271
    congruence, 274
Singular, 53, 126
Skew-Hermitian, 174, 193
Skew-symmetric form, 151
Skew-symmetric matrix, 151, 154, 299
Smith canonical form, 233, 242, 245
Span, 25
Spherical neighborhood, 286
Spread of a vector, 86
Square matrix, 42
Strategy, 298
Strictly positive, 285
Stripe matrix, 280
Submatrix, 63, 121
Subring, 196
Subspace, 24
    of $\mathscr{V}_n(\mathscr{F})$, 29
Substitution property, 134, 213
Sum, of linear transformations, 55
    of subspaces, 26
    of vectors, 3, 8, 10
Summation index, 37
Symmetric bilinear function, 167
Symmetric form, 151
Symmetric matrix, 151, 156, 169, 187
Symmetry, 132

Torsion space, 244
Total matrix algebra, 61
Transcendental, 198, 199
Transitivity, 132
Transpose, 70, 115
    of a function, 307
    of a product, 71
Triangle inequality, 182
Triangular matrix, 89, 113
Triangular spanning set, 89
Trivial solution, 11

Unimodular, 229
Unimodular group, 230

Unit, 4, 229
Unitary equivalence, 192
Unitary matrix, 192
Unitary space, 191
Unitary transformation, 192
Upper-triangular matrix, 89

$\mathscr{V}^*$, 58
$\mathscr{V}_n(\mathscr{F})$, 8
$\mathscr{V}_n^r$, 68
Vector, 2, 8, 10
  addition of, 8, 10
  component of, 3, 8

dependent on a set, 14
feasible, 293
product of with scalar, 3, 8, 10
strictly positive, 285
Vector function, 161
Vector space, 10, 56, 57, 238

Weyr numbers, 270

Zero, 4
Zero mapping, 56
Zero space, 24
Zero vector, 10